Relations for Discrete Cash Flows with End-of-I

Type	Find/Given	Factor Notation and Formula	Relation	Sample Cash Flow Diagram
Single Amount	F/P Compound amount	$(F/P,i,n) = (1 + i)^n$	$F = P(F/P,i,n)$	
	P/F Present worth	$(P/F,i,n) = \dfrac{1}{(1+i)^n}$	$P = F(P/F,i,n)$ (Sec. 2.1)	
Uniform Series	P/A Present worth	$(P/A,i,n) = \dfrac{(1+i)^n - 1}{i(1+i)^n}$	$P = A(P/A,i,n)$	
	A/P Capital recovery	$(A/P,i,n) = \dfrac{i(1+i)^n}{(1+i)^n - 1}$	$A = P(A/P,i,n)$ (Sec. 2.2)	
	F/A Compound amount	$(F/A,i,n) = \dfrac{(1+i)^n - 1}{i}$	$F = A(F/A,i,n)$	
	A/F Sinking fund	$(A/F,i,n) = \dfrac{i}{(1+i)^n - 1}$	$A = F(A/F,i,n)$ (Sec. 2.3)	
Arithmetic Gradient	P_G/G Present worth	$(P/G,i,n) = \dfrac{(1+i)^n - in - 1}{i^2(1+i)^n}$	$P_G = G(P/G,i,n)$	
	A_G/G Uniform series	$(A/G,i,n) = \dfrac{1}{i} - \dfrac{n}{(1+i)^n - 1}$	$A_G = G(A/G,i,n)$ (Sec. 2.5)	
Geometric Gradient	P_g/A_1 and g Present worth	$P_g = \begin{cases} \dfrac{A_1\left[1 - \left(\dfrac{1+g}{1+i}\right)^n\right]}{i - g} & g \neq i \\[4mm] A_1\dfrac{n}{1+i} & g = i \end{cases}$	$g \neq i$ $g = i$ (Sec. 2.6)	

ENGINEERING
Second Canadian Edition
ECONOMY

ENGINEERING ECONOMY

Second Canadian Edition

Leland Blank, P.E.
American University of Sharjah, United Arab Emirates
Texas A&M University

Anthony Tarquin, P.E.
University of Texas at El Paso

Scott Iverson, Ph.D.
University of Victoria—British Columbia

McGraw-Hill Ryerson
Connect. Learn. Succeed.

Engineering Economy
Second Canadian Edition

The Internet addresses listed in the text were accurate at the time of publication. The inclusion of a website does not indicate an endorsement by the authors or McGraw-Hill Ryerson, and McGraw-Hill Ryerson does not guarantee the accuracy of information presented at these sites.

ISBN-13: 978-0-07-007180-3
ISBN-10: 0-07-007180-2

1 2 3 4 5 6 7 8 9 10 QGF 1 9 8 7 6 5 4 3 2

Printed and bound in the United States of America

Care has been taken to trace ownership of copyright material contained in this text; however, the publisher will welcome any information that enables it to rectify any reference or credit for subsequent editions.

Executive Sponsoring Editor: *Leanna MacLean*
Marketing Manager: *Jeremy Guimond*
Developmental Editors: *Sarah Fulton and Amy Rydzanicz*
Supervising Editor: *Cathy Biribauer*
Editorial Associates: *Stephanie Giles and Erin Catto*
Copy Editor: *Rodney Rawlings*
Production Coordinator: *Tammy Mavroudi*
Cover and Inside Design: *Michelle Losier*
Composition: *SR Nova Pvt Ltd. Bangalore, India*
Cover Photo: *Getty Images*
Printer: *Quad/Graphics*

Library and Archives Canada Cataloguing in Publication Data

Blank, Leland T.
    Engineering economy / Leland Blank, Anthony Tarquin, Scott Iverson. — 2nd Canadian ed.

    Includes index.

    ISBN 978-0-07-007180-3

    1. Engineering economy — Textbooks.

    I. Tarquin, Anthony J. II. Iverson, Scott III. Title.

TA177.4.B53 2012   658.1502'462   C2011-904617-2

To my wife, Kathy, and my daughter, Kristen.

CONTENTS

LEVEL TWO   **TOOLS FOR EVALUATING ALTERNATIVES**

LEVEL THREE   **MAKING DECISIONS ON REAL-WORLD PROJECTS**

PREFACE

The primary purpose of this text is to present the principles and applications of economic analysis in a clearly written fashion, supported by a large number and wide range of engineering-oriented examples, end-of-chapter exercises, and electronic-based learning options. Through all editions of the book, our objective has been to present the material in the clearest, most concise fashion possible without sacrificing coverage or true understanding on the part of the learner. The sequence of topics and flexibility of chapter selection used to accommodate different course objectives are described later in the preface.

EDUCATION LEVEL AND USE OF TEXT

This text is best used in learning and teaching at the college and university level, and as a reference book for the basic computations of engineering economic analysis. It is well suited for a one-term undergraduate course in engineering economic analysis, project analysis, or engineering cost analysis. Additionally, because of its behavioural-based structure, it is perfect for individuals who wish to learn the material for the first time completely on their own, and for individuals who simply want to review. Students should be at least in year two of their engineering studies, so that they can better appreciate the engineering context of the problems. A background in calculus is not necessary to understand the calculations, but a basic familiarization with engineering terminology makes the material more meaningful and therefore easier and more enjoyable to learn. Nevertheless, the building-block approach used in the text's design allows a practitioner unacquainted with economics and engineering principles to use the text to learn, understand, and correctly apply the principles and techniques for effective decision making.

ABOUT THIS EDITION

This second Canadian edition is written to reflect content and applications specific to Canada. It strives to not only modify the engineering examples and economic procedures, but to also expand and introduce appropriate techniques that are particularly relevant to the context of Canadian priorities and values.

From the beginning of Confederation, Canadians have shown a willingness to be responsible for one another and to relate harmoniously to their diverse communities, nations, and the world. We use these experiences to manage compromise between conflicting and often contradictory values through dialogue, persuasion, peacekeeping, and diplomacy within international organizations and corporations. The microeconomics of **tradeoff analysis**, **linear programming optimization techniques**, **decision theory**, and **simulation** receive more attention in this context and are therefore expanded in this second Canadian edition. **Utility theory** and **game theory** are added to address the use of and the importance of these topics to the Canadian economy. The growing exploitation of these techniques in engineering design practice in Canada helps encourage decision making consistent with our nation's values.

As Canadians, we are justifiably proud of our social safety net and the building of our public infrastructure (transportation, universal health care, education, legal) and see their necessity for the promotion of individual freedom and a prosperous economy. Therefore, this Canadian edition expands **public sector decision making** and includes a discussion addressing the debates concerning the **implementation of public-private partnerships in Canada**.

Since taxes and depreciation are country-specific, these sections have been reworked to **reflect Canadian regulations.** The **macroeconomics of inflation and interest rates**, and an **introduction to monetary policy in Canada** are also included.

NEW TO THE SECOND CANADIAN EDITION

- Additional problems at the end of each chapter, emphasizing various engineering disciplines and Canadian companies offering sustainable energy and technology solutions
- Updated Canadian macroeconomic discussions in response to the global financial situation after the economic crisis of 2008, such as Bank of Canada objectives, CPI, inflation, and deflation
- Revised information on depreciation and income taxation, reflecting the most recent Revenue Canada tax regulations and depreciation practices
- Canadian mortgage rules and rates updated to current practices
- Enhanced coverage of Canadian public-private partnerships

STRUCTURE OF TEXT AND OPTIONS FOR PROGRESSION THROUGH THE CHAPTERS

The text is written in modular form, providing for topic integration in a variety of ways that serve different course purposes, structures, and time limitations. There are a total of 18 chapters in four levels. As indicated in the flowchart that follows, some of the chapters have to be covered in numerical sequence; however, the modular design allows for great flexibility in the selection and sequencing of topics. The chapter progression graphic (which follows the flowchart) shows some of the options for introducing chapters earlier than their numerical order. For example, if the course is designed to emphasize after-tax analysis early in the term, Chapter 15 and the initial sections of Chapter 16 may be introduced at any point after Chapter 6 without loss of foundation preparation. There are clear primary and alternative entry points for the major categories of inflation, estimation, taxes, and risk. Alternative entries are indicated by a dashed arrow on the graphic.

The material in Level One emphasizes basic computational skills, so these chapters are prerequisites for all the others in the book. The chapters in Level Two are primarily devoted to the most common analytical techniques for comparing alternatives. While it is advisable to cover all the chapters in this Level, only the first two (Chapters 5 and 6) are widely used in the remainder of the text. The three chapters of Level Three show how any of the techniques in Level Two can be used to evaluate presently owned assets or independent alternatives, while the chapters in Level Four emphasize the tax consequences of decision making and some additional concepts in cost estimation, activity-based costing, sensitivity analysis, and risk, as treated using simulation.

Organization of Chapters and End-of-Chapter Exercises   Each chapter contains a purpose and a series of progressive learning objectives, followed by the study material. Section headings correspond to each learning objective; for example, Section 5.1 contains the material pertaining to the first objective of the chapter. Each section contains one or more illustrative examples solved by hand, or by both hand and computer methods. Examples are separated from the textual material and include comments about the solution and pertinent connections to other topics in the book. The crisp end-of-chapter summaries neatly tie together the concepts and major topics covered to reinforce the learner's understanding prior to engaging in the end-of chapter exercises.

The end-of-chapter unsolved problems are grouped and labelled in the same general order as the sections in the chapter. This approach provides an opportunity to apply material on a section-by-section basis or to schedule problem solving when the chapter is completed.

Appendices A (in-text) and B (available in the Online Learning Centre) contain supplementary information: a basic introduction to the use of spreadsheets (Microsoft Excel) for readers unfamiliar with them and the basics of accounting and business reports and business ratios. Interest factor tables are located at the end of the text for easy access. Finally, the inside front covers offer a quick reference to factor notation, formulas, and cash flow diagrams, plus a guide to the format for commonly used spreadsheet functions. A glossary of common terms and symbols used in engineering economy appears inside the back cover.

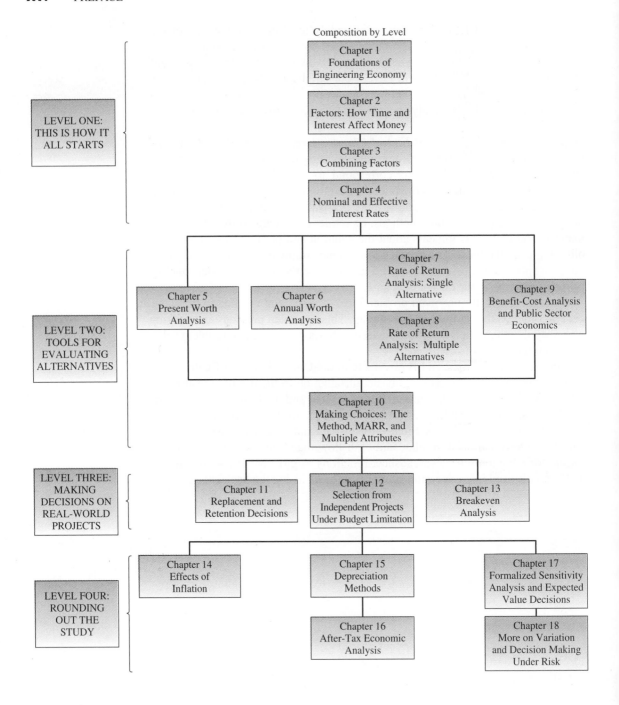

Composition by Level

LEVEL ONE:
THIS IS HOW IT
ALL STARTS

Chapter 1
Foundations of
Engineering Economy

Chapter 2
Factors: How Time and
Interest Affect Money

Chapter 3
Combining Factors

Chapter 4
Nominal and Effective
Interest Rates

LEVEL TWO:
TOOLS FOR
EVALUATING
ALTERNATIVES

Chapter 5
Present Worth
Analysis

Chapter 6
Annual Worth
Analysis

Chapter 7
Rate of Return
Analysis: Single
Alternative

Chapter 8
Rate of Return
Analysis: Multiple
Alternatives

Chapter 9
Benefit-Cost Analysis
and Public Sector
Economics

Chapter 10
Making Choices: The
Method, MARR, and
Multiple Attributes

LEVEL THREE:
MAKING
DECISIONS ON
REAL-WORLD
PROJECTS

Chapter 11
Replacement and
Retention Decisions

Chapter 12
Selection from
Independent Projects
Under Budget Limitation

Chapter 13
Breakeven
Analysis

LEVEL FOUR:
ROUNDING
OUT THE
STUDY

Chapter 14
Effects of
Inflation

Chapter 15
Depreciation
Methods

Chapter 17
Formalized Sensitivity
Analysis and Expected
Value Decisions

Chapter 16
After-Tax Economic
Analysis

Chapter 18
More on Variation
and Decision Making
Under Risk

OPTIONS FOR PROGRESSION THROUGH CHAPTERS

There is considerable flexibility in the sequencing of topics and chapters once the first six chapters are covered, as shown in the progression graphic on this page. If the course is designed to emphasize sensitivity and risk analysis, Chapters 17 and 18 can be covered immediately after Chapter 9. If depreciation and tax emphasis are vitally important to the goals of the course, Chapters 15 and 16 can be covered after Chapter 6. The progression graphic can help in the design of the course content and topic ordering.

Topics may be introduced at the point indicated or any point thereafter
(Alternative entry points are indicated by ← – – –)

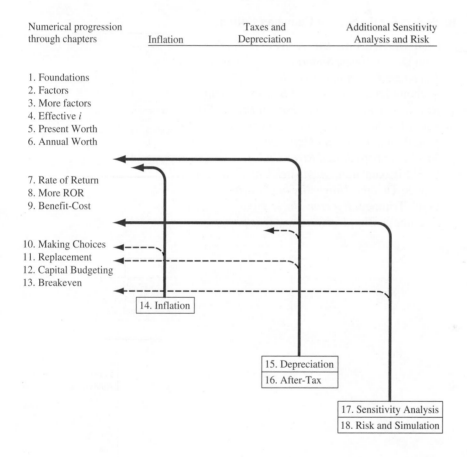

ACKNOWLEDGMENTS

I am deeply grateful to those who have assisted me in the preparation of the original Canadian edition and this second edition. The constructive and insightful comments I received from the reviewers were very useful in providing direction. I owe a great debt of thanks to my wife for her advice, support, and editing. I would also like to express my appreciation to the professional staff at McGraw-Hill Ryerson, including Leanna MacLean (Sponsoring Editor), Amy Rydzanicz and Sarah Fulton (Developmental Editors), Cathy Biribauer (Supervising Editor), and Rodney Rawlings (Copy Editor), who did an outstanding job assisting and facilitating the creation of this second edition.

Reviewers for the Second Canadian Edition

Craig M. Gelowitz, *University of Regina*
John Dewey Jones, *Simon Fraser University*
Ata Khan, *Carleton University*
Anthony Lau, *University of British Columbia*
Ronald Mackinnon, *University of British Columbia*
Samir El-Omari, *Concordia University*
Juan Pernia, *Lakehead University*
Vivek N. Sharma, *Red River College*
K. S. Sivakumaran, *McMaster University*
Claude Théoret, *University of Ottawa*
Frank Trimnell, *Ryerson University*
Zoe Jingyu Zhu, *University of Guelph*

GUIDED TOUR

LEARNING OBJECTIVES

Every chapter begins with a purpose, list of topics, and learning objectives for each corresponding section. This behavioural-based approach sensitizes the reader to what is ahead, leading to improved understanding and learning.

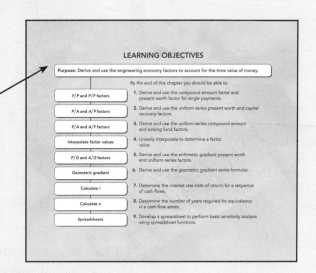

LEARNING OBJECTIVES

Purpose: Derive and use the engineering economy factors to account for the time value of money.

By the end of this chapter you should be able to

F/P and P/F factors	1. Derive and use the compound amount factor and present worth factor for single payments.
P/A and A/P factors	2. Derive and use the uniform series present worth and capital recovery factors.
F/A and A/F factors	3. Derive and use the uniform series compound amount and sinking fund factors.
Interpolate factor values	4. Linearly interpolate to determine a factor value.
P/G and A/G factors	5. Derive and use the arithmetic gradient present worth and uniform series factors.
Geometric gradient	6. Derive and use the geometric gradient series formulas.
Calculate i	7. Determine the interest rate (rate of return) for a sequence of cash flows.
Calculate n	8. Determine the number of years required for equivalence in a cash flow series.
Spreadsheets	9. Develop a spreadsheet to perform basic sensitivity analysis using spreadsheet functions.

EXTENDED EXERCISES

The extended exercises are designed to require spreadsheet analysis with a general emphasis on sensitivity analysis.

EXTENDED EXERCISE

INCREMENTAL ROR ANALYSIS WHEN ESTIMATED ALTERNATIVE LIVES ARE UNCERTAIN

Make-to-Specs is a software system under development by ABC Corporation. It will be able to translate digital versions of three-dimensional computer models, containing a wide variety of part shapes with machined and highly finished (ultra-smooth) surfaces. The product of the system is the numerically controlled (NC) machine code for the part's manufacturing. Additionally, Make-to-Specs will build the code for super-fine finishing of surfaces with continuous control of the finishing machines. There are two alternative computers that can provide the server function for the software interfaces and shared database updates on the manufacturing floor while Make-to-Specs is operating in parallel mode. The server first cost and estimated contribution to annual net cash flow are summarized below.

	Server 1	Server 2
First cost, $	$100,000	$200,000
Net cash flow, $/year	$35,000	$50,000 year 1, plus $5000 per year for years 2, 3, and 4 (gradient)
		$70,000 maximum for years 5 on, even if the server is replaced
Life, years	3 or 4	5 or 8

The life estimates were developed by two different individuals: a design engineer and a manufacturing manager. They have asked that at this stage of the project, all analyses be performed using both life estimates for each system.

Questions

Use computer analysis to answer the following:

1. If the MARR = 12%, which server should be selected? Use the PW or AW method to make the selection.

CASE STUDIES

All the case studies present real-world, in-depth treatments and exercises that cover the wide spectrum of economic analysis in the engineering profession.

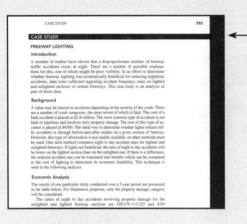

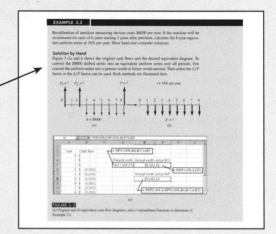

IN-CHAPTER EXAMPLES

Examples within the chapters are relevant to all engineering disciplines that use this text, including industrial, civil, environmental, mechanical, petroleum, and electrical engineering as well as engineering management and engineering technology programs.

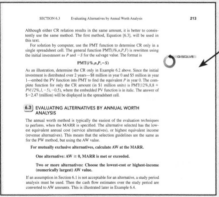

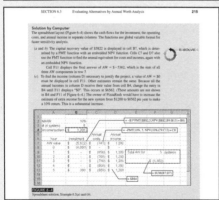

USE OF SPREADSHEETS

The text integrates spreadsheets and shows how easy they are to use in solving virtually any type of engineering economic analysis problem and how powerful they can be for altering estimates to achieve a better understanding of sensitivity and economic consequences of the uncertainties inherent in all forecasts. Beginning in Chapter 1, the authors illustrate their spreadsheet discussions with screenshots from Microsoft Excel©.

When a single-cell, built-in Excel function may be used to solve a problem, an icon ⭕ labelled *Q-Solve* (for *quick solve*) appears in the margin.

The *E-Solve* icon ⭕ indicates that a more complex, sophisticated spreadsheet is developed to solve the problem. The spreadsheet will contain data and several functions and possibly an Excel chart or graph to illustrate the answer and sensitivity analysis of the solution to changing data.

For both Q-Solve and E-Solve examples, the authors have included cells that show the exact Excel function needed to obtain the value in a specific cell. The E-Solve icon is also used throughout chapters to point out descriptions of how best to use the computer to address the engineering economy topic under discussion.

CROSS-REFERENCING

The text reinforces the engineering concepts presented throughout the book by making them easily accessible from other sections of the book. Cross-reference icons in the margins refer the reader to additional section numbers, specific examples, or entire chapters that contain either foundational (backward) or more advanced (forward) information that is relevant to that in the paragraph next to the icon.

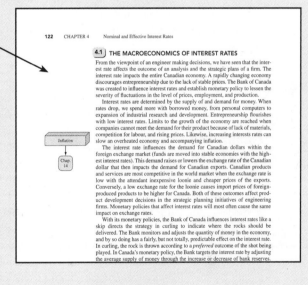

of the opponent's. In Canada, the economy scores a win when inflation and unemployment remain in check and the GDP is encouraged to grow. Just as curling is called "chess on ice" due to its subtle and intense strategic plays, monetary policy incorporates strategic interventions that result in dramatic effects on the Canadian economy (chess with loonies?).

In the Vancouver Olympics of 2010, Canada (the world's biggest curling nation with more than one million curlers) swept silver for the women and gold for the men by knocking the opposing team's rocks away from the target and locating their rocks closest to it. The Governor of the Bank of Canada, Mark Carney, hopes for gold-medal results in maintaining economic stability after the upheavals in the global financial system in 2008. Rapid and unprecedented intervention by the major central banks, along with massive government stimulus spending, is credited with saving the world from another Great Depression. International loans tied to troubled assets such as subprime-rate mortgages led to bank failures in many countries and a tightening of credit for businesses and individuals, with accompanying high levels of bankruptcies and unemployment. The central banks responded by improving the supply of global credit, keeping the money markets solvent and currencies relatively stable. Mark Carney maintained the Bank of Canada's emergency-level interest rate at 0.25%, its lowest level possible, until inflation reached the target level of 2%. Canada fared better than the United States and Europe through the recession, because its commercial banks were more stable due to tighter rules on how much debt they could carry and a more conservative approach to risk. The Governor states that his principal priority is to achieve a low and stable inflation rate. He stands ready to increase interest rates should inflation trend upward.

4.2 NOMINAL AND EFFECTIVE INTEREST RATE STATEMENTS

In Chapter 1, we learned that the primary difference between simple interest and compound interest is that compound interest includes interest on the interest earned in the previous period, while simple does not. Here we discuss *nominal and effective interest rates*, which have the same basic relationship. The difference is that the concepts of nominal and effective must be used when interest

---

THE CANADIAN PERSPECTIVE

The Canadian dimensions of this book are apparent throughout. Examples and sections dealing with Canadian tax and depreciation regulations, the macroeconomics of inflation and interest rates, and public sector decision-making are included. There is also an introduction to monetary policy in Canada, and material addressing the debates concerning public-private partnerships.

4.1 THE MACROECONOMICS OF INTEREST RATES

From the viewpoint of an engineer making decisions, we have seen that the interest rate affects the outcome of an analysis and the strategic plans of a firm. The interest rate impacts the entire Canadian economy. A rapidly changing economy discourages entrepreneurship due to the lack of stable prices. The Bank of Canada was created to influence interest rates and establish monetary policy to lessen the severity of fluctuations in the level of prices, employment, and production.

Interest rates are determined by the supply of and demand for money. When rates drop, we spend more with borrowed money, from personal computers to expansion of industrial research and development. Entrepreneurship flourishes with low interest rates. Limits to the growth of the economy are reached when companies cannot meet the demand for their product because of lack of materials, competition for labour, and rising prices. Likewise, increasing interests rates can slow an overheated economy and accompanying inflation.

The interest rate influences the demand for Canadian dollars within the foreign exchange market (funds are moved into stable economies with the highest interest rates). This demand raises or lowers the exchange rate of the Canadian dollar that then impacts the demand for Canadian exports. Canadian products and services are most competitive in the world market when the exchange rate is low with the attendant inexpensive loonie and cheaper prices of the exports. Conversely, a low exchange rate for the loonie causes import prices of foreign-produced products to be higher for Canada. Both of these outcomes affect product development decisions in the strategic planning initiatives of engineering firms. Monetary policies that affect interest rates will most often cause the same impact on exchange rates.

With its monetary policies, the Bank of Canada influences interest rates like a skip directs the strategy in curling to indicate where the rocks should be delivered. The Bank monitors and adjusts the quantity of money in the economy, and by so doing has a fairly, but not totally, predictable effect on the interest rate. In curling, the rock is thrown according to a *preferred* outcome of the shot being played. In Canada's monetary policy, the Bank targets the interest rate by adjusting the average supply of money through the increase or decrease of bank reserves.

ADDITIONAL RESOURCES

This edition of the text features an Online Learning Centre (OLC) available to both students and professors. The URL for the site is **www.mcgrawhill.ca/olc/blank**.

The OLC offers Appendix B: Basics of Accounting Reports and Business Ratios, the solutions to end-of-chapter problems, FE (Fundamentals of Engineering) exam prep quizzes, spreadsheet exercises, matching and true/false quizzes, links to important websites, chapter objectives, and more!

Additional resources, available to instructors only, include a computerized test bank stocked with hundreds of questions, complete PowerPoint® presentations for each chapter of *Engineering Economy*, Second Canadian Edition, and a full Instructor's Solutions Manual.

SUPERIOR SERVICE

Service takes on a whole new meaning with McGraw-Hill Ryerson and Cases in Strategic Management, Tenth Edition. More than just bringing you the textbook, we have consistently raised the bar in terms of innovation and educational research. These investments in learning and the education community have helped us understand the needs of students and educators across the country and allowed us to foster the growth of truly innovative, integrated learning.

INTEGRATED LEARNING

Your Integrated-Learning Sales Specialist is a McGraw-Hill Ryerson representative who has the experience, product knowledge, training, and support to help you assess and integrate our products, technology, and services into your course for optimum teaching and learning performance. Whether it's how to use our test bank software, helping your students to improve their grades, or how to put your entire course online, your *i*Learning Sales Specialist is there to help. Contact your *i*Learning Sales Specialist today to learn how to maximize all McGraw-Hill Ryerson resources!

*i*LEARNING SERVICES PROGRAM

At McGraw-Hill Ryerson, we take great pride in developing high-quality learning resources while working hard to provide you with the tools necessary to utilize them. We want to help bring your teaching to life, and we do this by integrating technology, events, conferences, training, and other services. We call it *i*Services. For more information, visit **www.mcgrawhill.ca/olc/iservices**.

BLACKBOARD

McGraw-Hill Higher Education and Blackboard have teamed up. Blackboard, the web-based course management system, has partnered with McGraw-Hill to better allow students and faculty to use online materials and activities to complement face-to-face teaching. Blackboard features exciting social learning and teaching tools that foster more logical, visually impactful and active learning opportunities for students. You'll transform your closed-door classrooms into communities where students remain connected to their educational experience 24 hours a day. This partnership allows you and your students access to McGraw-Hill's Connect™ and Create™ right from within your

Blackboard course—all with one single sign-on. Not only do you get single sign-on with Connect and Create, you also get deep integration of McGraw-Hill content and content engines right in Blackboard. Whether you're choosing a book for your course or building Connect assignments, all the tools you need are right where you want them—inside of Blackboard.

Gradebooks are now seamless. When a student completes an integrated Connect assignment, the grade for that assignment automatically (and instantly) feeds your Blackboard grade centre.

McGraw-Hill and Blackboard can now offer you easy access to industry-leading technology and content, whether your campus hosts it or we do. Be sure to ask your local McGraw-Hill representative for details.

CREATE

McGraw-Hill's Create Online gives you access to the most abundant resource at your fingertips—literally. With a few mouse clicks, you can create customized learning tools simply and affordably. McGraw-Hill Ryerson has included many of our market-leading textbooks within Create Online for eBook and print customization as well as many licensed readings and cases. For more information, go to **www.mcgrawhillcreate.com**.

COURSESMART

CourseSmart brings together thousands of textbooks across hundreds of courses in an eTextbook format, providing unique benefits to students and faculty. By purchasing an eTextbook, students can save up to 50 percent on the cost of a print textbook, reduce their impact on the environment, and gain access to powerful Web tools for learning including full-text search, notes and highlighting, and e-mail tools for sharing notes between classmates. For faculty, CourseSmart provides instant access for reviewing and comparing textbooks and course materials in their discipline area without the time, cost, and environmental impact of mailing print exam copies. For further details contact your *i*Learning Sales Specialist or go to **www.coursesmart.com**.

LEVEL 1

This Is How It All Starts

The foundations of engineering economy are introduced in these four chapters. When you have completed Level One, you will be able to understand and work problems that account for the *time value of money, cash flows* occurring at different times with different amounts, and *equivalence* at different interest rates. The techniques you master here form the basis of how an engineer in any discipline can take *economic value* into account in virtually any project environment.

The eight factors commonly used in all engineering economy computations are introduced and applied in this level. Combinations of these factors assist in moving monetary values forward and backward through time and at different interest rates. Also, after these four chapters, you should be comfortable with using many of the Excel spreadsheet functions to solve problems.

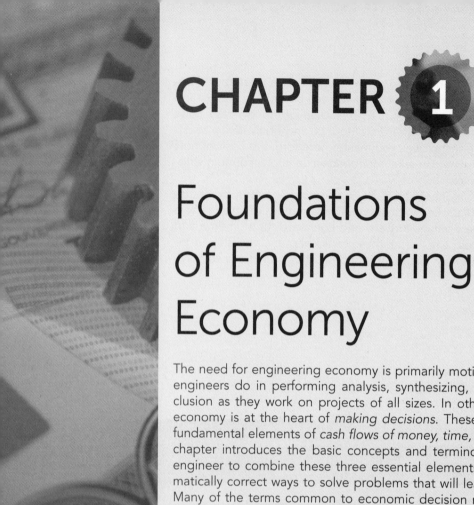

CHAPTER 1

Foundations of Engineering Economy

The need for engineering economy is primarily motivated by the work that engineers do in performing analysis, synthesizing, and coming to a conclusion as they work on projects of all sizes. In other words, engineering economy is at the heart of *making decisions*. These decisions involve the fundamental elements of *cash flows of money*, *time*, and *interest rates*. This chapter introduces the basic concepts and terminology necessary for an engineer to combine these three essential elements in organized, mathematically correct ways to solve problems that will lead to better decisions. Many of the terms common to economic decision making are introduced here and used in later chapters of the text. Icons in the margins serve as back and forward cross-references to more fundamental and additional material throughout the book.

The case studies included after the end-of-chapter problems focus on the development of engineering economy alternatives.

LEARNING OBJECTIVES

Purpose: Understand the fundamental concepts of engineering economy.

By the end of this chapter you should be able to

Questions	1. List the types of questions engineering economy can answer.
Decision making	2. Describe the role of engineering economy in the decision-making process.
Study approach	3. Identify what is needed to successfully perform an engineering economy study.
Interest rate	4. Perform calculations about interest rates and rate of return.
Equivalence	5. Understand what equivalence means in economic terms.
Simple and compound interest	6. Calculate simple interest and compound interest for one or more interest periods.
Symbols	7. Identify and use engineering economy terminology and symbols.
Spreadsheet functions	8. Identify the Excel© spreadsheet functions commonly used to solve engineering economy problems.
Minimum acceptable rate of return	9. Identify the meaning and use of minimum acceptable rate of return (MARR).
Cash flows	10. Estimate cash flows and graphically represent them.
Doubling time	11. Use the rule of 72 to estimate a compound interest rate or number of years for a present worth amount to double.
Spreadsheets	12. Develop a spreadsheet that involves simple and compound interest, incorporating sensitivity analysis.

1.1 WHY ENGINEERING ECONOMY IS IMPORTANT TO ENGINEERS (and other professionals)

Decisions made by engineers, managers, corporation presidents, and individuals are commonly the result of choosing one alternative over another. Decisions often reflect a person's educated choice of how to best invest funds, also called *capital*. The amount of capital is usually restricted, just as the cash available to an individual is usually limited. The decision of how to invest capital will invariably change the future, hopefully for the better; that is, it will be *value adding*. Engineers play a major role in capital investment decisions based on their analysis, synthesis, and design efforts. The factors considered in making the decision are a combination of economic and noneconomic factors. Additional factors may be intangible, such as convenience, goodwill, friendship, and others.

Fundamentally, engineering economy involves formulating, estimating, and evaluating the economic outcomes when alternatives to accomplish a defined purpose are available. Another way to define engineering economy is as a collection of mathematical techniques that simplify economic comparison.

For many corporations, especially larger ones, many of the projects and services are international in scope. They may be developed in one country for application in another. People and plants located in sites around the world routinely separate product design and manufacturing from each other, and from the customers who utilize the product. The approaches presented here are easily implemented in multinational settings or within a single country or location. Correct use of the techniques of engineering economy is especially important, since virtually any project—local, national, or international—will affect costs and/or revenues.

Some of the typical questions that can be addressed using the material in this book are posed below.

For Engineering Activities

- Should a new bonding technique be incorporated into the manufacture of automobile brake pads?
- If a computer-vision system replaces the human inspector in performing quality tests on an automobile welding line, will operating costs decrease over a time horizon of 5 years?
- Is it an economically wise decision to upgrade the composite material production centre of an airplane factory in order to reduce costs by 20%?
- Should a highway bypass be constructed around a city of 25,000 people, or should the current roadway through the city be expanded?
- Will we make the required rate of return if we install the newly offered technology onto our medical laser manufacturing line?

For Public Sector Projects and Government Agencies

- How much new tax revenue does the city need to generate to pay for an upgrade to the electric distribution system?

- Do the benefits outweigh the costs of a bridge connecting mainland British Columbia to Vancouver island versus ferry system upgrades?
- Is it cost-effective for the provincial government to cost-share with a contractor to construct a new toll road?

For Individuals

- Should I pay off my credit card balance with borrowed money?
- What are graduate studies worth financially over my professional career?
- Exactly what rate of return did we make on our stock investments?
- Should I buy or lease my next car, or keep the one I have now and pay off the loan?

EXAMPLE 1.1

Two lead engineers with a mechanical design company and a structural analysis firm work together often. They have decided that, due to their joint and frequent commercial airline travel around the region, they should evaluate the purchase of a plane co-owned by the two companies. What are some of the economics-based questions the engineers should answer as they evaluate the alternatives to (1) co-own a plane or (2) continue to fly commercially?

Solution
Some questions (and what is needed to respond) for each alternative are as follows:

- How much will it cost each year? (Cost estimates are needed.)
- How do we pay for it? (A financing plan is needed.)
- Are there tax advantages? (Tax law and tax rates are needed.)
- What is the basis for selecting an alternative? (A selection criterion is needed.)
- What is the expected rate of return? (Equations are needed.)
- What happens if we fly more or less than we estimate now? (Sensitivity analysis is needed.)

1.2 ROLE OF ENGINEERING ECONOMY IN DECISION MAKING

People make decisions; computers, mathematics, and other tools do not. The techniques and models of engineering economy *assist people in making decisions*. Since decisions affect what will be done, the time frame of engineering economy is primarily *the future*. Therefore, numbers used in an engineering economic analysis are *best estimates of what is expected to occur*. These estimates often involve the three essential elements mentioned earlier: cash flows, time of occurrence, and interest rates. These estimates are about the future, and will be somewhat different than what actually occurs, primarily because of changing circumstances and unplanned-for events. In other words, the *stochastic nature* of estimates will likely make the observed value in the future differ from the estimate made now.

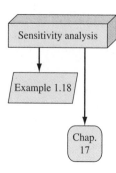

Sensitivity analysis

Example 1.18

Chap. 17

Commonly, *sensitivity analysis* is performed during the engineering economic study to determine how the decision might change based on varying estimates, especially those that may vary widely. For example, an engineer who expects initial software development costs to vary as much as ±20% from an estimated $250,000 should perform the economic analysis for first-cost estimates of $200,000, $250,000, and $300,000. Other uncertain estimates about the project can be "tweaked" using sensitivity analysis. (Sensitivity analysis is quite easy to perform using electronic spreadsheets. Tabular and graphical displays make analysis possible by simply changing the estimated values. The power of spreadsheets is used to advantage throughout this text and on the supporting website.)

Engineering economy can be used equally well to analyze outcomes of *the past.* Observed data are evaluated to determine if the outcomes have met or not met a specified criterion, such as a rate of return requirement. For example, suppose that 5 years ago, a Canadian-based engineering design company initiated a detailed-design service in Asia for automobile chassis. Now, the company president wants to know if the actual return on the investment has exceeded 15% per year.

There is an important procedure used to address the development and selection of alternatives. Commonly referred to as the *problem-solving approach* or the *decision-making process,* the steps in the approach follow.

1. **Understand the problem and define the objective.**
2. **Collect relevant information.**
3. **Define the feasible alternative solutions and make realistic estimates.**
4. **Identify the criteria for decision making using one or more attributes.**
5. **Evaluate each alternative, using sensitivity analysis to enhance the evaluation.**
6. **Select the best alternative.**
7. **Implement the solution.**
8. **Monitor the results.**

Engineering economy has a major role in all steps and is primary to steps 2 through 6. Steps 2 and 3 establish the alternatives and make the estimates for each one. Step 4 requires the analyst to identify attributes for alternative selection. This sets the stage for the technique to apply. Step 5 utilizes engineering economy models to complete the evaluation and perform any sensitivity analysis upon which a decision is based (step 6).

EXAMPLE 1.2

Reconsider the questions presented for the engineers in the previous example about co-owning an airplane. State some ways in which engineering economy contributes to decision making between the two alternatives.

Solution
Assume that the objective is the same for each engineer—available, reliable transportation that minimizes total cost. Use the steps above.

Steps 2 and 3: The framework for an engineering economy study assists in identifying what should be estimated or collected. For alternative 1 (buy the plane), estimate the purchase cost, financing method and interest rate, annual operating costs, possible increase in annual sales revenue, and income tax deductions. For alternative 2 (fly commercial) estimate commercial transportation costs, number of trips, annual sales revenue, and other relevant data.

Step 4: The selection criterion is a numerically valued attribute called a *measure of worth.* Some measures of worth are

Present worth (PW)	Future worth (FW)	Payback period
Annual worth (AW)	Rate of return (ROR)	Economic value added
Benefit-cost ratio (BCR)	Capitalized cost (CC)	

When determining a measure of worth, the fact that money today is worth a different amount in the future is considered; that is, the *time value of money* is accounted for.

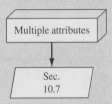

There are many noneconomic attributes—social, environmental, legal, political, personal, to name a few. This multiple-attribute environment may result in less reliance placed on the economic results in step 6. But this is exactly why the decision maker must have adequate information for all factors—economic and noneconomic—to make an informed selection. In our case, the economic analysis may favour the co-owned plane (alternative 1), but because of noneconomic factors, one or both engineers may select alternative 2.

Steps 5 and 6: The actual computations, sensitivity analysis, and alternative selection are accomplished here.

The concept of the *time value of money* was mentioned above. It is often said that money makes money. The statement is indeed true, for if we elect to invest money today, we inherently expect to have more money in the future. If a person or company borrows money today, by tomorrow more than the original loan principal will be owed. This fact is also explained by the time value of money.

The change in the amount of money over a given time period is called the *time value of money*; it is the most important concept in engineering economy.

1.3 PERFORMING AN ENGINEERING ECONOMY STUDY

Consider the terms *engineering economy, engineering economic analysis, economic decision making, capital allocation study, economic analysis,* and similar terms to be synonymous throughout this book. There is a general approach, called the *Engineering Economy Study Approach,* that provides an overview of the engineering economic study. It is outlined in Figure 1–1 for two alternatives. The decision-making process steps are keyed to the blocks in Figure 1–1.

Alternative Description   The result of decision-making process step 1 is a basic understanding of what the problem requires for solution. There may initially be many alternatives, but only a few will be feasible and actually evaluated.

If alternatives A, B, and C have been identified for analysis, when method D, though not recognized as an alternative, is the most attractive, the wrong decision is certain to be made.

Alternatives are stand-alone options that involve a word description and best estimates of parameters, such as *first cost* (including purchase price, development, installation), *useful life, estimated annual incomes and expenses, salvage value* (resale or residual value), an *interest rate* (rate of return), and possibly *inflation* and *income tax effects.* Estimates of annual expenses are usually lumped together and called annual operating costs (AOC) or maintenance and operation (M&O) costs.

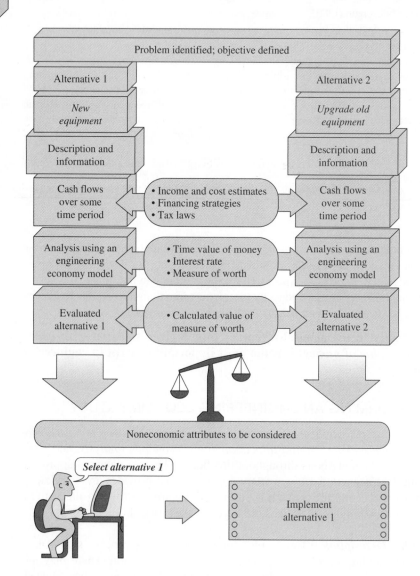

FIGURE 1–1

Engineering economy study approach.

Cash Flows   The estimated inflows (revenues) and outflows (costs) of money are called *cash flows*. These estimates are made for each alternative (step 3). Without cash flow estimates over a stated time period, no engineering economy study can be conducted. Expected variation in cash flows indicates a real need for sensitivity analysis in step 5.

Analysis Using Engineering Economy   Computations that consider the time value of money are performed on the cash flows of each alternative to obtain the measure of worth.

Alternative Selection   The measure-of-worth values are compared, and an alternative is selected. This is the result of the engineering economy analysis. For example, the result of a rate-of-return analysis may be: Select alternative 1, where the rate of return is estimated at 18.4% per year, over alternative 2 with an expected 10% per year return. Some combination of economic criteria using the measure of worth, and the noneconomic and intangible factors, may be applied to help select one alternative.

If only one feasible alternative is defined, a second is often present in the form of the *do-nothing alternative*. This is the *as-is* or *status quo* alternative. Do nothing can be selected if no alternative has a favourable measure of worth.

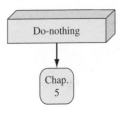

Whether we are aware of it or not, we use criteria every day to choose between alternatives. For example, when you drive to campus, you decide to take the "best" route. But how did you define *best*? Was the best route the safest, shortest, fastest, cheapest, most scenic, or what? Obviously, depending upon which criterion or combination of criteria is used to identify the best, a different route might be selected each time. In economic analysis, *financial units* (dollars or other currency) are generally used as the tangible basis for evaluation. Thus, when there are several ways of accomplishing a stated objective, the alternative with the lowest overall cost or highest overall net income is selected.

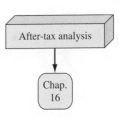

An *after-tax analysis* is performed during project evaluation, usually with only significant effects for asset depreciation and income taxes accounted for. Taxes imposed by local, provincial, federal, and international governments usually take the form of an income tax on revenues, value-added tax (VAT), import taxes, sales taxes, real estate taxes, and others. Taxes affect alternative estimates for cash flows; they tend to *improve* cash flow estimates for expenses, cost savings, and asset depreciation, while they *reduce* cash flow estimates for revenue and after-tax net income. This text delays the details of after-tax analysis until the fundamental tools and techniques of engineering economy are covered. Until then, it is assumed that all alternatives are taxed equally by prevailing tax laws. (If the effects of taxes must be considered earlier, it is recommended that Chapters 15 and 16 be covered after Chapter 6, 8, or 11.)

Now, we turn to some fundamentals of engineering economy that are applicable in the everyday life of engineering practice, as well as personal decision making.

1.4 INTEREST RATE AND RATE OF RETURN

Interest is the manifestation of the time value of money. Computationally, interest is the difference between an ending amount of money and the beginning amount. If the difference is zero or negative, there is no interest. There are always two perspectives to an amount of interest—interest paid and interest earned. Interest is *paid* when a person or organization borrowed money (obtained a loan) and repays a larger amount. Interest is *earned* when a person or organization saved, invested, or lent money and obtains a return of a larger amount. It is shown below that the computations and numerical values are essentially the same for both perspectives, but there are different interpretations.

Interest paid on borrowed funds (a loan) is determined by using the relation

$$\text{Interest} = \text{amount owed now} - \text{original amount} \qquad [1.1]$$

When interest paid over a *specific time unit* is expressed as a percentage of the original amount (principal), the result is called the *interest rate*.

$$\textbf{Interest rate } (\%) = \frac{\textbf{interest accrued per time unit}}{\textbf{original amount}} \times \textbf{100\%} \qquad [1.2]$$

The time unit of the rate is called the *interest period*. By far the most common interest period used to state an interest rate is 1 year. Shorter time periods can be used, such as, 1% per month. Thus, the interest period of the interest rate should always be included. If only the rate is stated, for example, 8.5%, a 1-year interest period is assumed.

EXAMPLE 1.3

An employee at LaserKinetics.com borrows $10,000 on May 1 and must repay a total of $10,700 exactly 1 year later. Determine the interest amount and the interest rate paid.

Solution

The perspective here is that of the borrower since $10,700 repays a loan. Apply Equation [1.1] to determine the interest paid.

$$\text{Interest earned} = \$10,700 - 10,000 = \$700$$

Equation [1.2] determines the interest rate paid for 1 year.

$$\text{Percent interest rate} = \frac{\$700}{\$10,000} \times 100\% = 7\% \text{ per year}$$

EXAMPLE 1.4

Stereophonics, Inc., plans to borrow $20,000 from a bank for 1 year at 6% interest for new recording equipment. (*a*) Compute the interest and the total amount due after 1 year. (*b*) Construct a column graph that shows the original loan amount and total amount due after 1 year used to compute the loan interest rate of 6% per year.

Solution

(a) Compute the total interest accrued by solving Equation [1.2] for interest accrued.

$$\text{Interest} = \$20{,}000(0.06) = \$1200$$

The total amount due is the sum of principal and interest.

$$\text{Total due} = \$20{,}000 + 1200 = \$21{,}200$$

(b) Figure 1–2 shows the values used in Equation [1.2]: $1200 interest, $20,000 original loan principal, 1-year interest period.

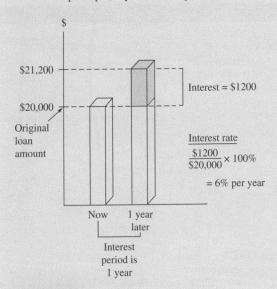

FIGURE 1–2
Values used to compute an interest rate of 6% per year, Example 1.4.

Comment

Note that in part (a), the total amount due may also be computed as

$$\text{Total due} = \text{principal}(1 + \text{interest rate}) = \$20{,}000(1.06) = \$21{,}200$$

Later we will use this method to determine future amounts for times longer than one interest period.

From the perspective of a saver, a lender, or an investor, interest earned is the final amount minus the initial amount, or principal.

$$\text{Interest earned} = \text{total amount now} - \text{original amount} \qquad [1.3]$$

Interest earned over a specific period of time is expressed as a percentage of the original amount and is called *rate of return (ROR).*

$$\textbf{Rate of return (\%)} = \frac{\textbf{interest accrued per time unit}}{\textbf{original amount}} \times \textbf{100\%} \qquad [1.4]$$

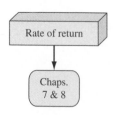

The time unit for rate of return is called the *interest period,* just as for the borrower's perspective. Again, the most common period is 1 year.

The term *return on investment (ROI)* is used equivalently with ROR in different industries and settings, especially where large capital funds are committed to engineering-oriented programs.

The numerical values in Equation [1.2] and Equation [1.4] are the same, but the term *interest rate paid* is more appropriate for the borrower's perspective, while the *rate of return earned* is better for the investor's perspective.

EXAMPLE 1.5

(*a*) Calculate the amount deposited 1 year ago to have $1000 now at an interest rate of 3% per year.

(*b*) Calculate the amount of interest earned during this time period.

Solution

(*a*) The total amount accrued ($1000) is the sum of the original deposit and the earned interest. If X is the original deposit,

$$\text{Total accrued} = \text{original} + \text{original (interest rate)}$$
$$\$1000 = X + X(0.03) = X(1 + 0.03) = 1.03X$$

The original deposit is

$$X = \frac{1000}{1.03} = \$970.87$$

(*b*) Apply Equation [1.3] to determine interest earned.

$$\text{Interest} = \$1000 - 970.87 = \$29.13$$

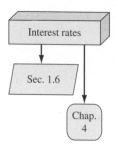

In Examples 1.3 to 1.5 the interest period was 1 year, and the interest amount was calculated at the end of one period. When more than one interest period is involved (e.g., if we wanted the amount of interest owed after 3 years in Example 1.4), it is necessary to state whether the interest is accrued on a *simple* or *compound* basis from one period to the next.

An additional economic consideration for any engineering economy study is *inflation.* Several comments about the fundamentals of inflation are warranted at this early stage. First, inflation represents a decrease in the value of a given currency. That is, $1 now will not purchase the same number of apples (or most other things) as $1 did 20 years ago. The changing value of the currency affects market interest rates. In simple terms, bank interest rates reflect two things: a so-called real rate of return *plus* the expected inflation rate. The real rate of return allows the investor to purchase more than he or she could have purchased before the investment.

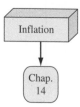

From the borrower's perspective, the rate of inflation is simply another interest rate *tacked on to the real interest rate.* And, from the vantage point of the saver or investor in a fixed-interest account, inflation *reduces the real rate of*

return on the investment. Inflation means that cost and revenue cash flow estimates increase over time. This increase is due to the changing value of money that is forced upon a country's currency by inflation, thus making a unit of currency (one dollar) worth less relative to its value at a previous time. We see the effect of inflation in that money purchases less now than it did at a previous time. Inflation contributes to

* A reduction in purchasing power of the currency.
* An increase in the CPI (consumer price index).
* An increase in the cost of equipment and its maintenance.
* An increase in the cost of salaried professionals and hourly employees.
* A reduction in the real rate of return on personal savings and certain corporate investments.

In other words, inflation can materially contribute to changes in corporate and personal economic analysis.

Commonly, engineering economy studies assume that inflation affects all estimated values equally. Accordingly, an interest rate or rate of return, such as 8% per year, is applied throughout the analysis without accounting for an additional inflation rate. However, if inflation were explicitly taken into account, and it was reducing the value of money at, say, an average of 4% per year, it would be necessary to perform the economic analysis using an inflated interest rate of 12.32% per year. (The relevant relations are derived in Chapter 14.) On the other hand, if the stated ROR on an investment is 8% with inflation included, the same inflation rate of 4% per year results in a real rate of return of only 3.85% per year!

1.5 EQUIVALENCE

Equivalent terms are used very often in the transfer from one scale to another. For example:

Length: 100 centimetres = 1 metre   1000 metres = 1 kilometre

Pressure: 1 pascal = 1 newton/metre^2
             1 atmosphere = 10^5 pascals

Many equivalent measures are a combination of two or more scales.

When considered together, the time value of money and the interest rate help develop the concept of *economic equivalence,* which means that different sums of money at different times would be equal in economic value. For example, if the interest rate is 6% per year, $100 today (present time) is equivalent to $106 one year from today.

$$\text{Amount accrued} = 100 + 100(0.06) = 100(1 + 0.06) = \$106$$

So, if someone offered you a gift of $100 today or $106 one year from today, it would make no difference which offer you accepted from an economic perspective. In either case you have $106 one year from today. However, the two sums of money are equivalent to each other *only* when the interest rate is 6% per year. At a higher or lower interest rate, $100 today is not equivalent to $106 one year from today.

In addition to future equivalence, we can apply the same logic to determine equivalence for previous years. A total of $100 now is equivalent to $100/1.06 = $94.34 one year ago at an interest rate of 6% per year. From these illustrations, we can state the following: $94.34 last year, $100 now, and $106 one year from now are equivalent at an interest rate of 6% per year. The fact that these sums are equivalent can be verified by computing the two interest rates for 1-year interest periods.

$$\frac{\$6}{\$100} \times 100\% = 6\% \text{ per year}$$

and

$$\frac{\$5.66}{\$94.34} \times 100\% = 6\% \text{ per year}$$

Figure 1–3 indicates the amount of interest each year necessary to make these three different amounts equivalent at 6% per year.

FIGURE 1–3

Equivalence of three amounts at a 6% per year interest rate.

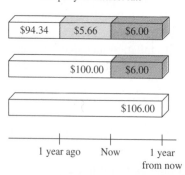

EXAMPLE 1.6

AC-Delco makes auto batteries available to General Motors dealers through privately owned distributorships. In general, batteries are stored throughout the year, and a 5% cost increase is added each year to cover the inventory carrying charge for the distributorship owner. Assume you own the City Centre Delco facility. Make the calculations necessary to show which of the following statements are true and which are false about battery costs.

(a)   The amount of $98 now is equivalent to a cost of $105.60 one year from now.
(b)   A truck battery cost of $200 one year ago is equivalent to $205 now.
(c)   A $38 cost now is equivalent to $39.90 one year from now.
(d)   A $3000 cost now is equivalent to $2887.14 one year ago.
(e)   The carrying charge accumulated in 1 year on an investment of $2000 worth of batteries is $100.

Solution

(a) Total amount accrued = 98(1.05) = $102.90 ≠ $105.60; therefore, it is false. Another way to solve this is as follows: Required original cost is 105.60/1.05 = $100.57 ≠ $98.

(b) Required old cost is 205.00/1.05 = $195.24 ≠ $200; therefore, it is false.

(c) The cost 1 year from now is $38(1.05) = $39.90; true.

(d) Cost now is 2887.14(1.05) = $3031.50 ≠ $3000; false.

(e) The charge is 5% per year interest, or 2000(0.05) = $100; true.

1.6 SIMPLE AND COMPOUND INTEREST

The terms *interest, interest period,* and *interest rate* (introduced in Section 1.4) are useful in calculating equivalent sums of money for one interest period in the past and one period in the future. However, for more than one interest period, the terms *simple interest* and *compound interest* become important.

Simple interest is calculated using the principal only, ignoring any interest accrued in preceding interest periods. The total simple interest over several periods is computed as

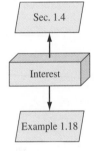

$$\text{Interest} = \text{(principal)(number of periods)(interest rate)} \qquad [1.5]$$

where the interest rate is expressed in decimal form.

EXAMPLE 1.7

Pacific Savings Credit Union lent money to an engineer for a radio-controlled model airplane. The loan is for $1000 for 3 years at 5% per year simple interest. How much money will the engineer repay at the end of 3 years? Tabulate the results.

Solution
The interest for each of the 3 years is

$$\text{Interest per year} = 1000(0.05) = \$50$$

Total interest for 3 years from Equation [1.5] is

$$\text{Total interest} = 1000(3)(0.05) = \$150$$

The amount due after 3 years is

$$\text{Total due} = \$1000 + 150 = \$1150$$

The $50 interest accrued in the first year and the $50 accrued in the second year do not earn interest. The interest due each year is calculated only on the $1000 principal.

The details of this loan repayment are tabulated in Table 1–1 from the perspective of the borrower. The year zero represents the present, that is, when the money is borrowed. No payment is made until the end of year 3. The amount owed each year increases uniformly by $50, since simple interest is figured on only the loan principal.

TABLE 1–1 Simple Interest Computations

(1) End of Year	(2) Amount Borrowed	(3) Interest	(4) Amount Owed	(5) Amount Paid
0	$1000			
1	—	$50	$1050	$ 0
2	—	50	1100	0
3	—	50	1150	1150

For *compound interest,* the interest accrued for each interest period is calculated on the *principal plus the total amount of interest accumulated in all previous periods.* Thus, compound interest means interest on top of interest. Compound interest reflects the effect of the time value of money on the interest also. Now the interest for one period is calculated as

$$\text{Interest} = (\text{principal} + \text{all accrued interest})(\text{interest rate}) \qquad [1.6]$$

EXAMPLE 1.8

If an engineer borrows $1000 from a credit union at 5% per year compound interest, compute the total amount due after 3 years. Graph and compare the results of this and the previous example.

Solution
The interest and total amount due each year are computed separately using Equation [1.6].

Year 1 interest:	$1000(0.05) = $50.00
Total amount due after year 1:	$1000 + 50.00 = $1050.00
Year 2 interest:	$1050(0.05) = $52.50
Total amount due after year 2 :	$1050 + 52.50 = $1102.50
Year 3 interest:	$1102.50(0.05) = $55.13
Total amount due after year 3:	$1102.50 + 55.13 = $1157.63

The details are shown in Table 1–2. The repayment plan is the same as that for the simple interest example—no payment until the principal plus accrued interest is due at the end of year 3.

Figure 1–4 shows the amount owed at the end of each year for 3 years. The difference due to the time value of money is recognized for the compound interest case. An extra $1157.63 − $1150 = $7.63 of interest is paid compared with simple interest over the 3-year period.

TABLE 1–2 Compound Interest Computations, Example 1.8

(1)	(2)	(3)	(4)	(5)
End of Year	Amount Borrowed	Interest	Amount Owed	Amount Paid
0	$1000			
1	—	$50.00	$1050.00	$ 0
2	—	52.50	1102.50	0
3	—	55.13	1157.63	1157.63

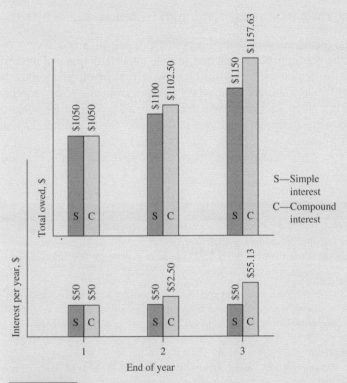

S—Simple interest
C—Compound interest

FIGURE 1–4

Comparison of simple and compound interest calculations, Examples 1.7 and 1.8.

Comment

The difference between simple and compound interest grows each year. If the computations are continued for more years, for example, 10 years, the difference is $128.90; after 20 years compound interest is $653.30 more than simple interest.

If $7.63 does not seem like a significant difference in only 3 years, remember that the beginning amount here is $1000. If we make these same calculations for an initial amount of $100,000 or $1 million, multiply the difference by 100 or 1000, and we are talking real money. This indicates that the power of compounding is vitally important in all economics-based analyses.

Another and shorter way to calculate the total amount due after 3 years in Example 1.8 is to combine calculations rather than perform them on a year-by-year basis. The total due each year is as follows:

$$\text{Year 1:} \quad \$1000(1.05)^1 = \$1050.00$$

$$\text{Year 2:} \quad \$1000(1.05)^2 = \$1102.50$$

$$\text{Year 3:} \quad \$1000(1.05)^3 = \$1157.63$$

The year 3 total is calculated directly; it does not require the year 2 total. In general formula form

$$\text{Total due after a number of years} = \text{principal}(1 + \text{interest rate})^{\text{number of years}}$$

This fundamental relation is used many times in upcoming chapters.

We combine the concepts of interest rate, simple interest, compound interest, and equivalence to demonstrate that different loan repayment plans may be equivalent, but differ substantially in monetary amounts from one year to another. This also shows that there are many ways to take into account the time value of money. The following example illustrates equivalence for five different loan repayment plans.

EXAMPLE 1.9

(*a*) Demonstrate the concept of equivalence using the different loan repayment plans described below. Each plan repays a $5000 loan in 5 years at 8% interest per year.

- **Plan 1: Simple interest, pay all at end.** No interest or principal is paid until the end of year 5. Interest accumulates each year on the principal only.
- **Plan 2: Compound interest, pay all at end.** No interest or principal is paid until the end of year 5. Interest accumulates each year on the total of principal and all accrued interest.
- **Plan 3: Simple interest paid annually, principal repaid at end.** The accrued interest is paid each year, and the entire principal is repaid at the end of year 5.
- **Plan 4: Compound interest and portion of principal repaid annually.** The accrued interest and one-fifth of the principal (or $1000) is repaid each year. The outstanding loan balance decreases each year, so the interest for each year decreases.
- **Plan 5: Equal payments of compound interest and principal made annually.** Equal payments are made each year with a portion going toward principal repayment and the remainder covering the accrued interest. Since the loan balance

decreases at a rate slower than that in plan 4 due to the equal end-of-year payments, the interest decreases, but at a slower rate.

(b) Make a statement about the equivalence of each plan at 8% simple or compound interest, as appropriate.

Solution

(a) Table 1–3 presents the interest, payment amount, total owed at the end of each year, and total amount paid over the 5-year period (column 4 totals).

	(1)	(2)	(3)	(4)	(5)
	End of Year	Interest Owed for Year	Total Owed at End of Year	End-of-Year Payment	Total Owed After Payment
TABLE 1–3 Different Repayment Schedules over 5 Years for $5000 at 8% per Year Interest					
Plan 1: Simple Interest, Pay All at End					
	0				$5000.00
	1	$400.00	$5400.00	—	5400.00
	2	400.00	5800.00	—	5800.00
	3	400.00	6200.00	—	6200.00
	4	400.00	6600.00	—	6600.00
	5	400.00	7000.00	$7000.00	
	Totals			$7000.00	
Plan 2: Compound Interest, Pay All at End					
	0				$5000.00
	1	$400.00	$5400.00	—	5400.00
	2	432.00	5832.00	—	5832.00
	3	466.56	6298.56	—	6298.56
	4	503.88	6802.44	—	6802.44
	5	544.20	7346.64	$7346.64	
	Totals			$7346.64	
Plan 3: Simple Interest Paid Annually, Principal Repaid at End					
	0				$5000.00
	1	$400.00	$5400.00	$ 400.00	5000.00
	2	400.00	5400.00	400.00	5000.00
	3	400.00	5400.00	400.00	5000.00
	4	400.00	5400.00	400.00	5000.00
	5	400.00	5400.00	5400.00	
	Totals			$7000.00	

TABLE 1–3   (Continued)

(1) End of Year	(2) Interest Owed for Year	(3) Total Owed at End of Year	(4) End-of-Year Payment	(5) Total Owed After Payment
Plan 4: Compound Interest and Portion of Principal Repaid Annually				
0				$5000.00
1	$400.00	$5400.00	$1400.00	4000.00
2	320.00	4320.00	1320.00	3000.00
3	240.00	3240.00	1240.00	2000.00
4	160.00	2160.00	1160.00	1000.00
5	80.00	1080.00	1080.00	
Totals			$6200.00	
Plan 5: Equal Annual Payments of Compound Interest and Principal				
0				$5000.00
1	$400.00	$5400.00	$1252.28	4147.72
2	331.82	4479.54	1252.28	3227.25
3	258.18	3485.43	1252.28	2233.15
4	178.65	2411.80	1252.28	1159.52
5	92.76	1252.28	1252.28	
Totals			$6261.41	

The amounts of interest (column 2) are determined as follows:

Plan 1   Simple interest = (original principal)(0.08)
Plan 2   Compound interest = (total owed previous year)(0.08)
Plan 3   Simple interest = (original principal)(0.08)
Plan 4   Compound interest = (total owed previous year)(0.08)
Plan 5   Compound interest = (total owed previous year)(0.08)

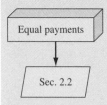

Equal payments

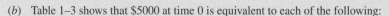

Sec. 2.2

Note that the amounts of the annual payments are different for each repayment schedule and that the total amounts repaid for most plans are different, even though each repayment plan requires exactly 5 years. The difference in the total amounts repaid can be explained (1) by the time value of money, (2) by simple or compound interest, and (3) by the partial repayment of principal prior to year 5.

(*b*)   Table 1–3 shows that $5000 at time 0 is equivalent to each of the following:

Plan 1 $7000 at the end of year 5 at 8% simple interest.
Plan 2 $7346.64 at the end of year 5 at 8% compound interest.
Plan 3 $400 per year for 4 years and $5400 at the end of year 5 at 8% simple interest.

Plan 4 Decreasing payments of interest and partial principal in years 1 ($1400) through 5 ($1080) at 8% compound interest.

Plan 5 $1252.28 per year for 5 years at 8% compound interest.

An engineering economy study uses plan 5; interest is compounded, and a constant amount is paid each period. This amount covers accrued interest and a partial amount of principal repayment.

1.7 TERMINOLOGY AND SYMBOLS

The equations and procedures of engineering economy utilize the following terms and symbols. Sample units are indicated.

P = value or amount of money at a time designated as the present or time 0. Also P is referred to as present worth (PW), present value (PV), net present value (NPV), discounted cash flow (DCF), and capitalized cost (CC); dollars

F = value or amount of money at some future time. Also F is called future worth (FW) and future value (FV); dollars

A = series of consecutive, equal, end-of-period amounts of money. Also A is called the annual worth (AW) and equivalent uniform annual worth (EUAW); dollars per year, dollars per month

n = number of interest periods; years, months, days

i = interest rate or rate of return per time period; percent per year, percent per month, percent per day

t = time, stated in periods; years, months, days

The symbols P and F represent one-time occurrences: A occurs with the same value once each interest period for a specified number of periods. It should be clear that a present value P represents a single sum of money at some time prior to a future value F or prior to the first occurrence of an equivalent series amount A.

It is important to note that the symbol A always represents a uniform amount (i.e., the same amount each period) that extends through *consecutive* interest periods. Both conditions must exist before the series can be represented by A.

The interest rate i is assumed to be a compound rate, unless specifically stated as simple interest. The rate i is expressed in percent per interest period, for example, 12% per year. Unless stated otherwise, assume that the rate applies throughout the entire n years or interest periods. The decimal equivalent for i is always used in engineering economy computations.

All engineering economy problems involve the element of time n and interest rate i. In general, every problem will involve at least four of the symbols $P, F, A, n,$ and i, with at least three of them estimated or known.

EXAMPLE 1.10

A new college graduate has a job with Bombardier. She plans to borrow $10,000 now to help in buying a car. She has arranged to repay the entire principal plus 8% per-year interest after 5 years. Identify the engineering economy symbols involved and their values for the total owed after 5 years.

Solution

In this case, P and F are involved, since all amounts are single payments, as well as n and i. Time is expressed in years.

$$P = \$10,000 \qquad i = 8\% \text{ per year} \qquad n = 5 \text{ years} \qquad F = ?$$

The future amount F is unknown.

EXAMPLE 1.11

Assume you borrow $2000 now at 7% per year for 10 years and must repay the loan in equal yearly payments. Determine the symbols involved and their values.

Solution

Time is in years.

$$P = \$2000$$
$$A = ? \text{ per year for 5 years}$$
$$i = 7\% \text{ per year}$$
$$n = 10 \text{ years}$$

In Examples 1.10 and 1.11, the P value is a receipt to the borrower, and F or A is a disbursement from the borrower. It is equally correct to use these symbols in the reverse roles.

EXAMPLE 1.12

On July 1, 2008, your new employer Canadian Pacific Railways deposits $5000 into your savings account, as part of your employment bonus. The account pays interest at 5% per year. You expect to withdraw an equal annual amount for the following 10 years. Identify the symbols and their values.

Solution

Time is in years.

$$P = \$5000$$
$$A = ? \text{ per year}$$
$$i = 5\% \text{ per year}$$
$$n = 10 \text{ years}$$

EXAMPLE 1.13

You plan to make a lump-sum deposit of $5000 now into an investment account that pays 6% per year, and you plan to withdraw an equal end-of-year amount of $1000 for 5 years, starting next year. At the end of the sixth year, you plan to close your account by withdrawing the remaining money. Define the engineering economy symbols involved.

Solution
Time is expressed in years.

$$P = \$5000$$
$$A = \$1000 \text{ per year for 5 years}$$
$$F = ? \text{ at end of year 6}$$
$$i = 6\% \text{ per year}$$
$$n = 5 \text{ years for the } A \text{ series and 6 for the } F \text{ value}$$

EXAMPLE 1.14

Last year Jane's grandmother offered to put enough money into a savings account to generate $1000 this year to help pay Jane's expenses at university. (*a*) Identify the symbols and (*b*) calculate the amount that had to be deposited exactly 1 year ago to earn $1000 in interest now, if the rate of return is 6% per year.

Solution
(*a*) Time is in years.

$$P = ?$$
$$i = 6\% \text{ per year}$$
$$n = 1 \text{ year}$$
$$F = P + \text{interest}$$
$$= ? + \$1000$$

(*b*) Refer to Equations [1.3] and [1.4]. Let F = total amount now and P = original amount. We know that $F - P = \$1000$ is the accrued interest. Now we can determine P for Jane and her grandmother.

$$F = P + P(\text{interest rate})$$

The $1000 interest can be expressed as

$$\text{Interest} = F - P = [P + P(\text{interest rate})] - P$$
$$= P(\text{interest rate})$$
$$\$1000 = P(0.06)$$
$$P = \frac{1000}{0.06} = \$16,666.67$$

1.8 INTRODUCTION TO SOLUTION BY COMPUTER

The functions on a computer spreadsheet can greatly reduce the amount of hand and calculator work for equivalency computations involving *compound interest* and the terms P, F, A, i, and n. The power of the electronic spreadsheet often makes it possible to enter a predefined spreadsheet function into one cell and obtain the final answer immediately. Any spreadsheet system can be used—one off the shelf, such as Microsoft Excel©, or one specially developed with built-in financial functions and operators. Excel is used throughout this book because it is readily available and easy to use.

Appendix A is a primer on using spreadsheets and Excel. The functions used in engineering economy are described there in detail, with explanations of all the parameters (also called *arguments*) placed between parentheses after the function identifier. The Excel online help function provides similar information. Appendix A also includes a section on spreadsheet layout that is useful when the economic analysis is presented to someone else—a coworker, a boss, or a professor.

A total of six Excel functions can perform most of the fundamental engineering economy calculations. However, these functions are no substitute for knowing how the time value of money and compound interest work. The functions are great supplemental tools, but they do not replace the understanding of engineering economy relations, assumptions, and techniques.

Using the symbols P, F, A, i, and n exactly as defined in the previous section, the Excel functions most used in engineering economic analysis are formulated as follows.

To find the present value P: PV($i\%,n,A,F$)

To find the future value F: FV($i\%,n,A,P$)

To find the equal, periodic value A: PMT($i\%,n,P,F$)

To find the number of periods n: NPER($i\%,A,P,F$)

To find the compound interest rate i: RATE(n,A,P,F)

To find the compound interest rate i: IRR(first_cell:last_cell)

To find the present value P of any series: NPV($i\%$,second_cell:last_cell) + first_cell

If some of the parameters don't apply to a particular problem, they can be omitted and zero is assumed. If the parameter omitted is an interior one, the comma must be entered. The last two functions require that a series of numbers be entered into contiguous spreadsheet cells, but the first five can be used with no supporting data. In all cases, the function must be preceded by an equals sign (=) in the cell where the answer is to be displayed.

Each of these functions will be introduced and illustrated at the point in this text where they are most useful. However, to get an idea of how they work, look back at Examples 1.10 and 1.11. In Example 1.10, the future amount F is unknown, as indicated by $F = ?$ in the solution. In the next chapter, we will learn how the time value of money is used to find F, given P, i, and n. To find F in this example using a spreadsheet, simply enter the FV function preceded by an equals sign into any cell. The format is =FV($i\%,n,,P$) or =FV(8%,5,,10000).

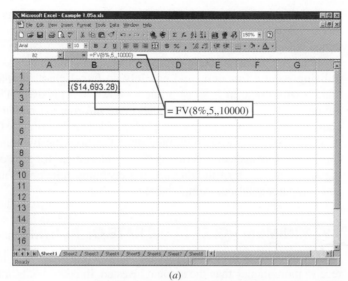

(a)

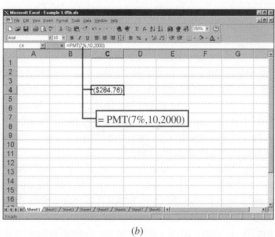

(b)

FIGURE 1–5

Excel spreadsheet functions for (a) Example 1.10 and (b) Example 1.11.

The third comma is still entered even though there is no *A* involved. Figure 1–5*a* is a screen image of the Excel spreadsheet with the FV function entered into cell B2. The answer of $-14,693.28 is displayed. The answer is in red on the actual Excel screen, to indicate a negative amount from the borrower's perspective to repay the loan after 5 years. The FV function is shown in the formula bar above the worksheet itself. Also, we have added a cell tag to show the format of the FV function.

In Example 1.11, the uniform annual amount *A* is sought, and *P*, *i*, and *n* are known. Find *A*, using the function PMT(*i*%,*n*,*P*) or, in this example, PMT(7%,10,2000). Figure 1–5*b* shows the result in cell C4. The format of the FV function is shown in the formula bar and the cell tag.

Because these functions can be used so easily and rapidly, we will detail them in many of the examples throughout the book. A special icon with *Q-Solve* (for quick solution) printed on it (shown here) is placed in the margin when just one function is needed to get an answer. In the introductory chapters of Level One,

the entire spreadsheet and detailed functions are shown. In succeeding chapters, the Q-Solve icon is shown in the margin, and the spreadsheet function is contained within the solution of the example.

When the power of the computer is used to solve a more complex problem utilizing several functions and possibly an Excel chart (graph), an icon in the margin with the term *E-Solve* printed (shown here) is used. These spreadsheets are more complex and contain much more information and computation, especially when sensitivity analysis is performed. The Solution by Computer answer to an example is always presented after the Solution by Hand. As mentioned earlier, the spreadsheet function is not a replacement for the correct understanding and application of the engineering economy relations. Therefore, the hand and computer solutions complement each other.

1.9 MINIMUM ACCEPTABLE RATE OF RETURN

For any investment to be profitable, the investor (corporate or individual) expects to receive more money than the amount invested. In other words, a fair *rate of return,* or *return on investment,* must be realizable. The definition of ROR in Equation [1.4] is used in this discussion, that is, amount earned divided by the original amount.

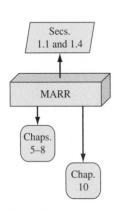

Engineering alternatives are evaluated upon the prognosis that a reasonable ROR can be expected. Therefore, some reasonable rate must be established for the selection criteria phase of the engineering economy study (Figure 1–1). The reasonable rate is called the *minimum acceptable rate of return (MARR)* and is higher than the rate expected from a bank or some safe investment that involves minimal investment risk. Figure 1–6 indicates the relations between different rate of return values. In Canada, the Prime Rate of the Bank of Canada is usually used as the benchmark safe rate.

The MARR is also referred to as the *hurdle rate* for projects; that is, to be considered financially viable the expected ROR must meet or exceed the MARR or hurdle rate. Note that the MARR is not a rate that is calculated like a ROR. The MARR is established by (financial) managers and is used as a criterion against which an alternative's ROR is measured, when making the accept/reject decision.

To develop a foundation-level understanding of how a MARR value is established and used, we must return to the term *capital* introduced in Section 1.1. Capital is also referred to as *capital funds* and *capital investment money.* It always costs money in the form of interest to raise capital. The interest, stated as a percentage rate, is a significant part of the *cost of capital.* Another cost of capital is the opportunity to invest in an alternative project of similar risk. For example, if you want to purchase a new music system, but don't have sufficient money (capital), you could obtain a credit union loan at some interest rate, say, 9% per year and use that cash to pay the merchant now. Or you could use your (newly acquired) credit card and pay off the balance on a monthly basis. This approach will probably cost you at least 18% per year. Or you could use funds from your savings account that earns 3% per year and pay cash. The 9%, 18%, and 3% rates are your cost of capital estimates to raise the capital for the system by different methods of capital financing. In analogous ways, corporations estimate the cost

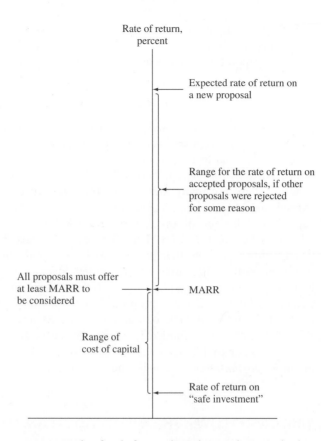

FIGURE 1–6
Size of MARR relative
to other rate of return
values.

of capital from different sources to raise funds for engineering projects and other types of projects.

In general, capital is developed in two ways—equity financing and debt financing. A combination of these two is very common for most projects. Chapter 10 covers these in greater detail, but a snapshot description follows.

Equity financing. The corporation uses its own funds from cash on hand, stock sales, or retained earnings. Individuals can use their own cash, savings, or investments. In the example above, using money from the 5% savings account is equity financing.

Debt financing. The corporation borrows from outside sources and repays the principal and interest according to some schedule, much like the plans in Table 1–3. Sources of debt capital may be bonds, loans, mortgages, venture capital pools, and many others. Individuals, too, can utilize debt sources, such as the credit card and credit union options described in the music system example.

Combinations of debt-equity financing mean that a weighted average cost of capital (WACC) results. If the music system is purchased with 40% credit card money at 18% per year and 60% savings account funds earning 5% per year, the weighted average cost of capital is $0.4(18) + 0.6(5) = 10.2\%$ per year.

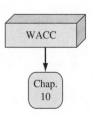

For a corporation, the *established MARR* used as a criterion to accept or reject an alternative will always be *higher than the weighted average cost of capital* that the corporation must bear to obtain the necessary capital funds. So the inequality

$$\text{ROR} \geq \text{MARR} > \text{cost of capital} \qquad [1.7]$$

must be correct for an accepted project. Exceptions may be government-regulated requirements (safety, security, environmental, legal, etc.), economically lucrative ventures expected to lead to other opportunities, etc. Value-added engineering projects usually follow Equation [1.7].

Often there are many alternatives that are expected to yield a ROR that exceeds the MARR as indicated in Figure 1–6, but there may not be sufficient capital available for all, or the project's risk may be estimated as too high to take the investment chance. Therefore, new projects that are undertaken are usually those projects that have an expected return at least as great as the return on another alternative not yet funded. Such a selected new project would be a proposal represented by the top ROR arrow in Figure 1–6. For example, assume MARR = 12% and proposal 1 with an expected ROR = 13% cannot be funded due to a lack of capital funds. Meanwhile, proposal 2 has a ROR = 14.5% and is funded from available capital. Since proposal 1 is not undertaken due to the lack of capital, its estimated ROR of 13% is referred to as the *opportunity cost*; that is, the opportunity to make an additional 13% return is forgone.

1.10 CASH FLOWS: THEIR ESTIMATION AND DIAGRAMMING

In Section 1.3 cash flows are described as the inflows and outflows of money. These cash flows may be estimates or observed values. Every person or company has cash receipts—revenue and income (inflows); and cash disbursements—expenses, and costs (outflows). These receipts and disbursements are the cash flows, with a plus sign representing cash inflows and a minus sign representing cash outflows. Cash flows occur during specified periods of time, such as 1 month or 1 year.

Of all the elements of the engineering economy study approach (Figure 1–1), cash flow estimation is likely the most difficult and inexact. Cash flow estimates are just that—estimates about an uncertain future. Once estimated, the techniques of this book guide the decision-making process. The forecasted cash inflows and outflows for each alternative influences the quality of the economic analysis and conclusion.

Cash inflows, or receipts, may comprise the following, depending upon the nature of the proposed activity and the type of business involved.

Samples of Cash Inflow Estimates

Revenues (usually *incremental* resulting from an alternative)

Operating cost reductions (resulting from an alternative)

Asset salvage value

Receipt of loan principal

Income tax savings

Receipts from stock and bond sales

Construction and facility cost savings

Saving or return of corporate capital funds

Cash outflows, or disbursements, may comprise the following, again depending upon the nature of the activity and type of business.

Samples of Cash Outflow Estimates

First cost of assets

Engineering design costs

Operating costs (annual and incremental)

Periodic maintenance and rebuild costs

Loan interest and principal payments

Major expected/unexpected upgrade costs

Income taxes

Expenditure of corporate capital funds

Background information for estimates may be available in departments such as accounting, finance, marketing, sales, engineering, design, manufacturing, production, field services, and computer services. The accuracy of estimates is largely dependent upon the experiences of the person making the estimate with similar situations. Usually *point estimates* are made; that is, a single-value estimate is developed for each economic element of an alternative. If a statistical approach to the engineering economy study is undertaken, a *range estimate* or *distribution estimate* may be developed. Though more involved computationally, a statistical study provides more complete results when key estimates are expected to vary widely. We will use point estimates throughout most of this book. Final chapters discuss decision making under risk.

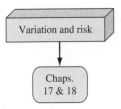

Once the cash inflow and outflow estimates are developed, the net cash flow can be determined.

$$\textbf{Net cash flow} = \textbf{receipts} - \textbf{disbursements}$$

$$= \textbf{cash inflows} - \textbf{cash outflows} \qquad \textbf{[1.8]}$$

Since cash flows normally take place at varying times within an interest period, a simplifying assumption is made.

> The *end-of-period convention* **means that all cash flows are assumed to occur at the end of an interest period. When several receipts and disbursements occur within a given interest period, the *net* cash flow is assumed to occur at the *end* of the interest period.**

However, it should be understood that, although F or A amounts are located at the end of the interest period by convention, the end of the period is not necessarily December 31. In Example 1.12 the deposit took place on July 1, 2008, and the withdrawals will take place on July 1 of each succeeding year for 10 years. *Thus, end of the period means end of interest period, not end of calendar year.*

The *cash flow diagram* is a very important tool in an economic analysis, especially when the cash flow series is complex. It is a graphical representation of cash flows drawn on a time scale. The diagram includes what is known, what is estimated, and what is needed. That is, once the cash flow diagram is complete, another person should be able to work the problem by looking at the diagram.

Cash flow diagram time $t = 0$ is the present, and $t = 1$ is the end of time period 1. We assume that the periods are in years for now. The time scale of Figure 1–7 is set up for 5 years. Since the end-of-year convention places cash flows at the end of years, the "1" marks the end of year 1.

While it is not necessary to use an exact scale on the cash flow diagram, you will probably avoid errors if you make a neat diagram to approximate scale for both time and relative cash flow magnitudes.

The direction of the arrows on the cash flow diagram is important. A vertical arrow pointing up indicates a positive cash flow. Conversely, an arrow pointing down indicates a negative cash flow. Figure 1–8 illustrates a receipt (cash inflow) at the end of year 1 and equal disbursements (cash outflows) at the end of years 2 and 3.

The perspective or vantage point must be determined prior to placing a sign on each cash flow and diagramming it. As an illustration, if you borrow $2500 to buy a $2000 used Yamaha V-Star motorcycle for cash, and you use the remaining $500 for a new paint job, there may be several different perspectives taken. Possible perspectives, cash flow signs, and amounts are as follows.

Perspective	Cash Flow, $
Credit union	−2500
You as borrower	+2500
You as purchaser,	−2000
and as paint customer	−500
Used cycle dealer	+2000
Paint shop owner	+500

FIGURE 1–7

A typical cash flow time scale for 5 years.

FIGURE 1–8

Example of positive and negative cash flows.

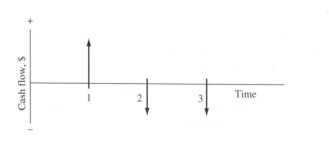

EXAMPLE 1.15

Reread Example 1.10, where $P = \$10,000$ is borrowed at 8% per year and F is sought after 5 years. Construct the cash flow diagram.

Solution

Figure 1–9 presents the cash flow diagram from the vantage point of the borrower. The present sum P is a cash inflow of the loan principal at year 0, and the future sum F is the cash outflow of the repayment at the end of year 5. The interest rate should be indicated on the diagram.

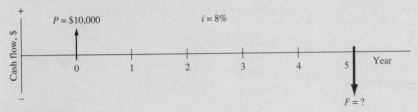

FIGURE 1–9
Cash flow diagram, Example 1.15.

EXAMPLE 1.16

Each year Esso Petroleum expends large amounts of funds for mechanical safety features throughout its worldwide operations. Michelle Fortier, a lead engineer for Quebec and Atlantic region operations, plans expenditures of $1 million now and each of the next 4 years just for the improvement of field-based pressure-release valves. Construct the cash flow diagram to find the equivalent value of these expenditures at the end of year 4, using a cost of capital estimate for safety-related funds of 12% per year.

Solution

Figure 1–10 indicates the uniform and negative cash flow series (expenditures) for five periods, and the unknown F value (positive cash flow equivalent) at exactly the same time as the fifth expenditure. Since the expenditures start immediately, the first $1 million is shown at time 0, not time 1. Therefore, the last negative cash flow occurs at the end of the fourth year, when F also occurs. To make this diagram appear similar to that of Figure 1–9 with a full 5 years on the time scale, the addition of the year -1 prior to year 0 completes the diagram for a full 5 years. This addition demonstrates that year 0 is the end-of-period point for the year -1.

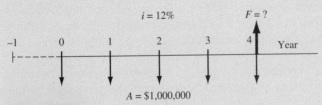

FIGURE 1–10
Cash flow diagram, Example 1.16.

EXAMPLE 1.17

A father wants to deposit an unknown lump-sum amount into an investment opportunity 2 years from now that is large enough to withdraw $4000 per year for university tuition for 5 years starting 3 years from now. If the rate of return is estimated to be 7% per year, construct the cash flow diagram.

Solution

Figure 1–11 presents the cash flows from the father's perspective. The present value P is a cash outflow 2 years hence and is to be determined ($P = ?$). Note that this present value does not occur at time $t = 0$, but it does occur one period prior to the first A value of $4000, which is the cash inflow to the father.

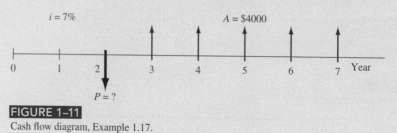

FIGURE 1–11
Cash flow diagram, Example 1.17.

Additional Examples 1.19 and 1.20.

1.11 RULE OF 72: ESTIMATING DOUBLING TIME AND INTEREST RATE

Sometimes it is helpful to estimate the number of years n or the rate of return i required for a single cash flow amount to double in size. The *rule of 72* for compound interest rates can be used to estimate i or n, given the other value. The estimation is simple; the time required for an initial single amount to double in size with compound interest is approximately equal to 72 divided by the rate of return in percent.

$$\text{Estimated } n = \frac{72}{i} \qquad [1.9]$$

For example, at a rate of 5% per year, it would take approximately $72/5 = 14.4$ years for a current amount to double. (The actual time required is 14.3 years, as will be shown in Chapter 2.) Table 1–4 compares the times estimated from the rule of 72 to the actual times required for doubling at several compounded rates.

Alternatively, the compound rate i in percent required for money to double in a specified period of time n can be estimated by dividing 72 by the specified n value.

$$\text{Estimated } i = \frac{72}{n} \qquad [1.10]$$

In order for money to double in a time period of 12 years, for example, a compound rate of return of approximately $72/12 = 6\%$ per year would be required. The exact answer is 5.946% per year.

If the interest is simple, a rule of 100 may be used in the same way. As illustrations, money doubles in 12 years at $100/12 = 8.33\%$ simple interest. Or at 5% simple interest it takes exactly $100/5 = 20$ years to double.

These are all approximations and should be used with caution.

TABLE 1–4   Doubling Time Estimates Using the Rule of 72 and the Actual Time Using Compound Interest Calculations

Rate of Return, % per Year	Doubling Time, Years	
	Rule-of-72 Estimate	Actual Years
1	72	70
2	36	35.3
5	14.4	14.3
10	7.2	7.5
20	3.6	3.9
40	1.8	2.0

1.12 SPREADSHEET APPLICATION—SIMPLE AND COMPOUND INTEREST, AND CHANGING CASH FLOW ESTIMATES

The example below demonstrates how an Excel spreadsheet can be used to obtain equivalent future values. A key feature is the use of mathematical relations developed in the cells to perform sensitivity analysis for changing cash flow estimates and the interest rate. To answer these basic questions using hand solution can be time-consuming; the spreadsheet makes it much easier.

E-SOLVE

EXAMPLE 1.18

A Japan-based architectural firm has asked a Canada-based software engineering group to infuse GIS (geographical information system) sensing capability via satellite into monitoring software for high-rise structures in order to detect greater-than-expected horizontal movements. This software could be very beneficial as an advance warning of serious tremors in earthquake-prone areas. The inclusion of accurate GIS data is estimated to increase annual revenue over that for the current software system by $200,000 for each of the next 2 years, and by $300,000 for each of years 3 and 4. The planning horizon is only 4 years due to the rapid advances made internationally in building-monitoring software. Develop spreadsheets to answer the questions below.

(a) Determine the equivalent future value in year 4 of the increased cash flows, using an 8% per year rate of return. Obtain answers for both simple and compound interest.

(b) Rework part (a) if the cash flow estimates in years 3 and 4 increase from $300,000 to $600,000.

(c) The financial manager of the Canadian company wants to consider the effects of 4% per year inflation in the analysis of part (a). As mentioned in Section 1.4, inflation reduces the real rate of return. For the 8% rate of return, an inflation rate of 4% per year compounded each year reduces the return to 3.85% per year.

Solution by Computer

Refer to Figure 1–12a to c for the solutions. All three spreadsheets contain the same information, but the cell values are altered as required by the question. (Actually, all the questions posed here can be answered on one spreadsheet by simply changing the numbers. Three spreadsheets are shown here for explanation purposes only.)

The Excel functions are constructed with reference to the cells, not the values themselves, so that sensitivity analysis can be performed without function changes. This approach treats the value in a cell as a *global variable* for the spreadsheet. For example, the 8% (simple or compound interest) rate in cell B4 will be referenced in all functions as B4, not 8%. Thus, a change in the rate requires only one alteration in the cell B4 entry, not in every spreadsheet relation and function where 8% is used. Key Excel relations are detailed in the cell tags.

(a) *8% simple interest.* Refer to Figure 1–12a, columns C and D, for the answers. Simple interest earned each year (column C) incorporates Equation [1.5] one year at a time into the interest relation by using only the end-of-year (EOY) cash flow amounts ($200,000 or $300,000) to determine interest for the next year. This interest is added to the interest from all previous years. In $1000 units,

Year 2:   C13 = B12*B4 = $200(0.08) = $16 (see the cell tag)

Year 3:   C14 = C13 + B13*B4 = $16 + 200(0.08) = $32

Year 4:   C15 = C14 + B14*B4 = $32 + 300(0.08) = $56 (see the cell tag)

(a)

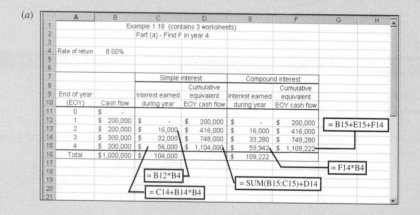

(b)

	A	B	C	D	E	F
1						
2			(b) Find F with increased cash flow estimates			
3						
4	Rate of return	8.00%				
5						
6						
7			Simple interest		Compound interest	
8				Cumulative		Cumulative
9	End of year		Interest earned	equivalent	Interest earned	equivalent
10	(EOY)	Cash flow	during year	EOY cash flow	during year	EOY cash flow
11	0	$ -				
12	1	$ 200,000	$ -	$ 200,000	$ -	$ 200,000
13	2	$ 200,000	$ 16,000	$ 416,000	$ 16,000	$ 416,000
14	3	$ 600,000	$ 32,000	$ 1,048,000	$ 33,280	$ 1,049,280
15	4	$ 600,000	$ 80,000	$ 1,728,000	$ 83,942	$ 1,733,222
16	Total	$1,600,000	$ 128,000		$ 133,222	

(c)

	A	B	C	D	E	F
1						
2			(c) Find F with 4% per year inflation			
3						
4	Rate of return	3.85%				
5						
6						
7			Simple interest		Compound interest	
8				Cumulative		Cumulative
9	End of year		Interest earned	equivalent	Interest earned	equivalent
10	(EOY)	Cash flow	during year	EOY cash flow	during year	EOY cash flow
11	0	$ -				
12	1	$ 200,000	$ -	$ 200,000	$ -	$ 200,000
13	2	$ 200,000	$ 7,700	$ 407,700	$ 7,700	$ 407,700
14	3	$ 300,000	$ 15,400	$ 723,100	$ 15,696	$ 723,396
15	4	$ 300,000	$ 26,950	$ 1,050,050	$ 27,851	$ 1,051,247
16	Total	$ 1,000,000	$ 50,050		$ 51,247	

FIGURE 1–12
Spreadsheet solution including sensitivity analysis, Example 1.18(a)–(c).

Remember, an = sign must precede each relation in the spreadsheet. Cell C16 contains the function SUM(C12:C15) to display the total simple interest of $104,000 over the 4 years. The future value is in D15. It is $F = \$1,104,000$ which includes the cumulative amount of all cash flows and all simple interest. In $1000 units, example functions are

Year 2:   D13 = SUM(B13:C13) + D12 = ($200 +16) + 200 = $416

Year 4:   D15 = SUM(B15:C15) + D14 = ($300 + 56) + 748 = $1104

8% compound interest. See Figure 1–12a, columns E and F. The spreadsheet structure is the same, except that Equation [1.6] is incorporated into the compound interest values in column E, thus adding interest on top of earned interest. Interest at 8% is based on the accumulated cash flow at the end of the previous year. In $1000 units,

Year 2 interest: E13 = F12*B4 = $200(0.08) = $16

Cumulative cash flow: F13 = B13 + E13 + F12 = $200 + 16 + 200 = $416

Year 4 interest: E15 = F14*B4 = $749.28(0.08) = $59.942

(see the cell tag)

Cumulative cash flow: F15 = B15 + E15 + F14

$$= \$300 + 59.942 + 749.280 = \$1109.222$$

The equivalent future value is in cell F15, where $F = \$1,109,222$ is shown.

The cash flows are equivalent to $1,104,000 at a simple 8% interest rate, and $1,109,222 at a compound 8% interest rate. Using a compound interest rate increases the F value by $5222.

Note that it is not possible to use the FV function in this case because the A values are not the same for all 4 years. We will learn how to use all the basic functions in more versatile ways in the next few chapters.

(b) Refer to Figure 1–12b. In order to initialize the spreadsheet with the two increased cash flow estimates, replace the $300,000 values in B14 and B15 with $600,000. All spreadsheet relations are identical, and the new interest and accumulated cash flow values are shown immediately. The equivalent fourth-year F values have increased for both the 8% simple and compound interest rates (D15 and F15, respectively).

(c) Figure 1–12c is identical to the spreadsheet in Figure 1–12a, except the cell B4 now contains the rate of 3.85%. The corresponding F value for compound interest in F15 has decreased to $1,051,247 from the $1,109,222 at 8%. This represents an effect of inflation of $57,975 in only four years. It is no surprise that governments, corporations, engineers, and all individuals are concerned when inflation rises and the currency is worth less over time.

Comment

When working with an Excel spreadsheet, it is possible to display all of the entries and functions on the screen by simultaneously touching the <Ctrl> and <`> keys, which may be in the upper left of the keyboard on the key with <~>. Additionally, it may be necessary to widen some columns in order to display the entire function statement.

ADDITIONAL EXAMPLES

EXAMPLE 1.19

CASH FLOW DIAGRAMS

A rental company spent $2500 on a new air compressor 7 years ago. The annual rental income from the compressor has been $750. Additionally, the $100 spent on maintenance during the first year has increased each year by $25. The company plans to sell the compressor at the end of next year for $150. Construct the cash flow diagram from the company's perspective.

Solution
Use now as time $t = 0$. The incomes and costs for years -7 through 1 (next year) are tabulated below with net cash flow computed using Equation [1.8]. The net cash flows (one negative, eight positive) are diagrammed in Figure 1–13.

End of year	Income	Cost	Net Cash Flow
−7	$ 0	$2500	$−2500
−6	750	100	650
−5	750	125	625
−4	750	150	600
−3	750	175	575
−2	750	200	550
−1	750	225	525
0	750	250	500
1	750 + 150	275	625

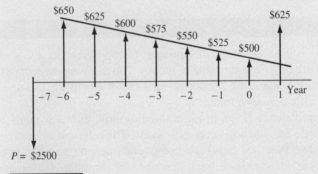

$P = \$2500$

FIGURE 1–13
Cash flow diagram, Example 1.19.

EXAMPLE 1.20

CASH FLOW DIAGRAMS

An electrical engineer wants to deposit an amount P now such that she can withdraw an equal annual amount of $A_1 = \$2000$ per year for the first 5 years starting 1 year after the deposit, and a different annual withdrawal of $A_2 = \$3000$ per year for the following 3 years. How would the cash flow diagram appear if $i = 5\%$ per year?

Solution

The cash flows are shown in Figure 1–14. The negative cash outflow P occurs now. The first withdrawal (positive cash inflow) for the A_1 series occurs at the end of year 1, and A_2 occurs in years 6 through 8.

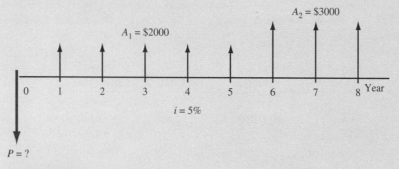

FIGURE 1–14
Cash flow diagram with two different A series, Example 1.20.

CHAPTER SUMMARY

Engineering economy is the application of economic factors and criteria to evaluate alternatives, considering the time value of money. The engineering economy study involves computing a specific economic measure of worth for estimated cash flows over a specific period of time.

The concept of *equivalence* helps in understanding how different sums of money at different times are equal in economic terms. The differences between simple interest (based on principal only) and compound interest (based on principal and interest upon interest) have been described in formulas, tables, and graphs. This power of compounding is very noticeable, especially over long periods of time, as is the effect of inflation, introduced here.

The MARR is a reasonable rate of return established as a hurdle rate to determine if an alternative is economically viable. The MARR is always higher than the return from a safe investment.

Also, we learned about cash flows:

Difficulties with their estimation

Difference between estimated and actual value

End-of-year convention for cash flow location

Net cash flow computation

Different perspectives in determining the cash flow sign

Construction of a cash flow diagram

PROBLEMS

Basic Concepts

1.1 What is meant by the term *time value of money?*

1.2 List three intangible factors.

1.3 (*a*) What is meant by evaluation criterion?
(*b*) What is the primary evaluation criterion used in economic analysis?

1.4 List three evaluation criteria besides the economic one for selecting the best restaurant.

1.5 Discuss the importance of *identifying* alternatives in the engineering economic process.

1.6 What is the difference between simple and compound interest?

1.7 What is meant by minimum attractive rate of return?

1.8 What is the difference between debt and equity financing? Give an example of each.

Interest Rate and Rate of Return

1.9 Trucking giant Transcontinent agreed to purchase rival C2C Transport for $966 million in order to reduce so-called back-office costs (e.g., payroll and insurance) by $45 million per year. If the savings were realized as planned, what would be the rate of return on the investment?

1.10 If Shaw Communication's profits increased from 22 cents per share to 29 cents per share in the April–June quarter compared to the previous quarter, what was the rate of increase in profits for that quarter?

1.11 A broadband service company borrowed $2 million for new equipment and repaid the principal of the loan plus $275,000 interest after 1 year. What was the interest rate on the loan?

1.12 A design-build engineering firm completed a pipeline project wherein the company realized a profit of $2.3 million in 1-year. If the amount of money the company had invested was $6 million, what was the rate of return on the investment?

1.13 Chapman's Ice Cream in Markdale, Ontario, the largest Canadian-owned ice cream company, wants to double the size of its old facility after it was destroyed by fire. If the company borrowed $1.6 million at 10% per year interest and repaid the loan in a lump-sum amount after 2 years, what would be (*a*) the amount of the payment and (*b*) the amount of the interest?

1.14 Pureflo Filters received a contract for a small water desalting plant whereby the company expected to make a 28% rate of return on its investment. If the company invested $8 million in equipment the first year, what was the amount of the profit in that year?

1.15 A publicly traded construction company reported that it just paid off a loan that it received 1 year earlier. If the total amount of money the company paid was $1.6 million and the interest rate on the loan was 10% per year, how much money did the company borrow 1 year ago?

1.16 A startup chemical company has established a goal of making at least a 35% per year rate of return on its investment. If the company acquired $50 million in venture capital, how much did it have to earn in the first year?

Equivalence

1.17 AdventureZone Parks has invested $280,000 in a venture that earns 15% per year. The company wants to expand to a third site in Nova Scotia that would offer an obstacle course of ziplines, Tarzan swings, scramble nets, and swinging logs. How many years will it take the investment to reach the required amount of at least $425,000?

1.18 At an interest rate of 8% per year, $10,000 today is equivalent to how much (*a*) 1 year from now and (*b*) 1 year ago?

1.19 A medium-size consulting engineering firm is trying to decide whether it should replace its office furniture now or wait and do it 1 year from now. If it waits 1 year, the cost is expected to be $16,000. At an interest rate of 10% per year, what would be the equivalent cost now?

1.20 An investment of $40,000 one year ago and $50,000 now are equivalent at what interest rate?

1.21 At what interest rate would $100,000 now be equivalent to $80,000 one year ago?

Simple and Compound Interest

1.22 Silverstar Minerals placed $580,000 in an investment 2 years ago that returned simple interest of 9% per year. If the company now invests the total accumulated amount at 9% per year compound interest, how much will the investment be worth in 2 years?

1.23 A certain investment accumulates interest at 10% per year simple interest. If a company invests $240,000 now for the purchase of a new machine 3 years from now, how much will the company have at the end of the 3-year period?

1.24 A local bank is offering to pay compound interest of 7% per year on new savings accounts. An e-bank is offering 7.5% per year simple interest on a 5-year investment certificate. Which offer is more attractive to a company that wants to set aside $1,000,000 now for a plant expansion 5 years from now?

1.25 Beaver Pump Company invested $500,000 five years ago in a new product line that is now worth $1,000,000. What rate of return did the company earn (*a*) on a simple interest basis and (*b*) on a compound interest basis?

1.26 How long will it take for an investment to double at 5% per year (*a*) simple interest and (*b*) compound interest?

1.27 A company that manufactures regenerative thermal oxidizers made an investment 10 years ago that is now worth $1,300,000. How much was the initial investment at an interest rate of 15% per year (*a*) simple interest and (*b*) compound interest?

1.28 Companies frequently borrow money under an arrangement that requires them to make periodic payments of only interest and then pay the principal of the loan all at once. A company that manufactures odour control chemicals borrowed $400,000 for 3 years at 10% per year compound interest under such an arrangement. What is the difference in the *total amount paid* between this arrangement (identified as plan 1) and plan 2, in which the company makes no interest payments until the loan is due and then pays it off in one lump sum?

1.29 A company that manufactures in-line mixers for bulk manufacturing is considering borrowing $1.75 million to update a production line. If it borrows the money now, it can do so at an interest rate of 7.5% per year simple interest for 5 years. If it borrows next year, the interest rate will be 8% per year compound interest, but it will be for only 4 years. (*a*) How much interest (total) will be paid under each scenario, and (*b*) should the company borrow now or 1 year from now? Assume the total amount due will be paid when the loan is due in either case.

Symbols and Spreadsheets

1.30 Define the symbols involved when a construction company wants to know how much money it can spend 3 years from now in lieu of spending $50,000 now to purchase a new truck, when the compound interest rate is 15% per year.

1.31 State the purpose for each of the following built-in Excel functions:
(a) FV($i\%,n,A,P$)
(b) IRR(first_cell:last_cell)
(c) PMT($i\%,n,P,F$)
(d) PV($i\%,n,A,F$)

1.32 What are the values of the engineering economy symbols P, F, A, i, and n in the following Excel functions? Use a ? for the symbol that is to be determined.
(a) FV(7%,10,2000,9000)
(b) PMT(11%,20,14000)
(c) PV(8%,15,1000,800)

1.33 Write the engineering economy symbol that corresponds to each of the following Excel functions.
(a) PV
(b) PMT
(c) NPER
(d) IRR
(e) FV

1.34 In a built-in Excel function, if a certain parameter does not apply, under what circumstances can it be left blank? When must a comma be entered in its place?

MARR and Cost of Capital

1.35 Identify each of the following as either a safe investment or a risky one.
(a) New restaurant business
(b) Savings account in a bank
(c) Guaranteed investment certificate
(d) Government bond
(e) Relative's "get rich quick" idea

1.36 Identify each of the following as either equity or debt financing.
(a) Money from savings
(b) Money from a guaranteed investment certificate
(c) Money from a relative who is a partner in the business
(d) Bank loan
(e) Credit card

1.37 Rank the following from highest to lowest rate of return or interest rate: government bond, corporate bond, credit card, bank loan to new business, interest on chequing account.

1.38 Rank the following from highest to lowest interest rate: cost of capital, acceptable rate of return on a risky investment, minimum acceptable rate of return, rate of return on a safe investment, interest on chequing account, interest on savings account.

1.39 Five separate projects have calculated rates of return of 8, 11, 12.4, 14, and 19% per year. An engineer wants to know which projects to accept on the basis of rate of return. She learns from the finance department that company funds, which have a cost of capital of 18% per year, are commonly used to fund 25% of all capital projects. Later, she is told that borrowed money is currently costing 10% per year. If the MARR is established at exactly the weighted average cost of capital, which projects should she accept?

Cash Flows

1.40 What is meant by the end-of-period convention?

1.41 Identify the following as cash inflows or outflows to DaimlerChrysler: income taxes, loan interest, salvage value, rebates to dealers, sales revenues, accounting services, cost reductions.

1.42 Construct a cash flow diagram for the following cash flows: $10,000 outflow at time zero, $3000 per year outflow in years 1 through 3 and $9000 inflow in years 4 through 8 at an interest rate of 10% per year, and an unknown future amount in year 8.

1.43 Construct a cash flow diagram to find the present worth of a future outflow of $40,000 in year 5 at an interest rate of 15% per year.

Doubling the Value

1.44 Use the rule of 72 to estimate the time it would take for an initial investment of $10,000 to accumulate to $20,000 at a compound rate of 8% per year.

1.45 Estimate the time it would take (according to the rule of 72) for money to quadruple in value at a compound interest rate of 9% per year.

1.46 Use the rule of 72 to estimate the interest rate that would be required for $5000 to accumulate to $10,000 in 4 years.

1.47 If you now have $62,500 in your retirement account and you want to retire when the account is worth $2 million, estimate the rate of return that the account must earn if you want to retire in 20 years without adding any more money to the account.

EXTENDED EXERCISE

EFFECTS OF COMPOUND INTEREST

In an effort to maintain compliance with noise emission standards on the processing floor, West Coast Mill & Paper requires the use of noise-measuring instruments. The company plans to purchase new portable systems at the end of next year at a cost of $9000 each. National estimates the maintenance cost to be $500 per year for 3 years, after which they will be salvaged for $2000 each.

Questions

E-SOLVE

1.   Construct the cash flow diagram. For a compound interest rate of 8% per year, find the equivalent F value after 4 years, using calculations by hand.
2.   Find the F value in question 1, using a spreadsheet.
3.   Find the F value if the maintenance costs are $300, $500, and $1000 for each of the 3 years. By how much has the F value changed?
4.   Find the F value in question 1 in terms of dollars needed in the future with an adjustment for inflation of 4% per year. This increases the interest rate from 8% to 12.32% per year.

CASE STUDY

DESCRIBING ALTERNATIVES FOR PRODUCING REFRIGERATOR PANELS

Background

Canada's leading manufacturers of refrigerators may subcontract the fabrication of their insulation panels. One prime Canadian subcontractor is Thermo Solutions in Saskatoon, Saskatchewan. Natural Resources Canada's (NRCan) Office of Energy Efficiency is proposing to amend Canada's energy efficiency regulations to require dealers of commercial food service refrigerators to comply with minimum energy performance standards. Effective for January 2008, the maximum daily energy consumed (kWh) shall not exceed 0.00964AV + 1.65 where

AV (adjusted volume) is equal to the refrigerator volume plus 1.63 times the freezer volume. NRCan has determined that the improved efficiency required by these changes is expected to provide positive benefits to Canadians through the reduction of greenhouse gas emissions.

As an engineer for Thermo Solutions, you have been asked for a recommendation on whether the company should plan on offering an advanced vacuum panel that will provide a significant improvement to its insulating value. Improved technology will be needed to enter this market. A complete engineering economic analysis is not required due to the lack of available information. However, you are asked to formulate reasonable alternatives, an estimate of the necessary capital investment to enter this market, determine what data and estimates are needed for each one, and ascertain what criteria (economic and noneconomic) should be utilized to make the final decision.

Information

Some information useful at this time is as follows:

- The technology and equipment are expected to last about 10 years before new methods are developed.
- Inflation and income taxes will not be considered in the analysis.
- The expected returns on capital investment used for the last three new technology projects were compound rates of 15, 5, and 18%. The 5% rate was the criterion for enhancing an employee-safety system.
- Equity capital financing beyond $5 million is not possible. The amount of debt financing and its cost are unknown.
- Annual operating costs have been averaging 8% of first cost for major equipment.
- Increased annual training costs and salary requirements for operating new equipment can range from $800,000 to $1.2 million.

There are two manufacturers working on the new technologies. You label these options alternatives A and B.

Case Study Exercises

1. Use the first four steps of the decision-making process to generally describe the alternatives and identify what economic-related estimates you will need to complete an engineering economy analysis.

2. Identify any noneconomic factors and criteria to be considered in making the alternative selection.

3. During your inquiries about alternative B from its manufacturer, you learn that this company has already produced a prototype technology and has sold it to a company in Germany for $3 million. Upon inquiry, you further discover that the German company already has unused capacity on the equipment for manufacturing panels. The company is willing to sell time on the equipment to Thermo Solutions immediately to produce its own panels. This could allow an earlier market entry. Consider this as alternative C, and develop the estimates necessary to evaluate C at the same time as alternatives A and B.

CHAPTER  2

Factors: How Time and Interest Affect Money

In the previous chapter we learned the basic concepts of engineering economy and their role in decision making. The cash flow is fundamental to every economic study. Cash flows occur in many configurations and amounts—isolated single values, series that are uniform, and series that increase or decrease by constant amounts or constant percentages. This chapter develops derivations for all the commonly used engineering economy factors that take the time value of money into account.

The application of factors is illustrated using their mathematical forms and a standard notation format. Spreadsheet functions are introduced in order to rapidly work with cash flow series and to perform sensitivity analysis.

The case study focuses on the significant impacts that compound interest and time make on the value and amount of money.

LEARNING OBJECTIVES

Purpose: Derive and use the engineering economy factors to account for the time value of money.

By the end of this chapter you should be able to

F/P and P/F factors	**1.** Derive and use the compound amount factor and present worth factor for single payments.
P/A and A/P factors	**2.** Derive and use the uniform series present worth and capital recovery factors.
F/A and A/F factors	**3.** Derive and use the uniform series compound amount and sinking fund factors.
Interpolate factor values	**4.** Linearly interpolate to determine a factor value.
P/G and A/G factors	**5.** Derive and use the arithmetic gradient present worth and uniform series factors.
Geometric gradient	**6.** Derive and use the geometric gradient series formulas.
Calculate i	**7.** Determine the interest rate (rate of return) for a sequence of cash flows.
Calculate n	**8.** Determine the number of years required for equivalence in a cash flow series.
Spreadsheets	**9.** Develop a spreadsheet to perform basic sensitivity analysis using spreadsheet functions.

2.1 SINGLE-PAYMENT FACTORS (F/P and P/F)

The most fundamental factor in engineering economy is the one that determines the amount of money F accumulated after n years (or periods) from a *single* present worth P, with interest compounded one time per year (or period). Recall that compound interest refers to interest paid on top of interest. Therefore, if an amount P is invested at time $t = 0$, the amount F_1 accumulated 1 year hence at an interest rate of i percent per year will be

$$F_1 = P + Pi$$
$$= P(1 + i)$$

where the interest rate is expressed in decimal form. At the end of the second year, the amount accumulated F_2 is the amount after year 1 plus the interest from the end of year 1 to the end of year 2 on the entire F_1.

$$F_2 = F_1 + F_1 i$$
$$= P(1 + i) + P(1 + i)i \qquad [2.1]$$

This is the logic used in Chapter 1 for compound interest, specifically in Examples 1.8 and 1.18. The amount F_2 can be expressed as

$$F_2 = P(1 + i + i + i^2)$$
$$= P(1 + 2i + i^2)$$
$$= P(1 + i)^2$$

Similarly, the amount of money accumulated at the end of year 3, using Equation [2.1], will be

$$F_3 = F_2 + F_2 i$$

Substituting $P(1 + i)^2$ for F_2 and simplifying, we get

$$F_3 = P(1 + i)^3$$

From the preceding values, it is evident by mathematical induction that the formula can be generalized for n years to

$$F = P(1 + i)^n \qquad [2.2]$$

The factor $(1+i)^n$ is called the *single-payment compound amount factor* (SPCAF), but it is usually referred to as the *F/P factor*. This is the conversion factor that, when multiplied by P, yields the future amount F of an initial amount P after n years at interest rate i. The cash flow diagram is seen in Figure 2–1a.

Reverse the situation to determine the P value for a stated amount F that occurs n periods in the future. Simply solve Equation [2.2] for P.

$$P = F\left[\frac{1}{(1 + i)^n}\right] \qquad [2.3]$$

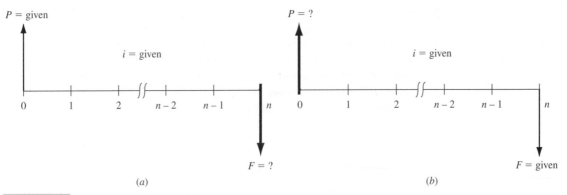

FIGURE 2–1
Cash flow diagrams for single-payment factors: (*a*) find *F* and (*b*) find *P*.

The expression in brackets is known as the *single-payment present worth factor* (SPPWF), or the *P/F factor*. This expression determines the present worth *P* of a given future amount *F* after *n* years at interest rate *i*. The cash flow diagram is shown in Figure 2–1*b*.

Note that the two factors derived here are for *single payments*; that is, they are used to find the present or future amount when only one payment or receipt is involved.

A standard notation has been adopted for all factors. The notation includes two cash flow symbols, the interest rate, and the number of periods. It is always in the general form (*X/Y,i,n*). The letter *X* represents what is sought, while the letter *Y* represents what is given. For example, *F/P* means *find F when given P*. The *i* is the interest rate in percent, and *n* represents the number of periods involved. Thus, (*F/P*,6%,20) represents the factor that is used to calculate the future amount *F* accumulated in 20 periods if the interest rate is 6% per period. The *P* is given. The standard notation, simpler to use than formulas and factor names, will be used hereafter.

Table 2–1 summarizes the standard notation and equations for the *F/P* and *P/F* factors. This information is also included inside the front cover.

To simplify routine engineering economy calculations, at the back of this book we have provided tables of factor values for interest rates from 0.25 to 50% and time periods from 1 to large *n* values, depending on the *i* value. The tables

TABLE 2–1   *F/P* and *P/F* Factors: Notation and Equations

Factor			Standard Notation	Equation	Excel
Notation	Name	Find/Given	Equation	with Factor Formula	Functions
(*F/P,i,n*)	Single-payment compound amount	*F/P*	$F = P(F/P,i,n)$	$F = P(1 + i)^n$	FV(*i*%,*n*,,*P*)
(*P/F,i,n*)	Single-payment present worth	*P/F*	$P = F(P/F,i,n)$	$P = F[1/(1 + i)^n]$	PV(*i*%,*n*,,*F*)

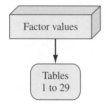

Factor values

Tables 1 to 29

are arranged with the factors across the top and the number of periods n down the left. The word *discrete* in the title of each table emphasizes that these tables utilize the end-of-period convention and that interest is compounded once each interest period. For a given factor, interest rate, and time, the correct factor value is found at the intersection of the factor name and n. For example, the value of the factor $(P/F,5\%,10)$ is found in the P/F column of Table 10 at period 10 as 0.6139. This value is determined by using Equation [2.3].

$$(P/F,5\%,10) = \frac{1}{(1+i)^n}$$

$$= \frac{1}{(1.05)^{10}}$$

$$= \frac{1}{1.6289} = 0.6139$$

Q-SOLVE

For *solution by computer,* the F value is calculated by the FV function using the format

$$\textbf{FV}(i\%,n,,P)$$

An $=$ sign must precede the function when it is entered. The amount P is determined using the PV function with the format

$$\textbf{PV}(i\%,n,,F)$$

These functions are included in Table 2–1. Refer to Appendix A or Excel online help for more information on the FV and PV functions. Examples 2.1 and 2.2 illustrate solutions by computer using both of these functions.

EXAMPLE 2.1

An industrial engineer received a bonus of $12,000 that he will invest now. He wants to calculate the equivalent value after 24 years, when he plans to use all the resulting money as the down payment on an island vacation home. Assume a rate of return of 8% per year for each of the 24 years. (*a*) Find the amount he can pay down, using both the standard notation and the factor formula. (*b*) Use a computer to find the amount he can pay down.

(a) Solution by Hand
The symbols and their values are

$$P = \$12{,}000 \qquad F = ? \qquad i = 8\% \text{ per year} \qquad n = 24 \text{ years}$$

The cash flow diagram is the same as that in Figure 2–1*a*.
   Standard notation: Determine F, using the F/P factor for 8% and 24 years. Table 13 at the back of the book provides the factor value.

$$F = P(F/P,i,n) = 12{,}000(F/P,8\%,24)$$
$$= 12{,}000(6.3412)$$
$$= \$76{,}094.40$$

Factor formula: Apply Equation [2.2] to calculate the future worth *F*.

$$F = P(1 + i)^n = 12,000(1 + 0.08)^{24}$$
$$= 12,000(6.341181)$$
$$= \$76,094.17$$

The slight difference in answers is due to the round-off error introduced by the tabulated factor values. An equivalence interpretation of this result is that \$12,000 today is worth \$76,094 after 24 years of growth at 8% per year, compounded annually.

(b) Solution by Computer

To find the future value use the FV function that has the format $FV(i\%,n,A,P)$. The spreadsheet will look like the one in Figure 1–5*a*, except the cell entry is FV(8%,24,,12000). The *F* value displayed by Excel is (\$76,094.17) in red to indicate a cash outflow. The FV function has performed the computation $F = P(1 + i)^n = 12,000(1 + 0.08)^{24}$ and presented the answer on the screen.

Q-SOLVE

EXAMPLE 2.2

The recent enhancements made by Ipsco, Inc., to its large-diameter spiral pipe mill in Regina are estimated to save \$50,000 in reduced maintenance this year.

(*a*) If the steel maker considers these types of savings worth 20% per year, find the equivalent value of this result after 5 years.

(*b*) If the \$50,000 maintenance savings occurs now, find its equivalent value 3 years earlier with interest at 20% per year.

(*c*) Develop a spreadsheet to answer the two parts above at compound rates of 20% and 5% per year. Additionally develop an Excel column chart indicating the equivalent values at the three different times for both rate-of-return values.

Solution

(*a*) The cash flow diagram appears as in Figure 2–1*a*. The symbols and their values are

$$P = \$50,000 \qquad F = ? \qquad i = 20\% \text{ per year} \qquad n = 5 \text{ years}$$

Use the *F/P* factor to determine *F* after 5 years.

$$F = P(F/P,i,n) = \$50,000(F/P,20\%,5)$$
$$= 50,000(2.4883)$$
$$= \$124,415.00$$

The function FV(20%,5,,50000) provides the same answer. See Figure 2–2*a*, cell C4.

Q-SOLVE

(*b*) In this case, the cash flow diagram appears as in Figure 2–1*b* with *F* placed at time $t = 0$ and the *P* value placed 3 years earlier at $t = -3$. The symbols and their values are

$$P = ? \qquad F = \$50,000 \qquad i = 20\% \text{ per year} \qquad n = 3 \text{ years}$$

(a)

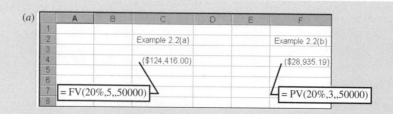

(b)

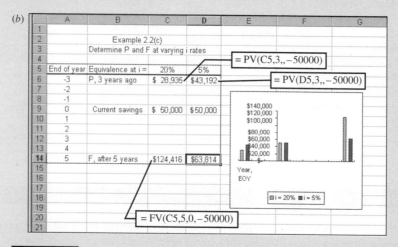

FIGURE 2–2

(a) Q-Solve spreadsheet for Example 2.2(a) and (b); (b) complete spreadsheet with graphic, Example 2.2.

Use the P/F factor to determine P three years earlier.

$$P = F(P/F, i, n) = \$50,000(P/F, 20\%, 3)$$
$$= 50,000(0.5787) = \$28,935.00$$

An equivalence statement is that \$28,935 three years ago is the same as \$50,000 today, which will grow to \$124,415 five years from now, provided a 20% per year compound interest rate is realized each year.

Q-SOLVE

Use the PV function PV($i\%, n, A, F$) and omit the A value. Figure 2–2a shows the result of entering PV(20%,3,,50000) in cell F4 to be the same as using the P/F factor.

Solution by Computer

(c) Figure 2–2b is a complete spreadsheet solution on one worksheet with the chart. Two columns are used for 20% and 5% computations primarily so the graph can

E-SOLVE

be developed to compare the F and P values. Row 14 shows the F values using the FV function with the format FV($i\%, 5, 0, -50000$) where the i values are taken from cells C5 and D5. The future worth $F = \$124,416$ in cell C14 is the same (round-off considered) as that calculated above. The minus sign on 50,000 makes the result a positive number for the chart.

The PV function is used to find the P values in row 6. For example, the present worth at 20% in year -3 is determined in cell C6 using the PV function. The result $P = \$28,935$ is the same as that obtained by using the P/F factor previously. The chart graphically shows the noticeable difference that 20% versus 5% makes over the 8-year span.

EXAMPLE 2.3

An independent engineering consultant reviewed records and found that the cost of office supplies varied as shown in the pie chart of Figure 2–3. If the engineer wants to know the equivalent value in year 10 of only the three largest amounts, what is it at an interest rate of 5% per year?

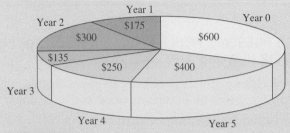

FIGURE 2–3
Pie chart of costs, Example 2.3.

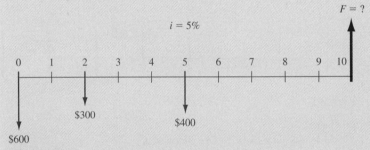

FIGURE 2–4
Diagram for a future worth in year 10, Example 2.3.

Solution
Draw the cash flow diagram for the values $600, $300, and $400 from the engineer's perspective (Figure 2–4). Use F/P factors to find F in year 10.

$$F = 600(F/P,5\%,10) + 300(F/P,5\%,8) + 400(F/P,5\%,5)$$
$$= 600(1.6289) + 300(1.4775) + 400(1.2763)$$
$$= \$1931.11$$

The problem could also be solved by finding the present worth in year 0 of the $300 and $400 costs using the P/F factors and then finding the future worth of the total in year 10.

$$P = 600 + 300(P/F,5\%,2) + 400(P/F,5\%,5)$$
$$= 600 + 300(0.9070) + 400(0.7835)$$
$$= \$1185.50$$
$$F = 1185.50(F/P,5\%,10) = 1185.50(1.6289)$$
$$= \$1931.06$$

Comment

It should be obvious that there are a number of ways the problem could be worked, since any year could be used to find the equivalent total of the costs before finding the future value in year 10. As an exercise, work the problem using year 5 for the equivalent total and then determine the final amount in year 10. All answers should be the same except for round-off error.

2.2 UNIFORM-SERIES PRESENT WORTH FACTOR AND CAPITAL RECOVERY FACTOR (P/A and A/P)

The equivalent present worth P of a uniform series A of end-of-period cash flows is shown in Figure 2–5a. An expression for the present worth can be determined by considering each A value as a future worth F, calculating its present worth

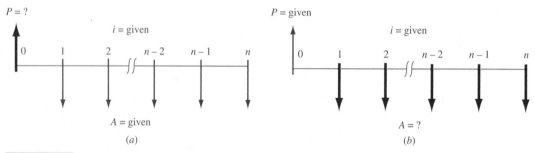

FIGURE 2–5

Cash flow diagrams used to determine (a) P of a uniform series and (b) A for a present worth.

with the P/F factor, and summing the results. The equation is

$$P = A\left[\frac{1}{(1+i)^1}\right] + A\left[\frac{1}{(1+i)^2}\right] + A\left[\frac{1}{(1+i)^3}\right] + \cdots$$
$$+ A\left[\frac{1}{(1+i)^{n-1}}\right] + A\left[\frac{1}{(1+i)^n}\right]$$

The terms in brackets are the P/F factors for years 1 through n, respectively. Factor out A.

$$P = A\left[\frac{1}{(1+i)^1} + \frac{1}{(1+i)^2} + \frac{1}{(1+i)^3} + \cdots + \frac{1}{(1+i)^{n-1}} + \frac{1}{(1+i)^n}\right] \qquad [2.4]$$

To simplify Equation [2.4] and obtain the P/A factor, multiply the n-term geometric progression in brackets by the $(P/F,i\%,1)$ factor, which is $1/(1+i)$. This results in Equation [2.5] below. Then subtract the two equations, [2.4] from [2.5], and simplify to obtain the expression for P when $i \neq 0$ (Equation [2.6]). This progression follows.

$$\frac{P}{1+i} = A\left[\frac{1}{(1+i)^2} + \frac{1}{(1+i)^3} + \frac{1}{(1+i)^4} + \cdots + \frac{1}{(1+i)^n} + \frac{1}{(1+i)^{n+1}}\right] \quad [2.5]$$

$$\frac{1}{1+i}P = A\left[\frac{1}{(1+i)^2} + \frac{1}{(1+i)^3} + \cdots + \frac{1}{(1+i)^n} + \frac{1}{(1+i)^{n+1}}\right]$$

$$-P = A\left[\frac{1}{(1+i)^1} + \frac{1}{(1+i)^2} + \cdots + \frac{1}{(1+i)^{n-1}} + \frac{1}{(1+i)^n}\right]$$

$$\frac{-i}{1+i}P = A\left[\frac{1}{(1+i)^{n+1}} - \frac{1}{(1+i)^1}\right]$$

$$P = \frac{A}{-i}\left[\frac{1}{(1+i)^n} - 1\right]$$

$$P = A\left[\frac{(1+i)^n - 1}{i(1+i)^n}\right] \qquad i \neq 0 \qquad\qquad [2.6]$$

The term in brackets in Equation [2.6] is the conversion factor referred to as the *uniform-series present worth factor* (USPWF). It is the P/A factor used to calculate the *equivalent P value in year 0* for a uniform end-of-period series of A values beginning at the end of period 1 and extending for n periods. The cash flow diagram is Figure 2–5a.

To reverse the situation, the present worth P is known and the equivalent uniform-series amount A is sought (Figure 2–5b). The first A value occurs at the end of period 1, that is, one period after P occurs. Solve Equation [2.6] for A to obtain

$$A = P\left[\frac{i(1+i)^n}{(1+i)^n - 1}\right] \qquad\qquad [2.7]$$

The term in brackets is called the *capital recovery factor* (CRF), or *A/P factor.* It calculates the equivalent uniform annual worth A over n years for a given P in year 0, when the interest rate is i.

> **These formulas are derived with the present worth P and the first uniform annual amount A *one year (period) apart*. That is, the present worth P must always be located *one period* prior to the first A.**

The factors and their use to find P and A are summarized in Table 2–2, and inside the front cover. The standard notations for these two factors are $(P/A,i\%,n)$ and $(A/P,i\%,n)$. Tables 1 through 29 at the end of the text include the factor values. As an example, if $i = 15\%$ and $n = 25$ years, the P/A factor value from Table 19 is $(P/A,15\%,25) = 6.4641$. This will find the equivalent present worth at 15%

TABLE 2–2 P/A and A/P Factors: Notation and Equations

| Factor | | | Factor | Standard | Excel |
Notation	Name	Find/Given	Formula	Notation Equation	Function
$(P/A,i,n)$	Uniform-series present worth	P/A	$\dfrac{(1+i)^n-1}{i(1+i)^n}$	$P = A(P/A,i,n)$	PV($i\%,n,A$)
$(A/P,i,n)$	Capital recovery	A/P	$\dfrac{i(1+i)^n}{(1+i)^n-1}$	$A = P(A/P,i,n)$	PMT($i\%,n,P$)

per year for any amount A that occurs uniformly from years 1 through 25. When the bracketed relation in Equation [2.6] is used to calculate the P/A factor, the result is the same except for round-off errors.

$$(P/A,15\%,25) = \frac{(1+i)^n-1}{i(1+i)^n} = \frac{(1.15)^{25}-1}{0.15(1.15)^{25}} = \frac{31.91895}{4.93784} = 6.46415$$

Spreadsheet functions are capable of determining both P and A values in lieu of applying the P/A and A/P factors. The PV function that we used in the last section also calculates the P value for a given A over n years, and a separate F value in year n, if it is given. The format, introduced in Section 1.8, is

PV($i\%,n,A,F$)

Similarly, the A value is determined using the PMT function for a given P value in year 0 and a separate F, if given. The format is

PMT($i\%,n,P,F$)

The PMT function was demonstrated in Section 1.18 (Figure 1–5b) and is used in later examples. Table 2–2 includes the PV and PMT functions for P and A, respectively. Example 2.4 demonstrates the PV function.

EXAMPLE 2.4

How much money should you be willing to pay now for a guaranteed $600 per year for 9 years starting next year, at a rate of return of 16% per year?

Solution

The cash flow diagram (Figure 2–6) fits the P/A factor. The present worth is

$$P = 600(P/A,16\%,9) = 600(4.6065) = \$2763.90$$

The PV function PV(16%,9,600) entered into a single spreadsheet cell will display the answer $P = \$2763.93$.

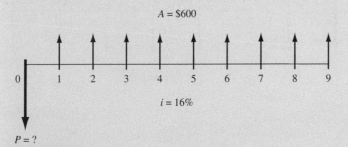

A = $600

$i = 16\%$

P = ?

FIGURE 2–6
Diagram to find P using the P/A factor, Example 2.4.

Comment
Another solution approach is to use P/F factors for each of the nine receipts and add the resulting present worths to get the correct answer. Another way is to find the future worth F of the $600 payments and then find the present worth of the F value. There are many ways to solve an engineering economy problem. Only the most direct method is presented here.

2.3 SINKING FUND FACTOR AND UNIFORM-SERIES COMPOUND AMOUNT FACTOR (A/F and F/A)

The simplest way to derive the A/F factor is to substitute into factors already developed. If P from Equation [2.3] is substituted into Equation [2.7], the following formula results.

$$A = F\left[\frac{1}{(1+i)^n}\right]\left[\frac{i(1+i)^n}{(1+i)^n-1}\right]$$

$$A = F\left[\frac{i}{(1+i)^n-1}\right] \qquad [2.8]$$

The expression in brackets in Equation [2.8] is the A/F or sinking fund factor. It determines the uniform annual series that is equivalent to a given future worth F. This is shown graphically in Figure 2–7a.

The uniform series A begins at the end of period 1 and continues *through the period of the given F*.

Equation [2.8] can be rearranged to find F for a stated A series in periods 1 through n (Figure 2–7b).

$$F = A\left[\frac{(1+i)^n-1}{i}\right] \qquad [2.9]$$

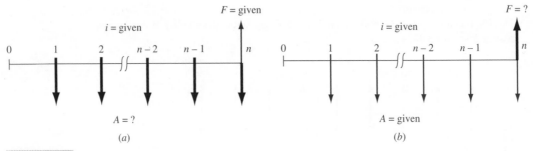

FIGURE 2–7
Cash flow diagrams to (*a*) find *A*, given *F*, and (*b*) find *F*, given *A*.

The term in brackets is called the *uniform-series compound amount factor* (USCAF), or *F/A* factor. When multiplied by the given uniform annual amount *A*, it yields the future worth of the uniform series. It is important to remember that the future amount *F* occurs in the same period as the last *A*.

Standard notation follows the same form as that of other factors. They are (*F/A,i,n*) and (*A/F,i,n*). Table 2–3 summarizes the notations and equations, as does the inside front cover. Tables 1 through 29 include *F/A* and *A/F* factor values.

The uniform-series factors can be symbolically determined by using an abbreviated factor form. For example, *F/A* = (*F/P*)(*P/A*), where cancellation of the *P* is correct. Using the factor formulas, we have

$$(F/A,i,n) = \left[(1+i)^n \right] \left[\frac{(1+i)^n - 1}{i(1+i)^n} \right] = \frac{(1+i)^n - 1}{i}$$

Also the *A/F* factor in Equation [2.8] may be derived from the *A/P* factor by subtracting *i*.

$$(A/F,i,n) = (A/P,i,n) - i$$

TABLE 2–3   *F/A* and *A/F* Factors: Notation and Equations

Notation	Factor Name	Find/Given	Factor Formula	Standard Notation Equation	Excel Functions
(*F/A,i,n*)	Uniform-series compound amount	*F/A*	$\dfrac{(1+i)^n - 1}{i}$	$F = A(F/A,i,n)$	FV(*i%,n,A*)
(*A/F,i,n*)	Sinking fund	*A/F*	$\dfrac{i}{(1+i)^n - 1}$	$A = F(A/F,i,n)$	PMT(*i%,n,,F*)

This relation can be verified empirically in any interest factor table in the rear of the text, or mathematically by simplifying the equation to derive the A/F factor formula. This relation is used later to compare alternatives by the annual worth method.

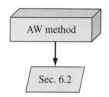

For solution by computer, the FV spreadsheet function calculates F for a stated A series over n years. The format is

$$\mathbf{FV}(i\%,n,A,P)$$

The P may be omitted when no separate present worth value is given. The PMT function determines the A value for n years, given F in year n, and possibly a separate P value in year 0. The format is

$$\mathbf{PMT}(i\%,n,P,F)$$

If P is omitted, the comma must be entered so the computer knows the last entry is an F value. These functions are included in Table 2–3. The next two examples include the FV and PMT functions.

EXAMPLE 2.5

Formasa Plastics has major fabrication plants in Toronto and Hong Kong. The president wants to know the equivalent future worth of a $1 million capital investment each year for 8 years, starting 1 year from now. Formasa capital earns at a rate of 14% per year.

Solution
The cash flow diagram (Figure 2–8) shows the annual payments starting at the end of year 1 and ending in the year the future worth is desired. Cash flows are indicated in $1000 units. The F value in 8 years is

$$F = 1000(F/A,14\%,8) = 1000(13.2328) = \$13,232.80$$

The actual future worth is $13,232,800. The FV function is FV(14%,8,1000000).

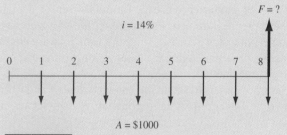

FIGURE 2–8
Diagram to find F for a uniform series, Example 2.5.

EXAMPLE 2.6

How much money must Carol deposit every year starting 1 year from now at $5\frac{1}{2}\%$ per year in order to accumulate $6000 seven years from now?

Solution
The cash flow diagram from Carol's perspective (Figure 2–9) fits the A/F factor.

$$A = \$6000(A/F,5.5\%,7) = 6000(0.12096) = \$725.76 \text{ per year}$$

Q-SOLVE

The A/F factor value of 0.12096 was computed using the factor formula in Equation [2.8]. Alternatively, use the PMT function, PMT(5.5%,7,6000), to obtain $A = \$725.79$ per year.

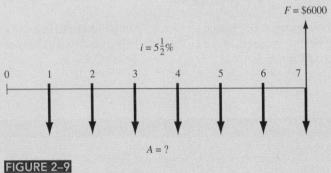

FIGURE 2–9
Cash flow diagram, Example 2.6.

2.4 INTERPOLATION IN INTEREST TABLES

When it is necessary to locate a factor value for an i or n not in the interest tables, the desired value can be obtained in one of two ways: (1) by using the formulas derived in Sections 2.1 to 2.3 or (2) by linearly interpolating between the tabulated values. It is generally easier and faster to use the formulas from a calculator or spreadsheet that has them preprogrammed. Furthermore, the value obtained through linear interpolation is not exactly correct, since the equations are nonlinear. Nevertheless, interpolation is sufficient in most cases as long as the values of i or n are not too distant from one another.

The first step in linear interpolation is to set up the known (values 1 and 2) and unknown factors, as shown in Table 2–4. A ratio equation is then set up and solved for c, as follows:

$$\frac{a}{b} = \frac{c}{d} \qquad or \qquad c = \frac{a}{b}d \qquad\qquad [2.10]$$

where *a*, *b*, *c*, and *d* represent the differences between the numbers shown in the interest tables. The value of *c* from Equation [2.10] is added to or subtracted from value 1, depending on whether the factor is increasing or decreasing in value, respectively. The following examples illustrate the procedure just described.

TABLE 2–4   Linear Interpolation Setup

i or *n*	Factor
tabulated	value 1
a ⌐ desired	*c* ⌐ unlisted
b ⌐ tabulated	*d* ⌐ value 2

EXAMPLE 2.7

Determine the value of the *A/P* factor for an interest rate of 7.3% and *n* of 10 years, that is, (*A/P*,7.3%,10).

Solution
The values of the *A/P* factor for interest rates of 7 and 8% and *n* = 10 are listed in Tables 12 and 13, respectively.

$$
\begin{array}{ccc}
 & 7\% & 0.14238 \\
a\left[\begin{array}{c} \\ \end{array}\right. & 7.3\% & X \quad c \\
b\left[\begin{array}{c} \\ \end{array}\right. & 8\% & 0.14903 \quad d
\end{array}
$$

The unknown *X* is the desired factor value. From Equation [2.10],

$$
c = \left(\frac{7.3 - 7}{8 - 7}\right)(0.14903 - 0.14238)
$$

$$
= \frac{0.3}{1}(0.00665) = 0.00199
$$

Since the factor is increasing in value as the interest rate increases from 7 to 8%, the value of *c* must be *added* to the value of the 7% factor. Thus,

$$
X = 0.14238 + 0.00199 = 0.14437
$$

Comment
It is good practice to check the reasonableness of the final answer by verifying that *X* lies *between* the values of the known factors in approximately the correct proportions. In this case, since 0.14437 is less than 0.5 of the distance between 0.14238 and 0.14903, the answer seems reasonable. If Equation [2.7] is applied, the exact factor value is 0.144358.

EXAMPLE 2.8

Find the value of the $(P/F,4\%,48)$ factor.

Solution
From Table 9 for 4% interest, the values of the P/F factor for 45 and 50 years are found.

From Equation [2.10],

$$c = \frac{a}{b}(d) = \frac{48-45}{50-45}(0.1712 - 0.1407) = 0.0183$$

Since the value of the factor decreases as n increases, c is subtracted from the factor value for $n = 45$.

$$X = 0.1712 - 0.0183 = 0.1529$$

Comment
Though it is possible to perform two-way linear interpolation, it is much easier and more accurate to use the factor formula or a spreadsheet function.

2.5 ARITHMETIC GRADIENT FACTORS (*P/G* and *A/G*)

An *arithmetic gradient* is a *cash flow series* that either increases or decreases by a constant amount. The cash flow, whether income or disbursement, changes by the same arithmetic amount each period. The *amount* of the increase or decrease is the *gradient*. For example, if a manufacturing engineer predicts that the cost of maintaining a robot will increase by $500 per year until the machine is retired, a gradient series is involved and the amount of the gradient is $500.

Formulas previously developed for an *A* series have year-end amounts of equal value. In the case of a gradient, each year-end cash flow is different, so new formulas must be derived. First, assume that the cash flow at the end of year 1 is not part of the gradient series, but is rather a *base amount*. This is convenient because in actual applications, the base amount is usually larger or smaller than the gradient increase or decrease. For example, if you purchase a used car with a 1-year warranty, you might expect to pay the gasoline and insurance costs during the first year of operation. Assume these cost

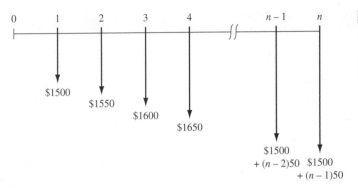

FIGURE 2–10
Diagram of an arithmetic
gradient series with a
base amount of $1500
and a gradient of $50.

$1500; that is, $1500 is the base amount. After the first year, you absorb the cost of repairs, which could reasonably be expected to increase each year. If you estimate that total costs will increase by $50 each year, the amount the second year is $1550, the third $1600, and so on to year *n*, when the total cost is $1500 + (n-1)50$. The cash flow diagram is shown in Figure 2–10. Note that the gradient ($50) is first observed between year 1 and year 2, and the base amount ($1500 in year 1) is not equal to the gradient.

Define the symbol *G* for gradients as

> **_G_ = constant arithmetic change in the magnitude of receipts or disbursements from one time period to the next; _G_ may be positive or negative.**

The cash flow in year *n* (CF_n) may be calculated as

$$CF_n = \text{base amount} + (n-1)G$$

If the base amount is ignored, a generalized arithmetic (increasing) gradient cash flow diagram is as shown in Figure 2–11. Note that the gradient begins between years 1 and 2. This is called a *conventional gradient*.

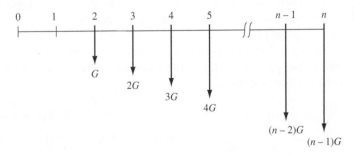

FIGURE 2–11
Conventional arithmetic
gradient series without
the base amount.

EXAMPLE 2.9

A sports apparel company has initiated a logo-licensing program. It expects to realize a revenue of $80,000 in fees next year from the sale of its logo. Fees are expected to increase uniformly to a level of $200,000 in 9 years. Determine the arithmetic gradient and construct the cash flow diagram.

Solution

The base amount is $80,000 and the total revenue increase is

$$\text{Increase in 9 years} = 200{,}000 - 80{,}000 = 120{,}000$$

$$\text{Gradient} = \frac{\text{increase}}{n-1}$$

$$= \frac{120{,}000}{9-1} = \$15{,}000 \text{ per year}$$

The cash flow diagram is shown in Figure 2–12.

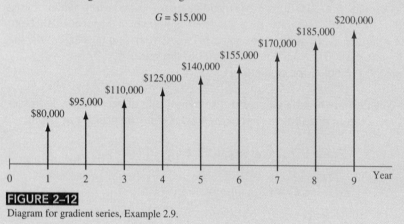

FIGURE 2–12
Diagram for gradient series, Example 2.9.

In this text, three factors are derived for arithmetic gradients: the P/G factor for present worth, the A/G factor for annual series, and the F/G factor for future worth. There are several ways to derive them. We use the single-payment present worth factor ($P/F,i,n$), but the same result can be obtained using the F/P, F/A, or P/A factor.

In Figure 2–11, the present worth at year 0 of only the gradient is equal to the sum of the present worths of the individual values, where each value is considered a future amount.

$$P = G(P/F,i,2) + 2G(P/F,i,3) + 3G(P/F,i,4) + \cdots$$
$$+ \big[(n-2)G\big](P/F,i,n-1) + \big[(n-1)G\big](P/F,i,n)$$

Factor out *G* and use the *P/F* formula.

$$P = G\left[\frac{1}{(1+i)^2} + \frac{2}{(1+i)^3} + \frac{3}{(1+i)^4} + \cdots + \frac{n-2}{(1+i)^{n-1}} + \frac{n-1}{(1+i)^n}\right] \qquad [2.11]$$

Multiplying both sides of Equation [2.11] by $(1 + i)^1$ yields

$$P(1+i)^1 = G\left[\frac{1}{(1+i)^1} + \frac{2}{(1+i)^2} + \frac{3}{(1+i)^3} + \cdots + \frac{n-2}{(1+i)^{n-2}} + \frac{n-1}{(1+i)^{n-1}}\right]$$

$$[2.12]$$

Subtract Equation [2.11] from Equation [2.12] and simplify.

$$iP = G\left[\frac{1}{(1+i)^1} + \frac{1}{(1+i)^2} + \cdots + \frac{1}{(1+i)^{n-1}} + \frac{1}{(1+i)^n}\right] - G\left[\frac{n}{(1+i)^n}\right] \qquad [2.13]$$

The left bracketed expression is the same as that contained in Equation [2.4], where the *P/A* factor was derived. Substitute the closed-end form of the *P/A* factor from Equation [2.6] into Equation [2.13] and solve for *P* to obtain a simplified relation.

$$\boldsymbol{P = \frac{G}{i}\left[\frac{(1+i)^n - 1}{i(1+i)^n} - \frac{n}{(1+i)^n}\right]} \qquad \textbf{[2.14]}$$

Equation [2.14] is the general relation to convert an arithmetic gradient *G* (not including the base amount) for *n* years into a present worth at year 0. Figure 2–13*a* is converted into the equivalent cash flow in Figure 2–13*b*. The *arithmetic-gradient present worth factor,* or *P/G factor,* may be expressed in two forms:

$$(P/G,i,n) = \frac{1}{i}\left[\frac{(1+i)^n - 1}{i(1+i)^n} - \frac{n}{(1+i)^n}\right]$$

or $\qquad\qquad (P/G,i,n) = \frac{(1+i)^n - in - 1}{i^2(1+i)^n} \qquad\qquad [2.15]$

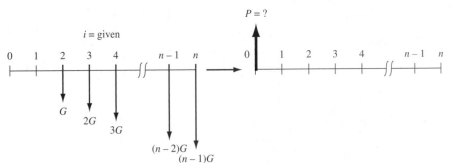

P = ?

FIGURE 2–13

Conversion diagram from an arithmetic gradient to a present worth.

(*a*)   (*b*)

Remember: The gradient starts in year 2 and P is located in year 0. Equation [2.14] expressed as an engineering economy relation is

$$P = G(P/G,i,n) \qquad [2.16]$$

The equivalent uniform annual series (A value) for an arithmetic gradient G is found by multiplying the present worth in Equation [2.16] by the $(A/P,i,n)$ factor expression. In standard notation form, the equivalent of algebraic cancellation of P can be used to obtain the $(A/G,i,n)$ factor.

$$A = G(P/G,i,n)(A/P,i,n)$$
$$= G(A/G,i,n)$$

In equation form,

$$A = \frac{G}{i}\left[\frac{(1+i)^n - 1}{i(1+i)^n} - \frac{n}{(1+i)^n}\right]\left[\frac{i(1+i)^n}{(1+i)^n - 1}\right]$$

$$= G\left[\frac{1}{i} - \frac{n}{(1+i)^n - 1}\right] \qquad [2.17]$$

The expression in brackets in Equation [2.17] is called the *arithmetic-gradient uniform-series factor* and is identified by $(A/G,i,n)$. This factor converts Figure 2–14a into Figure 2–14b.

The P/G and A/G factors and relations are summarized inside the front cover. Factor values are tabulated in the two rightmost columns of Tables 1 through 29 at the back of this text.

There is no direct, single-cell spreadsheet function to calculate P or A for an arithmetic gradient. Use the NPV function for P, and the PMT function for A, after all cash flows are entered into cells. (The use of NPV and PMT functions for this type of cash flow series is illustrated in Chapter 3.)

FIGURE 2–14

Conversion diagram of an arithmetic gradient series to an equivalent uniform annual series.

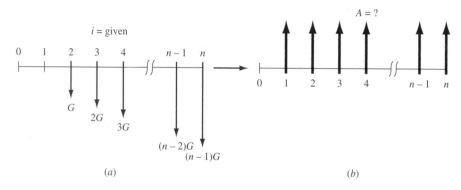

An *F/G factor* (*arithmetic-gradient future worth factor*) can be derived by multiplying the *P/G* and *F/P* factors. The resulting factor, (*F/G,i,n*), in brackets, and engineering economy relation is

$$F = G\left[\left(\frac{1}{i}\right)\left(\frac{(1+i)^n - 1}{i} - n\right)\right]$$

The total present worth P_T for a gradient series must consider the base and the gradient separately. Thus, for cash flow series involving conventional gradients:

- The *base amount* is the uniform-series amount *A* that begins in year 1 and extends through year *n*. Its present worth is represented by P_A.
- For an increasing gradient, the *gradient amount* must be added to the uniform-series amount. The present worth is P_G.
- For a decreasing gradient, the gradient amount must be subtracted from the uniform-series amount. The present worth is $-P_G$.

The general equations for calculating total present worth P_T of conventional arithmetic gradients are

$$P_T = P_A + P_G \quad \textbf{and} \quad P_T = P_A - P_G \qquad \text{[2.18]}$$

Similarly, the equivalent total annual series are

$$A_T = A_A + A_G \quad \textbf{and} \quad A_T = A_A - A_G \qquad \text{[2.19]}$$

where A_A is the annual base amount and A_G is the equivalent annual amount of the gradient series.

EXAMPLE 2.10

CN Rail is considering the deposit of $500,000 in an account for the repair of old and safety-questionable bridges in British Columbia. Further, they estimate that the deposits will increase by $100,000 per year for only 9 years thereafter, then cease. Determine the equivalent (*a*) present worth and (*b*) annual series amounts if the funds earn interest at a rate of 5% per year.

Solution

(*a*) The cash flow diagram from CN's perspective is shown in Figure 2–15. Two computations must be made and added: the first for the present worth of the base amount P_A and a second for the present worth of the gradient P_G. The total resent worth P_T occurs in year 0. This is illustrated by the partitioned cash flow diagram in Figure 2–16. In $1000 units, the present worth, from

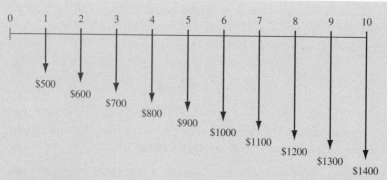

FIGURE 2–15
Cash flow series with a conventional arithmetic gradient (in $1000 units), Example 2.10.

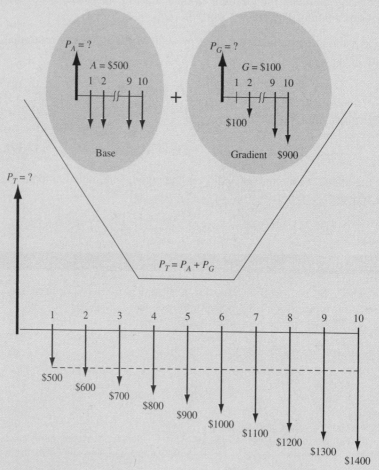

FIGURE 2–16
Partitioned cash flow diagram (in $1000 units), Example 2.10.

Equation [2.18], is

$$P_T = 500(P/A,5\%,10) + 100(P/G,5\%,10)$$
$$= 500(7.7217) + 100(31.652)$$
$$= \$7026.05 \quad (\$7,026,050)$$

(b) Here, too, it is necessary to consider the gradient and the base amount separately. The total annual series A_T is found by using Equation [2.19].

$$A_T = 500 + 100(A/G,5\%,10) = 500 + 100(4.0991)$$
$$= \$909.91 \text{ per year} \quad (\$909,910)$$

And A_T occurs from year 1 through year 10.

Comment
Remember: The P/G and A/G factors determine the present worth and annual series of the *gradient only.* Any other cash flow must be considered separately.

If the present worth is already calculated (as in part (a)), P_T can be multiplied by the appropriate A/P factor to get A_T.

$$A_T = P_T(A/P,5\%,10) = 7026.05(0.12950)$$
$$= \$909.87 \quad (\$909,870)$$

Round off accounts for the $40 difference.

Additional Example 2.16.

2.6 GEOMETRIC GRADIENT SERIES FACTORS

It is common for cash flow series, such as operating costs, construction costs, and revenues, to increase or decrease from period to period by a *constant percentage,* for example, 5% per year. This uniform rate of change defines a *geometric gradient series* of cash flows. In addition to the symbols i and n used thus far, we now need the term

g = constant rate of change, in decimal form, by which amounts increase or decrease from one period to the next

Figure 2–17 presents cash flow diagrams for geometric gradient series with increasing and decreasing uniform rates. The series starts in year 1 at an initial amount A_1, which is *not* considered a base amount as in the arithmetic gradient. The relation to determine the total present worth P_g for the entire cash flow series may be derived by multiplying each cash flow in Figure 2–17a by the P/F factor $1/(1+i)^n$.

$$P_g = \frac{A_1}{(1+i)^1} + \frac{A_1(1+g)}{(1+i)^2} + \frac{A_1(1+g)^2}{(1+i)^3} + \cdots + \frac{A_1(1+g)^{n-1}}{(1+i)^n}$$

$$= A_1 \left[\frac{1}{1+i} + \frac{1+g}{(1+i)^2} + \frac{(1+g)^2}{(1+i)^3} + \cdots + \frac{(1+g)^{n-1}}{(1+i)^n} \right] \qquad [2.20]$$

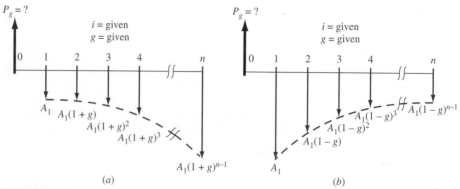

FIGURE 2–17

Cash flow diagram of (a) increasing and (b) decreasing geometric gradient series and present worth P_g.

Multiply both sides by $(1+g)/(1+i)$, subtract Equation [2.20] from the result, factor out P_g, and obtain

$$P_g\left(\frac{1+g}{1+i}-1\right)=A_1\left[\frac{(1+g)^n}{(1+i)^{n+1}}-\frac{1}{1+i}\right]$$

Solve for P_g and simplify.

$$P_g=A_1\left[\frac{1-\left(\dfrac{1+g}{1+i}\right)^n}{i-g}\right]\qquad g\neq i \qquad [2.21]$$

The term in brackets in Equation [2.21] is the geometric-gradient-series present worth factor for values of g not equal to the interest rate i. The standard notation used is $(P/A,g,i,n)$. When $g=i$, substitute i for g in Equation [2.20] to obtain

$$P_g=A_1\left(\frac{1}{(1+i)}+\frac{1}{(1+i)}+\frac{1}{(1+i)}+\cdots+\frac{1}{(1+i)}\right)$$

The term $1/(1+i)$ appears n times, so

$$P_g=\frac{nA_1}{(1+i)}\qquad\qquad [2.22]$$

In summary, the engineering economy relation and factor formulas to calculate P_g in period $t=0$ for a geometric gradient series starting in period 1 in the amount A_1 and increasing by a constant rate of g each period are

$$P_g=A_1(P/A,g,i,n)\qquad\qquad [2.23]$$

$$(P/A,g,i,n)=\begin{cases}\dfrac{1-\left(\dfrac{1+g}{1+i}\right)^n}{i-g} & g\neq i\\[2em]\dfrac{n}{1+i} & g=i\end{cases}\qquad [2.24]$$

It is possible to derive factors for the equivalent A and F values; however, it is easier to determine the P_g amount and then multiply by the A/P or F/P factor.

As with the arithmetic gradient series, there are no direct spreadsheet functions for geometric gradients series. Once the cash flows are entered, P and A are determined by using the NPV and PMT functions, respectively. However, it is always an option to develop on the spreadsheet a function that uses the factor equation to determine a P, F, or A value. Example 2.11 demonstrates this approach to find the present worth of a geometric gradient series using Equations [2.24].

EXAMPLE 2.11

Engineers at La Ronde, the large amusement park in Montreal, are considering an innovation on the existing Monster roller coaster to make it more exciting. The modification costs only $8000 and is expected to last 6 years with a $1300 salvage value for the solenoid mechanisms. The maintenance cost is expected to be high at $1700 the first year, increasing by 11% per year thereafter. Determine the equivalent present worth of the modification and maintenance cost by hand and by computer. The interest rate is 8% per year.

Solution by Hand
The cash flow diagram (Figure 2–18) shows the salvage value as a positive cash flow and all costs as negative. Use Equation [2.24] for $g \neq i$ to calculate P_g. The total P_T is

$$P_T = -8000 - P_g + 1300(P/F,8\%,6)$$

$$= -8000 - 1700\left[\frac{1-(1.11/1.08)^6}{0.08-0.11}\right] + 1300(P/F,8\%,6)$$

$$= -8000 - 1700(5.9559) + 819.26 = \$-17,305.85 \qquad [2.25]$$

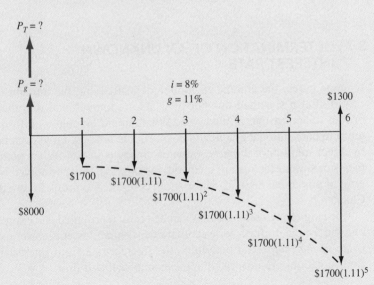

FIGURE 2–18
Cash flow diagram of a geometric gradient, Example 2.11.

Solution by Computer

Figure 2–19 presents a spreadsheet with the total present worth in cell B13. The function used to determine $P_T = \$-17,305.89$ is detailed in the cell tag. It is a rewrite of Equation [2.25]. Since it is complex, column C and D cells also contain the three elements of P_T, which are summed in D13 to obtain the same result.

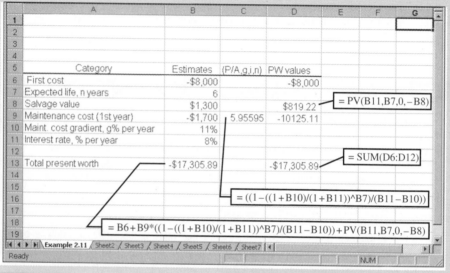

FIGURE 2–19

Spreadsheet used to determine present worth of a geometric gradient with $g = 11\%$, Example 2.11.

2.7 DETERMINATION OF AN UNKNOWN INTEREST RATE

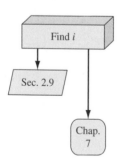

In some cases, the amount of money deposited and the amount of money received after a specified number of years are known, and it is the interest rate or rate of return that is unknown. When single amounts, uniform series, or a uniform conventional gradient is involved, the unknown rate i can be determined by direct solution of the time value of money equation. When nonuniform payments or several factors are involved, the problem must be solved by a trial-and-error or numerical method. These more complicated problems are deferred until Chapter 7.

The single-payment formulas can be easily rearranged and expressed in terms of i, but for the uniform series and gradient equations, it is easier to *solve for the value of the factor* and determine the interest rate from interest factor tables. Both situations are illustrated in the examples that follow.

EXAMPLE 2.12

If Laurel can make an investment in a friend's business of $3000 now in order to receive $5000 five years from now, determine the rate of return. If Laurel can receive 7% per year interest on a guaranteed investment certificate, which investment should be made?

Solution
Since only single payment amounts are involved, i can be determined directly from the P/F factor.

$$P = F(P/F, i, n) = F \frac{1}{(1+i)^n}$$

$$3000 = 5000 \frac{1}{(1+i)^5}$$

$$0.600 = \frac{1}{(1+i)^5}$$

$$i = \left(\frac{1}{0.6}\right)^{0.2} - 1 = 0.1076 \ (10.76\%)$$

Alternatively, the interest rate can be found by setting up the standard notation P/F relation, solving for the factor value, and interpolating in the tables.

$$P = F(P/F, i, n)$$

$$\$3000 = 5000(P/F, i, 5)$$

$$(P/F, i, 5) = \frac{3000}{5000} = 0.60$$

From the interest tables, a P/F factor of 0.6000 for $n = 5$ lies between 10 and 11%. Interpolate between these two values to obtain $i = 10.76\%$.

Since 10.76% is greater than the 7% available from a guaranteed investment certificate, Laurel should make the business investment. Since the higher rate of return would be received on the business investment, Laurel would probably select this option instead of the investment certificate. However, the degree of risk associated with the business investment was not specified. Obviously, risk is an important parameter that may cause selection of the lower rate of return investment. Unless specified to the contrary, equal risk for all alternatives is assumed in this text.

The IRR spreadsheet function is one of the most useful of all those available. IRR means internal rate of return, which is a topic unto itself, discussed in detail in Chapter 7. However, even at this early stage of engineering economic analysis, the IRR function can be used beneficially to find the interest rate (or rate of return) for any cash flow series that is entered into a series of contiguous spreadsheet cells, vertical or horizontal. It is very important that any years (periods) with a zero cash flow have an entry of 0 in the cell. A cell left blank is not sufficient, because an incorrect value of i will be displayed by the IRR function. The basic format is

E-SOLVE

IRR(first_cell:last_cell)

The *first_cell* and *last_cell* are the cell references for the start and end of the cash flow series. Example 2.13 illustrates the IRR function.

The RATE function, also very useful, is an alternative to IRR. RATE is a one-cell function that displays the compound interest rate (or rate of return) only when the annual cash flows, that is, A values, are the same. Present and future values different from the A value can be entered. The format is

$$\textbf{RATE(number\_years},A,P,F)$$

The F value does not include the amount A that occurs in year n. No entry into spreadsheet cells of each cash flow is necessary to use RATE, so it should be used whenever there is a uniform series over n years with associated P and/or F values stated. Example 2.13 illustrates the RATE function.

EXAMPLE 2.13

Professional Engineers, Inc., requires that $500 per year be placed into a sinking fund account to cover any unexpected major rework on field equipment. In one case, $500 was deposited for 15 years and covered a rework costing $10,000 in year 15. What rate of return did this practice provide to the company? Solve by hand and by computer.

Solution by Hand

The cash flow diagram is shown in Figure 2–20. Either the A/F or F/A factor can be used. Using A/F,

$$A = F(A/F,i,n)$$
$$500 = 10,000(A/F,i,15)$$
$$(A/F,i,15) = 0.0500$$

From interest Tables 8 and 9 under the A/F column for 15 years, the value 0.0500 lies between 3 and 4%. By interpolation, $i = 3.98\%$. (This is considered a low return for an engineering project.)

FIGURE 2–20
Diagram to determine the rate of return, Example 2.13.

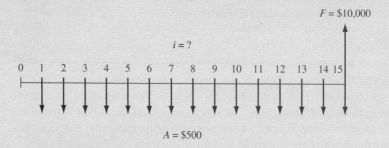

Solution by Computer

Refer to the cash flow diagram (Figure 2–20) while completing the spreadsheet (Figure 2–21). A single-cell solution using the RATE function can be applied since $A = \$-500$ occurs each year and the $F = \$10,000$ value takes place in the last year of the series. Cell A3 contains the function RATE(15,−500,,10000), and the answer displayed is 3.98%. The minus sign on 500 indicates the annual deposit. The extra comma is necessary to indicate that no *P* value is present. This function is fast, but it allows only limited sensitivity analysis; all the *A* values have to change by the same amount. The IRR function is much better for answering "What if?" questions.

To apply the IRR function and obtain the same answer, enter the value 0 in a cell (for year 0), followed by −500 for 14 years and 9500 (from 10,000 − 500) in year 15. Figure 2–21 contains these numbers in cells D2 through D17. In any cell on the spreadsheet, enter the IRR function IRR(D2:D17). The answer $i = 3.98\%$ is displayed in cell E3. It is advisable to enter the year numbers 0 through *n* (15 in this example) in the column immediately to the left of the cash flow entries. The IRR function does not need these numbers, but it makes the cash flow entry activity easier and more accurate. Now any cash flow can be changed, and a new rate will be displayed immediately via IRR.

	A	B	C	D	E	F	G
1			Year	Cash flow			
2	Using RATE		0	0	Using IRR		
3	3.98%		1	−500	3.98%		
4			2	−500			
5			3	−500			
6	= RATE(15,−500,,10000)		4	−500	= IRR(D2:D17)		
7			5	−500			
8			6	−500			
9			7	−500			
10			8	−500			
11			9	−500			
12			10	−500			
13			11	−500			
14			12	−500			
15			13	−500			
16			14	−500			

FIGURE 2–21
Spreadsheet solution for rate of return using the RATE and IRR functions, Example 2.13.

2.8 DETERMINATION OF UNKNOWN NUMBER OF YEARS

It is sometimes necessary to determine the number of years (periods) required for a cash flow series to provide a stated rate of return. Other times it is desirable to determine when specified amounts will be available from an investment. In both cases, the unknown value is *n*. Techniques similar to those of the preceding section are used to find *n*. Some problems can be solved directly for *n* by manipulation of the single-payment and uniform-series formulas. In other cases, *n* is found through interpolation in the interest tables, as illustrated below.

The spreadsheet function NPER can be used to quickly find the number of years (periods) *n* for given *A*, *P*, and/or *F* values. The format is

$$\textbf{NPER}(i\%,A,P,F)$$

If the future value *F* is not involved, *F* is omitted; however, a present worth *P* and uniform amount *A* must be entered. The *A* entry can be zero when only single amounts *P* and *F* are known, as in the next example. At least one of the entries must have a sign opposite the others to obtain an answer from NPER.

EXAMPLE 2.14

How long will it take for $1000 to double if the interest rate is 5% per year?

Solution
The n value can be determined using either the F/P or P/F factor. Using the P/F factor,

$$P = F(P/F,i,n)$$
$$1000 = 2000(P/F,5\%,n)$$
$$(P/F,5\%,n) = 0.500$$

Q-SOLVE

In the 5% interest table, the value 0.500 lies between 14 and 15 years. By interpolation, $n = 14.2$ years. Use the function NPER(5%,0,−1000,2000) to display an n value of 14.21 years.

2.9 SPREADSHEET APPLICATION—BASIC SENSITIVITY ANALYSIS

We have performed engineering economy computations with the spreadsheet functions PV, FV, PMT, IRR, and NPER that were introduced in Section 1.8. Most functions took only a single spreadsheet cell to find the answer. The example below illustrates how to solve a slightly more complex problem that involves sensitivity analysis; that is, it helps answer "What if?" questions.

EXAMPLE 2.15

E-SOLVE

An engineer and a medical doctor have teamed up to develop a major improvement in laparoscopic surgery for gallbladder operations. They formed a small business corporation to handle the financial aspects of their partnership. The company has invested $500,000 in the project already this year ($t = 0$), and it expects to spend $500,000 annually for the next 4 years, and possibly for more years. Develop a spreadsheet that helps answer the following questions.

(a) Assume the $500,000 is expended for only 4 additional years. If the company sells the rights to use the new technology at the end of year 5 for $5 million, what is the anticipated rate of return?

(b) The engineer and doctor estimate that they will need $500,000 per year for more than 4 additional years. How many years from now do they have to finish their development work and receive the $5 million licence fee to make at least 10% per year? Assume the $500,000 per year is expended through the year immediately *prior* to the receipt for the $5 million.

Solution by Computer
Figure 2–22 presents the spreadsheet, with all financial values in $1000 units. The IRR function is used throughout.

(a) The function IRR(B6:B11) in cell B15 displays $i = 24.07\%$. Note there is a cash flow of $−500 in year 0. The equivalence statement is: Spending $500,000 now and

$500,000 each year for 4 more years is equivalent to receiving $5 million at the end
of year 5, when the interest rate is 24.07% per year.

(b) Find the rate of return for an increasing number of years that the $500 is expended.
Columns C and D in Figure 2–22 present the results of IRR functions with the $5000
cash flow in different years. Cells C15 and D15 show returns on opposite sides of
10%. Therefore, the $5 million must be received some time prior to the end of year 7
to make more than the 8.93% shown in cell D15. The engineer and doctor have less
than 6 years to complete their development work.

	A	B	C	D
2				
3		Part (a)	Part (b)	
4		Find i	Fnd n such that i > 10%	
5	Year	Get $5 million in yr 5	Get $5 million in yr 6	Get $5 million in yr 7
6	0	$ (500)	$ (500)	$ (500)
7	1	$ (500)	$ (500)	$ (500)
8	2	$ (500)	$ (500)	$ (500)
9	3	$ (500)	$ (500)	$ (500)
10	4	$ (500)	$ (500)	$ (500)
11	5	$ 5,000	$ (500)	$ (500)
12	6		$ 5,000	$ (500)
13	7			$ 5,000
14				
15	Rate of returns	24.07%	14.80%	8.93%
16				
17				
18		= IRR(B6:B11)	= IRR(C6:C12)	= IRR(D6:D13)
19				

FIGURE 2–22
Spreadsheet solution including sensitivity analysis, Example 2.15.

ADDITIONAL EXAMPLE

EXAMPLE 2.16

P, F, AND *A* CALCULATIONS

Explain why the uniform series factors cannot be used to compute *P* or *F* directly for any
of the cash flows shown in Figure 2–23.

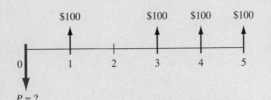

FIGURE 2–23
Sample cash
flow diagrams,
Example 2.16.

(*a*)

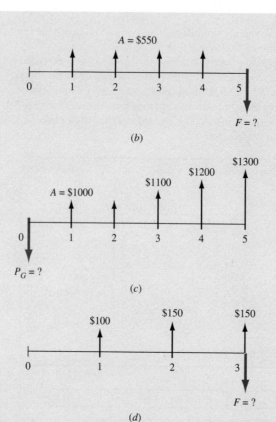

(b)

(c)

(d)

Solution

(a) The P/A factor cannot be used to compute P since the $100 per year receipt does not occur each year from 1 through 5.

(b) Since there is no $A = 550$ in year 5, the F/A factor cannot be used. The relation $F = 550(F/A,i,4)$ would furnish the future worth in year 4, not year 5.

(c) The first gradient amount $G = 100$ occurs in year 3. Use of the relation $P_G = 100(P/G,i\%,4)$ will compute P_G in year 1, not year 0. (The present worth of the base amount of $1000 is not included here.)

(d) The receipt values are unequal; thus the relation $F = A(F/A,i,3)$ cannot be used to compute F.

CHAPTER SUMMARY

Formulas and factors derived and applied in this chapter perform equivalence calculations for present, future, annual, and gradient cash flows. Capability in using these formulas and their standard notation manually and with spreadsheets is critical to complete an engineering economy study. Using these formulas and spreadsheet functions, you can convert single cash flows into uniform cash flows, gradients into present worths, and much more. You can solve for rate of return i or time n. A thorough understanding of how to manipulate cash flows using the material in this chapter will help you address financial questions in professional practice as well as in everyday living.

PROBLEMS

Use of Interest Tables

2.1 Find the correct numerical value for the following factors from the interest tables.
1. $(F/P,8\%,25)$
2. $(P/A,3\%,8)$
3. $(P/G,9\%,20)$
4. $(F/A,15\%,18)$
5. $(A/P,30\%,15)$

Determination of F, P, and A

2.2 Cenovus Energy is using "wedge well" technology (patent pending) to access stranded bitumen between its steam-assisted gravity drainage (SAGD) well pairs. If Cenovus spends $2.7 million now to drill 2 wedge wells at its Christina Lake installation near Fort McMurray to test for commercial applications, what dollar value of oil production three years from now is necessary to recover the investment at 20%-per-year interest?

2.3 The Canadian military is considering the purchase of a new helicopter for peace-keeping operations. A similar helicopter was purchased 4 years ago at a cost of $140,000. At an interest rate of 7% per year, what would be the equivalent value today of that $140,000 expenditure?

2.4 Pressure Systems, Inc., manufactures high-accuracy liquid-level transducers. It is investigating whether it should update certain equipment now or wait to do it later. If the cost now is $200,000, what will the equivalent amount be 3 years from now at an interest rate of 10% per year?

2.5 Petroleum Products, Inc., is a pipeline company that provides petroleum products to wholesalers in Canada and the northern United States. The company is considering purchasing insertion turbine flowmeters to allow for better monitoring of pipeline integrity. If these meters would prevent one major disruption (through early detection of product loss) valued at $600,000 four years from now, how much could the company afford to spend now at an interest rate of 12% per year?

2.6 Sensotech Inc., a maker of microelectro-mechanical systems, believes it can reduce product recalls by 10% if it purchases new software for detecting faulty parts. The cost of the new software is $225,000. (*a*) How much would the company have to save each year for 4 years to recover its investment if it uses a minimum attractive rate of return of 15% per year? (*b*) What was the cost of recalls per year before the software was purchased if the company did exactly recover its investment in 4 years from the 10% reduction?

2.7 Thompson Mechanical Products is planning to set aside $150,000 now for possibly replacing its large synchronous refiner motors whenever it becomes necessary. If the replacement isn't needed for 7 years, how much will the company have in its investment set-aside account if it achieves a rate of return of 18% per year?

2.8 French car maker Renault signed a $75 million contract with ABB of Zurich, Switzerland, for automated underbody assembly lines, body assembly workshops, and line control systems. If ABB will be paid in 2 years (when the systems are ready), what is the present worth of the contract at 18% per year interest?

2.9 Atlas Long-Haul Transportation is considering installing Valutemp temperature loggers in all of its refrigerated trucks for monitoring temperatures during transit. If the systems will reduce insurance claims by $100,000 two years from now, how much should the company be willing to spend now if it uses an interest rate of 12% per year?

2.10 GE Marine Systems is planning to supply a Japanese shipbuilder with aero-derivative gas turbines to power 11 DD-class destroyers for the Japanese Self-Defense Force. The buyer can pay the total contract price of $1,700,000 now or an equivalent amount 1 year from now (when the turbines will be needed). At an interest rate of 18% per year, what is the equivalent future amount?

2.11 What is the present worth of a future cost of $162,000 to Digitech, Inc., 6 years from now at an interest rate of 12% per year?

2.12 How much could Cryogenics Inc., a maker of superconducting magnetic energy storage systems, afford to spend now on new equipment in lieu of spending $125,000 five years from now if the company's rate of return is 14% per year?

2.13 V-Tek Systems is a manufacturer of vertical compactors, and it is examining its cash flow requirements for the next 5 years. The company expects to replace office machines and computer equipment at various times over the 5-year planning period. Specifically, the company expects to spend $9000 two years from now, $8000 three years from now, and $5000 five years from now. What is the present worth of the planned expenditures at an interest rate of 10% per year?

2.14 A manufacturer of toilet flush valves wants to have $2,800,000 available 10 years from now so that a new product line can be initiated. If the company plans to deposit money each year, starting 1 year from now, how much will it have to deposit each year at 6% per year interest in order to have the $2,800,000 available immediately after the last deposit is made?

2.15 The current cost of liability insurance for a certain consulting firm is $65,000. If the insurance cost is expected to increase by 4% each year, what will be the cost 5 years from now?

2.16 Grand Bay Gas Products manufactures a device that empties the contents of old aerosol cans in 2 to 3 seconds. This eliminates having to dispose of the cans as hazardous wastes. If a certain paint company can save $75,000 per year in waste disposal costs, how much could the company afford to spend now on the device if it wants to recover its investment in 3 years at an interest rate of 20% per year?

2.17 Atlantic Metals and Plastic uses austenitic nickel-chromium alloys to manufacture resistance heating wire. The company is considering a new annealing-drawing process to reduce costs. If the new process will cost $1.8 million now, how much must be saved each year to recover the investment in 6 years at an interest rate of 12% per year?

2.18 A green algae, *Chlamydomonas rein-hardtii,* can produce hydrogen when temporarily deprived of sulfur for up to 2 days at a time. A small company needs to purchase equipment costing $3.4 million to commercialize the process. If the company wants to earn a rate of return of 20% per year and recover its investments in 8 years, what must be the net value of the hydrogen produced each year?

2.19 How much money could RTT Environmental Services borrow to finance a site reclamation project if it expects revenues of $280,000 per year over a 5-year cleanup period? Expenses associated with the project are expected to be $90,000 per year. Assume the interest rate is 10% per year.

2.20 Edmonton Playland and Aquatics Park spends $75,000 each year in consulting services for ride inspection. New actuator element technology enables engineers to simulate complex computer-controlled movements in any direction. How much could the amusement park afford to spend now on the new technology if the annual consulting services will no longer be needed? Assume the park uses an interest rate of 15% per year and it wants to recover its investment in 5 years.

2.21 Under an agreement with the Internet Service Providers (ISPs) Association, SBC Communications reduced the price it charges ISPs to resell its high-speed digital subscriber line (DSL) service from $458 to $360 per year per customer line. A particular ISP, which has 20,000 customers, plans to pass 90% of the savings along to its customers. What is the total future worth of these savings over a 5-year horizon at an interest rate of 8% per year?

2.22 A new biomass-powered energy system run on mill waste is helping to put the Fraser Papers lumber mill in western New Brunswick back on the track to profitability. If the combustor is upgraded, determine the future worth in year 5 of savings of $70,000 now and $90,000 two years from now at an interest rate of 10% per year.

2.23 A civil engineer deposits $10,000 per year into a retirement account that achieves a rate of return of 12% per year. Determine the amount of money in the account at the end of 25 years.

2.24 A recent engineering graduate was given a raise (beginning in year 1) of $2000. At an interest rate of 8% per year, what is the present value of the $2000 per year over her expected 35-year career?

2.25 Ontario Moving and Storage wants to have enough money to purchase a new tractor-trailer in 3 years. If the unit will cost $250,000, how much should the company set aside each year if the account earns 9% per year?

2.26 Vision Technologies, Inc., is a small company that uses ultra-wideband technology to develop devices that can detect objects (including people) inside buildings, behind walls, or below ground. The company expects to spend $100,000 per year for labour and $125,000 per year for supplies before a product can be marketed. At an interest rate of 15% per year, what is the total equivalent future amount of the company's expenses at the end of 3 years?

Factor Values

2.27 Find the numerical value of the following factors by (a) interpolation and (b) using the appropriate formula.
1. (P/F,18%,33)
2. (A/G,12%,54)

2.28 Find the numerical value of the following factors by (a) interpolation and (b) using the appropriate formula.
1. (F/A,19%,20)
2. (P/A,26%,15)

Arithmetic Gradient

2.29 A cash flow sequence starts in year 1 at $3000 and decreases by $200 each year through year 10. (a) Determine the value of the gradient G; (b) determine the amount of cash flow in year 8; and (c) determine the value of n for the gradient.

2.30 Manulife expects sales to be described by the cash flow sequence (6000 + 5k), where k is in years and cash flow is in millions. Determine (a) the value of the gradient G; (b) the amount of cash flow in year 6; and (c) the value of n for the gradient if the cash flow ends in year 12.

2.31 For the cash flow sequence that starts in year 1 and is described by 900 − 100k, where k represents years 1 through 5, (a) determine the value of the gradient G and (b) determine the cash flow in year 5.

2.32 Omega Instruments has budgeted $300,000 per year to pay for certain ceramic parts over the next 5 years. If the company expects the cost of the parts to increase uniformly according to an arithmetic gradient of $10,000 per year, what is it expecting the cost to be in year 1, if the interest rate is 10% per year?

2.33 Petro-Canada expects receipts from a group of stripper wells (wells that produce less than 10 barrels per day) to decline according to an arithmetic gradient of $50,000 per year. This year's receipts are expected to be $280,000 (i.e., end of year 1), and the company expects the useful life of the wells to be 5 years. (a) What is the amount of the cash flow in year 3, and (b) what is the equivalent uniform annual worth in years 1 through 5 of the income from the wells at an interest rate of 12% per year?

2.34 Income from cardboard recycling at Moose Jaw has been increasing at a constant rate of $1000 in each of the last 3 years. If this year's income (i.e., end of year 1) is expected to be $4000 and the increased income trend continues through year 5, (a) what will the income be 3 years from now (i.e., end of year 3) and (b) what is the present worth of the income over that 5-year period at an interest rate of 10% per year?

2.35 McGraw-Hill Ryerson is considering purchasing a sophisticated computer system to "cube" a book's dimensions—measure its height, length, and width so that the proper box size will be used for shipment. This will save packing material, cardboard, and labour. If the savings will be $150,000 the first year, $160,000 the second year, and amounts increasing by $10,000 each year for 8 years, what is the present worth of the system at an interest rate of 15% per year?

2.36 West Coast Marine and RV is considering replacing its wired pendant controllers on its heavy-duty cranes with new portable infrared keypad controllers. The company expects to achieve cost savings of $14,000 the first year and amounts increasing by $1500 each year thereafter for the next 4 years. At an interest rate of 12% per year, what is the equivalent annual worth of the savings?

2.37 Ford Motor Company was able to reduce by 80% the cost required for installing data acquisition instrumentation on test vehicles by using MTS-developed spinning wheel force transducers. (*a*) If this year's cost (i.e., end of year 1) is expected to be $2000, what was the cost the year before installation of the transducers? (*b*) If the costs are expected to increase by $250 each year for the next 4 years (i.e., through year 5), what is the equivalent annual worth of the costs (years 1 through 5) at an interest rate of 18% per year?

2.38 For the cash flow shown below, determine the value of G that will make the future worth in year 4 equal to $6000 at an interest rate of 15% per year.

Year	0	1	2	3	4
Cash flow	0	$2000	2000−G	2000−2G	2000−3G

2.39 A major drug company anticipates that in future years it could be involved in litigation regarding perceived side effects of one of its antidepressant drugs. To prepare a "war chest," the company wants to have money available 6 years from now that has a present worth today of $50 million. The company expects to set aside $6 million the first year and uniformly increasing amounts in each of the next 5 years. If the company can earn 12% per year on the money it sets aside, by how much must it increase the amount set aside each year to achieve its goal?

2.40 A startup direct marketer of car parts expects to spend $1 million the first year

for advertising, with amounts decreasing by $100,000 each year. Income is expected to be $4 million the first year, increasing by $500,000 each year. Determine the equivalent annual worth in years 1 through 5 of the company's *net cash flow* at an interest rate of 16% per year.

Geometric Gradient

2.41 Assume you were told to prepare a table of factor values (like those at the back of this book) for calculating the present worth of a geometric gradient series. Determine the first three values (i.e., for $n = 1, 2,$ and 3) for an interest rate of 10% per year and a rate of change g of 4% per year.

2.42 A chemical engineer planning for her retirement will deposit 10% of her salary each year into a high-technology stock fund. If her salary this year is $60,000 (i.e., end of year 1) and she expects her salary to increase by 4% each year, what will be the present worth of the fund after 15 years if it earns 4% per year?

2.43 The effort required to maintain a scanning electron microscope is known to increase by a fixed percentage each year. A high-tech equipment maintenance company has offered it services for a fee of $25,000 for the first year (i.e., end of year 1) with increases of 6% per year thereafter. If a biotechnology company wants to pay for a 3-year contract up front, how much should it be willing to pay if it uses an interest rate of 15% per year?

2.44 Hughes Cable Systems plans to offer its employees a salary enhancement package that has revenue sharing as its main component. Specifically, the company will set aside 1% of total sales for year-end bonuses for all its employees. The sales are expected to be $5 million the first year, $6 million the second year, and amounts increasing by 20% each year for the next 5 years. At an interest rate of 10% per year, what is the equivalent annual worth in years 1 through 5 of the bonus package?

2.45 Determine how much money would be in a savings account that started with a deposit of $2000 in year 1 with each succeeding amount increasing by 10% per year. Use an interest rate of 15% per year and a 7-year period.

2.46 The future worth in year 10 of a geometric gradient series of cash flows was found to be $80,000. If the interest rate was 15% per year and the annual rate of increase was 9% per year, what was the cash flow amount in year 1?

2.47 Frederiction Furniture Industries offers several types of high-performance fabrics that are capable of withstanding chemicals as harsh as chlorine. A certain New Brunswick manufacturing company that uses fabric in several products has a report showing that the present worth of fabric purchases over a certain 5-year period was $900,000. If the costs were known to geometrically increase by 5% per year during that time and the company used an interest rate of 15% per year for investments, what was the cost of the fabric in year 2?

2.48 Find the present worth of a series of investments that starts at $1000 in year 1 and increases by 10% per year for 20 years. Assume the interest rate is 10% per year.

2.49 A Windsor consulting firm wants to start saving money for replacement of network servers. If the company invests $3000 at the end of year 1 and increases the amount invested by 5% each year, how much will be in the account 4 years

from now if it earns interest at a rate of 8% per year?

2.50 A company that manufactures purgable hydrogen sulfide monitors is planning to make deposits such that each one is 5% larger than the preceding one. How large must the first deposit be (at the end of year 1) if the deposits extend through year 10 and the fourth deposit is $1250? Use an interest rate of 10% per year.

Interest Rate and Rate of Return

2.51 What compound interest rate per year is equivalent to a 12% per year simple interest rate over a 15-year period?

2.52 A publicly traded consulting engineering firm pays a bonus to each engineer at the end of the year based on the company's profit for that year. If the company's initial investment was $1.2 million, what rate of return has it made on its investment if each engineer's bonus has been $3000 per year for the past 10 years? Assume the company has six engineers and that the bonus money represents 5% of the company's profit.

2.53 Danson Iron Works, Inc., manufactures angular contact ball bearings for pumps that operate in harsh environments. If the company invested $2.4 million in a process that resulted in profits of $760,000 per year for 5 years, what rate of return did the company make on its investment?

2.54 An investment of $600,000 increased to $1,000,000 over a 5-year period. What was the rate of return on the investment?

2.55 A small company that specializes in powder coating expanded its building and purchased a new oven that is large enough to handle automobile frames. The building and oven cost $125,000, but new business from hot-rodders has increased annual income by $520,000. If operating expenses for gas, materials, labour, etc., amount to $470,000 per year, what rate of return will be made on the investment if only the cash flows that occur over the next 4 years are included in the calculation?

2.56 The business plan for a startup company that manufactures multigas portable detectors showed equivalent annual cash flows of $400,000 for the first 5 years. If the cash flow in year 1 was $320,000 and the increase thereafter was $50,000 per year, what interest rate was used in the calculation?

2.57 A new company that makes medium-voltage soft starters spent $85,000 to build a new website. Net income was $60,000 the first year, increasing by $15,000 each year. What rate of return did the company make in its first 5 years?

Number of Years

2.58 A company that manufactures plastic control valves has a fund for equipment replacement that contains $500,000. If the company spends $75,000 per year on new equipment, how many years will it take to reduce the fund to less than $75,000 at an interest rate of 10% per year?

2.59 An engineering consulting firm is considering purchasing the building it currently occupies under a long-term lease because the owner of the building suddenly put it up for sale. The building is being offered at a price of $170,000. Since the lease is already paid for this year, the next annual lease payment of $30,000 isn't due until the end of this year. Because the firm has been a good tenant, the owner has offered to sell to them for $160,000. If the firm purchases the building with no down payment, how long will it be before the company recovers its investment at an interest rate of 12% per year?

2.60 An engineer who invested very well plans to retire now because she has $2,000,000 in her retirement account. How long will she be able to withdraw $100,000 per year (beginning 1 year from now) if her account earns interest at a rate of 4% per year?

2.61 A company that manufactures ultrasonic wind sensors invested $1.5 million 2 years ago to acquire part ownership in an innovative chip-making company. How long would it take (from the date of the initial investment) for its share of the chip company to be worth $3 million if that company is growing at a rate of 20% per year?

2.62 Roger Lareveur owns a mutual fund that has averaged an 18% annual rate of return since he bought it two years ago with $100,000. In the unlikely event that these stellar results should continue, how long will it be (from the time he started) before he can retire with $1.6 million?

2.63 How many years will it take for a uniform annual deposit of size A to accumulate to 10 times the size of a single deposit if the rate of return is 10% per year?

2.64 How many years would it take for an investment of $10,000 in year 1 with increases of 10% per year to have a present worth of $1,000,000 at an interest rate of 7% per year?

2.65 You were told that a certain cash flow sequence started at $3000 in year 1 and increased by $2000 each year. How many years were required for the equivalent annual worth of the sequence to be $12,000 at an interest rate of 10% per year?

WHAT A DIFFERENCE THE YEARS AND COMPOUND INTEREST CAN MAKE

Stock Option Program Purchase

A young B.Eng. graduate from the Dalhousie Faculty of Engineering went to work for a microelectronics company at the age of 22 and placed $50 per month into the stock purchase option. He left the company after a full 60 months of employment at age 27, and he did not sell the stock. The engineer did not inquire about the value of the stock until age 57, some 30 years later.

1. Construct the cash flow diagram for ages 22 through 57.

2. The engineer has learned that over the 35 intervening years, the stock earned at a rate of 1.25% per month. Determine the value of the funds accumulated in the stock purchase option when the engineer left the company after a total of 60 purchases.

3. Determine the value of the engineer's company stock at age 57. Again, observe the significant difference that 30 years have made at a 15% per year compound rate.

4. Assume the engineer did not leave the funds invested in the stock at age 27. Now determine the amount he would have to deposit each year, starting at age 50, to be equivalent to the value at age 57 you calculated in (3) above. Assume the 7 years of deposits make a return of 15% per year.

5. Finally, compare the total amount of money deposited during the 5 years when the engineer was in his twenties with the total amount he would have to deposit during the 7 years in his fifties to have the equal and equivalent amount at age 57, as determined in (3) above.

CHAPTER 3

Combining Factors

Most estimated cash flow series do not fit exactly the series for which the factors and equations in Chapter 2 were developed. Therefore, it is necessary to combine the equations. For a given sequence of cash flows, there are usually several correct ways to determine the equivalent present worth P, future worth F, or annual worth A. This chapter explains how to combine the engineering economy factors to address more complex situations involving shifted uniform series and gradient series. Spreadsheet functions are used to speed up the computations.

LEARNING OBJECTIVES

Purpose: Use hand and spreadsheet computations that combine several engineering economy factors.

By the end of this chapter you should be able to

Shifted series	**1.** Determine P, F, or A of a uniform series starting at a time other than period 1.
Shifted series and single amounts	**2.** Calculate P, F, or A of randomly placed single amounts and uniform series.
Shifted gradients	**3.** Make equivalence calculations for cash flows involving shifted arithmetic or geometric gradients.
Decreasing gradients	**4.** Make equivalence calculations for cash flows involving decreasing arithmetic gradients.
Spreadsheets	**5.** Apply different spreadsheet functions and compare computer and hand solutions.

3.1 CALCULATIONS FOR UNIFORM SERIES THAT ARE SHIFTED

When a uniform series begins at a time other than at the end of period 1, it is called a *shifted series*. In this case several methods can be used to find the equivalent present worth P. For example, P of the uniform series shown in Figure 3–1 could be determined by any of the following methods:

- Use the P/F factor to find the present worth of each disbursement at year 0 and add them.
- Use the F/P factor to find the future worth of each disbursement in year 13, add them, and then find the present worth of the total using $P = F(P/F,i,13)$.
- Use the F/A factor to find the future amount $F = A(F/A,i,10)$, and then compute the present worth using $P = F(P/F,i,13)$.
- Use the P/A factor to compute the "present worth" (which will be located in year 3 not year 0), and then find the present worth in year 0 by using the $(P/F,i,3)$ factor. (Present worth is enclosed in quotation marks here only to represent the present worth as determined by the P/A factor in year 3, and to differentiate it from the present worth in year 0.)

Typically the last method is used for calculating the present worth of a uniform series that does not begin at the end of period 1. For Figure 3–1, the "present worth" obtained using the P/A factor is located in year 3. This is shown as P_3 in Figure 3–2. Note that a P value is always located *1 year or period prior* to the beginning of the first series amount. Why? Because the P/A factor was derived with P in time period 0 and A beginning at the end of period 1. The most common mistake made in working problems of this type is improper placement of P. Therefore, it is extremely important to remember:

The present worth is always located one period prior to the first uniform-series amount when using the P/A factor.

To determine a future worth or F value, recall that the F/A factor derived in Section 2.3 had the F located in the *same* period as the last uniform-series amount. Figure 3–3 shows the location of the future worth when F/A is used for Figure 3–1 cash flows.

FIGURE 3–1

A uniform series that is shifted.

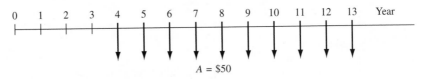

FIGURE 3–1

A uniform series that is shifted.

FIGURE 3–2

Location of present worth for the shifted uniform series in Figure 3–1.

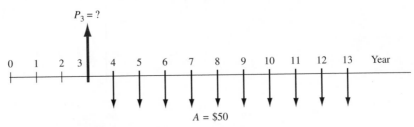

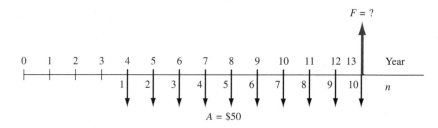

The future worth is always located in the same period as the last uniform-series amount when using the F/A factor.

It is also important to remember that the number of periods n in the P/A or F/A factor is equal to the number of uniform-series values. It may be helpful to *renumber* the cash flow diagram to avoid errors in counting. Figure 3–3 shows Figure 3–1 renumbered to determine $n = 10$.

As stated above, there are several methods that can be used to solve problems containing a uniform series that is shifted. However, it is generally more convenient to use the uniform-series factors than the single-amount factors. There are specific steps that should be followed in order to avoid errors:

1. Draw a diagram of the positive and negative cash flows.
2. Locate the present worth or future worth of each series on the cash flow diagram.
3. Determine n for each series by renumbering the cash flow diagram.
4. Draw another cash flow diagram representing the desired equivalent cash flow.
5. Set up and solve the equations.

These steps are illustrated below.

EXAMPLE 3.1

An engineering technology group just purchased new CAD software for $5000 now and annual payments of $500 per year for 6 years starting 3 years from now for annual upgrades. What is the present worth of the payments if the interest rate is 8% per year?

Solution

The cash flow diagram is shown in Figure 3–4. The symbol P_A is used throughout this chapter to represent the present worth of a uniform annual series A, and P'_A represents the present worth at a time other than period 0. Similarly, P_T represents the total present worth at time 0. The correct placement of P'_A and the diagram renumbering to obtain n are also indicated. Note that P'_A is located in actual year 2, not year 3. Also, $n = 6$, not 8, for the P/A factor. First find the value of P'_A of the shifted series.

$$P'_A = \$500(P/A,8\%,6)$$

Since P'_A is located in year 2, now find P_A in year 0.

$$P_A = P'_A(P/F,8\%,2)$$

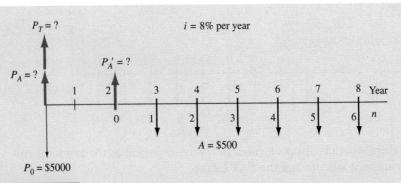

FIGURE 3-4
Cash flow diagram with placement of P values, Example 3.1.

The total present worth is determined by adding P_A and the initial payment P_0 in year 0.

$$P_T = P_0 + P_A$$
$$= 5000 + 500(P/A,8\%,6)(P/F,8\%,2)$$
$$= 5000 + 500(4.6229)(0.8573)$$
$$= \$6981.60$$

The more complex cash flow series become, the more useful are the spreadsheet functions. When the uniform series A is shifted, the NPV function is used to determine P, and the PMT function finds the equivalent A value. The NPV function, like the PV function, determines the P values, but NPV can handle any combination of cash flows directly from the cells in the same way as the IRR function. Enter the net cash flows in contiguous cells (column or row), making sure to enter 0 for all zero cash flows. Use the format

NPV($i\%$,second_cell:last_cell) + first_cell

First_cell contains the cash flow for year 0 and must be listed separately for NPV to correctly account for the time value of money. The cash flow in year 0 may be 0.

The easiest way to find an equivalent A over n years for a shifted series is with the PMT function, where the P value is from the NPV function above. The format is the same as we learned earlier, but the entry for P is a cell reference, not a number.

PMT($i\%$,n,cell_with_P,F)

Alternatively, the same technique can be used when an F value was obtained using the FV function. Now the last entry in PMT is "cell_with_F."

It is very useful that any parameter in a spreadsheet function can itself be a function. Thus, it is possible to write the PMT function in a single cell by embedding the NPV function (and FV function, if needed). The format is

$$\text{PMT}(i\%,n,\text{NPV}(i\%,\text{second\_cell:last\_cell})+\text{first\_cell},F)$$

Q-SOLVE

Of course, the answer for A is the same for the two-cell operation or a single-cell, embedded function. All three of these functions are illustrated in the next example.

EXAMPLE 3.2

Recalibration of sensitive measuring devices costs $8000 per year. If the machine will be recalibrated for each of 6 years starting 3 years after purchase, calculate the 8-year equivalent uniform series at 16% per year. Show hand and computer solutions.

Solution by Hand
Figure 3–5a and b shows the original cash flows and the desired equivalent diagram. To convert the $8000 shifted series into an equivalent uniform series over all periods, first convert the uniform series into a present worth or future worth amount. Then either the A/P factor or the A/F factor can be used. Both methods are illustrated here.

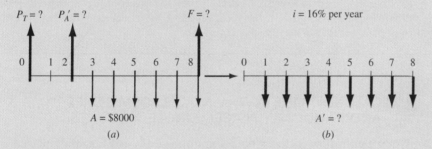

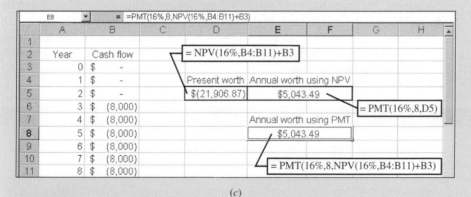

(c)

FIGURE 3–5
(a) Original and (b) equivalent cash flow diagrams, and (c) spreadsheet functions to determine A; Example 3.2.

Present worth method. (Refer to Figure 3–5a.) Calculate P_A' for the shifted series in year 2 and P_T in year 0.

$$P_A' = 8000(P/A,16\%,6)$$
$$P_T = P_A'(P/F,16\%,2) = 8000(P/A,16\%,6)(P/F,16\%,2)$$
$$= 8000(3.6847)(0.7432) = \$21,907.75$$

The equivalent series A' *for 8 years* can now be determined via the A/P factor.

$$A' = P_T(A/P,16\%,8) = \$5043.60$$

Future worth method. (Refer to Figure 3–5a.) First calculate the future worth F in year 8.

$$F = 8000(F/A,16\%,6) = \$71,820$$

The A/F factor is now used to obtain A' over all 8 years.

$$A' = F(A/F,16\%,8) = \$5043.20$$

Solution by Computer

(Refer to Figure 3–5c.) Enter the cash flows in B3 through B11 with entries of 0 in the first three cells. Enter NPV(16%,B4:B11)+B3 in cell D5 to display the P of $21,906.87.

There are two ways to obtain the equivalent A over 8 years. Of course, only one of these PMT functions needs to be entered. Either enter the PMT function making direct reference to the NPV value (see cell tag for E/F5), or embed the NPV function into the PMT function (see cell tag for E/F8 or the formula bar).

3.2 CALCULATIONS INVOLVING UNIFORM-SERIES AND RANDOMLY PLACED SINGLE AMOUNTS

When a cash flow includes both a uniform series and randomly placed single amounts, the procedures of Section 3.1 are applied to the uniform series and the single-amount formulas are applied to the one-time cash flows. This approach, illustrated in Examples 3.3 and 3.4, is merely a combination of previous ones. For spreadsheet solutions, it is necessary to enter the net cash flows before using the NPV and other functions.

EXAMPLE 3.3

An engineering company in British Columbia that owns 50 hectares of valuable land has decided to lease the mineral rights to a mining company. The primary objective is to obtain long-term income to finance ongoing projects 6 and 16 years from the present time. The engineering company makes a proposal to the mining company that it pay $20,000 per year for 20 years beginning 1 year from now, plus $10,000 six years from now and $15,000 sixteen years from now. If the mining company wants to pay off its lease immediately, how much should it pay now if the investment should make 16% per year?

Solution

The cash flow diagram is shown in Figure 3–6 from the owner's perspective. Find the present worth of the 20-year uniform series and add it to the present worth of the two one-time amounts.

$$P = 20,000(P/A,16\%,20) + 10,000(P/F,16\%,6) + 15,000(P/F,16\%,16)$$
$$= \$124,075$$

Note that the $20,000 uniform series starts at the end of year 1, so the P/A factor determines the present worth at year 0.

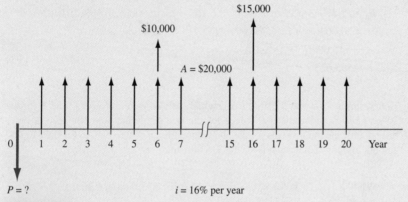

FIGURE 3–6

Diagram including a uniform series and single amounts, Example 3.3.

When you calculate the A value for a cash flow series that includes randomly placed single amounts and uniform series, *first convert everything to a present worth or a future worth.* Then the A value is obtained by multiplying P or F by the appropriate A/P or A/F factor. Example 3.4 illustrates this procedure.

EXAMPLE 3.4

Assume similar cash flow estimates to those projected in the previous example (Example 3.3) for the engineering company planning to lease its mineral rights. However, move the beginning year for the $20,000 per year series forward 2 years to start in year 3. It will now continue through year 22. Utilize engineering economy relations by hand and by computer to determine the five *equivalent values* listed below at 16% per year.

1. Total present worth P_T in year 0
2. Future worth F in year 22
3. Annual series over all 22 years
4. Annual series over the first 10 years
5. Annual series over the last 12 years

Solution by Hand

Figure 3–7 presents the cash flows with equivalent P and F values indicated in the correct years for the P/A, P/F, and F/A factors.

1. First determine the present worth of the series in year 2. Then the total present worth P_T is the sum of three P values: the series present worth value moved back to $t = 0$ with the P/F factor, and the P values at $t = 0$ for the two single amounts in years 6 and 16.

$$P'_A = 20,000(P/A,16\%,20)$$
$$P_T = P'_A(P/F,16\%,2) + 10,000(P/F,16\%,6) + 15,000(P/F,16\%,16)$$
$$= 20,000(P/A,16\%,20)(P/F,16\%,2) + 10,000(P/F,16\%,6)$$
$$+ 15,000(P/F,16\%,16)$$
$$= \$93,625 \qquad\qquad [3.1]$$

2. To determine F in year 22 from the original cash flows (Figure 3–7), find F for the 20-year series and add the F values for the two single amounts. Be sure to carefully determine the n values for the single amounts: $n = 22-6 = 16$ for the \$10,000 amount and $n = 22 - 16 = 6$ for the \$15,000 amount.

$$F = 20,000(F/A,16\%,20) + 10,000(F/P,16\%,16) + 15,000(F/P,16\%,6)$$
$$= \$2,451,626 \qquad\qquad [3.2]$$

3. Multiply the present worth amount $P_T = \$93,625$ from (1) above by the A/P factor for 22 years to determine an equivalent 22-year A series, referred to as A_{1-22} here.

$$A_{1-22} = P_T(A/P,16\%,22) = 93,625(0.16635) = \$15,575 \qquad\qquad [3.3]$$

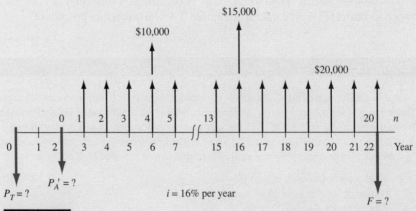

FIGURE 3–7
Diagram from Figure 3–6 with the A series shifted 2 years forward, Example 3.4.

An alternative way to determine the 22-year series uses the F value from (2) above. In this case, the computation is $A_{1-22} = F(A/F,16\%,22) = \$15,575$. Note that in both methods, the equivalent total P or F value is determined first, then the A/P or A/F factor for 22 years is applied.

4. This and item 5, which follows, are special cases that often occur in engineering economy studies. The equivalent A series is calculated for a number of years different from that covered by the original cash flows. This occurs when a defined *study period* or *planning horizon* is preset for the analysis. (More is mentioned about study periods later.) To determine the equivalent A series for years 1 through 10 only (call it A_{1-10}) the P_T *value must be used* with the A/P factor for $n = 10$. This computation will transform the original cash flows in Figure 3–7 into the equivalent series A_{1-10} in Figure 3–8a.

$$A_{1-10} = P_T(A/P,16\%,10) = 93,625(0.20690) = \$19,371 \qquad [3.4]$$

5. For the equivalent 12-year series for years 11 through 22 (call it A_{11-22}), the F *value must be used* with the A/F factor for 12 years. This transforms Figure 3–7 into the 12-year series A_{11-22} in Figure 3–8b.

$$A_{11-22} = F(A/F,16\%,12) = 2,451,626(0.03241) = \$79,457 \qquad [3.5]$$

Notice the huge difference of more than $60,000 in equivalent annual amounts that occurs when the present worth of $93,625 is allowed to compound at 16% per year for the first 10 years. This is another demonstration of the time value of money.

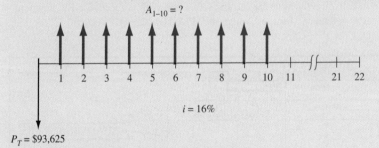

(a)

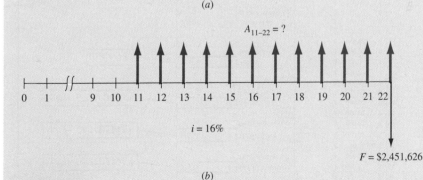

(b)

FIGURE 3–8

Cash flows of Figure 3–7 converted to equivalent uniform series for (a) years 1 to 10 and (b) years 11 to 22.

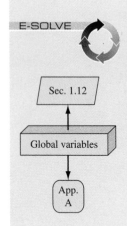

E-SOLVE

Sec. 1.12

Global variables

App. A

Solution by Computer

Figure 3–9 is a spreadsheet image with answers for all five questions. The $20,000 series and the two single amounts have been entered into separate columns, B and C. The zero cash flow values are all entered so that the functions will work correctly. This is an excellent example demonstrating the versatility of the NPV, FV, and PMT functions. In order to prepare for sensitivity analysis, the functions are developed using cell reference format or global variables, as indicated in the cell tags. This means that virtually any number—the interest rate, any cash flow estimate in the series or the single amounts, and the timing within the 22-year time frame—can be changed and the new answers will be immediately displayed. This is the general spreadsheet structure utilized for performing an engineering economy analysis with sensitivity analysis on the estimates.

1. Present worth values for the series and single amounts are determined in cells E6 and E10, respectively, using the NPV function. The sum of these in E14 is $P_T = \$93,622$, which corresponds to the value in Equation [3.1].
2. The FV function in cell E18 uses the P value in E14 (preceded by a minus sign) to determine F twenty-two years later. This is significantly easier than Equation [3.2], which determines the three separate F values and adds them to obtain $F = \$2,451,626$. Of course, either method is correct.
3. To find the 22-year A series of $15,574 starting in year 1, the PMT function in E21 references the P value in cell E14. This is effectively the same procedure used in Equation [3.3] to obtain A_{1-22}.

    For the spreadsheet enthusiast, it is possible to find the 22-year A series value in E21 directly by using the PMT function with embedded NPV functions. The cell reference format would be PMT(D1,22,−(NPV(D1,B6:B27)+B5+ NPV(D1,C6:C27)+C5)).

FIGURE 3–9

Spreadsheet using cell reference format, Example 3.4.

	D1	▼	=	16%				
	A	B	C	D	E	F	G	H	I
1			Interest rate	16.00%				
2								
3			Cash flows					
4	Year	Series	Single	Results from functions				
5	0	$ ·	$ ·	Present worth			= NPV(D1,B6:B27) + B5	
6	1	$ ·	$ ·	of series =	$88,122			
7	2	$ ·	$ ·					
8	3	$ 20,000	$ ·					
9	4	$ 20,000	$ ·	Present worth				
10	5	$ 20,000	$ ·	of singles =	$5,500			
11	6	$ 20,000	$ 10,000					
12	7	$ 20,000	$ ·					
13	8	$ 20,000	$ ·	1. Present worth			= E6 + E10	
14	9	$ 20,000	$ ·	total =	$ 93,622			
15	10	$ 20,000	$ ·					
16	11	$ 20,000	$ ·					
17	12	$ 20,000	$ ·	2. Future worth			= FV(D1,22,0, –E14)	
18	13	$ 20,000	$ ·	total =	$ 2,451,621			
19	14	$ 20,000	$ ·					
20	15	$ 20,000	$ ·	3. Annual series			= PMT(D1,22, –E14)	
21	16	$ 20,000	$ 15,000	amt (22 yrs) =	$ 15,574			
22	17	$ 20,000	$ ·					
23	18	$ 20,000	$ ·	4. Annual series			= PMT(D1,10, –E14)	
24	19	$ 20,000	$ ·	for first 10 yrs =	$ 19,370			
25	20	$ 20,000	$ ·					
26	21	$ 20,000	$ ·	5. Annual series			= PMT(D1,12,0, –E18)	
27	22	$ 20,000	$ ·	for last 12 yrs =	$ 79,469			

|◄ ◄ ► ►|\ **Sheet1** / Sheet2 / Sheet3 / Sheet4 / Sheet5 / Sheet6 / Sheet |◄ |

Ready   NUM

4. and 5. It is quite simple to determine an equivalent uniform series over any number of periods using a spreadsheet, provided the series starts one period after the P value is located or ends in the same period that the F value is located. These are both true for the series requested here—the first 10-year series can reference P in cell E14, and the last 12-year series can anchor on F in cell E18. The results in E24 and E27 are the same as A_{1-10} and A_{11-22} in Equations [3.4] and [3.5], respectively.

Comment

Remember that some round-off error will always be present when comparing hand and computer results. The spreadsheet functions carry more decimal places than the tables during calculations. Also, be very careful when constructing spreadsheet functions. It is easy to miss a value, such as the P or F in PMT and FV functions, or a minus sign between entries. Always check your function entries carefully before hitting <Enter>.

When using spreadsheets and calculators, it is important to remember that the results carry more decimal places than justified by the data's precision. The answer must be adjusted for significant figures. Normally, a single decimal place is indicative of the precision of the forecasted data used in the calculation. Two decimal places (indicating rounding to the nearest cent) are often used for small amounts of money. When the results are in the thousands of dollars, rounding to the nearest dollar is appropriate.

3.3 CALCULATIONS FOR SHIFTED GRADIENTS

In Section 2.5, we derived the relation $P = G(P/G,i,n)$ to determine the present worth of the arithmetic gradient series. The P/G factor, Equation [2.15], was derived for a present worth in year 0 with the gradient starting between periods 1 and 2.

The present worth of an arithmetic gradient will always be located *two periods before the gradient starts*.

Refer to Figure 2–13 as a refresher for the cash flow diagrams.

The relation $A = G(A/G,i,n)$ was also derived in Section 2.5. The A/G factor in Equation [2.17] performs the equivalence transformation of a gradient only into an A series from years 1 through n, as indicated in Figure 2–14. Recall that when there is a base amount, it and the arithmetic gradient must be treated separately. Then the equivalent P or A values can be summed to obtain the equivalent total present worth P_T and total annual series A_T, according to Equations [2.18] and [2.19].

A conventional gradient series starts between periods 1 and 2 of the cash flow sequence. A gradient starting at any other time is called a *shifted gradient*. The n value in the P/G and A/G factors for a shifted gradient is determined by renumbering the time scale. The period in which the *gradient first appears is labelled period 2*. The n value for the factor is determined by the renumbered period where the last gradient increase occurs.

Partitioning a cash flow series into the arithmetic gradient series and the remainder of the cash flows can make very clear what the gradient n value should be. Example 3.5 illustrates this partitioning.

EXAMPLE 3.5

Claire, an engineer at Saguenay Industries, has tracked the average inspection cost on a robotics manufacturing line for 8 years. Cost averages were steady at $100 per completed unit for the first 4 years, but have increased consistently by $50 per unit for each of the last 4 years. Claire plans to analyze the gradient increase using the P/G factor. Where is the present worth located for the gradient? What is the general relation used to calculate total present worth in year 0?

Solution

Claire constructed the cash flow diagram in Figure 3–10a. It shows the base amount $A = \$100$ and the arithmetic gradient $G = \$50$ starting between periods 4 and 5.

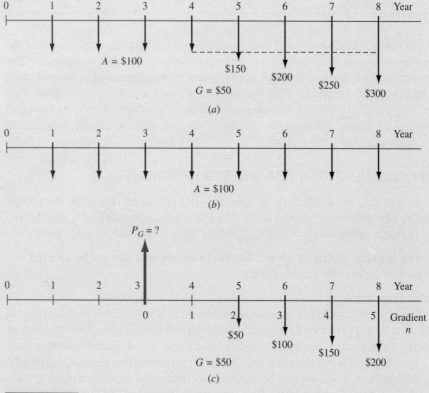

FIGURE 3–10
Partitioned cash flow, $(a) = (b) + (c)$, Example 3.5.

Figure 3–10b and c partitions these two series. Gradient year 2 is placed in year 5 of the entire sequence in Figure 3–10c. It is clear that $n = 5$ for the P/G factor. The $P_G = ?$ arrow is correctly placed in gradient year 0, which is year 3 in the cash flow series.

The general relation for P_T is taken from Equation [2.18]. The uniform series $A = \$100$ occurs for all 8 years, and the $G = \$50$ gradient present worth appears in year 3.

$$P_T = P_A + P_G = 100(P/A,i,8) + 50(P/G,i,5)(P/F,i,3)$$

The P/G and A/G factor values for the shifted gradients in Figure 3–11 are shown below each diagram. Determine the factors and compare the answers with these values.

It is important to note that the A/G factor *cannot* be used to find an equivalent A value in periods 1 through n for cash flows involving a shifted gradient. Consider the cash flow diagram of Figure 3–11b. To find the equivalent annual series in years 1 through 10 for the gradient series only, first find the present worth of the gradient in year 5, take this present worth back to year 0, and then annualize the present worth for 10 years with the A/P factor. If you apply the annual series gradient factor ($A/G,i,5$) directly, the gradient is converted into an equivalent annual series over years 6 through 10 only. Remember:

To find the equivalent A series of a shifted gradient through all the periods, first find the present worth of the gradient at actual time 0, then apply the $(A/P,i,n)$ factor.

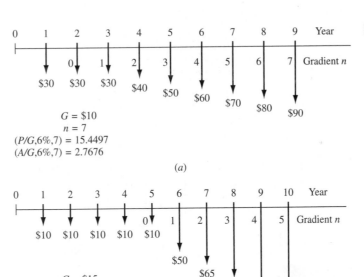

FIGURE 3–11
Determination of G and n values used in factors for shifted gradients.

EXAMPLE 3.6

Set up the engineering economy relations to compute the equivalent annual series in years 1 through 7 for the cash flow estimates in Figure 3–12.

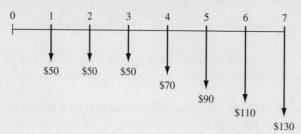

FIGURE 3–12
Diagram of a shifted gradient, Example 3.6.

Solution
The base amount annual series is A_B = $50 for all 7 years (Figure 3–13). Find the present worth P_G in year 2 of the $20 gradient that starts in actual year 4. The gradient year is $n = 5$.

$$P_G = 20(P/G,i,5)$$

Bring the gradient present worth back to actual year 0.

$$P_0 = P_G(P/F,i,2) = 20(P/G,i,5)(P/F,i,2)$$

Annualize the gradient present worth from year 0 through year 7 to obtain A_G.

$$A_G = P_0(A/P,i,7)$$

Finally, add the base amount to the gradient annual series.

$$A = 20(P/G,i,5)(P/F,i,2)(A/P,i,7) + 50$$

Q-SOLVE

For a spreadsheet, enter the cash flows in cells B3 through B9 and use an embedded NPV function in the PMT. The single-cell function is PMT($i\%$,7,$-$NPV($i\%$, B3:B9)).

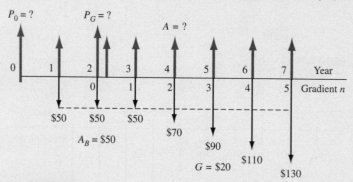

FIGURE 3–13
Diagram used to determine A for a shifted gradient, Example 3.6.

Sec. 2.6

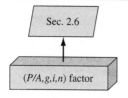

($P/A,g,i,n$) factor

If the cash flow series involves a *geometric gradient* and the gradient starts at a time other than between periods 1 and 2, it is a shifted gradient. The P_g is located in a manner similar to that for P_G above, and Equation [2.24] is the factor formula.

EXAMPLE 3.7

Chemical engineers at Revelstoke Recreation, Inc., have determined that a small amount of a newly available chemical additive will increase the water repellency of their tent fabric by 20%. The plant superintendent has arranged to purchase the additive through a 5-year contract at $7000 per year, starting 1 year from now. He expects the annual price to increase by 12% per year thereafter for the next 8 years. Additionally, an initial investment of $35,000 was made now to prepare a site suitable for the contractor to deliver the additive. Use $i = 15\%$ to determine the equivalent total present worth for all these cash flows.

Solution
Figure 3–14 presents the cash flows. The total present worth P_T is found using $g = 0.12$ and $i = 0.15$. Equation [2.24] is used to determine the present worth P_g for the entire geometric series at actual year 4, which is moved to year 0 using $(P/F,15\%,4)$.

$$P_T = 35,000 + A(P/A,15\%,4) + A_1(P/A,12\%,15\%,9)(P/F,15\%,4)$$

$$= 35,000 + 7000(2.8550) + \left[7000 \frac{1-(1.12/1.15)^9}{0.15-0.12} \right](0.5718)$$

$$= 35,000 + 19,985 + 28,247$$

$$= \$83,232$$

Note that $n = 4$ in the $(P/A,15\%,4)$ factor because the $7000 in year 5 is the initial amount A_1 in Equation [2.23].

For solution by computer, enter the cash flows of Figure 3–14. If cells B1 through B14 are used, the function to find $P = \$83,230$ is

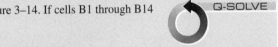
Q-SOLVE

$$NPV(15\%,B2:B14)+B1$$

The fastest way to enter the geometric series is to enter $7840 for year 6 (into cell B7) and set up each succeeding cell multiplied by 1.12 for the 12% increase.

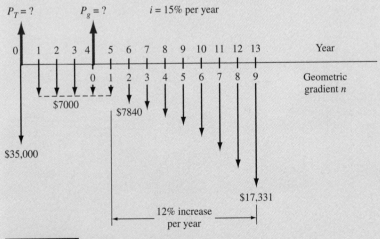

FIGURE 3–14
Cash flow diagram including a geometric gradient with $g = 12\%$, Example 3.7.

3.4 SHIFTED DECREASING ARITHMETIC GRADIENTS

Sec. 2.5

$-P_G$ and $-A_G$

The use of the arithmetic gradient factors is the same for increasing and decreasing gradients, except that in the case of decreasing gradients the following are true:

1. The base amount is equal to the *largest* amount in the gradient series, that is, the amount in period 1 of the series.
2. The gradient amount is *subtracted* from the base amount instead of added to it.
3. The term $-G(P/G,i,n)$ or $-G(A/G,i,n)$ is used in the computations and in Equations [2.18] and [2.19] for P_T and A_T, respectively.

The present worth of the gradient will still take place two periods before the gradient starts, and the equivalent A value will start at period 1 of the gradient series and continue through period n.

Figure 3–15 partitions a decreasing gradient series with $G = \$-100$ that is shifted 1 year forward. P_G occurs in actual year 1, and P_T is the sum of three components.

$$P_T = \$800(P/F,i,1) + 800(P/A,i,5)(P/F,i,1) - 100(P/G,i,5)(P/F,i,1)$$

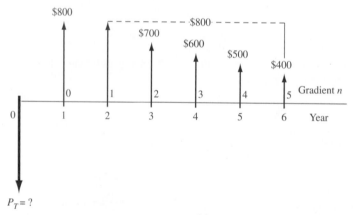

(a)

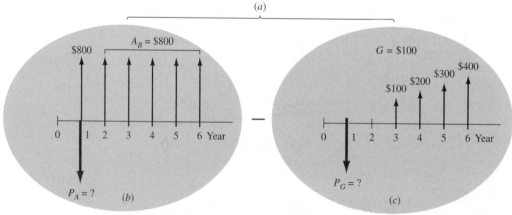

(b)   (c)

FIGURE 3–15

Partitioned cash flow of a shifted arithmetic gradient, $(a) = (b) - (c)$.

EXAMPLE 3.8

Assume that you are planning to invest money at 7% per year as shown by the increasing gradient of Figure 3–16. Further, you expect to withdraw according to the decreasing gradient shown. Find the net present worth and equivalent annual series for the entire cash flow sequence and interpret the results.

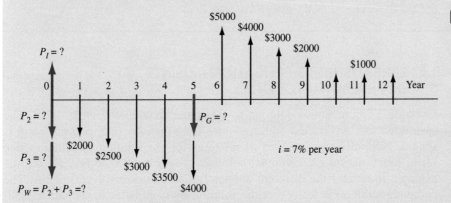

FIGURE 3–16

Investment and withdrawal series, Example 3.8.

Solution
For the investment sequence, G is $500, the base amount is $2000, and $n = 5$. For the withdrawal sequence through year 10, G is -1000, the base amount is $5000, and $n = 5$. There is a 2-year annual series with $A = \$1000$ in years 11 and 12. For the investment series,

$$P_I = \text{present worth of deposits}$$
$$= 2000(P/A,7\%,5) + 500(P/G,7\%,5)$$
$$= 2000(4.1002) + 500(7.6467)$$
$$= \$12,023.75$$

For the withdrawal series, let P_W represent the present worth of the withdrawal base amount and gradient series in years 6 through 10 (P_2), plus the present worth of withdrawals in years 11 and 12 (P_3). Then

$$P_W = P_2 + P_3$$
$$= P_G(P/F,7\%,5) + P_3$$
$$= [5000(P/A,7\%,5) - 1000(P/G,7\%,5)](P/F,7\%,5)$$
$$\quad + 1000(P/A,7\%,2)(P/F,7\%,10)$$
$$= [5000(4.1002) - 1000(7.6467)](0.7130) + 1000(1.8080)(0.5083)$$
$$= \$9165.12 + 919.00 = \$10,084.12$$

Since P_I is actually a negative cash flow and P_W is positive, the net present worth is

$$P = P_W - P_I = 10,084.12 - 12,023.75 = \$-1939.63$$

The A value may be computed using the $(A/P,7\%,12)$ factor.

$$A = P(A/P,7\%,12)$$
$$= \$-244.20$$

The interpretation of these results is as follows: In present-worth equivalence, you will invest $1939.63 more than you expect to withdraw. This is equivalent to an annual savings of $244.20 per year for the 12-year period.

3.5 SPREADSHEET APPLICATION—USING DIFFERENT FUNCTIONS

E-SOLVE

Example 3.9 compares a solution by computer with a solution by hand. The cash flows are two shifted uniform series for which the total present worth is sought. Naturally, only one set of relations for the solution by hand, or one set of functions for the computer solution, would be used to find P_T, but the example illustrates the different approaches and work involved in each. The computer solution is faster, but the solution by hand helps in the understanding of how the time value of money is accounted for by engineering economy factors.

EXAMPLE 3.9

Determine the total present worth P_T in period 0 at 15% per year for the two shifted uniform series in Figure 3–17. Use two approaches: by computer with different functions and by hand using three different factors.

$i = 15\%$ per year

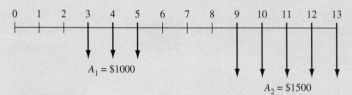

FIGURE 3–17
Uniform series used to compute present worth by several methods, Example 3.9.

Solution by Computer
Figure 3–18 finds P_T using the NPV and PV functions.

NPV function: This is by far the easiest way to determine $P_T = \$3370$. The cash flows are entered into cells, and the NPV function is developed using the format

Q-SOLVE

$$\text{NPV}(i\%,\text{second\_cell:last\_cell}) + \text{first\_cell} \quad \text{or} \quad \text{NPV}(\text{B1,B6:B18}) + \text{B5}$$

	B1		=	15%				
	A	B	C	D	E	F	G
1	Interest rate	15%					
2							
3			Present worth				
4	Year	Cash flow	by PV function				
5	0	$ -	$ -	Present worth			
6	1	$ -	$ -	by NPV function			
7	2	$ -	$ -				
8	3	$ 1,000	$ 658	$ 3,370	= NPV(B1,B6:B18) + B5		
9	4	$ 1,000	$ 572				
10	5	$ 1,000	$ 497	= -PV(B1,A10,,B10)			
11	6	$ -	$ -				
12	7	$ -	$ -				
13	8	$ -	$ -				
14	9	$ 1,500	$ 426				
15	10	$ 1,500	$ 371				
16	11	$ 1,500	$ 322				
17	12	$ 1,500	$ 280				
18	13	$ 1,500	$ 244				
19		Sum of PV values	$ 3,370	= SUM(C5:C18)			
20							

FIGURE 3–18

Spreadsheet determination of total present worth using NPV and PV functions, Example 3.9.

The value $i = 15\%$ is in cell B1. With the NPV parameters in cell-reference form, any value can be changed, and the new P_T value is displayed immediately. Additionally, if more than 13 years are needed, simply add the cash flows at the end of column B and increase the B18 entry accordingly. *Remember: The NPV function requires that all spreadsheet cells representing a cash flow have an entry, including those periods that have a zero cash flow value.* The wrong answer is generated if cells are left blank.

PV function: Column C entries in Figure 3–18 include PV functions that determine P in period 0 for each cash flow separately. They are added in C19 using the SUM function. This approach takes more keyboard time, but it does provide the P value for each cash flow, if these amounts are needed. Also, the PV function does not require that each zero cash flow entry be made.

FV function: It is not efficient to determine P_T using the FV function, because the FV format does not allow direct entry of cell references like the NPV function. Each cash flow must first be taken to the last period using the general format FV(15%,years_remaining,, cash_flow), where they are summed using the SUM function. This SUM is then moved back to period 0 via the PV(15%,13,,SUM) function. In this case, both the NPV and PV functions, especially NPV, provide a much more efficient use of spreadsheet capabilities than FV.

Solution by Hand

There are numerous ways to find P_T. The two simplest are probably the *present worth* and *future worth methods.* For a third method, use year 7 as an anchor point. This is called the *intermediate year method.*

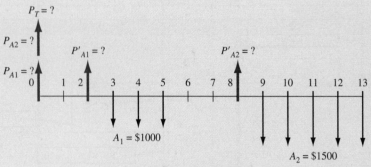

(*a*) Present worth method

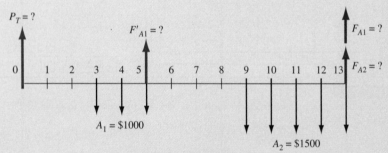

(*b*) Future worth method

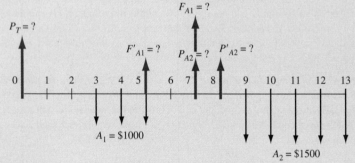

(*c*) Intermediate year method

FIGURE 3–19

Computation of the present worth of Figure 3–17 by three methods, Example 3.9.

Present worth method: See Figure 3–19a. The use of P/A factors for the uniform series, followed by the use of P/F factors to obtain the present worth in year 0, finds P_T.

$$P_T = P_{A1} + P_{A2}$$
$$P_{A1} = P'_{A1}(P/F,15\%,2) = A_1(P/A,15\%,3)(P/F,15\%,2)$$
$$= 1000(2.2832)(0.7561)$$
$$= \$1726$$
$$P_{A2} = P'_{A2}(P/F,15\%,8) = A_2(P/A,15\%,5)(P/F,15\%,8)$$
$$= 1500(3.3522)(0.3269)$$
$$= \$1644$$
$$P_T = 1726 + 1644 = \$3370$$

Future worth method: See Figure 3–19b. Use the F/A, F/P, and P/F factors.

$$P_T = (F_{A1} + F_{A2})(P/F,15\%,13)$$
$$F_{A1} = F'_{A1}(F/P,15\%,8) = A_1(F/A,15\%,3)(F/P,15\%,8)$$
$$= 1000(3.4725)(3.0590) = \$10,622$$
$$F_{A2} = A_2(F/A,15\%,5) - 1500(6.7424) = \$10,113$$
$$P_T = (F_{A1} + F_{A2})(P/F,15\%,13) = 20,735(0.1625) = \$3369$$

Intermediate year method: See Figure 3–19c. Find the equivalent worth of both series at year 7 and then use the P/F factor.

$$P_T = (F_{A1} + P_{A2})(P/F,15\%,7)$$

The P_{A2} value is computed as a present worth; but to find the total value P_T at year 0, it must be treated as an F value. Thus,

$$F_{A1} = F'_{A1}(F/P,15\%,2) = A_1(F/A,15\%,3)(F/P,15\%,2)$$
$$= 1000(3.4725)(1.3225) = \$4592$$
$$P_{A2} = P'_{A2}(P/F,15\%,1) = A_2(P/A,15\%,5)(P/F,15\%,1)$$
$$= 1500(3.3522)(0.8696) = \$4373$$
$$P_T = (F_{A1} + P_{A2})(P/F,15\%,7)$$
$$= 8965(0.3759) = \$3370$$

ADDITIONAL EXAMPLE

EXAMPLE 3.10

PRESENT WORTH BY COMBINING FACTORS

Calculate the total present worth of the following series of cash flows at $i = 18\%$ per year.

Year	0	1	2	3	4	5	6	7
Cash flow, $	+460	+460	+460	+460	+460	+460	+460	−5000

Solution

The cash flow diagram is shown in Figure 3–20. Since the receipt in year 0 is equal to the A series in years 1 through 6, the P/A factor can be used for either 6 or 7 years. The problem is worked both ways.

Using P/A and $n = 6$: The receipt P_0 in year 0 is added to the present worth of the remaining amounts, since the P/A factor for $n = 6$ will place P_A in year 0.

$$P_T = P_0 + P_A - P_F$$
$$= 460 + 460(P/A,18\%,6) - 5000(P/F,18\%,7)$$
$$= \$499.40$$

Using P/A and $n = 7$: By using the P/A factor for $n = 7$, the "present worth" is located in year -1, not year 0, because the P is one period prior to the first A. It is necessary to move the P_A value 1 year forward with the F/P factor.

$$P = 460(P/A,18\%,7)(F/P,18\%,1) - 5000(P/F,18\%,7)$$
$$= \$499.38$$

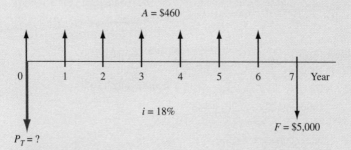

FIGURE 3–20
Cash flow diagram, Example 3.10.

CHAPTER SUMMARY

In Chapter 2, we derived the equations to calculate the present, future, or annual worth of specific cash flow series. In this chapter, we have shown that these equations apply to cash flow series different from those for which the basic relations are derived. For example, when a uniform series does not begin in period 1, we still use the P/A factor to find the "present worth" of the series, except the P value is located one period ahead of the first A value, not at time 0. For arithmetic and geometric gradients, the P value is two periods ahead of where the gradient starts. With this information, it is possible to solve for any symbol—P, A, or F—for any conceivable cash flow series.

We have experienced some of the power of spreadsheet functions in determining P, F, and A values once the cash flow estimates are entered into spreadsheet cells.

PROBLEMS

Present Worth Calculations

3.1 Green rainwater management practices such as porous pavements, green roofs, sidewalk planter boxes, grassy boulevards, and retention ponds have been recommended to manage problems associated with polluted storm-water runoff. Requiring all new developments in Duncan, B.C., to retrofit its developed areas with green infrastructure is estimated to save the city $60,000 now and $50,000 per year afterwards. What is the present worth of the savings for the first 3 years at an interest rate of 10% per year?

3.2 Because unintended lane changes by distracted drivers are responsible for 43% of all highway fatalities, Ford Motor Co. and Volvo launched a program to develop technologies to prevent accidents by sleepy drivers. A device costing $260 tracks lane markings and sounds an alert during lane changes. If these devices are included in 100,000 new cars per year beginning 3 years from now, what would be the present worth of their cost over a 10-year period at an interest rate of 10% per year?

3.3 Part of a bargaining agreement with the teachers' union was a plan for the Province to pay an additional $56 for every student K through Grade 4 toward reducing class sizes. If there are 50,000 such students in the district and the cash flow begins 2 years from now, what is the present worth of the plan over a 5-year planning period at an interest rate of 8% per year?

3.4 Dofasco may purchase a new machine for ram cambering large I-beams. The company expects to bend 80 beams at $2000 per beam in each of the first 3 years, after which the company expects to bend 100 beams per year at $2500 per beam through year 8. If the company's minimum attractive rate of return is 18% per year, what is the present worth of the expected income?

3.5 Labelle Plastics plans to purchase a rectilinear robot for pulling parts from an injection molding machine. Because of the robot's speed, the company expects production costs to decrease by $100,000 per year in each of the first 3 years and by $200,000 per year in the next 2 years. What is the present worth of the cost savings if the company uses an interest rate of 15% per year on such investments?

3.6 Toyco Watercraft has a contract with a parts supplier that involves purchases amounting to $150,000 per year, with the first purchase to be made now, followed by similar purchases over the next 5 years. Determine the present worth of the contract at an interest rate of 10% per year.

3.7 Calculate the present worth in year 0 of the following series of disbursements. Assume that $i = 10\%$ per year.

Year	Disbursement, $	Year	Disbursement, $
0	0	6	5000
1	3500	7	5000
2	3500	8	5000
3	3500	9	5000
4	5000	10	5000
5	5000		

Annual Worth Calculations

3.8 Cisco's *gross revenue* (the percentage of revenue left after subtracting the cost of goods sold) was 70.1% of total revenue over a certain 4-year period. If the *total revenue* was $5.4 billion for the first 2 years and $6.1 billion for the last 2 years, what was the equivalent annual worth of the *gross revenue* over that 4-year period at an interest rate of 20% per year?

3.9 BKM Systems sales revenues are shown below. Calculate the equivalent annual worth (years 1 through 7), using an interest rate of 10% per year.

Year	Disbursement, $	Year	Disbursement, $
0		4	5000
1	4000	5	5000
2	4000	6	5000
3	4000	7	5000

3.10 A metallurgical engineer decides to set aside money for his newborn daughter's college education. He estimates that her needs will be $20,000 on her 17th, 18th, 19th, and 20th birthdays. If he plans to make uniform deposits starting 3 years from now and continue through year 16, what should be the size of each deposit, if the account earns interest at a rate of 8% per year?

3.11 Calculate the annual worth in years 1 through 10 of the following series of incomes and expenses, if the interest rate is 10% per year.

Year	Income, $/Year	Expense, $/Year
0	10,000	2000
1–6	800	200
7–10	900	300

3.12 How much money would you have to pay each year in 8 equal payments, starting 2 years from today, to repay a $20,000 loan received from a relative today, if the interest rate is 8% per year?

3.13 An industrial engineer is planning for his early retirement 25 years from now. He believes he can comfortably set aside $10,000 each year starting *now*. If he plans to start withdrawing money 1 year after he makes his last deposit (i.e., year 26), what uniform amount could he withdraw each year for 30 years, if the account earns interest at a rate of 8% per year?

3.14 A rural utility company provides standby power to pumping stations using diesel-powered generators. An alternative has arisen whereby the utility could use natural gas to power the generators, but it will be a few years before the gas is available at remote sites. The utility estimates that by switching to gas, it will save $15,000 per year, starting 2 years from now. At an interest rate of 8% per year, determine the equivalent annual worth (years 1 through 10) of the projected savings.

3.15 The operating cost of a pulverized coal cyclone furnace is expected to be $80,000 per year. If the steam produced will be needed only for 5 years beginning now (i.e., years 0 through 5), what is the equivalent annual worth in years 1 through 5 of the operating cost at an interest rate of 10% per year?

3.16 An entrepreneurial electrical engineer has approached a large water utility with a proposal that promises to reduce the utility's power bill by at least 15% per year for the next 5 years through installation of patented surge protectors. The proposal states that the engineer will get $5000 now and annual payments that are equivalent to 75% of the power savings achieved from the devices. Assuming the savings are the same every year (i.e., 15%) and that the utility's power bill is $1 million per year, what would be the equivalent uniform amount (years 1 through 5) of the payments to the engineer? Assume the utility uses an interest rate of 6% per year.

3.17 A large water utility is planning to upgrade its system for controlling well pumps, booster pumps, and disinfection equipment, so that everything can be controlled from one site. The first phase will reduce labour and travel costs by $28,000 per year. The second phase will reduce costs by an additional $20,000 per year. If phase I savings occur in years 0, 1, 2, and 3 and phase II occurs in years 4 through 10, what is the equivalent annual worth of the upgraded system in years 1 through 10 at an interest rate of 8% per year?

3.18 A mechanical engineer who recently graduated with a master's degree is contemplating starting his own commercial heating and cooling company. He can purchase a Web page design package aimed at delivering information only for $600 per year. If his business is successful, he will purchase a more elaborate e-commerce package costing $4000 per year. If the engineer

purchases the less expensive page now (beginning-of-year payments) and he purchases the e-commerce package 1 year from now (also beginning-of-year payments), what is the equivalent annual worth of costs for the website for a 5-year period (years 1 through 5) at an interest rate of 12% per year?

Future Worth Calculations

3.19 If an engineer invests $10,000 in a savings account now and $10,000 each year for the next 20 years, how much will be in the account immediately after the last deposit if the account grows by 15% per year?

3.20 How much money was deposited each year for 5 years if the account is now worth $100,000 and the last deposit was made 10 years ago? Assume the account earned interest at 7% per year.

3.21 Calculate the future worth (in year 11) of the following income and expenses, if the interest rate is 8% per year.

Year	Income, $	Expense, $
0	12,000	3000
1–6	800	200
7–11	900	200

Random Placement and Uniform Series

3.22 What is the equivalent worth in year 5 of the following series of income and disbursements, if the interest rate is 12% per year?

Year	Income, $	Expense, $
0	0	9000
1–5	6000	6000
6–8	6000	3000
9–14	8000	5000

3.23 Use the cash flow diagram below to calculate the amount of money in year 5 that is equivalent to all the cash flows shown, if the interest rate is 12% per year.

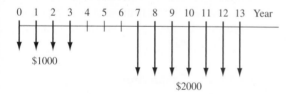

3.24 By spending $10,000 now and $25,000 three years from now, a plating company can increase its income in years 4 through 10. At an interest rate of 12% per year, how much extra income per year would be needed in years 4 through 10 to recover the investment?

3.25 ENMAX Corporation is considering the purchase of a hillside ranch for its Taber Wind Power Generation Project. The owner of the 500-hectare ranch will sell for $3000 per hectare if the company will pay her in two payments—one payment now and another that is twice as large 3 years from now. If the transaction interest rate is 8% per year, what is the amount of the first payment?

3.26 Two equal deposits made 20 and 21 years ago, respectively, will allow a retiree to withdraw $10,000 now and $10,000 per year for 14 more years. If the account earned interest at 10% per year, how large was each deposit?

3.27 A concrete and building materials company has a fund for future equipment replacement. The company has already deposited $20,000 in each of the last 5 years. How much must be deposited now in order for the fund to have $350,000 three years from now, if the fund grows at a rate of 15% per year?

3.28 Find the value of x below such that the positive cash flows will be exactly equivalent to the negative cash flows, if the interest rate is 14% per year.

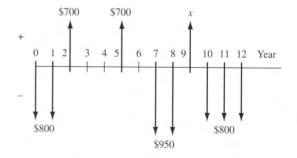

3.29 In attempting to obtain a loan from a local bank, a general contractor was asked to provide an estimate of annual expenses. One component of the expenses is shown in the cash flow diagram below. Convert the amounts shown into an equivalent uniform annual amount in years 1 through 8, using an interest rate of 12% per year.

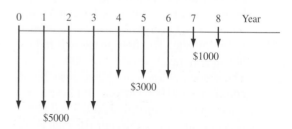

3.30 Determine the value in year 8 that is equivalent to the cash flows below. Use an interest rate of 12% per year.

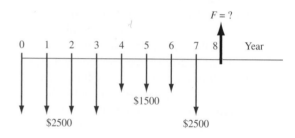

3.31 Find the value of x in the diagram below that will make the equivalent present worth of the cash flow equal to $15,000, if the interest rate is 15% per year.

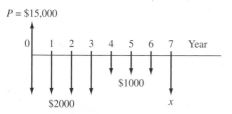

P = $15,000

3.32 Calculate the amount of money in year 3 that is equivalent to the following cash flows, if the interest rate is 16% per year.

Year	Amount, $	Year	Amount, $
0	900	5	3000
1	900	6	−1500
2	900	7	500
3	900	8	500
4	3000		

3.33 Calculate the annual worth (years 1 through 7) of the following series of disbursements. Assume that $i = 12\%$ per year.

Year	Disbursement, $	Year	Disbursement, $
0	5000	4	5000
1	3500	5	5000
2	3500	6	5000
3	3500	7	5000

3.34 Calculate the value of x for the cash flows below such that the equivalent total value in year 8 is $20,000, using an interest rate of 15% per year.

Year	Cash Flow, $	Year	Cash Flow, $
0	2000	6	x
1	2000	7	x
2	x	8	x
3	x	9	1000
4	x	10	1000
5	x	11	1000

Shifted Arithmetic Gradients

3.35 Red Deer Oil is considering various oil field development options. One field under consideration is expected to generate revenues of $4.1 million per year for the first 4 years, after which declining production will decrease revenue each year by $50,000 per year. If the field will be totally depleted in 25 years, what is the present worth of this option at an interest rate of 6% per year?

3.36 If a person begins saving money by depositing $1000 now and then increases the deposit by $500 each year through year 10, determine the amount that will be in the account in year 10 at an interest rate of 10% per year.

3.37 Ontario Northern is considering the elimination of a railroad grade crossing by constructing a dual-track overpass. The railroad subcontracts for maintenance of its crossing gates at $11,500 per year. Beginning 4 years from now, however, the costs are expected to increase by $1000 per year into the foreseeable future (that is, $12,500 four years from now, $13,500 five years from now, etc.). The overpass will cost $1.4 million (now) to build, but it will eliminate 100% of the auto-train collisions that have cost an average of $250,000 per year. If the railroad uses a 10-year study period and an interest rate of 10% per year, determine whether the railroad should build the overpass.

3.38 Syncrude is working to reduce fluid tailings, which are a mixture of water, clay, sand, and residual bitumen resulting from oil sands mining. Syncrude is testing 3 main methods: covering tailings with water in lakes, combining tailings with settling agents, and centrifugation. If the water capping option at one of their tailing pits costs $500,000 now (year 0) and is expected to increase by $40,000 every year through year 12, what is the equivalent uniform annual worth in years 1 to 12 of the costs at an interest rate of 10% per year?

3.39 Levi Strauss has some of its jeans stone-washed under a contract with independent Grimbsy Garment Corp. If Grimbsy's operating cost per machine is $22,000 per year for years 1 and 2 and then it increases by $1000 per year through year 5, what is the equivalent uniform annual cost per machine (years 1 through 5) at an interest rate of 12% per year?

3.40 Herman Trucking Company's receipts and disbursements (in $1000) are shown below. Calculate the future worth in year 7 at an interest rate of 10% per year.

Year	Cash Flow, $	Year	Cash Flow, $
0	−10,000	4	5,000
1	4,000	5	−1,000
2	3,000	6	7,000
3	4,000	7	8,000

3.41 Peyton Packing has a ham cooker that has the cost stream below. If the interest rate is 15% per year, determine the annual worth (in years 1 through 7) of the costs.

Year	Cost, $	Year	Cost, $
0	4,000	4	6,000
1	4,000	5	8,000
2	3,000	6	10,000
3	2,000	7	12,000

3.42 A startup company selling colour-keyed carnuba car wax borrows $40,000 at an interest rate of 10% per year and wishes to repay the loan over a 5-year period with annual payments such that the third through fifth payments are $2000 greater than the first two. Determine the size of the first two payments.

3.43 For the cash flows below, find the value of x that makes the present worth in year 0

equal to $11,000 at an interest rate of 12% per year.

Year	Cash Flow, $	Year	Cash Flow, $
0	200	5	700
1	300	6	800
2	400	7	900
3	x	8	1000
4	600	9	1100

Shifted Geometric Gradients

3.44 A company that manufactures hydrogen sulfide monitors is planning to make deposits such that each one is 5% larger than the preceding one. How large must the first deposit be (at the end of year 1) if the deposits extend through year 10 and the fourth deposit is $1250? Use an interest rate of 10% per year.

3.45 A successful alumnus is planning to make a contribution to the university from which he graduated. The donation is to be made over a 5-year period beginning *now*, a total of six payments. It will support five engineering students per year for 20 years, with the first scholarship to be awarded immediately (a total of 21 scholarships). The cost of tuition at the school is $4000 per year and is expected to stay at that amount for 3 more years. After that time (i.e., year 4), the tuition is expected to increase by 8% per year. If the university can invest the money and earn interest at a rate of 10% per year, what size must the donations be?

3.46 Calculate the present worth (year 0) of a lease that requires a payment of $20,000 now and amounts increasing by 5% per year through year 10. Use an interest rate of 14% per year.

3.47 Calculate the present worth for a machine that has an initial cost of $29,000, a life of 10 years, and an annual operating cost of $13,000 for the first 4 years, increasing by

10% per year thereafter. Use an interest rate of 10% per year.

3.48 A-1 Box Company is planning to lease a computer system that will cost (with service) $15,000 in year 1, $16,500 in year 2, and amounts increasing by 10% each year thereafter. Assume the lease payments must be made *at the beginning of the year* and that a 5-year lease is planned. What is the present worth (year 0) if the company uses a minimum acceptable rate of return of 16% per year?

3.49 Hi-C Steel signed a contract that will generate revenue of $210,000 now, $222,600 in year 1, and amounts increasing by 8% per year through year 5. Calculate the future worth of the contract at an interest rate of 8% per year.

Shifted Decreasing Gradients

3.50 Find the present worth (at time 0) of the chrome plating costs in the cash flow diagram. Assume $i = 12\%$ per year.

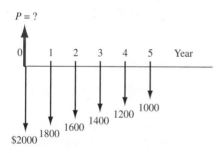

3.51 Compute the present worth (year 0) of the following cash flows at $i = 12\%$ per year.

Year	Amount, $	Year	Amount, $
0	5000	8	700
1–5	1000	9	600
6	900	10	500
7	800	11	400

3.52 For the cash flow tabulation, calculate the equivalent uniform annual worth in periods 1 through 10, if the interest rate is 10% per year.

Year	Amount, $	Year	Amount, $
0	2000	6	2400
1	2000	7	2300
2	2000	8	2200
3	2000	9	2100
4	2000	10	2000
5	2500		

3.53 Prudential Realty has an escrow account for one of its property management clients that currently contains $20,000. How long will it take to deplete the account if the client withdraws $5000 now, $4500 one year from now, and amounts decreasing by $500 each year thereafter, if the account earns interest at a rate of 8% per year?

3.54 The cost of spacers used around fuel rods in liquid-metal fast breeder reactors has been decreasing because of the availability of improved temperature-resistant ceramic materials. Determine the present worth (in year 0) of the costs shown in the diagram below, using an interest rate of 15% per year.

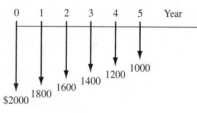

3.55 Compute the future worth in year 10 at $i = 10\%$ per year for the cash flow shown below.

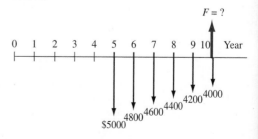

EXTENDED EXERCISE

NEW PROVINCIAL PARK FOR B.C. GULF ISLANDS

The Land Acquisitions of Parks and Protected Areas Branch of the British Columbia Ministry of Environment is considering a request that it manage the purchase of 50 hectares of ecologically sensitive, forested, waterfront property containing a large protected stand of Garry oak trees for the development of a new provincial park in the Gulf Islands. The land will be acquired in increments over the next 5 years with $4 million expended immediately on property purchases. Total annual purchase amounts will decrease 25% each year through its final phase in the fifth year. The Land Conservancy of B.C. has committed $3 million to support these purchases and is conducting a campaign with the Gulf Island's Conservancy to collect community donations for the remaining amount.

The civil engineers working on public access trails, a visitors' centre, and a campground intend to complete all the development over a 3-year period starting in year 4, when the amount budgeted is $550,000. Increases in construction costs are expected to be $100,000 each year through year 6.

The initial phase will consume the Conservancy's funds with the remaining amount coming from a loan by the B.C. Ministry of Environment reserves encumbered for the project. The remaining project funds will be raised over the first 2 years in equal annual amounts to pay back this loan.

Alternatively, if the Ministry of Environment finances the park's development by providing the required funds over those committed by the Conservancy until the park's development is initiated in year 4, those funds could be reimbursed to the Ministry during the last 3 years of the project.

All interest rates are to be evaluated at 7% per year.

Questions

Use hand or computer computations to find the following:

1. For each of the first 2 years, what is the equivalent annual amount necessary to supply the remaining project funds?

2. If the Ministry of Environment agrees to bankroll all costs above the $3 million committed by the Conservancy until year 4, determine the equivalent annual amount that must be raised in years 4 through 6 to pay the borrowed funds used to support the project.

CHAPTER 4

Nominal and Effective Interest Rates

In all engineering economy relations developed thus far, the interest rate has been a constant, annual value. For a substantial percentage of the projects evaluated by professional engineers in practice, the interest rate is compounded more frequently than once a year; frequencies such as semi-annual, quarterly, and monthly are common. In fact, weekly, daily, and even continuous compounding may be experienced in some project evaluations. Also, in our own personal lives, many of the financial considerations we make—loans of all types (home mortgages, credit cards, automobiles, boats), checking and savings accounts, investments, stock option plans, etc.—have interest rates compounded for a time period shorter than 1 year. This requires the introduction of two new terms—nominal and effective interest rates.

This chapter explains how to understand and use nominal and effective interest rates in engineering practice and in daily life situations. The flowchart on calculating an effective interest rate in the appendix to this chapter serves as a reference throughout the sections on nominal and effective rates, as well as continuous compounding of interest. This chapter also develops equivalence calculations for any compounding frequency in combination with any cash flow frequency.

The case study includes an evaluation of several financing plans for the purchase of a house.

LEARNING OBJECTIVES

Purpose: Make economic calculations for interest rates and cash flows that occur on a time basis other than 1 year.

By the end of this chapter you should be able to

Nominal and effective	**1.** Interpret and apply nominal and effective interest rate statements.
Effective annual interest rate	**2.** Derive and use the formula for the effective annual interest rate.
Effective interest rate	**3.** Determine the effective interest rate for any time period.
Compare PP and CP	**4.** Determine the correct method for equivalence calculations for different payment and compounding periods.
Single amounts: PP $\geq$ CP	**5.** Make equivalence calculations for payment periods equal to or longer than the compounding period when only single amounts occur.
Series: PP $\geq$ CP	**6.** Make equivalence calculations when uniform or gradient series occur for payment periods equal to or longer than the compounding period.
Single and series: PP $<$ CP	**7.** Make equivalence calculations for payment periods shorter than the compounding period.
Continuous compounding	**8.** Calculate and use an effective interest rate for continuous compounding.
Varying rates	**9.** Account for interest rates that vary over time when performing equivalency computations.

4.1) THE MACROECONOMICS OF INTEREST RATES

From the viewpoint of an engineer making decisions, we have seen that the interest rate affects the outcome of an analysis and the strategic plans of a firm. The interest rate impacts the entire Canadian economy. A rapidly changing economy discourages entrepreneurship due to the lack of stable prices. The Bank of Canada was created to influence interest rates and establish monetary policy to lessen the severity of fluctuations in the level of prices, employment, and production.

Interest rates are determined by the supply of and demand for money. When rates drop, we spend more with borrowed money, from personal computers to expansion of industrial research and development. Entrepreneurship flourishes with low interest rates. Limits to the growth of the economy are reached when companies cannot meet the demand for their product because of lack of materials, competition for labour, and rising prices. Likewise, increasing interests rates can slow an overheated economy and accompanying inflation.

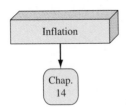

The interest rate influences the demand for Canadian dollars within the foreign exchange market (funds are moved into stable economies with the highest interest rates). This demand raises or lowers the exchange rate of the Canadian dollar that then impacts the demand for Canadian exports. Canadian products and services are most competitive in the world market when the exchange rate is low with the attendant inexpensive loonie and cheaper prices of the exports. Conversely, a low exchange rate for the loonie causes import prices of foreign-produced products to be higher for Canada. Both of these outcomes affect product development decisions in the strategic planning initiatives of engineering firms. Monetary policies that affect interest rates will most often cause the same impact on exchange rates.

With its monetary policies, the Bank of Canada influences interest rates like a skip directs the strategy in curling to indicate where the rocks should be delivered. The Bank monitors and adjusts the quantity of money in the economy, and by so doing has a fairly, but not totally, predictable effect on the interest rate. In curling, the rock is thrown according to a *preferred* outcome of the shot being played. In Canada's monetary policy, the Bank targets the interest rate by adjusting the average supply of money through the increase or decrease of bank reserves. In curling, the rock is delivered by sliding with it for 25 feet (about 7.6 m) and imparting a rotation to the handle for a desired arc. Control is then handed over to the teammates, who may vigorously sweep its path for the last 100 feet (about 30.5 m) of travel.

The Bank's adjustments are analogous to the spin or rotation imparted by the player throwing the rock. It uses various monetary policy actions and tools for the task. The curlers sweeping the path have various options to affect the friction between the ice and rock. For the Bank of Canada, after it has established its adjustment, control is handed over to the chartered banks and other financial institutions as the reserves impact their ability to make loans to firms and households. This action influences consumption and investment.

In curling, the team with the rock closest to the centre of the target, or house, scores a point for each rock in the house that is closer to the centre than any of the opponent's. In Canada, the economy scores a win when inflation and unemployment remain in check and the GDP is encouraged to grow. Just as curling is called "chess on ice" due to its subtle and intense strategic plays, monetary policy incorporates strategic interventions that result in dramatic effects on the Canadian economy (chess with loonies?).

In the Vancouver Olympics of 2010, Canada (the world's biggest curling nation with more than one million curlers) swept silver for the women and gold for the men by knocking the opposing team's rocks away from the target and locating their rocks closest to it. The Governor of the Bank of Canada, Mark Carney, hopes for gold-medal results in maintaining economic stability after the upheavals in the global financial system in 2008. Rapid and unprecedented intervention by the major central banks, along with massive government stimulus spending, is credited with saving the world from another Great Depression. International loans tied to troubled assets such as subprime-rate mortgages led to bank failures in many countries and a tightening of credit for businesses and individuals, with accompanying high levels of bankruptcies and unemployment. The central banks responded by improving the supply of global credit, keeping the money markets solvent and currencies relatively stable. Mark Carney maintained the Bank of Canada's emergency-level interest rate at 0.25%, its lowest level possible, until inflation reached the target level of 2%. Canada fared better than the United States and Europe through the recession, because its commercial banks were more stable due to tighter rules on how much debt they could carry and a more conservative approach to risk. The Governor states that his principal priority is to achieve a low and stable inflation rate. He stands ready to increase interest rates should inflation trend upward.

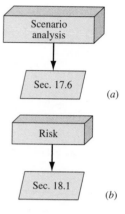

4.2 NOMINAL AND EFFECTIVE INTEREST RATE STATEMENTS

In Chapter 1, we learned that the primary difference between simple interest and compound interest is that compound interest includes interest on the interest earned in the previous period, while simple does not. Here we discuss *nominal and effective interest rates,* which have the same basic relationship. The difference is that the concepts of nominal and effective must be used when interest is compounded more than once each year. For example, if an interest rate is expressed as 1% per month, the terms *nominal* and *effective* interest rates must be considered.

To understand and correctly handle effective interest rates is important in engineering practice, as well as for individual finances. Engineering projects, as discussed in Chapter 1, are funded by capital raised through debt and equity financing. The interest amounts for loans, mortgages, bonds, and stocks are based upon interest rates compounded more frequently than annually. The engineering economy study must account for these effects. In our own personal finances, we manage most cash disbursements and receipts on a nonannual time basis. Again, the effect of compounding more frequently than once per year is present. First, consider a nominal interest rate.

Nominal interest rate, *r*, **is an interest rate that does not include any consideration of compounding. By definition,**

$$r = \text{interest rate per period} \times \text{number of periods} \qquad \textbf{[4.1]}$$

A nominal rate *r* may be stated for any time period—1 year, 6 months, quarter, month, week, day, etc. Equation [4.1] can be used to find the equivalent *r* for any other shorter or longer time period. For example, the nominal rate of *r* = 1.5% per month is the same as each of the following rates.

r = 1.5% per month × 24 months
  = 36% per 2-year period   (longer than 1 month)

  = 1.5% per month × 12 months
  = 18% per year   (longer than 1 month)

  = 1.5% per month × 6 months
  = 9% per semiannual period   (longer than 1 month)

  = 1.5% per month × 3 months
  = 4.5% per quarter   (longer than 1 month)

  = 1.5% per month × 1 month
  = 1.5% per month   (equal to 1 month)

  = 1.5% per month × 0.231 month
  = 0.346% per week   (shorter than 1 month)

Note that none of these nominal rates make mention of the compounding frequency. They all have the format "*r*% per time period *t*."

Now, consider an effective interest rate.

Effective interest rate **is the actual rate that applies for a stated period of time. The compounding of interest during the time period of the corresponding nominal rate is accounted for by the effective interest rate. It is commonly expressed on an annual basis as the effective annual rate** i_a, **but any time basis can be used. This is sometimes referred to as the "periodic rate" or the "rate per period."**

An effective rate has the compounding frequency attached to the nominal rate statement. If the compounding frequency is not stated, it is assumed to be the same as the time period of *r*, in which case the nominal and effective rates have the same value. All the following are nominal rate statements; however, they will not have the same effective interest rate value over all time periods, due to the different compounding frequencies.

4% per year, compounded monthly   (compounding more often than time period)

12% per year, compounded quarterly   (compounding more often than time period)

9% per year, compounded daily	(compounding more often than time period)
3% per quarter, compounded monthly	(compounding more often than time period)
6% per 6 months, compounded weekly	(compounding more often than time period)
3% per quarter, compounded daily	(compounding more often than time period)

Note that all these rates make mention of the compounding frequency. They all have the format "r% per time period t, compounded m-ly." The m is a month, a quarter, a week, or some other time unit. The formula to calculate the effective interest rate value for any nominal or effective rate statement is discussed in the next section.

All the interest formulas, factors, tabulated values, and spreadsheet relations must have the effective interest rate to properly account for the time value of money.

Therefore, it is very important to determine the effective interest rate before performing time value of money calculations in the engineering economy study. This is especially true when the cash flows occur at other than annual intervals.

The terms *APR* and *APY* are used in many individual financial situations instead of nominal and effective interest rates. The annual percentage rate (APR) is the same as the nominal interest rate, and annual percentage yield (APY) is used in lieu of effective interest rate. All definitions and interpretations are the same as those developed in this chapter.

Based on these descriptions, there are always three time-based units associated with an interest rate statement.

Time period—the period over which the interest is expressed. This is the t in the statement of r% per time period t, for example, 1% *per month*. The time unit of 1 year is by far the most common. It is assumed when not stated otherwise.

Compounding period (CP)—the shortest time unit over which interest is charged or earned. This is defined by the compounding term in the interest rate statement, for example, 8% per year *compounded monthly*. If not stated, it is assumed to be 1 year.

Compounding frequency—the number of times that m compounding occurs within the time period t. If the compounding period CP and the time period t are the same, the compounding frequency is 1, for example, 1% *per month compounded monthly*.

Consider the rate 8% per year, compounded monthly. It has a time period t of 1 year, a compounding period CP of 1 month, and a compounding frequency m of 12 times per year. A rate of 6% per year, compounded weekly, has $t = 1$ year, CP = 1 week, and $m = 52$, based on the standard of 52 weeks per year.

In previous chapters, all interest rates have t and m values of 1 year. This means the rates are both the effective and the nominal rate because the same time unit of 1 year is used. It is common to express the effective rate on the same time basis as the compounding period. The corresponding effective rate per CP is determined by using the relation

$$\textbf{Effective rate per CP} = \frac{r\%\ \textbf{per time period}\ t}{m\ \textbf{compounding periods per}\ t} = \frac{r}{m} \qquad [4.2]$$

As an illustration, assume $r = 9\%$ per year, compounded monthly; then $m = 12$. Equation [4.2] is used to obtain the effective rate of $9\%/12 = 0.75\%$ per month, compounded monthly. It is important to note that changing the basic time period t does not alter the compounding period, which is 1 month in this illustration.

EXAMPLE 4.1

The different bank loan rates for three separate electric generation equipment projects are listed below. Determine the effective rate on the basis of the compounding period for each quote.

(a)   9% per year, compounded quarterly
(b)   9% per year, compounded monthly
(c)   4.5% per 6-months, compounded weekly

Solution
Apply Equation [4.2] to determine the effective rate per CP for different compounding frequencies. The accompanying graphic indicates how the interest rate is distributed over time.

Nominal r% per t	Compounding Period	m	Effective Rate per CP	Distribution over Time Period t
(a) 9% per year	Quarter	4	2.25%	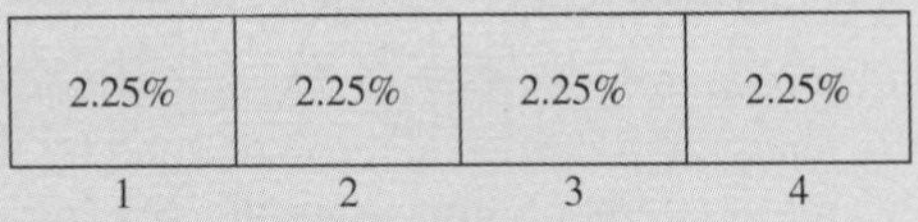
(b) 9% per year	Month	12	0.75%	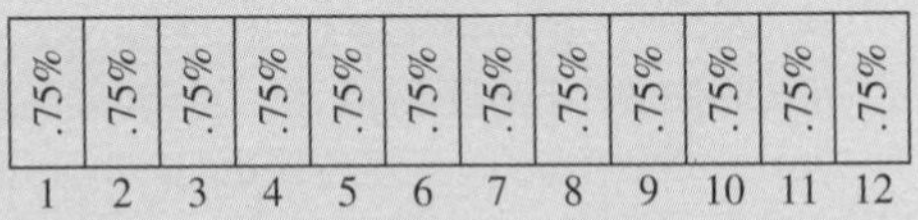
(c) 4.5% per 6 months	Week	26	0.173%	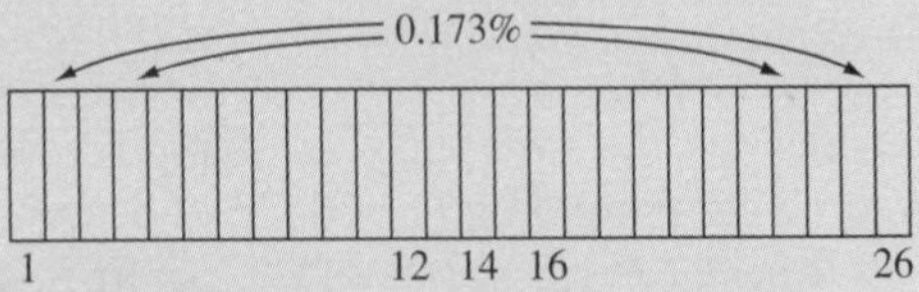

TABLE 4–1   Various Ways to Express Nominal and Effective Interest Rates

Format of Rate Statement	Examples of Statement	What About the Effective Rate?
1. Nominal rate stated, compounding period stated	8% per year, compounded quarterly	Find effective rate
2. Effective rate stated	Effective 8.243% per year, compounded quarterly	Use effective rate directly
3. Interest rate stated, no compounding period stated	8% per year or 2% per quarter	Rate is effective only for time period stated; find effective rate for all other time periods

Sometimes it is not obvious whether a stated rate is a nominal or an effective rate. Basically there are three ways to express interest rates, as detailed in Table 4–1. The right column includes a statement about the effective rate. For format 1, no statement of nominal or effective is given, but the compounding frequency is stated. The effective rate must be calculated (discussed in the next sections). In format 2, the stated rate is identified as effective (or APY could also be used), so the rate is used directly in computations.

In format 3, no compounding frequency is identified, for example, 8% per year. This rate is effective only over the time (compounding) period of a year, in this case. The effective rate for any other time period must be calculated.

4.3 EFFECTIVE ANNUAL INTEREST RATES

In this section, only effective *annual* interest rates are discussed. Therefore, the year is used as the time period t, and the compounding period can be any time unit less than 1 year. For example, a *nominal* 6% per year, compounded quarterly is the same as an *effective* rate of 6.136% per year. These are by far the most commonly quoted rates in everyday business and industry. The symbols used for nominal and effective interest rates are

r = nominal interest rate per year

m = number of compounding periods per year

i = effective interest rate per compounding period (CP) = r/m

i_a = effective interest rate per year

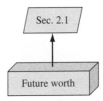

Sec. 2.1

Future worth

As mentioned earlier, treatment for nominal and effective interest rates parallels that of simple and compound interest. Like compound interest, an effective interest rate at any point during the year includes (compounds) the interest rate for all previous compounding periods during the year. Therefore, the derivation

FIGURE 4–1

Future worth calculation at a rate i, compounded m times in a year.

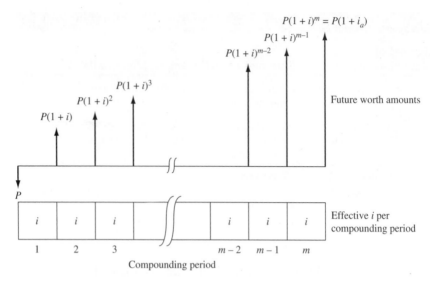

of an effective interest rate formula directly parallels the logic used to develop the future worth relation $F = P(1 + i)^n$.

The future worth F at the end of 1 year is the principal P plus the interest $P(i)$ through the year. Since interest may be compounded several times during the year, replace i with the effective annual rate i_a. Now write the relation for F at the end of 1 year.

$$F = P + Pi_a = P(1 + i_a) \qquad [4.3]$$

As indicated in Figure 4–1, the rate i per CP must be compounded through all m periods to obtain the total effect of compounding by the end of the year. This means that F can also be written as

$$F = P(1 + i)^m \qquad [4.4]$$

Consider the F value for a present worth P of $1. By equating the two expressions for F and substituting $1 for P, the *effective annual interest rate* formula for i_a is derived.

$$1 + i_a = (1 + i)^m$$
$$i_a = (1 + i)^m - 1 \qquad [4.5]$$

So Equation [4.5] calculates the effective annual interest rate for any number of compounding periods when i is the rate for one compounding period.

If the effective annual rate i_a and compounding frequency m are known, Equation [4.5] can be solved for i to determine the *effective interest rate per compounding period*.

$$i = (1 + i_a)^{1/m} - 1 \qquad [4.6]$$

Further, it is possible to determine the *nominal annual rate r* using the definition of *i* stated above, namely, $i = r/m$.

$$r\% \text{ per year} = (i\% \text{ per CP})(\text{no. of CPs per year}) = (i)(m) \qquad [4.7]$$

This is the same as Equation [4.1] where CP is the period of time.

EXAMPLE 4.2

Jacki obtained a new credit card from a bank with a stated rate of 18% per year compounded monthly. For a $1000 balance at the beginning of the year, find the effective annual rate and the total amount owed after 1 year, provided no payments are made during the year.

Solution
There are 12 compounding periods per year. Thus, $m = 12$ and $i = 18\%/12 = 1.5\%$ per month. For a $1000 balance that is not reduced during the year, apply Equation [4.5], then [4.3] to provide Jacki with the information.

$$i_a = (1 + 0.015)^{12} - 1 = 1.19562 - 1 = 0.19562$$
$$F = \$1000(1.19562) = \$1195.62$$

Jacki will pay 19.562%, or $195.62 plus the $1000 balance, for the use of the bank's money during the year.

Table 4–2 utilizes the rate of 18% per year, compounded over different times (yearly to weekly) to determine the effective annual interest rates over these various compounding periods. In each case, the compound period rate *i* is applied *m* times during the year. Table 4–3 summarizes the effective annual rate for frequently quoted nominal rates using Equation [4.5]. A standard of 52 weeks and 365 days per year is used throughout. The values in the continuous-compounding column are discussed in Section 4.8.

When Equation [4.5] is applied, the result is usually not an integer. Therefore, the engineering economy factor cannot be obtained directly from the interest factor tables. There are three alternatives to find the factor value.

- Linearly interpolate between two tabulated rates (as discussed in Section 2.4).
- Use the factor formula with the i_a rate substituted for *i*.
- Develop a spreadsheet using i_a or $i = r/m$ in the functions, as required by the spreadsheet function.

We use the second method in examples that are solved by hand and the last one in solutions by computer.

All the economic situations discussed in this section involve annual nominal and effective rates and annual cash flows. When cash flows are non-annual, it is necessary to remove the year assumption in the interest rate statement "*r%* per year, compounded *m*-ly." This is the topic of the next section.

TABLE 4-2   Effective Annual Interest Rates Using Equation [4.5]

$r = 18\%$ per year, compounded m-ly

Compounding Period	Times Compounded per Year, m	Rate per Compound Period, i	Distribution of i over the Year of Compounding Periods	Effective Annual Rate, i_a
Year	1	18%	18% (1)	$(1.18)^1 - 1 = 18\%$
6 months	2	9%	9% (1), 9% (2)	$(1.09)^2 - 1 = 18.81\%$
Quarter	4	4.5%	4.5% (1), 4.5% (2), 4.5% (3), 4.5% (4)	$(1.045)^4 - 1 = 19.252\%$
Month	12	1.5%	1.5% in each (1 2 3 4 5 6 7 8 9 10 11 12)	$(1.015)^{12} - 1 = 19.562\%$
Week	52	0.3461%	0.34615% in each (1 2 3 ... 24 26 28 ... 50 52)	$(1.0034615)^{52} - 1 = 19.684\%$

TABLE 4–3 Effective Annual Interest Rates for Selected Nominal Rates

Nominal Rate r%	Semiannually (m = 2)	Quarterly (m = 4)	Monthly (m = 12)	Weekly (m = 52)	Daily (m = 365)	Continuously (m = ∞; $e^r - 1$)
0.25	0.250	0.250	0.250	0.250	0.250	0.250
0.50	0.501	0.501	0.501	0.501	0.501	0.501
1.00	1.003	1.004	1.005	1.005	1.005	1.005
1.50	1.506	1.508	1.510	1.511	1.511	1.511
2	2.010	2.015	2.018	2.020	2.020	2.020
3	3.023	3.034	3.042	3.044	3.045	3.046
4	4.040	4.060	4.074	4.079	4.081	4.081
5	5.063	5.095	5.116	5.124	5.126	5.127
6	6.090	6.136	6.168	6.180	6.180	6.184
7	7.123	7.186	7.229	7.246	7.247	7.251
8	8.160	8.243	8.300	8.322	8.328	8.329
9	9.203	9.308	9.381	9.409	9.417	9.417
10	10.250	10.381	10.471	10.506	10.516	10.517
12	12.360	12.551	12.683	12.734	12.745	12.750
15	15.563	15.865	16.076	16.158	16.177	16.183
18	18.810	19.252	19.562	19.684	19.714	19.722
20	21.000	21.551	21.939	22.093	22.132	22.140
25	26.563	27.443	28.073	28.325	28.390	28.403
30	32.250	33.547	34.489	34.869	34.968	34.986
40	44.000	46.410	48.213	48.954	49.150	49.182
50	56.250	60.181	63.209	64.479	64.816	64.872

4.4 EFFECTIVE INTEREST RATES FOR ANY TIME PERIOD

The concepts of nominal and effective annual interest rates have been introduced. Now, in addition to the compounding period (CP), it is necessary to consider the frequency of the payments or receipts, that is, the cash flow transaction period. For simplicity, this is called the *payment period (PP)*. It is important to distinguish between the compounding period and the payment period because in many instances the two do not coincide. For example, if a company deposits money each month into an account that pays a nominal interest rate of 14% per year, compounded semiannually, the payment period is 1 month while the compounding period is 6 months (Figure 4–2). Similarly, if a person deposits money each year into a savings account which compounds interest quarterly, the payment period is 1 year, while the compounding period is 3 months.

To evaluate cash flows that occur more frequently than annually, that is, PP < 1 year, the effective interest rate over the PP must be used in the engineering economy relations. The effective annual interest rate formula is easily generalized to any nominal rate by substituting r/m for the period interest rate in Equation [4.5].

$$\textbf{Effective } i = (1 + r/m)^m - 1 \qquad\qquad \textbf{[4.8]}$$

where

r = nominal interest rate per payment period (PP)

m = number of compounding periods per payment period (CP per PP)

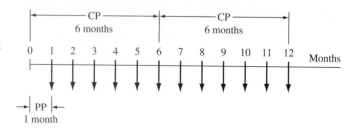

FIGURE 4–2

One-year cash flow diagram for a monthly payment period (PP) and semiannual compounding period (CP).

Instead of i_a, this general expression uses i as the symbol for effective interest. This conforms to all other uses of i for the remainder of the text. With Equation [4.8], it is possible to take a nominal rate ($r\%$ per year or any other time period) and convert it to an effective rate i for any time basis, the most common of which will be the PP time period. The next two examples illustrate how to do this.

EXAMPLE 4.3

An engineer for Quebecor World Inc., the Montreal-based commercial printing unit of Quebecor Inc., is evaluating bids for new state-of-the-art printing machines as part of a major overhaul to cut costs and deal with pricing pressures. Three vendor bids include the interest rates that follow. Quebecor World will make payments on a semiannual basis only. The engineer is confused about the effective interest rates—what they are annually and over the payment period of 6 months.

Bid 1:   9% per year, compounded quarterly
Bid 2:   3% per quarter, compounded quarterly
Bid 3:   8.8% per year, compounded monthly

(a)   Determine the effective rate for each bid on the basis of semiannual payments, and construct cash flow diagrams similar to Figure 4–2 for each bid rate.
(b)   What are the effective annual rates? These are to be a part of the final bid selection.
(c)   Which bid has the lowest effective annual rate?

Solution
(a)   Set the payment period (PP) at 6 months, convert the nominal rate $r\%$ to a semian-nual basis, then determine m. Finally, use Equation [4.8] to calculate the effective semiannual interest rate i. For bid 1, the following are correct:

$$PP = 6 \text{ months}$$
$$r = 9\% \text{ per year} = 4.5\% \text{ per 6 months}$$
$$m = 2 \text{ quarters per 6 months}$$

$$\text{Effective } i\% \text{ per 6 months} = \left(1 + \frac{0.045}{2}\right)^2 - 1 = 1.0455 - 1 = 4.55\%$$

Table 4–4 (left section) summarizes the effective semiannual rates for all three bids. Figure 4–3a is the cash flow diagram for bids 1 and 2, semiannual payments

(PP = 6 months) and quarterly compounding (CP = 1 quarter). Figure 4–3b is the same for monthly compounding (bid 3).

(b) For the effective annual rate, the time basis in Equation [4.8] is 1 year. This is the same as PP = 1 year. For bid 1,

$$r = 9\% \text{ per year} \quad m = 4 \text{ quarters per year}$$

$$\text{Effective } i\% \text{ per year} = \left(1 + \frac{0.09}{4}\right)^4 - 1 = 1.0931 - 1 = 9.31$$

The right section of Table 4–4 includes a summary of the effective annual rates.

(c) Bid 3 includes the lowest effective annual rate of 9.16%, which is equivalent to an effective semiannual rate of 4.48%.

TABLE 4–4   Effective Semiannual and Annual Interest Rates for Three Bid Rates, Example 4.3

	Semiannual Rates			Annual Rates		
Bid	Nominal per 6 Months, r	CP per PP, m	Equation [4.8], Effective i	Nominal per Year, r	CP per Year, m	Equation [4.8], Effective i
1	4.5%	2	4.55%	9%	4	9.31%
2	6.0%	2	6.09%	12%	4	12.55%
3	4.4%	6	4.48%	8.8%	12	9.16%

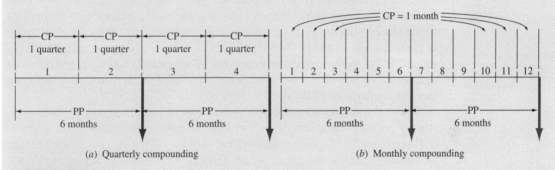

(a) Quarterly compounding   (b) Monthly compounding

FIGURE 4–3
Cash flow diagram showing CP and PP for (a) bids 1 and 2 and (b) bid 3, Example 4.3.

Comment

The effective rates for bid 2 only may be found directly in Table 4–3. For the effective semiannual rate, look at the nominal 6% line under $m = 2$, which is the number of quarters per 6 months. The effective semiannual rate is 6.09%. Similarly, for the nominal 12% rate, there are $m = 4$ quarters per year, so effective annual $i = 12.551\%$. Although Table 4–3 was originally designed for nominal annual rates, it is correct for other nominal rate periods, provided the appropriate m value is included in the column headings.

| EXAMPLE 4.4 | |

A dot-com company plans to place money in a new venture capital fund that currently returns 18% per year, compounded daily. What effective rate is this (*a*) yearly and (*b*) semiannually?

Solution

(*a*) Use Equation [4.8], with $r = 0.18$ and $m = 365$.

$$\text{Effective } i\% \text{ per year} = \left(1 + \frac{0.18}{365}\right)^{365} - 1 = 19.716\%$$

(*b*) Here $r = 0.09$ per 6 months and $m = 182$ days.

$$\text{Effective } i\% \text{ per 6 months} = \left(1 + \frac{0.09}{182}\right)^{182} - 1 = 9.415\%$$

4.5 EQUIVALENCE RELATIONS: COMPARING PAYMENT PERIOD AND COMPOUNDING PERIOD LENGTHS (PP versus CP)

In a large percentage of equivalency computations, the frequency of cash flows does not equal the frequency of interest compounding. For example, cash flows may occur monthly, and compounding occurs annually, quarterly, or more often. Consider deposits made to a savings account each month, while the earning rate is compounded quarterly. The length of the CP is a quarter, while the PP is a month. To correctly perform any equivalence computation, it is essential that the compounding period and payment period be placed on the same time basis, and that the interest rate be adjusted accordingly.

The next three sections describe procedures to determine correct *i* and *n* values for engineering economy factors and spreadsheet solutions. First, compare the length of PP and CP, then identify the cash flow series as only single amounts (*P* and *F*) or as a series (*A*, *G*, or *g*). Table 4–5 provides the section reference. When only single amounts are involved, there is no payment period PP per se defined by the cash flows. The length of PP is, therefore, defined by the time period *t* of the interest rate statement. If the rate is 8% per 6 months, compounded quarterly, the PP is 6 months, the CP is 3 months, and PP > CP.

Note that the section references in Table 4–5 are the same when PP = CP and PP > CP. The equations to determine *i* and *n* are the same. Additionally, the technique to account for the time value of money is the same, because it is only when cash flows occur that the effect of the interest rate is determined. For example, assume that cash flows occur every 6 months (PP is semiannual), and that interest is compounded each 3 months (CP is a quarter). After 3 months there is no cash flow and no need to determine the effect of

TABLE 4–5	Section References for Equivalence Calculations Based on Payment Period and Compounding Period Comparison	
Length of Time	Involves Single Amounts (*P* and *F* only)	Involves Uniform Series or Gradient Series (*A, G,* or *g*)
PP = CP	Section 4.6	Section 4.7
PP > CP	Section 4.6	Section 4.7
PP < CP	Section 4.8	Section 4.8

quarterly compounding. However, at the 6-month time point, it is necessary to consider the interest accrued during the previous two quarterly compounding periods.

4.6 EQUIVALENCE RELATIONS: SINGLE AMOUNTS WITH PP ≥ CP

When only single-amount cash flows are involved, there are two equally correct ways to determine i and n for P/F and F/P factors. Method 1 is easier to apply, because the interest tables in the back of the text can usually provide the factor value. Method 2 likely requires a factor formula calculation, because the resulting effective interest rate is not an integer. For spreadsheets, either method is acceptable; however, method 1 is usually easier.

Method 1:   Determine the effective interest rate over the *compounding period CP*, and set n equal to the number of compounding periods between P and F. The relations to calculate P and F are

$$P = F(P/F, \text{effective } i\% \text{ per CP, total number of periods } n) \quad \textbf{[4.9]}$$

$$F = P(F/P, \text{effective } i\% \text{ per CP, total number of periods } n) \quad \textbf{[4.10]}$$

For example, assume that a nominal 15% per year, compounded monthly, is the stated credit card rate. Here CP is a month. To find P or F over a 2-year span, calculate the effective monthly rate of $15\%/12 = 1.25\%$ and the total months of $2(12) = 24$. Then 1.25% and 24 are used in the P/F and F/P factors.

Any time period can be used to determine the effective interest rate; however, CP is the best basis. The CP is best because only over the CP can the effective rate have the same numerical value as the nominal rate over the same time period as the CP. This was discussed in Section 4.1 and Table 4–1. This means that the effective rate over CP is usually a whole number. Therefore, the factor tables in the back of the text can be used.

Method 2:   Determine the effective interest rate for the *time period t of the nominal rate,* and set n equal to the total number of periods using this same time period. The P and F relations are the same as in Equations [4.9] and [4.10] with the term *effective i% per t* substituted for the interest rate.

For a credit card rate of 15% per year, compounded monthly, the time period t is 1 year. The effective rate over 1 year and n values are

$$\text{Effective } i\% \text{ per year} = \left(1 + \frac{0.15}{12}\right)^{12} - 1 = 16.076\%$$

$$n = 2 \text{ years}$$

The P/F factor is the same by both methods: $(P/F, 1.25\%, 24) = 0.7422$ using Table 5; and $(P/F, 16.076\%, 2) = 0.7422$ using the P/F factor formula.

EXAMPLE 4.5

An engineer working as a private consultant made deposits into a special account to cover unreimbursed travel expenses. Figure 4–4 is the cash flow diagram. Find the amount in the account after 10 years at an interest rate of 12% per year, compounded semiannually.

Solution

Only P and F values are involved. Both methods are illustrated to find F in year 10.

Method 1: Use the semiannual CP to express the effective semiannual rate of 6% per 6-month period. There are $n = (2)(\text{number of years})$ semiannual periods for each cash flow. Using the factor values from Table 11, we see that the future worth by Equation [4.10] is

$$F = 1000(F/P, 6\%, 20) + 3000(F/P, 6\%, 12) + 1500(F/P, 6\%, 8)$$
$$= 1000(3.2071) + 3000(2.0122) + 1500(1.5938)$$
$$= \$11,634$$

Method 2: Express the effective annual rate, based on semiannual compounding.

$$\text{Effective } i\% \text{ per year} = \left(1 + \frac{0.12}{2}\right)^{2} - 1 = 12.36\%$$

The n value is the actual number of years. Use the factor formula $(F/P, i, n) = (1.1236)^n$ and Equation [4.10] to obtain the same answer as with method 1.

$$F = 1000(F/P, 12.36\%, 10) + 3000(F/P, 12.36\%, 6) + 1500(F/P, 12.36\%, 4)$$
$$= 1000(3.2071) + 3000(2.0122) + 1500(1.5938)$$
$$= \$11,634$$

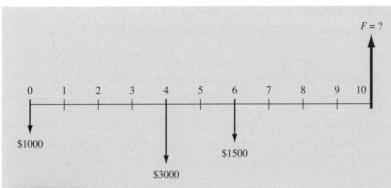

FIGURE 4–4
Cash flow diagram, Example 4.5.

Comment
For single-amount cash flows, any combination of i and n derived from the stated nominal rate can be used in the factors, provided they are on the same time basis. Using 12% per year, *compounded monthly*, Table 4–6 presents various acceptable combinations of i and n. Other combinations are correct, such as the effective weekly rate for i and weeks for n.

TABLE 4–6 Various i and n Values for Single-Amount Equations Using $r = 12\%$ per Year, Compounded Monthly	
Effective Rate i	**Units for n**
1% per month	Months
3.03% per quarter	Quarters
6.15% per 6 months	Semiannual periods
12.68% per year	Years
26.97% per 2 years	2-year periods

4.7 EQUIVALENCE RELATIONS: SERIES WITH PP ≥ CP

When uniform or gradient series are included in the cash flow sequence, the procedure is basically the same as method 2 above, except that PP is now defined by the frequency of the cash flows. This also establishes the time unit of the effective interest rate. For example, if cash flows occur on a *quarterly* basis, PP is a *quarter* and the effective *quarterly* rate is necessary. The n value is the total number of *quarters*. If PP is a quarter, 5 years translates to an n value of 20 quarters. This is a direct application of the following general guideline:

When cash flows involve a series (i.e., A, G, g) and the payment period equals or exceeds the compounding period in length,

- **Find the effective *i* per payment period.**
- **Determine *n* as the total number of payment periods.**

In performing equivalence computations for series, *only* these values of *i* and *n* can be used in interest tables, factor formulas, and spreadsheet functions. In other words, there are no other combinations that give the correct answers, as there are for single amount cash flows.

Table 4–7 shows the correct formulation for several cash flow series and interest rates. Note that *n* is always equal to the total number of payment periods and *i* is an effective rate expressed over the same time period as *n*.

EXAMPLE 4.6

For the past 7 years, a quality manager has paid $500 every 6 months for the software mainte-nance contract of a LAN. What is the equivalent amount after the last payment, if these funds are taken from a pool that has been returning 10% per year, compounded quarterly?

Solution
The cash flow diagram is shown in Figure 4–5. The payment period (6 months) is longer than the compounding period (quarter); that is, PP > CP. Applying the guideline, we need to determine an effective semiannual interest rate. Use Equation [4.8] with $r = 0.05$ per 6-month period and $r = 2$ quarters per semiannual period.

$$\text{Effective } i\% \text{ per 6 months} = \left(1 + \frac{0.05}{2}\right)^{2} - 1 = 5.063\%$$

The effective semiannual interest rate can also be obtained from Table 4–3 by using the r value of 5% and $m = 2$ to get $i = 5.063\%$.

The value $i = 5.063\%$ seems reasonable, since we expect the effective rate to be slightly higher than the nominal rate of 5% per 6-month period. The total number of semiannual payment periods is $n = 2(7) = 14$. The relation for F is

$$F = A(F/A,5.063\%,14)$$
$$= 500(28.4891)$$
$$= \$14,244.50$$

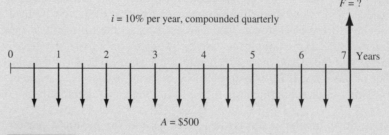

i = 10% per year, compounded quarterly

$A = \$500$

FIGURE 4–5
Diagram of semiannual deposits used to determine *F*, Example 4.6.

TABLE 4–7 Examples of *n* and *i* Values Where PP = CP or PP > CP

Cash Flow Series	Interest Rate	What to Find; What Is Given	Standard Notation
$500 semiannually for 5 years	8% per year, compounded semiannually	Find P; given A	$P = 500(P/A,4\%,10)$
$75 monthly for 3 years	12% per year, compounded monthly	Find F; given A	$F = 75(F/A,1\%,36)$
$180 quarterly for 15 years	5% per quarter	Find F; given A	$F = 180(F/A,5\%,60)$
$25 per month increase for 4 years	1% per month	Find P; given G	$P = 25(P/G,1\%,48)$
$5000 per quarter for 6 years	1% per month	Find A; given P	$A = 5000(A/P,3.03\%,24)$

EXAMPLE 4.7

Suppose you plan to purchase a car and carry a loan of $12,500 at 9% per year, compounded monthly. Payments will be made monthly for 4 years. Determine the monthly payment. Compare the computer and hand solutions.

Solution

A monthly series A is sought; the PP and CP are both a month. Use the steps for PP = CP when a uniform series is present. The effective interest per month is $9\%/12 = 0.75\%$, and the number of payments is (4 years)(12 months per year) = 48.

Enter PMT(9%/12,48,−12500) into any cell to display $311.06.

Figure 4–6 shows a complete spreadsheet with the PMT function in cell B5 using cell reference format. This monthly payment of $311.06 is equivalent to the following solution by hand, using standard notation and the factor tables.

$$A = \$12,500(A/P,0.75\%,48) = 12,500(0.02489) = \$311.13$$

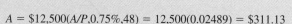

FIGURE 4–6

Spreadsheet for Example 4.7.

Comment

It is incorrect to use the effective annual rate of $i = 9.381\%$ and $n = 4$ years to calculate the monthly A value, whether solving by hand or by computer. The payment period, the effective rate, and the number of payments must all be on the same time basis, which is the *month* in this example.

EXAMPLE 4.8

Costco Canada is considering the purchase of automated prescription fulfillment systems for its 18 locations with pharmacies in Alberta and British Columbia. Assume the cost will be $3 million to install the systems and an estimated $200,000 per year for materials, operating, and maintenance costs. The expected life is 10 years. Costco wants to estimate the total revenue requirement for each 6-month period that is necessary to recover the investment, interest, and annual costs. Find this semiannual A value both by hand and by computer, if capital funds are evaluated at 8% per year using two different compounding periods:

1. 8% per year, compounded *semiannually*
2. 8% per year, compounded *monthly*

Solution

Figure 4–7 shows the cash flow diagram. Throughout the 20 semiannual periods, the annual cost occurs every other period, and the capital recovery series is sought for every 6-month period. This pattern makes the solution by hand quite involved if the *P/F* factor, not the *P/A* factor, is used to find P for the 10 annual $200,000 costs. The computer solution is recommended in cases such as this.

Solution by hand—rate 1: Steps to find the semiannual A value are summarized below:

   PP = CP at 6 months; find the effective rate per semiannual period
   Effective semiannual $i = 8\%/2 = 4\%$ per 6 months, compounded semiannually
   Number of semiannual periods $n = 2(10) = 20$

Calculate P, using the *P/F* factor for $n = 2, 4, \ldots, 20$ periods since the costs are annual, not semiannual. Then use the *A/P* factor over 20 periods to find the semiannual A.

FIGURE 4–7

Cash flow diagram with two different compounding periods, Example 4.8.

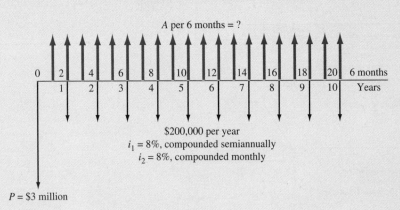

A per 6 months = ?

$200,000 per year
$i_1 = 8\%$, compounded semiannually
$i_2 = 8\%$, compounded monthly

$P = $3 million

$$P = 3{,}000{,}000 + 200{,}000\left[\sum_{k=2,4}^{20} (P/F,4\%,k)\right]$$

$$= 3{,}000{,}000 + 200{,}000(6.6620) = \$4.332.400$$

$$A = \$4{,}332{,}400(A/P,4\%,20) = \$318{,}778$$

Conclusion: Revenue of $318,778 is necessary every 6 months to cover all costs and interest at 8% per year, compounded semiannually.

Solution by hand—rate 2: The PP is semiannual, but the CP is now monthly; therefore, PP > CP. To find the effective semiannual rate, the effective interest rate, Equation [4.8], is applied with $r = 4\%$ and $m = 6$ months per semiannual period.

$$\text{Effective semiannual } i = \left(1 + \frac{0.04}{6}\right)^6 - 1 = 4.067\%$$

$$P = 3{,}000{,}000 + 200{,}000\left[\sum_{k=2,4}^{20} (P/F,4.067\%,k)\right]$$

$$= 3{,}000{,}000 + 200{,}000(6.6204) = \$4.324.080$$

$$A = \$4{,}324{,}080(A/P,4.067\%,20) = \$320{,}064$$

Now, $320,064, or $1286 more semiannually, is required to cover the more frequent compounding of the 8% per year interest. Note that all *P/F* and *A/P* factors must be calculated with factor formulas at 4.067%. This method is usually more calculation-intensive and error-prone than with a spreadsheet solution.

Solution by computer—rates 1 and 2: Figure 4–8 presents a general solution for the problem at both rates. (Several rows at the bottom of the spreadsheet are not printed. They continue the cash flow pattern of $200,000 every other 6 months through cell B32.) The functions in C8 and E8 are general expressions for the effective rate per PP, expressed in months. This allows some sensitivity analysis to be performed for different PP and CP values. Note the function in C7 and E7 to determine *m* for the effective rate relations. This technique works well for spreadsheets once PP and CP are entered in the time unit of the CP.

Each 6-month period is included in the cash flows, including the $0 entries, so the NPV and PMT functions work correctly. The final *A* values in D14 ($318,784) and F14 ($320,069) are the same (except for rounding) as those above.

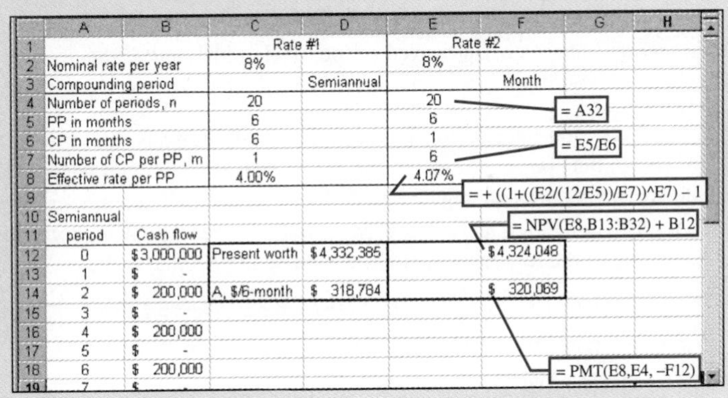

	A	B	C	D	E	F
1			Rate #1		Rate #2	
2	Nominal rate per year		8%		8%	
3	Compounding period			Semiannual		Month
4	Number of periods, n		20		20	
5	PP in months		6		6	
6	CP in months		6		1	
7	Number of CP per PP, m		1		6	
8	Effective rate per PP		4.00%		4.07%	
9						
10	Semiannual					
11	period	Cash flow				
12	0	$3,000,000	Present worth	$4,332,385		$4,324,048
13	1	$ -				
14	2	$ 200,000	A, $/6-month	$ 318,784		$ 320,069
15	3	$ -				
16	4	$ 200,000				
17	5	$ -				
18	6	$ 200,000				
19	7	$				

FIGURE 4–8
Spreadsheet solution for semiannual *A* series for different compounding periods, Example 4.8.

4.8 EQUIVALENCE RELATIONS: SINGLE AMOUNTS AND SERIES WITH PP < CP

If a person deposits money each month into a savings account where interest is compounded quarterly, do all the monthly deposits earn interest before the next quarterly compounding time? If a person's credit card payment is due with interest on the 15th of the month, and if the full payment is made on the 1st, does the financial institution reduce the interest owed, based on early payment? The usual answers are no. However, if a monthly payment on a $10 million, quarterly-compounded, bank loan were made early by a large corporation, the corporate financial officer would likely insist that the bank reduce the amount of interest due, based on early payment. These are examples of PP < CP. The timing of cash flow transactions between compounding points introduces the question of how *interperiod compounding* is handled. Fundamentally, there are two policies: interperiod cash flows earn *no interest,* or they earn *compound interest.*

For a no-interperiod-interest policy, deposits (negative cash flows) are all regarded as *deposited at the end of the compounding period,* and withdrawals are all regarded as *withdrawn at the beginning.* As an illustration, when interest is compounded quarterly, all monthly deposits are moved to the end of the quarter (no interperiod interest is earned), and all withdrawals are moved to the beginning (no interest is paid for the entire quarter). This procedure can significantly alter the distribution of cash flows before the effective quarterly rate is applied to find P, F, or A. This effectively forces the cash flows into a PP = CP situation, as discussed in Sections 4.6 and 4.7. Example 4.9 illustrates this procedure and the economic fact that, within a one-compounding-period time frame, there is no interest advantage to making payments early. Of course, noneconomic factors may be present.

EXAMPLE 4.9

Rob is the on-site coordinating engineer for Aur Resources in Newfoundland where their Duck Pond copper-zinc-gold mine has new ore refining equipment being installed by a local contractor. Rob developed the cash flow diagram in Figure 4–9a in $1000 units from the project perspective. Included are payments to the contractor he has authorized for the current year and approved advances from Aur's home office. He knows that the interest rate on equipment "field projects" such as this is 12% per year, compounded quarterly, and that Aur does not bother with interperiod compounding of interest. Will Rob's project finances be in the red or the black at the end of the year? By how much?

Solution

With no interperiod interest considered, Figure 4–9b reflects the moved cash flows. The future worth after four quarters requires an F at an effective rate per quarter of 12%/4 = 3%. Figure 4–9b shows all negative cash flows (payments to contractor) moved to the end of the respective quarter, and all positive cash flows (receipts from home office) moved to the beginning of the respective quarter. Calculate the F value at 3%.

$$F = 1000[-150(F/P,3\%,4) - 200(F/P,3\%,3) + (-175 + 90)(F/P,3\%,2)$$
$$+ 165(F/P,3\%,1) - 50]$$
$$= \$-357{,}592$$

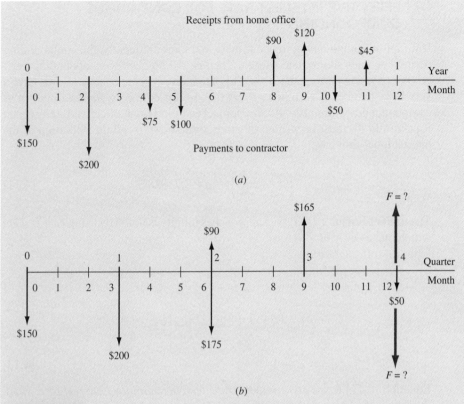

FIGURE 4–9
(a) Actual and (b) moved cash flows (in $1000) for quarterly compounding periods using no interperiod interest, Example 4.9.

Rob can conclude that the on-site project finances will be in the red about $357,600 by the end of the year.

If PP < CP and interperiod compounding is earned, the cash flows are not moved, and the equivalent *P*, *F*, or *A* values are determined using the effective interest rate per payment period. The engineering economy relations are determined in the same way as in the previous two sections for PP ≥ CP. The effective interest rate formula will have an *m* value less than 1, because there is only a fractional part of the CP within one PP. For example, weekly cash flows and quarterly compounding require that $m = 1/13$ of a quarter. When the nominal rate is 12% per year, compounded quarterly (the same as 3% per quarter, compounded quarterly), the effective rate per PP is

$$\text{Effective weekly } i\% = (1.03)^{1/13} - 1 = 0.228\% \text{ per week}$$

4.9 EFFECTIVE INTEREST RATE FOR CONTINUOUS COMPOUNDING

If we allow compounding to occur more and more frequently, the compounding period becomes shorter and shorter. Then m, the number of compounding periods per payment period, increases. This situation occurs in businesses that have a very large number of cash flows every day, so it is correct to consider interest as compounded continuously. As m approaches infinity, the effective interest rate, Equation [4.8], must be written in a new form. First, recall the definition of the natural logarithm base.

$$\lim_{h \to \infty} \left(1 + \frac{1}{h} \right)^h = e = 2.71828+ \qquad [4.11]$$

The limit of Equation [4.8] as m approaches infinity is found by using $r/m = 1/h$, which makes $m = hr$.

$$\lim_{m \to \infty} i = \lim_{m \to \infty} \left(1 + \frac{r}{m} \right)^m - 1$$

$$= \lim_{h \to \infty} \left(1 + \frac{1}{h} \right)^{hr} - 1 = \lim_{h \to \infty} \left[\left(1 + \frac{1}{h} \right)^h \right]^r - 1$$

$$\boldsymbol{i = e^r - 1} \qquad \textbf{[4.12]}$$

Equation [4.12] is used to compute the *effective continuous interest rate,* when the time periods on i and r are the same. As an illustration, if the nominal annual $r = 15\%$ per year, the effective continuous rate per year is

$$i\% = e^{0.15} - 1 = 16.183\%$$

For convenience, Table 4–3 includes effective continuous rates for the nominal rates listed.

EXAMPLE 4.10

(a) For an interest rate of 18% per year, compounded continuously, calculate the effective monthly and annual interest rates.

(b) An investor requires an effective return of at least 15%. What is the minimum annual nominal rate that is acceptable for continuous compounding?

Solution

(a) The nominal monthly rate is $r = 18\%/12 = 1.5\%$, or 0.015 per month. By Equation [4.12], the effective monthly rate is

$$i\% \text{ per month} = e^r - 1 = e^{0.015} - 1 = 1.511\%$$

Similarly, the effective annual rate using $r = 0.18$ per year is

$$i\% \text{ per year} = e^r - 1 = e^{0.18} - 1 = 19.72\%$$

(b) Solve Equation [4.12] for r by taking the natural logarithm.

$$e^r - 1 = 0.15$$
$$e^r = 1.15$$
$$\ln e^r = \ln 1.15$$
$$r\% = 13.976\%$$

Therefore, a rate of 13.976% per year, compounded continuously, will generate an effective 15% per year return.

Comment
The general formula to find the nominal rate, given the effective continuous rate i, is $r = \ln(1 + i)$.

EXAMPLE 4.11

Engineers Marci and Suzanne both invest $5000 for 10 years at 10% per year. Compute the future worth for both individuals if Marci receives annual compounding and Suzanne receives continuous compounding.

Solution
Marci: For annual compounding the future worth is

$$F = P(F/P,10\%,10) = 5000(2.5937) = \$12,969$$

Suzanne: Using Equation [4.12], first find the effective i per year for use in the F/P factor.

$$\text{Effective } i\% = e^{0.10} - 1 = 10.517\%$$
$$F = P(F/P,10.517\%,10) = 5000(2.7183) = \$13,591$$

Continuous compounding causes a $622 increase in earnings. For comparison, daily compounding yields an effective rate of 10.516% ($F = \$13,590$), only slightly less than the 10.517% for continuous compounding.

For some business activities, cash flows occur throughout the day. Examples of costs are energy and water costs, inventory costs, and labour costs. A realistic model for these activities is to increase the frequency of the cash flows to become continuous. In these cases, the economic analysis can be performed for continuous cash flow (also called continuous funds flow) and the continuous compounding of interest as discussed above. Different expressions must be derived for the factors for these cases. In fact, the monetary differences for continuous cash flows relative to the discrete cash flow and discrete compounding assumptions are usually not large. Accordingly, most engineering economy studies do not require the analyst to utilize these mathematical forms to make a sound economic project evaluation and decision.

4.10 INTEREST RATES THAT VARY OVER TIME

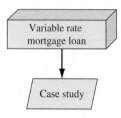

Variable rate mortgage loan

Case study

Real-world interest rates for a corporation vary from year to year, depending upon the financial health of the corporation, its market sector, the national and international economies, forces of inflation, and many other elements. Loan rates may increase from one year to another. Home mortgages financed using variable rate mortgage interest are a good example. The mortgage rate is slightly adjusted annually to reflect the age of the loan, the current cost of mortgage money, etc. An example of interest rates that rise over time is inflation-protected bonds that are issued by the Canadian government, the U.S. government, and other agencies. The dividend rate that the bond pays remains constant over its stated life, but the lump-sum amount due to the owner when the bond reaches maturity is adjusted upward with the inflation index of the consumer price index (CPI). This means the annual rate of return will increase annually in accordance with observed inflation. (Bonds and inflation are visited again in Chapters 5 and 14, respectively.)

When P, F, and A values are calculated using a constant or average interest rate over the life of a project, rises and falls in i are neglected. If the variation in i is large, the equivalent values will vary considerably from those calculated using the constant rate. Although an engineering economy study can accommodate varying i values mathematically, it is more involved computationally to do so.

To determine the P value for future cash flow values (F_t) at different i values (i_t) for each year t, we will assume *annual compounding*. Define

$$i_t = \text{ effective annual interest rate for year } t \ (t = \text{ years 1 to } n)$$

To determine the present worth, calculate the P of each F_t value, using the applicable i_t, and sum the results. Using standard notation and the P/F factor,

$$P = F_1(P/F,i_1,1) + F_2(P/F,i_1,1)(P/F,i_2,1) + \cdots$$
$$+ F_n(P/F,i_1,1)(P/F,i_2,1)\cdots(P/F,i_n,1)$$

[4.13]

When only single amounts are involved, that is, one P and one F in the final year n, the last term in Equation [4.13] is the expression for the present worth of the future cash flow.

$$P = F_n(P/F,i_1,1)(P/F,i_2,1), \cdots (P/F,i_n,1)$$

[4.14]

If the equivalent uniform series A over all n years is needed, first find P using either of the last two equations, then substitute the symbol A for each F_t symbol.

Since the equivalent P has been determined numerically using the varying rates, this new equation will have only one unknown, namely A. The following example illustrates this procedure.

EXAMPLE 4.12

CE, Inc., leases large earth tunnelling equipment. The net profit from the equipment for each of the last 4 years has been decreasing, as shown below. Also shown are the annual rates of return on invested capital. The return has been increasing. Determine the present worth P and equivalent uniform series A of the net profit series. Take the annual variation of rates of return into account.

Year	1	2	3	4
Net profit	$70,000	$70,000	$35,000	$25,000
Annual rate	7%	7%	9%	10%

Solution

Figure 4–10 shows the cash flows, rates for each year, and the equivalent P and A. Equation [4.13] is used to calculate P. Since for both years 1 and 2 the net profit is $70,000 and the annual rate is 7%, the P/A factor can be used for these 2 years only.

$$P = [70(P/A,7\%,2) + 35(P/F,7\%,2)(P/F,9\%,1)$$
$$+ 25(P/F,7\%,2)(P/F,9\%,1)(P/F,10\%,1)](1000)$$
$$= [70(1.8080) + 35(0.8013) + 25(0.7284)](1000)$$
$$= \$172.816 \hspace{3cm} [4.15]$$

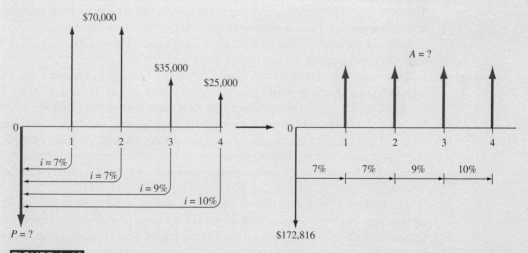

FIGURE 4–10
Equivalent P and A values for varying interest rates, Example 4.12.

To determine an equivalent annual series, substitute the symbol A for all net profit values on the right side of Equation [4.15], set it equal to $P = \$172,816$, and solve for A. This equation accounts for the varying i values each year. See Figure 4–10 for the cash flow diagram transformation.

$$\$172,816 = A[(1.8080) + (0.8013) + (0.7284)] = A[3.3377]$$

$$A = \$51,777 \text{ per year}$$

Comment

If the average of the four annual rates, that is, 8.25%, is used, the result is $A = \$52,467$. This is a \$690 per year overestimate of the required equivalent amount.

When there is a cash flow in year 0 and interest rates vary annually, this cash flow must be included when one is determining P. In the computation for the equivalent uniform series A over all years, including year 0, it is important to include this initial cash flow at $t = 0$. This is accomplished by inserting the factor value for $(P/F,i_0,0)$ into the relation for A. This factor value is always 1.00. It is equally correct to find the A value using a future worth relation for F in year n. In this case, the A value is determined using the F/P factor, and the cash flow in year n is accounted for by including the factor $(F/P,i_n,0) = 1.00$.

4.11 HOME MORTGAGE APPLICATION

A mortgage is often obtained from a bank to purchase a house or other residential property. In Canada, such loans can be amortized over a period of up to 35 years. This is the period it would take to repay the loan in full. The term of the mortgage is the time period, from 6 months to 10 years, over which the legal agreement is made. At the end of each term, the borrower again selects a mortgage loan to continue repayment of the mortgage.

There are many types of mortgages to choose from with interest rates that remain fixed over the term of the agreement or with interest rates that vary with the Bank of Canada prime lending rate or a premium interest rate set by the lender. For both fixed-rate and variable-rate mortgages, the regular payment stays the same during the term even if interest rates change. As rates change, a larger or smaller portion of the payment goes toward the amount you borrow, or principal. The interest is compounded semiannually on a monthly payment schedule.

The borrower must also choose between a closed or an open mortgage. The interest rate charged remains unchanged for the term of a closed mortgage, but prepayment costs usually apply if the loan if repaid, renegotiated, or refinanced before the end of the term. Some loans allow annual repayments of up to 10% or

15% of the original mortgage amount without penalty. An open mortgage may be repaid in part or in full at any time during the term without prepayment costs. This flexibility usually results in a higher interest rate being charged than for a closed mortgage.

New mortgage rules were put in place in 2011 to try to keep Canadian consumers from taking on too much debt. The government was concerned that historically low mortgage rates were contributing to speculation in real estate and that mortgage costs require an exceptionally high proportion of household incomes in some cities—costs that will increase if interest rates rise. A conventional mortgage loan in Canada requires that the borrower make a down payment of at least 20% of the value of the property. A smaller down payment necessitates the purchase of Canada Mortgage and Housing Corporation insurance that may cost up to 2.75% of the borrowed amount and a reduction in the maximum amortization period to 30 years from 35 years. Borrowers have to qualify for a loan on the basis of being able to make payments on a 5-year fixed-rate mortgage.

Because the amount of money paid over the lifetime of a mortgage loan can be quite large, it is wise to compare the various terms and conditions of mortgage loans available.

EXAMPLE 4.13

Fatima has just bought a house for $200,000. She paid $50,000 down and the rest of the cost was obtained with a closed mortgage having a 25-year term at 8% compounded semi-annually and a monthly payment period. Assume she renews the loan after each term at the same rate. Determine the total dollar amount (T) of her investment when the loan is paid in full.

Solution
This situation requires the calculation of an effective interest rate for a series where the PP is less than the CP. Assuming that interperiod compounding is earned, the

$$\text{Effective monthly } i\% = (1 + 0.08/2)^{1/6} - 1 = 0.656\% \text{ per month}$$
$$N = (25 \text{ years})(12 \text{ months/year}) = 300 \text{ months}$$
$$A = 150{,}000(A/P, 0.6558, 300) = \$1{,}144.80/\text{month}$$

Fatima paid $50,000 down and repays the loan for 25 years. Therefore,

$$T = \$50{,}000 + \$1{,}144.80(300 \text{ months})$$
$$T = \$343{,}400$$

CHAPTER SUMMARY

Since many real-world situations involve cash flow frequencies and compounding periods other than 1 year, it is necessary to use nominal and effective interest rates. When a nominal rate r is stated, the effective interest rate per payment period is determined by using the effective interest rate equation.

$$\text{Effective } i = \left(1 + \frac{r}{m}\right)^m - 1$$

The m is the number of compounding periods (CP) per payment period (PP). If interest compounding becomes more and more frequent, the length of a CP approaches zero, continuous compounding results, and the effective i is $e^r - 1$.

All engineering economy factors require the use of an effective interest rate. The i and n values placed in a factor depend upon the type of cash flow series. If only single amounts (P and F) are present, there are several ways to perform equivalence calculations using the factors. However, when series cash flows (A, G, and g) are present, only one combination of the effective rate i and number of periods n is correct for the factors. This requires that the relative lengths of PP and CP be considered as i and n are determined. *The interest rate and payment periods must have the same time unit* for the factors to correctly account for the time value of money.

From one year (or interest period) to the next, interest rates will vary. To accurately perform equivalence calculations for P and A when rates vary significantly, the applicable interest rate should be used, not an average or constant rate. Whether performed by hand or by computer, the procedures and factors are the same as those for constant interest rates; however, the number of calculations increases.

PROBLEMS

Nominal and Effective Rates

4.1 Identify the compounding period for the following interest statements: (*a*) 1% per month; (*b*) 2.5% per quarter; and (*c*) 9.3% per year compounded semiannually.

4.2 Identify the compounding period for the following interest statements: (*a*) nominal 7% per year compounded quarterly; (*b*) effective 6.8% per year compounded monthly; and (*c*) effective 3.4% per quarter compounded weekly.

4.3 Determine the number of times interest would be compounded in 1 year for the following interest statements: (*a*) 1% per month; (*b*) 2% per quarter; and (*c*) 8% per year compounded semiannually.

4.4 For an interest rate of 10% per year compounded quarterly, determine the number of times interest would be compounded (*a*) per quarter, (*b*) per year, and (*c*) per 3 years.

4.5 For an interest rate of 0.50% per quarter, determine the nominal interest rate per (*a*) semiannual period, (*b*) year, and (*c*) 2 years.

4.6 For an interest rate of 12% per year compounded every 2 months, determine the nominal interest rate per (*a*) 4 months, (*b*) 6 months, and (*c*) 2 years.

4.7 For an interest rate of 10% per year, compounded quarterly, determine the nominal rate per (*a*) 6 months and (*b*) 2 years.

4.8 Identify the following interest rate statements as either nominal or effective: (*a*) 1.3% per month; (*b*) 1% per week, compounded weekly; (*c*) nominal 15% per year, compounded monthly; (*d*) effective 1.5% per month, compounded daily; and (*e*) 15% per year, compounded semiannually.

4.9 What effective interest rate per 6 months is equivalent to 14% per year, compounded semiannually?

4.10 An interest rate of 16% per year, compounded quarterly, is equivalent to what effective interest rate per year?

4.11 What nominal interest rate per year is equivalent to an effective 16% per year, compounded semiannually?

4.12 What effective interest rate per year is equivalent to an effective 18% per year, compounded semiannually?

4.13 What compounding period is associated with nominal and effective rates of 18% and 18.81% per year, respectively?

4.14 An interest rate of 1% per month is equivalent to what effective rate per 2 months?

4.15 An interest rate of 12% per year, compounded monthly, is equivalent to what nominal and effective interest rates per 6 months?

4.16 (*a*) An interest rate of 6.8% per semiannual period, compounded weekly, is equivalent to what weekly interest rate?
    (*b*) Is the weekly rate a nominal or effective rate? Assume 26 weeks per 6 months.

Payment and Compounding Periods

4.17 Deposits of $100 per week are made into a savings account that pays interest of 6% per year, compounded quarterly. Identify the payment and compounding periods.

4.18 A certain bank advertises quarterly compounding for business chequing accounts. What payment and compounding periods are associated with deposits of daily receipts?

4.19 Determine the F/P factor for 3 years at an interest rate of 8% per year, compounded quarterly.

4.20 Determine the P/G factor for 5 years at an effective interest rate of 6% per year, compounded semiannually.

Equivalence for Single Amounts and Series

4.21 A plant to produce ethanol from non-edible plant materials in Prince Albert, Saskatchewan, is estimated to cost $14 million. How much money has to be set aside in a lump-sum investment *now* in order to have the money in 2 years, if the investment earns 14% interest per year compounded continuously?

4.22 A company that specializes in online security software development wants to have $85 million available in 3 years to pay stock dividends. How much money must the company set aside *now* in an account that earns interest at a rate of 8% per year, compounded quarterly?

4.23 An engineer analyzing cost data discovered that the information for the first three years was missing. However, he knew that the cost in year 4 was $1250 and that it increased by 5% per year thereafter. If the same trend applied to the first three years, calculate the cost in year 1.

4.24 A present sum of $5000 at an interest rate of 8% per year, compounded semiannually, is equivalent to how much money 8 years ago?

4.25 Cell phone users are increasingly aware that specific absorbed radiation (SAR) may be harmful to their health. Most cell phones operate with a SAR level of 1.6 watts per kilogram (W/kg) of tissue. A new cell phone company estimates that by advertising its favourable 1.2 SAR number, it will increase sales by $1.2 million 3 months from now when its phones go on sale. At an interest rate of 20% per year, compounded quarterly, what is the maximum amount the company can afford to spend *now* for advertising in order to break even?

4.26 Radio Frequency Identification (RFID) is technology that is used by drivers with speed passes at toll booths and ranchers who track livestock from farm to fork. Walmart expects to begin using the technology to track products within its stores. If RFID-tagged products will result in better inventory control that will save the company $1.3 million per month beginning 3 months from now, how much could the company afford to spend *now* to implement the technology at an interest rate of 12% per year, compounded monthly, if it wants to recover its investment in $2\frac{1}{2}$ years?

4.27 A plant manager wants to know the present worth of the maintenance costs for a certain assembly line. An industrial engineer, who designed the system, estimates that the maintenance costs are expected to be zero for the first 3 years, $2000 in year 4, $2500 in year 5, and amounts increasing by $500 each year through year 10. At an interest rate of 8% per year, compounded semiannually, calculate PW.

4.28 Video cards based on Nvidia's highly praised GeForce2 GTS processor typically cost $250. Nvidia released a light version of the chip that costs $150. If a certain video game maker was purchasing 3000 chips per quarter, what was the present worth of the savings associated with the cheaper chip over a 2-year period at an interest rate of 16% per year, compounded quarterly?

4.29 Exotic Faucets and Sinks, Ltd., guarantees that its new infrared sensor faucet will save any household that has two or more children at least $30 per month in water costs beginning 1 month after the faucet is installed. If the faucet is under full warranty for 5 years, calculate the minimum amount a family could afford to spend *now* on such a faucet at an interest rate of 6% per year, compounded monthly.

4.30 The optical products division of Panasonic is planning a $3.5 million building expansion for manufacturing its powerful Lumix DMC digital zoom camera. If the company uses an interest rate of 20% per year, compounded quarterly, for all new investments, what is the uniform amount per quarter the company must make to recover its investment in 3 years?

4.31 Thermal Systems, a company that specializes in odour control, made deposits of $10,000 now, $25,000 at the end of month 6, and $30,000 at the end of month 9. Determine the future worth (end of year 1) of the deposits at an interest rate of 16% per year, compounded quarterly.

4.32 Lotus Development has a software rental plan called SmartSuite that is available online. A number of programs are available at $2.99 for 48 hours. If a construction company uses the service an average of 48 hours per week, what is the present worth of the rental costs for 10 months at an interest rate of 1% per month, compounded weekly? (Assume 4 weeks per month.)

4.33 Superior Iron and Steel is considering getting involved in electronic commerce. A modest e-commerce package is available for $20,000. If the company wants to recover the cost in 2 years, what is the equivalent amount of new income that must be realized every 6 months, if the interest rate is 3% per quarter?

4.34 Royalties paid to holders of mineral rights tend to decrease with time as resources become depleted. In one particular case, the holder received a royalty cheque of $18,000 six months after the lease was signed. She continued to receive cheques at 6-month intervals, but the amount decreased by $2000 each time. At an interest rate of 6% per year, compounded semiannually, calculate the equivalent uniform

semiannual worth of the royalty payments through the first 4 years.

4.35 Scott Specialty Manufacturing is considering consolidating all its electronic services. The company can buy wireless e-mail and fax services for $6.99 per month. For $14.99 per month, the company will get unlimited Web access and personal organization functions. For a 2-year contract period, what is the present worth of the *difference* between the services at an interest rate of 12% per year, compounded monthly?

4.36 Magnetek Instrument and Controls, a manufacturer of liquid-level sensors, expects sales for one of its models to increase by 20% every 6 months into the foreseeable future. If the sales 6 months from now are expected to be $150,000, determine the equivalent semiannual worth of sales for a 5-year period at an interest rate of 14% per year, compounded semiannually.

4.37 Metalfab Pump and Filter projects that the cost of steel bodies for certain valves will increase by $2 every 3 months. If the cost for the first quarter is expected to be $80, what is the present worth of the costs for a 3-year period at an interest rate of 3% per quarter?

4.38 Fieldsaver Technologies, a manufacturer of precision laboratory equipment, borrowed $2 million to renovate one of its testing labs. The loan was repaid in 2 years through quarterly payments that increased by $50,000 each time. At an interest rate of 3% per quarter, what was the size of the first quarterly payment?

4.39 For the cash flows shown below, determine the present worth (time 0), using an interest rate of 18% per year, compounded monthly.

Month	Cash Flow, $/Month
0	1000
1–12	2000
13–28	3000

4.40 The cash flows (in thousands) associated with Barkley Sound's new digital music player are shown below. Determine the uniform quarterly series in quarters 0 through 8 that would be equivalent to the cash flows shown at an interest rate of 16% per year, compounded quarterly.

Quarter	Cash Flow, $/Quarter
1	1000
2–3	2000
5–8	3000

Equivalence When PP < CP

4.41 An engineer deposits $300 per month into a savings account that pays interest at a rate of 6% per year, compounded semiannually. How much will be in the account at the end of 15 years? Assume no interperiod compounding.

4.42 Coal gasification technology was chosen for use in Canada's first low-CO_2 power plant, built in Alberta by EPCOR Power Generation. Clean syngas will be produced from coal that will fire a gas turbine to provide electricity. Waste CO_2 will be sequestered in natural underground formations. If the cost of the sequestration process is $0.019 per kilowatt-hour, what is the present worth of the extra cost over a 3-year period when 100,000 kWh of energy per month is used, if the interest rate is 12% per year compounded quarterly?

4.43 At time $t = 0$, an engineer deposited $10,000 into an account that pays interest at 8% per year, compounded semiannually. If she withdrew $1000 in months 2, 11, and 23, what was the total value of the account at the end of 3 years? Assume no interperiod compounding.

4.44 For the transactions shown below, determine the amount of money in the account at the end of year 3 if the interest rate is 8% per year, compounded semiannually. Assume no interperiod compounding.

End of Quarter	Amount of Deposit $/Quarter	Amount of Withdrawal, $/Quarter
1	900	
2–4	700	
7	1000	2600
11	—	1000

4.45 Bonanza Creek Gold Mine occasionally rents a helicopter at $495 per hour. If the helicopter is used an average of 2 days per month for 6 hours each day, what is the equivalent future worth of the costs for 1 year at an interest rate of 6% per year, compounded quarterly (treat the costs as deposits)?

Continuous Compounding

4.46 What effective interest rate per year, compounded continuously, is equivalent to a nominal rate of 13% per year?

4.47 What effective interest rate per 6 months is equal to a nominal 2% per month, compounded continuously?

4.48 What nominal rate per quarter is equivalent to an effective rate of 12.7% per year, compounded continuously?

4.49 Corrosion problems and manufacturing defects rendered a gas pipeline between Regina and Winnipeg subject to longitudinal weld seam failures. Therefore, pressure was reduced to 80% of the design value. If the reduced pressure results in delivery of $100,000 per month less product, what will be the value of the lost revenue after a 2-year period at an interest rate of 15% per year, compounded continuously?

4.50 The city of Halifax is considering the conversion of public buses to biodiesel. If the value of the fuel saved each month is $6000, how much can the city afford to spend on the conversion process if it wants to recover the investment in 5 years at an interest rate of 18% per year, compounded continuously?

4.51 A Taiwan-based chemical company had to file for bankruptcy because of a nationwide phaseout of methyl tertiary butyl ether (MTBE). If the company reorganizes and invests $50 million in a new ethanol production facility, how much money must it make each month if it wants to recover its investment in 3 years at an interest rate of 2% per month, compounded continuously?

4.52 In order to have $85,000 four years from now for equipment replacement, a construction company plans to set aside money today in investment-grade corporate bonds. If the bonds earn interest at a rate of 6% per year, compounded continuously, how much money must the company invest?

4.53 How long would it take for a lump-sum investment to double in value at an interest rate of 1.5% per month, compounded continuously?

4.54 What effective interest rate per month, compounded continuously, would be required for a single deposit to triple in value in 5 years?

Varying Interest Rates

4.55 How much money could the maker of fluidized-bed scrubbers afford to spend now instead of spending $150,000 in year 5 if the interest rate is 10% in years 1 through 3 and 12% in years 4 and 5?

4.56 What is the future worth in year 8 of a present sum of $50,000 if the interest rate is 10% per year in years 1 through 4 and 1% per month in years 5 through 8?

4.57 For the cash flows shown below, determine (*a*) the future worth in year 5 and (*b*) the equivalent *A* value for years 0 through 5.

Year	Cash Flow, $/Year	Interest Rate per Year, %
0	5000	12
1–4	6000	12
5	6000	20

4.58 For the cash flow series shown below, find the equivalent *A* value in years 1 through 5.

Year	Cash Flow, $/Year	Interest Rate per Year, %
0	0	
1–3	5000	10
4–5	7000	12

FINANCING A HOUSE

Introduction

One of the most important considerations in purchasing a home is the financing. There are many methods of financing a residential property, each having advantages which make it the method of choice under a given set of circumstances. The selection of one method over another is the topic of this case study. Two methods of financing are described in detail. Plan A is evaluated; you are asked to evaluate plan B and perform some additional analyses.

The criterion for our decision is: Select the financing plan which has the largest amount of money remaining at the end of a 10-year period. Therefore, calculate the future worth of each plan, and select the one with the larest future worth value.

Sec. 4.11

Home mortgage

Plan	Description
A	10-year fixed rate of 8% per year interest, 10% down payment, amortized over 20 years
B	5-year variable rate at 6%, continued for second 5-year period (rate = 6% for years 1 and 2, 6.5% for year 3, 7% for years 4 and 5, 8% for years 6 and 7, 9% for year 8, 10% for year 9, and 10.5% for year 10) with 10% down payment

Other information:
- Price of condo is $200,000.
- Condo will be sold in 10 years for $250,000 (net proceeds after expenses).
- Taxes and insurance (T&I) are $300 per month.
- Amount available: maximum of $40,000 for the down payment, $1800 per month, including T&I.
- New loan expenses: appraisal fee = $200, home inspection = $300, land transfer tax = $2000, legal fees = $1500, title insurance = $250, insurance cost for high-ratio mortgage (less than 25% down) = 2% of mortgage for 10% down.
- Amortization period is 20 years.
- Any money not spent on the down payment or monthly payments will earn tax-free interest at $1/4$% per month.

Analysis of Financing Plans

Plan A: 10-Year Fixed Rate

The amount of money required up front is

(a)	Down payment (10% of 200,000)	$20,000
(b)	Appraisal fee	200
(c)	Home inspection	300
(d)	Land transfer tax	2,000
(e)	Legal fees	1,500
(f)	Title insurance	250
(g)	Insurance cost (2% of mortgage)	3,600
	Total	$27,850

The amount of the loan is \$180,000. The equivalent monthly principal and interest (P&I) payment is determined at 8%/12 per month for 20(12) = 240 months.

$$A = 180,000(A/P,8\%/12,240)$$
$$= \$1440$$

When T&I are added to P&I, the total monthly payment PMT_A is

$$PMT_A = 1440 + 300$$
$$= \$1740$$

We can now determine the future worth of plan A by summing three future worth amounts: the remaining funds not used for the down payment and up-front fees (F_{1A}) and for monthly payments (F_{2A}), and the increase in the value of the house (F_{3A}). Since non-expended money earns interest at $^1/_4\%$ per month, in 10 years the first future worth is

$$F_{1A} = (40,000 - 27,850)(F/P,0.25\%,120)$$
$$= \$16,395$$

The available money not spent on monthly payments is \$1800 − 1740 = \$60. Its future worth after 10 years is

$$F_{2A} = 60(F/A,0.25\%,120)$$
$$= \$8,384$$

Net money available from the sale of the condo is the difference between the net selling price and the balance of the loan. The balance of the loan is

$$\text{Loan balance} = 180,000 \, (F/P,8\%/12,120) - 1,440 \, (F/A,8\%/12,120)$$
$$= 405,000 - 265,003$$
$$= \$139,997$$

Since the net proceeds from the sale of the house are \$250,000,

$$F_{3A} = 250,000 - 139,997$$
$$= \$110,003$$

The total future worth of plan A is

$$F_A = F_{1A} + F_{2A} + F_{3A}$$
$$= 16,395 + 8,384 + 110,003$$
$$= \$134,782$$

Case Study Exercises

1. Evaluate plan B and select the best financing method.

2. What is the total amount of interest paid in plan A through the 10-year period?

3. What is the total amount of interest paid in plan B through the 10-year period?

4. Compare plans A and B to the future worth of renting a unit in the condominium for $1000 per month. The $20,000 that was to be used as a down payment is deposited in a 10-year GIC paying 5%. Assume rental rates increase every year by 3%, and that the difference between the rental and mortgage payment is invested at 5% per year.

Calculation of an Effective Interest Rate

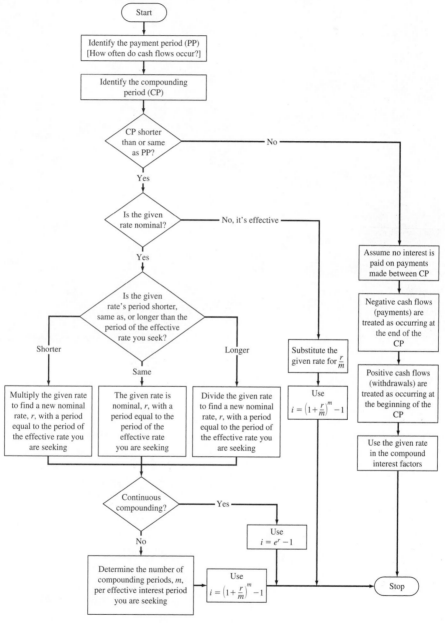

Contributed by Dr. Mathias Sutton, Purdue University.

LEVEL 2

Tools for Evaluating Alternatives

One or more engineering alternatives are formulated to solve a problem or provide specified results. In engineering economics, each alternative has cash flow estimates for the initial investment, periodic (usually annual) incomes and/or costs, and possibly a salvage value at the end of its estimated life. The chapters in this level develop the four different methods by which one or more alternatives can be evaluated economically using the factors and formulas learned in Level One.

In professional practice, it is typical that the evaluation method and parameter estimates necessary for the economic study are not specified. The last chapter in this level begins with a focus on selecting the best evaluation method for the study. It continues by treating the fundamental question of what MARR to use and the historical dilemma of how to consider noneconomic factors when selecting an alternative.

Important note: **If depreciation and/or after-tax analysis is to be considered along with the evaluation methods in Chapters 5 through 9, Chapter 15 and/or Chapter 16 should be covered, preferably after Chapter 6.**

LEVEL ③ Making Decisions on Real-World Projects	LEVEL ④ Rounding Out the Study
CHAPTER 11 Replacement and Retention Decisions	**CHAPTER 14** Effects of Inflation
CHAPTER 12 Selection from Independent Projects Under Budget Limitation	**CHAPTER 15** Depreciation Methods
CHAPTER 13 Breakeven Analysis	**CHAPTER 16** After-Tax Economic Analysis
	CHAPTER 17 Formalized Sensitivity Analysis and Expected Value Decisions
	CHAPTER 18 More on Variation and Decision Making Under Risk

CHAPTER

Present Worth Analysis

A future amount of money converted to its equivalent value now has a present worth (PW) that is always less than that of the actual cash flow, because for any interest rate greater than zero, all *P/F* factors have a value less than 1.0. For this reason, present worth values are often referred to as *discounted cash flows (DCF)*. Similarly, the interest rate is referred to as the *discount rate*. When performing Excel spreadsheet calculations, the PW function is named PV. Net present worth (NPW) is the difference between benefits and costs. Up to this point, present worth computations have been made for one project or alternative. In this chapter, techniques for comparing two or more mutually exclusive alternatives by the present worth method are treated.

Several extensions to PW analysis are covered here—future worth, capitalized cost, payback period, life-cycle costing, and bond analysis—these all use present worth relations to analyze alternatives.

In order to understand how to organize an economic analysis, this chapter begins with a description of independent and mutually exclusive projects, as well as revenue and service alternatives.

The case study examines the payback period and sensitivity for a public sector project.

LEARNING OBJECTIVES

Purpose: Compare mutually exclusive alternatives on a present worth basis, and apply extensions of the present worth method.

By the end of this chapter you should be able to

Formulating alternatives	**1.** Identify mutually exclusive and independent projects, and define a service and a revenue alternative.
PW of equal-life alternatives	**2.** Select the best of equal-life alternatives using present worth analysis.
PW of different-life alternatives	**3.** Select the best of different-life alternatives using present worth analysis.
FW analysis	**4.** Select the best alternative using future worth analysis.
Capitalized cost (CC)	**5.** Select the best alternative using capitalized cost calculations.
Payback period	**6.** Determine the payback period at $i = 0\%$ and $i > 0\%$, and state the shortcomings of payback analysis.
Life-cycle cost (LCC)	**7.** Perform a life-cycle cost analysis for the acquisition and operations phases of a (system) alternative.
PW of bonds	**8.** Calculate the present worth of a bond investment.
Spreadsheets	**9.** Develop spreadsheets that use PW analysis and its extensions, including payback period.

5.1 FORMULATING MUTUALLY EXCLUSIVE ALTERNATIVES

Section 1.3 explains that the economic evaluation of an alternative requires cash flow estimates over a stated time period and a criterion for selecting the best alternative. The alternatives are developed from project proposals to accomplish a stated purpose. This progression is depicted in Figure 5–1. Some projects are economically and technologically viable, and others are not. Once the viable projects are defined, it is possible to formulate the alternatives. For example, assume Med-supply.com, an Internet-based medical supply provider, wants to challenge its storefront competitors by significantly shortening the time between order placement and delivery to the hospital or clinic. Three projects have been proposed: closer networking with Purolator and FedEx for shortened delivery time; partnering with local medical supply houses in major cities to provide same-day delivery; and developing a 3-dimensional fax-like machine to ship items not physically larger than the machine. Economically (and technologically) only the first two project proposals can be pursued at this time; they are the two alternatives to evaluate.

The description above treats project proposals as precursors to economic alternatives. To help formulate alternatives, *categorize each project* as one of the following:

- **Mutually exclusive.** *Only one of the viable projects can be selected* by the economic analysis. Each viable project *is* an alternative.
- **Independent.** *More than one viable project may be selected* by the economic analysis. (There may be dependent projects requiring a particular project to be selected before another, and contingent projects where one project may be substituted for another.)

The *do-nothing (DN)* option is usually understood to be an alternative when the evaluation is performed. If it is absolutely required that one of the defined alternatives be selected, do nothing is not considered an option. (This may occur when a mandated function must be installed for safety, legal, or other purposes.) Selection of the DN alternative means that the current approach is maintained; nothing new is initiated. No new costs, revenues, or savings are generated by the DN alternative.

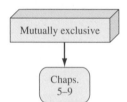

A mutually exclusive alternative selection takes place, for example, when an engineer must select the one best diesel-powered engine from several competing models. Mutually exclusive alternatives are, therefore, the same as the viable projects; each one is evaluated, and the one best alternative is chosen. Mutually exclusive alternatives *compete with one another* in the evaluation. All the analysis techniques through Chapter 9 are developed to compare mutually exclusive alternatives. Present worth is discussed in the remainder of this chapter. If no mutually exclusive alternative is considered economically acceptable, it is possible to reject all alternatives and (by default) accept the DN alternative. (This option is indicated in Figure 5–1 by the coloured arrow and type on the DN mutually exclusive alternative.)

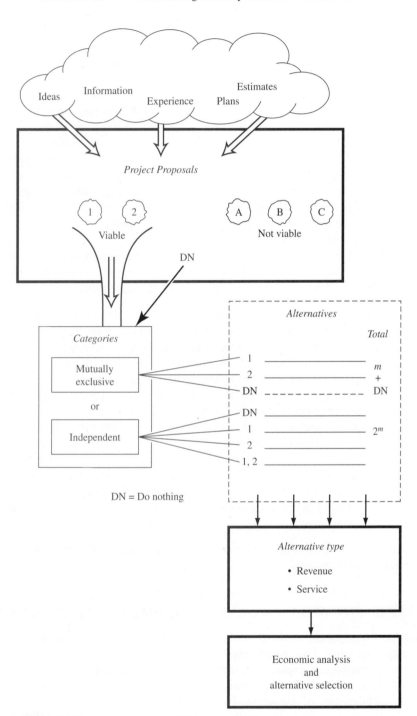

FIGURE 5–1
Progression from projects to alternatives to economic analysis.

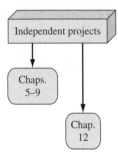

Independent projects

Chaps. 5–9

Chap. 12

Independent projects do not compete with one another in the evaluation. Because the projects are usually designed to accomplish different purposes, each one is evaluated separately, and thus the *comparison is between one project at a time and the do-nothing alternative.* If there are *m* independent projects, zero, one, two, or more may be selected. Since each project may be in or out of the selected group of projects, there are a total of 2^m mutually exclusive alternatives. This number includes the DN alternative, as shown in Figure 5–1. For example, if the engineer has three diesel engine models (A, B, and C) and may select any number of them, there are $2^3 = 8$ alternatives: DN, A, B, C, AB, AC, BC, ABC. Commonly, in real-world applications, there are restrictions, such as an upper budgetary limit, that eliminate many of the 2^m alternatives. Independent project analysis without budget limits is discussed in this chapter and through Chapter 9. Chapter 12 treats independent projects with a budget limitation; this is called the capital budgeting problem.

Finally, it is important to recognize the *nature or type of an alternative's cash flows* before starting an evaluation. The cash flows determine whether the alternatives are revenue-based or service-based. All the alternatives evaluated in one particular engineering economy study must be of the same type.

- **Revenue.** *Each alternative generates cost (or disbursement) and revenue (or receipt) cash flow estimates, and possibly savings* (which are treated like revenues). Revenues are dependent upon which alternative is selected. These alternatives usually involve new systems, products, and services that require capital investment to generate revenues and/or savings. Purchasing new equipment to increase productivity and sales is a revenue alternative. Profits are generated as the difference between the revenues received and total costs.
- **Service.** *Each alternative has only cost cash flow estimates.* Revenues or savings are not dependent upon the alternative selected, so these cash flows are assumed to be equal. These may be public sector (government) initiatives (as discussed in Chapter 9). Also, they may be legally mandated or safety improvements. Often an improvement is justified; however, the anticipated revenues or savings are not estimable. In these cases the evaluation is based only on cost estimates.

The alternative selection guidelines developed in the next section are tailored for both types of alternatives.

5.2 PRESENT WORTH ANALYSIS OF EQUAL-LIFE ALTERNATIVES

In present worth analysis, the *P* value, now called PW, is calculated at the MARR for each alternative. The present worth method is popular because future cost and revenue estimates are transformed into *equivalent dollars now*; that is, all future cash flows are converted into present dollars. This makes it easy to determine the economic advantage of one alternative over another.

The PW comparison of alternatives with equal lives is straightforward. If both alternatives are used in identical capacities for the same time period, they are termed *equal-service* alternatives.

Whether mutually exclusive alternatives involve disbursements only (service) or receipts and disbursements (revenue), the following guidelines are applied to select one alternative.

One alternative. Calculate PW at the MARR. If PW ≥ 0, the requested MARR is met or exceeded and the alternative is financially viable.

Two or more alternatives. Calculate the PW of each alternative at the MARR. *Select the alternative with the PW value that is numerically largest,* **that is, less negative or more positive, indicating a lower PW of cost cash flows or larger PW of net cash flows of receipts minus disbursements.**

Note that the guideline to select one alternative with the lowest cost or the highest income uses the criterion of *numerically largest.* This is *not the absolute value* of the PW amount, because the sign matters. The selections below correctly apply the guideline for the listed PW values.

PW_1	PW_2	Selected Alternative
$-1500	$-500	2
-500	+1000	2
+2500	-500	1
+2500	+1500	1

If the projects are *independent,* the selection guideline is as follows:

For one or more independent projects, select all projects with PW ≥ 0 at the MARR.

This compares each project with the do-nothing alternative. The sum of each project's cash flows must yield a PW value that exceeds zero; that is, each project must generate revenue for the company.

A PW analysis requires a MARR for use as the i value in all PW relations. The bases used to establish a realistic MARR were summarized in Chapter 1 and are discussed in detail in Chapter 10.

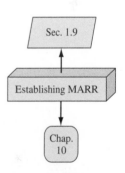

Sec. 1.9

Establishing MARR

Chap. 10

EXAMPLE 5.1

Perform a present worth analysis of equal-service machines with the costs shown below, if the MARR is 10% per year. Revenues for all three alternatives are expected to be the same.

	Electric-Powered	Gas-Powered	Solar-Powered
First cost, $	-2500	-3500	-6000
Annual operating cost (AOC), $	-900	-700	-50
Salvage value S, $	200	350	100
Life, years	5	5	5

Solution

These are service alternatives. The salvage values are considered a "negative" cost, so a + sign precedes them. (If it costs money to dispose of an asset, the estimated disposal cost has a − sign.) The PW of each machine is calculated at $i = 10\%$ for $n = 5$ years. Use subscripts E, G, and S.

$$PW_E = -2500 - 900(P/A,10\%,5) + 200(P/F,10\%,5) = \$-5788$$

$$PW_G = -3500 - 700(P/A,10\%,5) + 350(P/F,10\%,5) = \$-5936$$

$$PW_S = -6000 - 50(P/A,10\%,5) + 100(P/F,10\%,5) = \$-6127$$

The electric-powered machine is selected since the PW of its costs is the lowest; it has the numerically largest PW value.

5.3 PRESENT WORTH ANALYSIS OF DIFFERENT-LIFE ALTERNATIVES

When the present worth method is used to compare mutually exclusive alternatives that have different lives, the procedure of the previous section is followed with one exception:

The PW of the alternatives must be compared over the same number of years and end at the same time.

This is necessary, since a present worth comparison involves calculating the equivalent present value of all future cash flows for each alternative. A fair comparison can be made only when the PW values represent costs (and receipts) associated with equal service. Failure to compare equal service will always favour a shorter-lived alternative (for costs), even if it is not the most economical one, because fewer periods of costs are involved. The equal-service requirement can be satisfied by either of two approaches:

- Compare the alternatives over a period of time equal to the *least common multiple (LCM)* of their lives.
- Compare the alternatives using a *study period of length n years,* which does not necessarily take into consideration the useful lives of the alternatives. This is also called the *planning horizon* approach.

In either case, the PW of each alternative is calculated at the MARR, and the selection guideline is the same as that for equal-life alternatives. The LCM approach automatically makes the cash flows for all alternatives extend to the same time period. For example, alternatives with expected lives of 2 and 3 years are compared over a 6-year time period. Such a procedure requires that some assumptions be made about subsequent life cycles of the alternatives.

The assumptions of a PW analysis of different-life alternatives for the LCM method are as follows:

1. **The service provided by the alternatives will be needed for the LCM of years or more.**
2. **The selected alternative will be repeated over each life cycle of the LCM in exactly the same manner.**
3. **The cash flow estimates will be the same in every life cycle.**

As will be shown in Chapter 14, the third assumption is valid only when the cash flows are expected to change by exactly the inflation (or deflation) rate that is applicable through the LCM time period. If the cash flows are expected to change by any other rate, then the PW analysis must be conducted using constant-value dollars, which considers inflation (Chapter 14). A study period analysis is necessary if the first assumption about the length of time the alternatives are needed cannot be made. A present worth analysis over the LCM requires that the estimated salvage values be included in each life cycle.

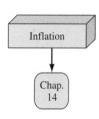

For the study period approach, a time horizon is chosen over which the economic analysis is conducted, and only those cash flows which occur during that time period are considered relevant to the analysis. All cash flows occurring beyond the study period are ignored. An estimated market value at the end of the study period must be made. The time horizon chosen might be relatively short, especially when short-term business goals are very important. The study period approach is often used in replacement analysis. It is also useful when the LCM of alternatives yields an unrealistic evaluation period, for example, 5 and 9 years.

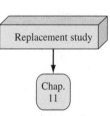

Example 5.2 includes evaluations based on the LCM and study period approaches. Also, Example 5.12 in Section 5.9 illustrates the use of spreadsheets in PW analysis for both different lives and a study period.

EXAMPLE 5.2

A project engineer with EnvironCare is assigned to start up a new office in a city where a 6-year contract has been finalized to take and to analyze ozone-level readings. Two lease options are available, each with a first cost, annual lease cost, and deposit-return estimates shown below.

	Location A	Location B
First cost, $	−15,000	−18,000
Annual lease cost, $ per year	−3,500	−3,100
Deposit return, $	1,000	2,000
Lease term, years	6	9

(*a*) Determine which lease option should be selected on the basis of a present worth comparison, if the MARR is 15% per year.

(b) EnvironCare has a standard practice of evaluating all projects over a 5-year period. If a study period of 5 years is used and the deposit returns are not expected to change, which location should be selected?

(c) Which location should be selected over a 6-year study period if the deposit return at location B is estimated to be $6000 after 6 years?

Solution

(a) Since the leases have different terms (lives), compare them over the LCM of 18 years. For life cycles after the first, the first cost is repeated in year 0 of each new cycle, which is the last year of the previous cycle. These are years 6 and 12 for location A and year 9 for B. The cash flow diagram is in Figure 5–2. Calculate PW at 15% over 18 years.

$$PW_A = -15{,}000 - 15{,}000(P/F,15\%,6) + 1000(P/F,15\%,6)$$
$$-15{,}000(P/F,15\%,12) + 1000(P/F,15\%,12) + 1000(P/F,15\%,18)$$
$$-3500(P/A,15\%,18)$$
$$= \$-45{,}036$$

$$PW_B = -18{,}000 - 18{,}000(P/F,15\%,9) + 2000(P/F,15\%,9)$$
$$+2000(P/F,15\%,18) - 3100(P/A,15\%,18)$$
$$= \$-41{,}384$$

Location B is selected, since it costs less in PW terms; that is, the PW_B value is numerically larger than PW_A.

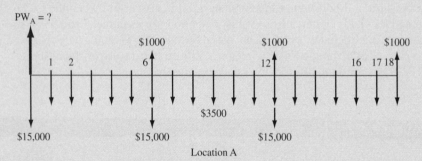

Location A

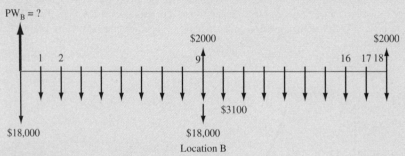

Location B

FIGURE 5–2
Cash flow diagram for different-life alternatives, Example 5.2(a).

(b) For a 5-year study period no cycle repeats are necessary. The PW analysis is

$$PW_A = -15{,}000 - 3500(P/A{,}15\%{,}5) + 1000(P/F{,}15\%{,}5)$$

$$= \$-26{,}236$$

$$PW_B = -18{,}000 - 3100(P/A{,}15\%{,}5) + 2000(P/F{,}15\%{,}5)$$

$$= \$-27{,}397$$

Location A is now the better choice.

(c) For a 6-year study period, the deposit return for B is $6000 in year 6.

$$PW_A = -15{,}000 - 3500(P/A{,}15\%{,}6) + 1000(P/F{,}15\%{,}6) = \$-27{,}813$$

$$PW_B = -18{,}000 - 3100(P/A{,}15\%{,}6) + 6000(P/F{,}15\%{,}6) = \$-27{,}138$$

Location B now has a small economic advantage. Noneconomic factors are likely to enter into the final decision.

Comments

In part (a) and Figure 5–2, the deposit return for each lease is recovered *after each life cycle,* that is, in years 6, 12, and 18 for A and in years 9 and 18 for B. In part (c), the increase of the deposit return from $2000 to $6000 (one year later), switches the selected location from A to B. The project engineer should reexamine these estimates before making a final decision.

5.4 FUTURE WORTH ANALYSIS

The future worth (FW) of an alternative may be determined directly from the cash flows by determining the future worth value, or by multiplying the PW value by the F/P factor, at the established MARR. Therefore, it is an extension of present worth analysis. The n value in the F/P factor depends upon which time period has been used to determine PW—the LCM value or a specified study period. Analysis of one alternative, or the comparison of two or more alternatives, using FW values is especially applicable to large capital investment decisions when a prime goal is to maximize the *future wealth* of a corporation's shareholders.

Future worth analysis is often utilized if the asset (equipment, a corporation, a building, etc.) might be sold or traded at some time after its startup or acquisition, but before the expected life is reached. An FW value at an intermediate year estimates the alternative's worth at the time of sale or disposal. Suppose an entrepreneur is planning to buy a company and expects to trade it within 3 years. FW analysis is the best method to help with the decision to sell or keep it 3 years hence. Example 5.3 illustrates this use of FW analysis. Another excellent application of FW analysis is for projects that will not come online until the end of the investment period. Alternatives such as electric generation facilities, toll roads, hotels, and the like can be analyzed using the FW value of investment commitments made during construction.

Once the FW value is determined, the selection guidelines are the same as with PW analysis; FW $\geq$ 0 means the MARR is met or exceeded (one alternative). For two (or more) mutually exclusive alternatives, select the one with the numerically larger (largest) FW value.

EXAMPLE 5.3

A British food distribution conglomerate purchased a Canadian food store chain for $75 million three years ago. There was a net loss of $10 million at the end of year 1 of ownership. Net cash flow is increasing with an arithmetic gradient of $+5$ million per year starting the second year, and this pattern is expected to continue for the foreseeable future. This means that breakeven net cash flow was achieved this year. Because of the heavy debt financing used to purchase the Canadian chain, the international board of directors wants a MARR of 25% per year from any sale.

(a) The British conglomerate has just been offered $159.5 million by a French company wishing to get a foothold in Canada. Use FW analysis to determine if the MARR will be realized at this selling price.

(b) If the British conglomerate continues to own the chain, what selling price must be obtained at the end of 5 years of ownership to make the MARR?

Solution

(a) Set up the future worth relation in year 3 (FW_3) at $i = 25\%$ per year and an offer price of $159.5 million. Figure 5–3a presents the cash flow diagram in million $ units.

$$FW_3 = -75(F/P,25\%,3) - 10(F/P,25\%,2) - 5(F/P,25\%,1) + 159.5$$
$$= -168.36 + 159.5 = \$-8.86 \text{ million}$$

No, the MARR of 25% will not be realized if the $159.5 million offer is accepted.

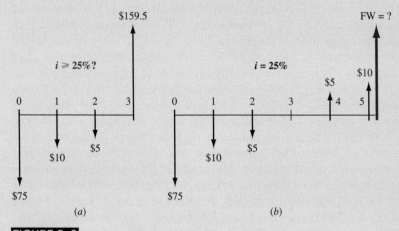

FIGURE 5–3

Cash flow diagrams for Example 5.3. (a) Is MARR $= 25\%$ realized? (b) What is FW in year 5? Amounts are in million $ units.

(b) Determine the future worth 5 years from now at 25% per year. Figure 5–3b presents the cash flow diagram. The A/G and F/A factors are applied to the arithmetic gradient.

$$FW_5 = -75(F/P,25\%,5) - 10(F/A,25\%,5) + 5(A/G,25\%,5)(F/A,25\%,5)$$

$$= \$-246.81 \text{ million}$$

The offer must be for at least \$246.81 million to make the MARR. This is approximately 3.3 times the purchase price only 5 years earlier, in large part based on the required MARR of 25%.

Comment

If the "rule of 72" in Equation [1.9] is applied at 25% per year, the sales price must double approximately every $72/25\% = 2.9$ years. This does not consider any annual net positive or negative cash flows during the years of ownership.

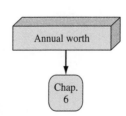

5.5 CAPITALIZED COST CALCULATION AND ANALYSIS

Capitalized cost (CC) is the present worth of an alternative that will last "forever." Public sector projects such as bridges, dams, irrigation systems, and railroads fall into this category, since they have useful lives of 30, 40, and more years. In addition, permanent and charitable organization endowments are evaluated using the capitalized cost methods.

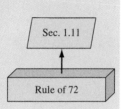

The formula to calculate CC is derived from the relation $P = A(P/A,i,n)$, where $n = \infty$. The equation for P using the P/A factor formula is

$$P = A\left[\frac{(1+i)^n - 1}{i(1+i)^n}\right]$$

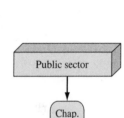

Divide the numerator and denominator by $(1 + i)^n$.

$$P = A\left[\frac{1 - \dfrac{1}{(1+i)^n}}{i}\right]$$

As n approaches ∞, the bracketed term becomes $1/i$, and the symbol CC replaces PW and P.

$$CC = \frac{A}{i} \qquad\qquad \text{[5.1]}$$

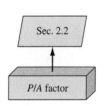

If the A value is an annual worth (AW) determined through equivalence calculations of cash flows over n years, the CC value is

$$CC = \frac{AW}{i} \qquad\qquad \text{[5.2]}$$

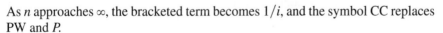

The validity of Equation [5.1] can be illustrated by considering the time value of money. If \$10,000 earns 10% per year, compounded annually, the maximum amount of money that can be withdrawn at the end of every year for *eternity* is $1000, or the interest accumulated each year. This leaves the original $10,000 to earn interest so that another $1000 will be accumulated the next year. Mathematically, the amount A of new money generated each consecutive interest period for an infinite number of periods is

$$A = Pi = CC(i) \qquad\qquad [5.3]$$

The capitalized cost calculation in Equation [5.1] is Equation [5.3] solved for P and renamed CC.

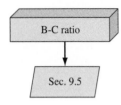

For a public sector alternative with an infinite or very long life, the A value determined by Equation [5.3] is used when the benefit-cost ratio (BCR) is the comparison basis for public projects. This method is covered in Chapter 9.

The cash flows (costs or receipts) in a capitalized cost calculation are usually of two types: *recurring,* also called periodic, and *nonrecurring.* An annual operating cost of $50,000 and a rework cost estimated at $40,000 every 12 years are examples of recurring cash flows. Examples of nonrecurring cash flows are the initial investment amount in year 0 and one-time cash flow estimates at future times, for example, $500,000 in royalty fees 2 years hence. The following procedure assists in calculating the CC for an infinite sequence of cash flows.

1. Draw a cash flow diagram showing all nonrecurring (one-time) cash flows and at least two cycles of all recurring (periodic) cash flows.
2. Find the present worth of all nonrecurring amounts. This is their CC value.
3. Find the equivalent uniform annual worth (A value) through *one life cycle* of all recurring amounts. This is the same value in all succeeding life cycles, as explained in Chapter 6. Add this to all other uniform amounts occurring in years 1 through infinity and the result is the total equivalent uniform annual worth (AW).
4. Divide the AW obtained in step 3 by the interest rate i to obtain a CC value. This is an application of Equation [5.2].
5. Add the CC values obtained in steps 2 and 4.

Drawing the cash flow diagram (step 1) is more important in CC calculations than elsewhere, because it helps separate nonrecurring and recurring amounts. In step 5 the present worths of all component cash flows have been obtained; the total capitalized cost is simply their sum.

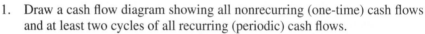

EXAMPLE 5.4

The property assessment department for Halifax, Nova Scotia, has just installed new software to track residential market values for property tax computations. The manager wants to know the total equivalent cost of all future costs incurred when it was agreed to purchase the software system. If the new system will be used for the indefinite future, find the equivalent value (*a*) now and (*b*) for each year hereafter.

The system has an installed cost of $150,000 and an additional cost of $50,000 after 10 years. The annual software maintenance contract cost is $5000 for the first

4 years and $8000 thereafter. In addition, there is expected to be a recurring major upgrade cost of $15,000 every 13 years. Assume that $i = 5\%$ per year for city funds.

Solution

(a) The five-step procedure is applied.

1. Draw a cash flow diagram for two cycles (Figure 5–4).
2. Find the present worth of the nonrecurring costs of $150,000 now and $50,000 in year 10 at $i = 5\%$. Label this CC_1.

$$CC_1 = -150,000 - 50,000(P/F,5\%,10) = \$-180,695$$

3. Convert the recurring cost of $15,000 every 13 years into an annual worth A_1 for the first 13 years.

$$A_1 = -15,000(A/F,5\%,13) = \$-847$$

The same value, $A_1 = \$-847$, applies to all the other 13-year periods as well.

4. The capitalized cost for the two annual maintenance cost series may be determined in either of two ways: (1) consider a series of -5000 from now to infinity and find the present worth of $-\$8000 - (\$-5000) = \$-3000$ from year 5 on; or (2) find the CC of $\$-5000$ for 4 years and the present worth of $\$-8000$ from year 5 to infinity. Using the first method, the annual cost (A_2) is $\$-5000$ forever. The capitalized cost CC_2 of $\$-3000$ from year 5 to infinity is found using Equation [5.1] times the P/F factor.

$$CC_2 = \frac{-3000}{0.05}(P/F,5\%,4) = \$-49,362$$

The two annual cost series are converted into a capitalized cost CC_3.

$$CC_3 = \frac{A_1 + A_2}{i} = \frac{-847 + (-5000)}{0.05} = \$-116,940$$

5. The total capitalized cost CC_T is obtained by adding the three CC values.

$$CC_T = -180,695 - 49,362 - 116,940 = \$-346,997$$

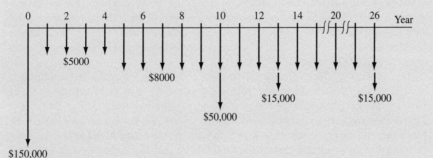

FIGURE 5–4
Cash flows for two cycles of recurring costs and all nonrecurring amounts, Example 5.4.

(*b*) Equation [5.3] determines the *A* value forever.

$$A = Pi = CC_T(i) = \$346{,}997(0.05) = \$17{,}350$$

Correctly interpreted, this means city officials have committed the equivalent of $17,350 forever to operate and maintain the property appraisal software.

Comment

The CC_2 value is calculated using $n = 4$ in the P/F factor because the present worth of the annual $3000 cost is located in year 4, since *P* is always one period ahead of the first *A*. Rework the problem using the second method suggested for calculating CC_2.

For the comparison of two or more alternatives on the basis of capitalized cost, use the procedure above to find CC_T for each alternative. Since the capitalized cost represents the total present worth of financing and maintaining a given alternative forever, the alternatives will automatically be compared for the same number of years (i.e., infinity). The alternative with the smaller capitalized cost will represent the more economical one. This evaluation is illustrated in Example 5.5.

As in present worth analysis, it is only the differences in cash flow between the alternatives that must be considered for comparative purposes. Therefore, whenever possible, the calculations should be simplified by eliminating the elements of cash flow which are common to both alternatives. On the other hand, if true capitalized cost values are needed to reflect actual financial obligations, actual cash flows should be used.

EXAMPLE 5.5

Two sites are currently under consideration for a bridge to cross a river in Ontario. The north site, which connects a major highway with a ring road around the city, would alleviate much of the local through traffic. The disadvantages of this site are that the bridge would do little to ease local traffic congestion during rush hours, and the bridge would have to stretch from one hill to another to span the widest part of the river, railroad tracks, and local highways below. This bridge would therefore be a suspension bridge. The south site would require a much shorter span, allowing for construction of a truss bridge, but it would require new road construction.

The suspension bridge will cost $500 million with annual inspection and maintenance costs of $350,000. In addition, the concrete deck would have to be resurfaced every 10 years at a cost of $1,000,000. The truss bridge and approach roads are expected to cost $250 million and have annual maintenance costs of $200,000. The bridge would have to be painted every 3 years at a cost of $400,000. In addition, the bridge would have to be sand-blasted every 10 years at a cost of $1,900,000. The cost of purchasing right-of-way is expected to be $20 million for the suspension bridge and $150 million for the truss bridge. Compare the alternatives on the basis of their capitalized cost if the interest rate is 6% per year.

Solution
Construct the cash flow diagrams over two cycles (20 years).

Capitalized cost of suspension bridge (CC_S):

CC_1 = capitalized cost of initial cost

$= -500 - 20 = \$-520$ million

The recurring operating cost is $A_1 = \$-350,000$, and the annual equivalent of the resurface cost is

$$A_2 = -1,000,000 (A/F,6\%,10) = \$-75,870$$

$$CC_2 = \text{capitalized cost of recurring costs} = \frac{A_1 + A_2}{i}$$

$$= \frac{-350,000 + (-75,870)}{0.06} = \$-7,097,833$$

The total capitalized cost is

$$CC_S = CC_1 + CC_2 = \$-527.1 \text{ million}$$

Capitalized cost of truss bridge (CC_T):

$CC_1 = -250 + (-150) = \$-400$ million

$A_1 = \$-200,000$

A_2 = annual cost of painting $= -400,000(A/F,6\%,3) = \$-125,640$

A_3 = annual cost of sandblasting $= -1,900,000(A/F,6\%,10) = \$-144,153$

$$CC_2 = \frac{A_1 + A_2 + A_3}{i} = \frac{\$-46,790}{0.06} = \$-7,829,833$$

$$CC_T = CC_1 + CC_2 = \$-407.83 \text{ million}$$

Conclusion: Build the truss bridge, since its capitalized cost is lower by \$119 million.

If a finite-life alternative (e.g., 5 years) is compared to one with an indefinite or very long life, capitalized costs can be used for the evaluation. To determine capitalized cost for the alternative with a finite life, calculate the equivalent A value for one life cycle and divide by the interest rate (Equation [5.1]). This procedure is illustrated in the next example.

EXAMPLE 5.6

APSco, a large electronics subcontractor, needs to immediately acquire 10 soldering machines with specially prepared jigs for assembling components onto printed circuit boards. More machines may be needed in the future. The lead production engineer has outlined below two simplified, but viable, alternatives. The company's MARR is 15% per year.

Alternative LT (long-term). For $8 million now, a contractor will provide the necessary number of machines (up to a maximum of 20), now and in the future, for as long as APSco needs them. The annual contract fee is a total of $25,000 with no additional per-machine annual cost. There is no time limit placed on the contract, and the costs do not escalate.

Alternative ST (short-term). APSco buys its own machines for $275,000 each and expends an estimated $12,000 per machine in annual operating cost (AOC). The useful life of a soldering system is 5 years.

Perform a capitalized cost evaluation by hand and by computer. Once the evaluation is complete, use the spreadsheet for sensitivity analysis to determine the maximum number of soldering machines that can be purchased now and still have a capitalized cost less than that of the long-term alternative.

Solution by Hand

For the LT alternative, find the CC of the AOC using Equation [5.1], $CC = A/i$. Add this amount to the initial contract fee, which is already a capitalized cost (present worth) amount.

$$CC_{LT} = CC \text{ of contract fee} + CC \text{ of AOC}$$

$$= -8 \text{ million} - 25,000/0.15 = \$-8,166,667$$

For the ST alternative, first calculate the equivalent annual amount for the purchase cost over the 5-year life, and add the AOC values for all 10 machines. Then determine the total CC using Equation [5.2].

$$AW_{ST} = AW \text{ for purchase} + AOC$$

$$= -2.75 \text{ million}(A/P,15\%,5) - 120,000 = \$-940,380$$

$$CC_{ST} = -940,380/0.15 = \$-6,269,200$$

The ST alternative has a lower capitalized cost by approximately $1.9 million present value dollars.

Solution by Computer

Figure 5–5 contains the solution for 10 machines in column B. Cell B8 uses the same relation as in the solution by hand. Cell B15 uses the PMT function to determine the equivalent annual amount A for the purchase of 10 machines, to which the AOC is added. Cell B16 uses Equation [5.2] to find the total CC for the ST alternative. As expected, alternative ST is selected. (Compare CC_{ST} for the hand and computer solutions to note that the round-off error using the tabulated interest factors gets larger for large P values.)

The type of sensitivity analysis requested here is easy to perform once a spreadsheet is developed. The PMT function in B15 is expressed generally in terms of cell B12, the number of machines purchased. Columns C and D replicate the evaluation for 13 and 14 machines. Thirteen is the maximum number of machines that can be purchased and have a CC for the ST alternative that is less than that of the LT contract. This conclusion is easily reached by comparing total CC values in rows 8 and 16. (*Note:* It is not necessary to duplicate column B into C and D to perform this sensitivity analysis. Changing the entry in cell B12 upward from 10 will provide the same information. Duplication is shown here in order to view all the results on one spreadsheet.)

	A	B	C	D	E	F	G
1							
2	Interest rate	15%	15%	15%			
3							
4	**Alternative LT (long term)**						
5	Initial contract cost	$ (8,000,000)	$ (8,000,000)	$ (8,000,000)			
6	Annual cost	$ (25,000)	$ (25,000)	$ (25,000)			
7							
8	**Capitalized cost for LT**	$ (8,166,667)	$ (8,166,667)	$ (8,166,667)		= D5 + D6/D2	
9							
10	**Alternative ST (short term)**						
11	Initial cost per machine	$ (275,000)	$ (275,000)	$ (275,000)			
12	Number of machines	10	13	14			
13	Expected life, years	5	5	5			
14	AOC per machine	$ (12,000)	$ (12,000)	$ (12,000)			
15	Equivalent annual value (AW)	$ (940,368)	$ (1,222,478)	$ (1,316,515)			
16	**Capitalized cost for ST**	$ (6,269,118)	$ (8,149,854)	$ (8,776,766)			
17							
18				= + B15/B2			
19							
20		= PMT(B2,B13,–B11*B12) + B14*B12					
21							

FIGURE 5–5

Spreadsheet solution for capitalized cost comparison, Example 5.6.

5.6 PAYBACK PERIOD ANALYSIS

Payback analysis (also called payout analysis) is another extension of the present worth method. Payback can take two forms: one for $i > 0\%$ (also called *discounted payback analysis*) and another for $i = 0\%$. There is a logical linkage between payback and breakeven analysis, which is used in several chapters and discussed in detail in Chapter 13.

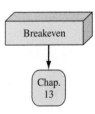

The payback period n_p is the estimated time, usually in years, it will take for the estimated revenues and other economic benefits *to recover the initial investment and a stated rate of return.* The n_p value is generally not an integer. It is important to remember the following:

> **The payback period n_p should never be used as the primary measure of worth to select an alternative. Rather, it should be determined in order to provide initial screening or supplemental information in conjunction with an analysis performed using present worth or another method.**

The payback period should be calculated using a required return that is greater than 0%. However, in practice the payback period is often determined with a no-return requirement ($i = 0\%$) to initially screen a project and determine whether it warrants further consideration.

To find the *discounted payback period* at a stated rate $i > 0\%$, calculate the years n_p that make the following expression correct.

$$0 = -P + \sum_{t=1}^{t=n_p} \text{NCF}_t(P/F,i,t) \qquad \text{[5.4]}$$

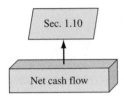

Sec. 1.10

Net cash flow

The amount P is the initial investment or first cost, and NCF is the estimated net cash flow for each year t as determined by Equation [1.8], NCF = receipts − disbursements. If the NCF values are expected to be equal each year, the P/A factor may be used, in which case the relation is

$$0 = -P + \text{NCF}(P/A,i,n_p) \qquad [5.5]$$

After n_p years, the cash flows will recover the investment and a return of $i\%$. If, in reality, the asset or alternative is used for more than n_p years a larger return may result; but if the useful life is less than n_p years, there is not enough time to recover the initial investment and the $i\%$ return. It is very important to realize that in payback analysis *all net cash flows occurring after n_p years are neglected.* Since this is significantly different from the approach of PW (or annual worth, or rate of return, as discussed later), where all cash flows for the entire useful life are included in the economic analysis, payback analysis can unfairly bias alternative selection. So use payback analysis only as a screening or supplemental technique.

When $i > 0\%$ is used, the n_p value does provide a sense of the risk involved if the alternative is undertaken. For example, if a company plans to produce a product under contract for only 3 years and the payback period for the equipment is estimated to be 6 years, the company should not undertake the contract. Even in this situation, the 3-year payback period is only supplemental information, not a good substitute for a complete economic analysis.

No-return payback or *simple payback* analysis determines n_p at $i = 0\%$. This n_p value serves merely as an initial indicator that a proposal is a viable alternative worthy of a full economic evaluation. Use $i = 0\%$ in Equation [5.4] and find n_p.

$$0 = -P + \sum_{t=1}^{t=n_p} \text{NCF}_t \qquad [5.6]$$

For a uniform net cash flow series, Equation [5.6] is solved for n_p directly.

$$n_p = \frac{P}{\text{NCF}} \qquad [5.7]$$

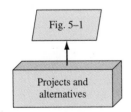

Fig. 5–1

Projects and alternatives

An example of the use of n_p as an initial screening of proposed projects would be a corporation president who absolutely insists that every project must return the investment in 3 years or less. Therefore, no proposed project with $n_p > 3$ should become an alternative.

It is incorrect to use the no-return payback period to make final alternative selections because it

1. **Neglects any required return, since the time value of money is omitted**
2. **Neglects all net cash flows after time n_p, including positive cash flows that may contribute to the return on the investment**

As a result, the selected alternative may be different from that selected by an economic analysis based on PW (or AW) computations. This fact is demonstrated later in Example 5.8.

EXAMPLE 5.7

The board of directors of SNC-Lavalin Group, Inc., has just approved an $18 million worldwide engineering construction design contract. The services are expected to generate new annual net cash flows of $3 million. The contract has a potentially lucrative repayment clause to SNC-Lavalin of $3 million at any time that the contract is cancelled by either party during the 10 years of the contract period. (a) If $i = 15\%$, compute the payback period. (b) Determine the no-return payback period and compare it with the answer for $i = 15\%$. This is an initial check to determine if the board made a good economic decision.

Solution

(a) The net cash flow each year is $3 million. The single $3 million payment (call it CV for cancellation value) could be received at any time within the 10-year contract period. Equation [5.5] is altered to include CV.

$$0 = -P + \text{NCF}(P/A,i,n) + \text{CV}(P/F,i,n)$$

In $1,000,000 units,

$$0 = -18 + 3(P/A,15\%,n) + 3(P/F,15\%,n)$$

The 15% payback period is $n_p = 15.3$ years. During the period of 10 years, the contract will not deliver the required return.

(b) If SNC-Lavalin requires absolutely no return on its $18 million investment, Equation [5.6] results in $n_p = 5$ years, as follows (in million $):

$$0 = -18 + 5(3) + 3$$

There is a very significant difference in n_p for 15% and 0%. At 15% this contract would have to be in force for 15.3 years, while the no-return payback period requires only 5 years. A longer time is always required for $i > 0\%$ for the obvious reason that the time value of money is considered.

Use NPER(15%,3,−18,3) to display 15.3 years. Change the rate from 15% to 0% to display the no-return payback period of 5 years.

Comment

The payback calculation provides the number of years required to recover the invested dollars. But from the points of view of engineering economic analysis and the time value of money, no-return payback analysis is not a reliable method for alternative selection.

If two or more alternatives are evaluated using payback periods to indicate that one may be better than the other(s), the second shortcoming of payback analysis (neglect of cash flows after n_p) may lead to an economically incorrect decision. When cash flows that occur after n_p are neglected, it is possible to favour short-lived assets even when longer-lived assets produce a higher return. In these cases, PW (or AW) analysis should always be the primary selection method. Comparison of short- and long-lived assets in Example 5.8 illustrates this incorrect use of payback analysis.

EXAMPLE 5.8

Two equivalent pieces of quality inspection equipment are being considered for purchase by Square D Electric. Machine 2 is expected to be versatile and technologically advanced enough to provide net income longer than machine 1.

	Machine 1	Machine 2
First cost, $	12,000	8,000
Annual NCF, $	3,000	1,000 (years 1–5), 3,000 (years 6–14)
Maximum life, years	7	14

The quality manager used a return of 15% per year and a PC-based economic analysis package. The software utilized Equations [5.4] and [5.5] to recommend machine 1 because it has a shorter payback period of 6.57 years at $i = 15\%$. The computations are summarized here.

Machine 1: $n_p = 6.57$ years, which is less than the 7-year life.

Equation used: $\quad 0 = -12{,}000 + 3000(P/A,15\%,n_p)$

Machine 2: $n_p = 9.52$ years, which is less than the 14-year life.

Equation used: $\quad 0 = -8000 + 1000(P/A,15\%,5)$
$\quad\quad\quad\quad\quad\quad + 3000(P/A,15\%,n_p-5)(P/F,15\%,5)$

Recommendation: Select machine 1.

Now, use a 15% PW analysis to compare the machines and comment on any difference in the recommendation.

Solution
For each machine, consider the net cash flows for all years during the estimated (maximum) life. Compare them over the LCM of 14 years.

$$PW_1 = -12{,}000 - 12{,}000(P/F,15\%,7) + 3000(P/A,15\%,14) = \$663$$

$$PW_2 = -8000 + 1000(P/A,15\%,5) + 3000(P/A,15\%,9)(P/F,15\%,5)$$

$$= \$2470$$

Machine 2 is selected since its PW value is numerically larger than that of machine 1 at 15%. This result is the opposite of the payback period decision. The PW analysis accounts for the increased cash flows for machine 2 in the later years. As illustrated in Figure 5–6 (for one life cycle for each machine), payback analysis neglects all cash flow amounts that may occur after the payback time has been reached.

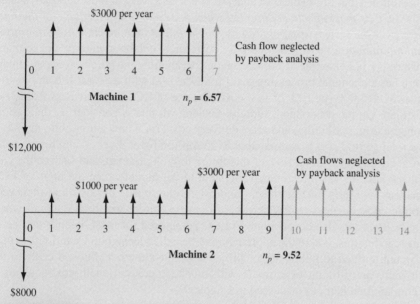

FIGURE 5–6

Illustration of payback periods and neglected net cash flows, Example 5.8.

Comment
This is a good example of why payback analysis is best used for initial screening and supplemental risk assessment. Often a shorter-lived alternative evaluated by payback analysis may appear to be more attractive, when the longer-lived alternative has cash flows estimated later in its life that make it more economically attractive.

5.7 LIFE-CYCLE COST

Life-cycle cost (LCC) is another extension of present worth analysis. The PW value at a stated MARR is utilized to evaluate one or more alternatives. The LCC method, as its name implies, is commonly applied to alternatives with cost estimates over the entire *system life span*. This means that costs from the very early stage of the project (needs assessment) through the final stage (phaseout and disposal) are estimated. Typical applications for LCC are buildings (new construction or purchases), new product lines, manufacturing plants, commercial aircraft, new automobile models, defence systems, and the like.

A PW analysis with all definable costs (and possibly incomes) estimated may be considered a LCC analysis. However, the broad definition of the LCC term *system life span* requires cost estimates not usually made for a regular PW analysis. Also, for large long-life projects, the longer-term estimates are less accurate. This implies that life-cycle cost analysis is not necessary in most alternative analysis. *LCC is most effectively applied when a substantial percentage of the total costs over the system life span, relative to the initial investment, will be operating and maintenance costs* (postpurchase costs such as labour, energy, upkeep, and materials). For example, if Petro-Canada is evaluating the purchase of equipment for a large chemical processing plant for $150,000 with a 5-year life and annual costs of $15,000 (or 10% of first cost), the use of LCC analysis is probably not justified. On the other hand, suppose General Motors is considering the design, construction, marketing, and after-delivery costs for a new automobile model. If the total startup cost is estimated at $125 million (over 3 years) and total annual costs are expected to be 20% of this figure to build, market, and service the cars for the next 15 years (estimated life span of the model), then the logic of LCC analysis will help GM engineers understand the profile of costs and their economic consequences in PW terms. (Of course, future worth and annual worth equivalents can also be calculated.) LCC is required for most defence and aerospace industries, where the approach may be called Design to Cost. LCC is usually not applied to public sector projects, because the benefits and costs to the citizenry are difficult to estimate with much accuracy. Benefit-cost analysis is better applied here, as discussed in Chapter 9.

To understand how a LCC analysis works, first we must understand the phases and stages of systems engineering or systems development. Many books and manuals are available on systems development and analysis. Generally, the LCC estimates may be categorized into a simplified format for the major phases of *acquisition* and *operation,* and their respective stages.

Acquisition phase: all activities prior to the delivery of products and services.

- Requirements definition stage—Includes determination of user/customer needs, assessing them relative to the anticipated system, and preparation of the system requirements documentation.
- Preliminary design stage—Includes feasibility study, conceptual, and early-stage plans; final go–no go decision is probably made here.
- Detailed design stage—Includes detailed plans for resources—capital, human, facilities, information systems, marketing, etc.; there is some acquisition of assets, if economically justifiable.

Operations phase: all activities are functioning, products and services are available.

- Construction and implementation stage—Includes purchases, construction, and implementation of system components; testing; preparation, etc.

- Usage stage—Uses the system to generate products and services.
- Phaseout and disposal stage—Covers time of clear transition to new system; removal/recycling of old system.

EXAMPLE 5.9

Cascades of Kingsey Falls, Quebec, is Canada's leading collector of waste paper. It is also one of Canada's Green 30 companies, an award given a company on the basis of how well it has made environmental responsibility a part of business. Cascades uses more than 2.1 million tonnes of recycled fibres in its products, uses six times less water than the Canadian industry average, and makes its fine paper with biogas resulting from landfill waste.

Maple Bay is a household products company that wishes to emulate Cascades' success in attracting the attention of the increasing numbers of people willing to pay extra for products perceived as environmentally friendly. The company wants to add a new product line that replaces the ammonia, sodium hydroxide, and phosphates in their products with natural ingredients. At this time only cost estimates have been addressed—not revenues or profits.

Assume that the major cost estimates below have been made based on a 6-month study about a new product line that could have a 10-year life span for the company. Some cost elements were not estimated (e.g., materials, product distribution, and phaseout). Use LCC analysis at the industry MARR of 18% to determine the size of the commitment in PW dollars. (Time is indicated in product-years. Since all estimates are for costs, they are not preceded by a minus sign.)

Consumer habits study (year 0)	$0.5 million
Preliminary product design (year 1)	0.9 million
Preliminary equipment/plant design (year 1)	0.5 million
Detail product designs and test marketing (years 1, 2)	1.5 million each year
Detail equipment/plant design (year 2)	1.0 million
Equipment acquisition (years 1 and 2)	$2.0 million each year
Current equipment upgrades (year 2)	1.75 million
New equipment purchases (years 4 and 8)	2.0 million (year 4) +10% per purchase thereafter
Annual equipment operating cost (AOC) (years 3–10)	200,000 (year 3) +4% per year thereafter
Marketing, year 2	$8.0 million
years 3–10	5.0 million (year 3) and −0.2 million per year thereafter
year 5 only	3.0 million extra
Human resources, 100 new employees for 2000 hours per year (years 3–10)	$20 per hour (year 3) +5% per year

Solution

LCC analysis can get complicated rapidly due to the number of elements involved. Calculate the PW by phase and stage, then add all PW values. Values are in million $ units.

Acquisition phase:
Requirements definition: Consumer study

$$PW = \$0.5$$

Preliminary design: Product and equipment

$$PW = 1.4(P/F,18\%,1) = \$1.187$$

Detailed design: Product and test marketing, and equipment

$$PW = 1.5(P/A,18\%,2) + 1.0(P/F,18\%,2) = \$3.067$$

Operations phase:
Construction and implementation: Equipment and AOC

$$PW = 2.0(P/A,18\%,2) + 1.75(P/F,18\%,2) + 2.0(P/F,18\%,4) + 2.2(P/F,18\%,8)$$

$$+ 0.2 \left[\frac{1 - \left(\frac{1.04}{1.18}\right)^8}{0.14} \right] (P/F,18\%,2) = \$6.512$$

Use: Marketing

$$PW = 8.0(P/F,18\%,2) + [5.0(P/A,18\%,8) - 0.2(P/G,18\%,8)](P/F,18\%,2)$$

$$+ 3.0(P/F,18\%,5)$$

$$= \$20.144$$

Use: Human resources: (100 employees)(2000 h/year)($20/h) = $4.0 million in year 3

$$PW = 4.0 \left[\frac{1 - \left(\frac{1.05}{1.18}\right)^8}{0.13} \right] (P/F,18\%,2) = \$13,412$$

The total LCC commitment at this time is the sum of all PW values.

$$PW = \$44.822 \text{ (effectively } \$45 \text{ million)}$$

As a point of interest, over 10 years at 18% per year, the future worth of the Maple Bay commitment, thus far, is FW = PW(F/P,18%,10) = $234.6 million.

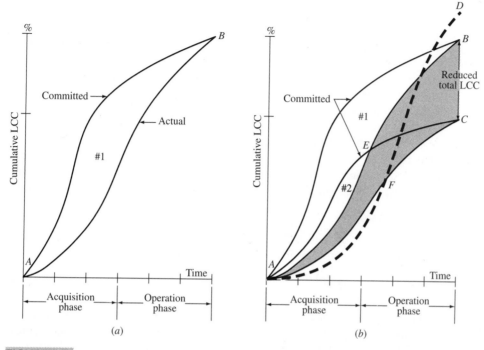

FIGURE 5–7

LCC envelopes for committed and actual costs: (*a*) design 1, (*b*) improved design 2.

The total LCC for a system is established or locked in early. It is not unusual to have 75 to 85% of the entire life span LCC committed during the preliminary and detail design stages. As shown in Figure 5–7*a*, the actual or observed LCC (bottom curve *AB*) will trail the committed LCC throughout the life span (unless some major design flaw increases the total LCC of design 1 above point *B*). *The potential for significantly reducing total LCC occurs primarily during the early stages.* A more effective design and more efficient equipment can reposition the envelope to design 2 in Figure 5–7*b*. Now the committed LCC curve *AEC* is below *AB* at all points, as is the actual LCC curve *AFC*. It is this lower envelope 2 we seek. The shaded area represents the reduction in actual LCC.

Even though an effective LCC envelope may be established early in the acquisition phase, it is not uncommon that unplanned cost-saving measures are introduced during the acquisition phase and early operation phase. These apparent "savings" may actually increase the total LCC, as shown by curve *AFD*. This style of ad hoc cost savings, often imposed by management early in the design stage and/or construction stage, can substantially increase costs later, especially in the after-sale portion of the use stage. For example, the use of inferior-strength concrete and steel has been the cause of structural failures many times, thus increasing the overall life span LCC.

5.8 PRESENT WORTH OF BONDS

A time-tested method of raising capital is through the issuance of an IOU, which is financing through debt, not equity, as discussed in Chapter 1. One very common form of IOU is a bond—a long-term note issued by a corporation or a government entity (the borrower) to finance major projects. The borrower receives money now in return for a promise to pay the *face value V* of the bond on a stated maturity date. Bonds are usually issued in face value amounts of $1000, $5000, or $10,000. *Bond interest I,* also called *bond dividend,* is paid periodically between the time the money is borrowed and the time the face value is repaid. The bond interest is paid c times per year. Expected payment periods are usually quarterly or semiannually. The amount of interest is determined using the stated interest rate, called the *bond coupon rate b.*

$$I = \frac{(\text{face value})(\text{bond coupon rate})}{\text{number of payment periods per year}}$$

$$I = \frac{Vb}{c} \qquad\qquad [5.8]$$

There are many types or classifications of bonds. Five general classifications are summarized in Table 5–1 according to their issuing entity, some fundamental characteristics, and example names or purposes. For example, *Treasury securities* are issued in different monetary amounts ($1000 and up) with varying periods of time to the maturity date. In Canada, Treasury securities are considered a very safe bond purchase because they are backed by the broad taxation power of the federal

TABLE 5–1 Classification and Characteristics of Bonds

Classification	Issued By:	Characteristics	Examples
Treasury securities	Federal government	Backed by Canadian government	Bills Marketable bonds Premium bonds Savings bonds
Provincial	Provincial government	May be guaranteed	Bonds
Municipal	Local governments	Issued against taxes received	Bonds
Mortgage	Corporation	Backed by specified assets or mortgage Low rate/low risk on first mortgage Foreclosure, if not repaid	First mortgage Second mortgage General mortgage
Debenture	Corporation	Not backed by collateral, but by reputation of corporation Bond rate may float Higher interest rates and higher risks	Convertible

government. The safe investment rate indicated in Figure 1–6 as the lowest level for establishing a MARR is the coupon rate on a Canada Savings Bond. As another illustration, *debenture bonds* are issued by corporations in order to raise capital, but they are not backed by any particular form of collateral. The corporation's reputation attracts bond purchasers, and the corporation may make the bond interest rate "float" to further attract buyers. Often debenture bonds are *convertible* to common stock of the corporation at a fixed rate prior to their maturity date.

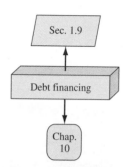

Sec. 1.9

Debt financing

Chap. 10

EXAMPLE 5.10

Loblaw Cos. Ltd. has issued $5,000,000 worth of $5000 ten-year debenture bonds. Each bond pays interest quarterly at 6%. (*a*) Determine the amount a purchaser will receive each 3 months and after 10 years. (*b*) Suppose a bond is purchased at a time when it is discounted by 2% to $4900. What are the quarterly interest amounts and the final payment amount at the maturity date?

Solution

(*a*) Use Equation [5.8] for the quarterly interest amount.

$$I = \frac{(5000)(0.06)}{4} = \$75$$

The face value of $5000 is repaid after 10 years.

(*b*) Purchasing the bond at a discount from face value does not change the interest or final repayment amounts. Therefore, $75 per quarter and $5000 after 10 years remain the amounts.

Finding the PW value of a bond is another extension of present worth analysis. When a corporation or government agency offers bonds, potential purchasers can determine how much they should be willing to pay in PW terms for a bond of a stated denomination. The amount paid at purchase time establishes the rate of return for the remainder of the bond life. The steps to calculate the PW of a bond are as follows:

1. Determine I, the interest per payment period, using Equation [5.8].
2. Construct the cash flow diagram of interest payments and face value repayment.
3. Establish the required MARR or rate of return.
4. Calculate the PW value of the bond interest payments and the face value at i = MARR. (If the bond interest payment period is not equal to the MARR compounding period, that is, PP ≠ CP, first use Equation [4.8] to determine the effective rate per payment period. Use this rate and the logic of Section 4.6 for PP ≥ CP to complete the PW calculations.)

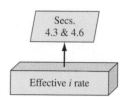

Secs. 4.3 & 4.6

Effective *i* rate

Use the following logic:

PW ≥ bond purchase price; MARR is met or exceeded, buy the bond.

PW < bond purchase price; MARR is not met, do not buy the bond.

EXAMPLE 5.11

Determine the purchase price you should be willing to pay now for a 4.5% $5000 10-year bond with interest paid semiannually. Assume your MARR is 8% per year, compounded quarterly.

Solution
First, determine the semiannual interest.

$$I = 5000(0.045)/2 = \$112.50 \text{ every 6 months}$$

The present worth of all bond payments to you (Figure 5–8) is determined in either of two ways.

1. *Effective semiannual rate.* Use the approach of Section 4.6. The cash flow period is PP = 6 months, and the compounding period is CP = 3 months; PP > CP. Find the effective semiannual rate, then apply P/A and P/F factors to the interest payments and $5000 receipt in year 10. The nominal semiannual MARR is $r = 8\%/2 = 4\%$. For $m = 2$ quarters per 6 months, Equation [4.8] yields

$$\text{Effective } i = \left(1 + \frac{0.04}{2}\right)^2 - 1 = 4.04\% \text{ per 6 months}$$

The PW of the bond is determined for $n = 2(10) = 20$ semiannual periods.

$$PW = \$112.50(P/A,4.04\%,20) + 5000(P/F,4.04\%,20) = \$3788$$

2. *Nominal quarterly rate.* Find the PW of each $112.50 semiannual bond interest receipt in year 0 separately with a P/F factor, and add the PW of the $5000 in year 10. The nominal quarterly MARR is $8\%/4 = 2\%$. The total number of periods is

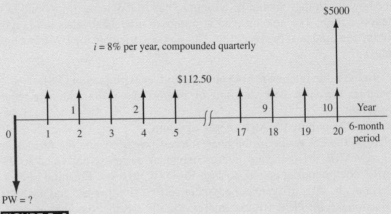

FIGURE 5–8
Cash flow for the present worth of a bond, Example 5.11.

$n = 4(10) = 40$ quarters, double those shown in Figure 5–8, since the payments are made semiannually while the MARR is compounded quarterly.

$$PW = 112.50(P/F,2\%,2) + 112.50(P/F,2\%,4) + \cdots + 112.50(P/F,2\%,40)$$
$$+ 5000(P/F,2\%,40)$$
$$= \$3788$$

If the asking price is more than $3788 for the bond, which is a discount of more than 24%, you will not make the MARR.

The spreadsheet function PV(4.04%,20,112.50,5000) displays the PW value of $3788.

Q-SOLVE

5.9 SPREADSHEET APPLICATIONS—PW ANALYSIS AND PAYBACK PERIOD

Example 5.12 illustrates how to set up a spreadsheet for PW analysis for different-life alternatives and for a specified study period. Example 5.13 demonstrates the technique and shortcomings of payback period analysis for $i > 0\%$. Both hand and computer solutions are presented for this second example.

Some general guidelines help organize spreadsheets for any PW analysis. The LCM of the alternatives dictates the number of row entries for initial investment and salvage/market values, based on the repurchase assumption that PW analysis requires. Some alternatives will be service-based (cost cash flows only); others are revenue-based (cost and income cash flows). Place the annual cash flows in separate columns from the investment and salvage amounts. This reduces the amount of number processing you have to do before entering a cash flow value. Determine the PW values for all columns pertinent to an alternative, and add them to obtain the final PW value.

Spreadsheets can become crowded very rapidly. However, placing the NPV functions at the head of each cash flow column and inserting a separate summary table make the component and total PW values stand out. Finally, place the MARR value in a separate cell, so sensitivity analysis on the required return can be easily accomplished. Example 5.12 illustrates these guidelines.

EXAMPLE 5.12

Lafarge Cement plans to open a new quarry. Two plans have been devised for movement of raw material from the quarry to the plant. Plan A requires the purchase of two earthmovers and construction of an unloading pad at the plant. Plan B calls for construction of a conveyor system from the quarry to the plant. The costs for each plan are detailed in Table 5–2. (*a*) Using spreadsheet-based PW analysis, determine which plan should be selected if money is worth 15% per year. (*b*) After only 6 years of operation a major environmental problem made Lafarge stop all operations at the quarry. Use a 6-year study period to determine if plan A or B was economically better. The market value of each mover after 6 years is $20,000, and the trade-in value of the conveyor after 6 years is only $25,000. The pad can be salvaged for $2000.

TABLE 5–2   Estimates for Plans to Move Rock from Quarry to Cement Plant

	Plan A		Plan B
	Mover	**Pad**	**Conveyor**
Initial cost, $	−45,000	−28,000	−175,000
Annual operating cost, $	−6,000	−300	−2,500
Salvage value, $	5,000	2,000	10,000
Life, years	8	12	24

Solution

(a) Evaluation must take place over the LCM of 24 years. Reinvestment in the two movers will occur in years 8 and 16, and the unloading pad must be rebuilt in year 12. No reinvestment is necessary for plan B. First, construct the cash flow diagrams for plans A and B over 24 years to better understand the spreadsheet analysis in Figure 5–9. Columns B, D, and F include all investments, reinvestments, and salvage values. (*Remember to enter zeros in all cells with no cash flows, or the NPV function will give an incorrect PW value.*) These are service-based alternatives, so columns C, E, and G display the AOC estimates, labelled "Annual CF." NPV functions provide the PW amounts in row 8 cells. These are added by alternative in cells H19 and H22.

   Conclusion: Select plan B because the PW of costs is smaller.

(b) Both alternatives are abruptly terminated after 6 years, and current market or trade-in values are estimated. To perform the PW analysis for a severely truncated study period, Figure 5–10 uses the same format as that for the 24-year analysis, except for two major alterations. Cells in row 16 now include the market and trade-in amounts, and all rows after 16 are deleted. See the cell tags in row 9 for the new NPV functions for the 6 years of cash flows. Cells D20 and D21 are the PW values found by summing the appropriate PW values in row 9.

   Conclusion: Plan A should have been selected, had the termination after 6 years been known at the design stage of the rock pit.

Comment

The spreadsheet solution for part (b) was developed by initially copying the entire worksheet in part (a) to sheet 2 of the Excel workbook. Then the changes outlined above were made to the copy. Another method uses the same worksheet to build the new NPV functions as shown in Figure 5–10 cell tags, but on the Figure 5–9 worksheet after inserting a new row 16 for year 6 cash flows. This approach is faster and less formal than the method demonstrated here. There is one real danger in using the one-worksheet approach to solving this (or any sensitivity analysis) problem. The altered worksheet now solves a different problem, so the functions display new answers. For example, when the cash flows are truncated to a 6-year study period, the old NPV functions in row 8 must be changed, or the new NPV functions must be added in row 9. But now the NPV functions of the old 24-year PW analysis display incorrect answers, or possibly an Excel error message. This introduces error possibilities into the decision making. For accurate, correct results, take the time to copy the first sheet to a new worksheet and make the changes on the copy. Store both solutions after documenting what each sheet is designed to analyze. This provides a historical record of what was altered during the sensitivity analysis.

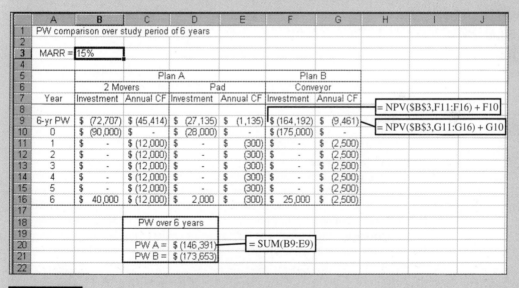

	A	B	C	D	E	F	G	H	I	J	K	L
1	PW comparison over LCM = 24 years m (2 worksheets included)											
2												
3	MARR =	15%										
4												
5				PLAN A			PLAN B					
6			2 Movers		Pad		Conveyor					
7	Year	Investment	Annual CF	Investment	Annual CF	Investment	Annual CF		= NPV($B$3,G11:G34) + G10			
8	24-yr PW	$ (124,352)	$(77,205)	$(32,790)	$(1,930)	$ (174,651)	$(16,084)					
9									= NPV($B$3,F11:F34) + F10			
10	0	$ (90,000)	$ -	$(28,000)	$ -	$ (175,000)	$ -					
11	1	$ -	$(12,000)	$ -	$ (300)	$ -	$ (2,500)					
12	2	$ -	$(12,000)	$ -	$ (300)	$ -	$ (2,500)					
13	3	$ -	$(12,000)	$ -	$ (300)	$ -	$ (2,500)					
14	4	$ -	$(12,000)	$ -	$ (300)	$ -	$ (2,500)					
15	5	$ -	$(12,000)	$ -	$ (300)	$ -	$ (2,500)					
16	6	$ -	$(12,000)	$ -	$ (300)	$ -	$ (2,500)	PW values over 24 years:				
17	7	$ -	$(12,000)	$ -	$ (300)	$ -	$ (2,500)					
18	8	$ (80,000)	$(12,000)	$ -	$ (300)	$ -	$ (2,500)	PW A= PW mover + PW pad		= SUM(B8:E8)		
19	9	$ -	$(12,000)	$ -	$ (300)	$ -	$ (2,500)	$ (236,277)				
20	10	$ -	$(12,000)	$ -	$ (300)	$ -	$ (2,500)					
21	11	$ -	$(12,000)	$ -	$ (300)	$ -	$ (2,500)	PW B = PW conveyor				
22	12	$ -	$(12,000)	$(26,000)	$ (300)	$ -	$ (2,500)	$ (190,735)				
23	13	$ -	$(12,000)	$ -	$ (300)	$ -	$ (2,500)					
24	14	$ -	$(12,000)	$ -	$ (300)	$ -	$ (2,500)					
25	15	$ -	$(12,000)	$ -	$ (300)	$ -	$ (2,500)					
26	16	$ (80,000)	$(12,000)	$ -	$ (300)	$ -	$ (2,500)					
27	17	$ -	$(12,000)	$ -	$ (300)	$ -	$ (2,500)					
28	18	$ -	$(12,000)	$ -	$ (300)	$ -	$ (2,500)					
29	19	$ -	$(12,000)	$ -	$ (300)	$ -	$ (2,500)					
30	20	$ -	$(12,000)	$ -	$ (300)	$ -	$ (2,500)					
31	21	$ -	$(12,000)	$ -	$ (300)	$ -	$ (2,500)					
32	22	$ -	$(12,000)	$ -	$ (300)	$ -	$ (2,500)					
33	23	$ -	$(12,000)	$ -	$ (300)	$ -	$ (2,500)					
34	24	$ 10,000	$(12,000)	$ 2,000	$ (300)	$ 10,000	$ (2,500)					

FIGURE 5–9
Spreadsheet solution using PW analysis of different-life alternatives, Example 5.12(*a*).

	A	B	C	D	E	F	G	H	I	J
1	PW comparison over study period of 6 years									
2										
3	MARR =	15%								
4										
5				Plan A			Plan B			
6			2 Movers		Pad		Conveyor			
7	Year	Investment	Annual CF	Investment	Annual CF	Investment	Annual CF		= NPV($B$3,F11:F16) + F10	
8										
9	6-yr PW	$ (72,707)	$ (45,414)	$ (27,135)	$ (1,135)	$ (164,192)	$ (9,461)		= NPV($B$3,G11:G16) + G10	
10	0	$ (90,000)	$ -	$ (28,000)	$ -	$ (175,000)	$ -			
11	1	$ -	$ (12,000)	$ -	$ (300)	$ -	$ (2,500)			
12	2	$ -	$ (12,000)	$ -	$ (300)	$ -	$ (2,500)			
13	3	$ -	$ (12,000)	$ -	$ (300)	$ -	$ (2,500)			
14	4	$ -	$ (12,000)	$ -	$ (300)	$ -	$ (2,500)			
15	5	$ -	$ (12,000)	$ -	$ (300)	$ -	$ (2,500)			
16	6	$ 40,000	$ (12,000)	$ 2,000	$ (300)	$ 25,000	$ (2,500)			
17										
18				PW over 6 years						
19										
20				PW A =	$ (146,391)		= SUM(B9:E9)			
21				PW B =	$ (173,653)					
22										

FIGURE 5–10
Spreadsheet solution for 6-year study period using PW analysis, Example 5.12(*b*).

EXAMPLE 5.13

Biothermics has agreed to a licensee agreement for safety engineering software that was developed in Australia and is being introduced into North America. The initial licence rights cost $60,000 with annual rights fees of $1800 the first year, increasing by $100 per year thereafter until the licence agreement is sold to another party or terminated. Biothermics must keep the agreement at least 2 years. Use hand and spreadsheet analysis to determine the payback period (in years) at $i = 8\%$ for two scenarios:

(a) Sell the software rights for $90,000 sometime beyond year 2.

(b) If the licence is not sold by the time determined in (a), the selling price will increase to $120,000 in future years.

Solution by Hand

(a) From Equation [5.4], it is necessary that PW = 0 at the 8% payback period n_p. Set up the PW relation for $n \geq 3$ years, and determine the number of years at which PW crosses the zero value.

$$0 = -60{,}000 - 1800(P/A,8\%,n) - 100(P/G,8\%,n) + 90{,}000(P/F,8\%,n)$$

n, years	3	4	5
PW value	$6562	$−274	$−6672

The 8% payback is between 3 and 4 years. By linear interpolation, $n_p = 3.96$ years.

(b) If the licence is not sold prior to 4 years, the price goes up to $120,000. The PW relation for 4 or more years and the PW values for n are

$$0 = -60{,}000 - 1800(P/A,8\%,n) - 100(P/G,8\%,n) + 120{,}000(P/F,8\%,n)$$

n, years	5	6	7
PW value	$13,748	$6247	$−755

The 8% payback is now between 6 and 7 years. By interpolation, $n_p = 6.90$ years.

Solution by Computer

E-SOLVE

(a and b) Figure 5–11 presents a spreadsheet that lists the software rights costs (column B) and expected selling price (columns C and E). The NPV functions in column D (selling price $90,000) show the payback period to be between 3 and 4 years, while the NPV results in column F (selling price $120,000) indicate PW switching from positive to negative between 6 and 7 years. The NPV functions reflect the relations presented in the hand solution, except the cost gradient of $100 has been incorporated into the costs in column B.

If more exact payback values are needed, interpolate between the PW results on the spreadsheet. The values will be the same as in the solution by hand, namely, 3.96 and 6.90 years.

	A	B	C	D	E	F	G
1							
2	Interest rate	8%					
3							
4		Licence	Price, if sold	PW, if sold	Price, if sold	PW, if sold	
5	Year	costs	this year	this year	this year	this year	
6	0	$(60,000)					
7	1	$ (1,800)					
8	2	$ (1,900)					
9	3	$ (2,000)	$ 90,000	$ 6,562			
10	4	$ (2,100)	$ 90,000	($274)	$ 120,000	$ 21,777	
11	5	$ (2,200)	$ 90,000	$ (6,672)	$ 120,000	$ 13,746	
12	6	$ (2,300)			$ 120,000	$ 6,247	
13	7	$ (2,400)			$ 120,000	$ (755)	
14							
15							
16	= NPV(B2,B7:B10) + B6 + C10*(1/(1 + B2)^A10)						
17				= NPV(B2,B7:B12) + B6 + E12*(1/(1 + B2)^A12)			

FIGURE 5–11

Determination of payback period using a spreadsheet, Example 5.13(*a*) and (*b*).

CHAPTER SUMMARY

The present worth method of comparing alternatives involves converting all cash flows to present dollars at the MARR. The alternative with the numerically larger (or largest) PW value is selected. When the alternatives have different lives, the comparison must be made for equal-service periods. This is done by performing the comparison over either the LCM of lives or a specific study period. Both approaches compare alternatives in accordance with the equal-service requirement. When a study period is used, any remaining value in an alternative is recognized through the estimated future market value.

Life-cycle cost analysis is an extension of PW analysis performed for systems that have relatively long lives and a large percentage of their lifetime costs in the form of operating expenses. If the life of the alternatives is considered to be infinite, capitalized cost is the comparison method. The CC value is calculated as A/i, because the P/A factor reduces to $1/i$ in the limit of $n = \infty$.

Payback analysis estimates the number of years necessary to recover the initial investment plus a stated rate of return (MARR). This is a supplemental analysis technique used primarily for initial screening of proposed projects prior to a full economic evaluation by PW or some other method. The technique has some drawbacks, especially for no-return payback analysis, where $i = 0\%$ is used as the MARR.

Finally, we learned about bonds. Present worth analysis determines if the MARR will be obtained over the life of a bond, given specific values for the bond's face value, term, and interest rate.

PROBLEMS

Types of Projects

5.1 What is meant by *service alternative*?

5.2 When you are evaluating projects by the present worth method, how do you know which one(s) to select if the projects are (*a*) independent and (*b*) mutually exclusive?

5.3 Read the statement in the following problems and determine if the cash flows define a revenue or a service project: (*a*) Problem 2.13, (*b*) Problem 2.33, (*c*) Problem 2.53, (*d*) Problem 3.7, (*e*) Problem 3.11, and (*f*) Problem 3.15.

5.4 A rapidly growing city is dedicated to neighbourhood integrity. However, increasing traffic and speed on a through street are of concern to residents. The city manager has proposed five independent options to slow traffic:

1. Stop sign at corner A
2. Stop sign at corner B
3. Low-profile speed bump at point C
4. Low-profile speed bump at point D
5. Speed dip at point E

There cannot be any of the following combinations in the final alternatives:

- No combination of dip and one or two bumps
- Not two bumps
- Not two stop signs

Use the five independent options and the restrictions to determine (*a*) the *total number* of mutually exclusive alternatives possible and (*b*) the *acceptable* mutually exclusive alternatives.

5.5 What is meant by the term *equal service*?

5.6 What two approaches can be used to satisfy the equal service requirement?

5.7 Define the term *capitalized cost* and give a real-world example of something that might be analyzed using that technique.

Alternative Comparison—Equal Lives

5.8 Bridgewater Systems Corp. of Ottawa develops technology that helps phone companies manage growing smartphone traffic and bill for services. Evaluate two possible service plans at a MARR of 9% per year. Plan A has an initial fee of $52,000 with annual fees starting at $1000 in contract year 1 and increasing by $500 every year. Alternatively, plan B costs $62,000 up front with annual fees starting at $5000 in contract year 1 and decreasing by $500 each year. The initial charge is considered a setup cost for which no salvage value is expected.

5.9 Lennon Hearth Products manufactures glass-door fireplace screens that have two types of mounting brackets for the frame. An L-shaped bracket is used for relatively small fireplace openings, and a U-shaped bracket is used for all others. The company includes both types of brackets in the box with the product, and the purchaser discards the one not needed. The cost of these two brackets with screws and other parts is $3.50. If the frame of the fireplace screen is redesigned, a single universal bracket can be used that will cost $1.20 to make. However, retooling will cost $6000. In addition, inventory write-downs will amount to another $8000. If the company sells 1200 fireplace units per year, should the company keep the old brackets or go with the new ones, assuming the company uses an interest rate of 15% per year and it wants to recover its investment in 5 years? Use the present worth method.

5.10 Two methods can be used for producing expansion anchors. Method A costs

$80,000 initially and will have a $15,000 salvage value after 3 years. The operating cost with this method will be $30,000 per year. Method B will have a first cost of $120,000, an operating cost of $8000 per year, and a $40,000 salvage value after its 3-year life. At an interest rate of 12% per year, which method should be used on the basis of a present worth analysis?

5.11 A software package created by Navarro & Associates can be used for analyzing and designing three-sided guyed towers and three- and four-sided self-supporting towers. A single-user licence will cost $4000 per year. A site licence has a one-time cost of $15,000. A structural engineering consulting company is trying to decide between two alternatives: first, to buy one single-user licence *now* and one each year for the next 4 years (which will provide 5 years of service); or second, to buy a site licence now. Determine which strategy should be adopted at an interest rate of 12% per year for a 5-year planning period, using the present worth method of evaluation.

5.12 A company that manufactures amplified pressure transducers is trying to decide between the machines shown below. Compare them on the basis of their present worth values, using an interest rate of 15% per year.

	Variable Speed	Dual Speed
First cost, $	−250,000	−224,000
Annual operating cost, $/year	−231,000	−235,000
Overhaul in year 3, $	—	−26,000
Overhaul in year 4, $	−140,000	—
Salvage value, $	50,000	10,000
Life, years	6	6

Alternative Comparison over Different Time Periods

5.13 The European Space Agency is considering two materials for use in a space probe. The costs are shown below. Which should be selected on the basis of a present worth comparison at an interest rate of 10% per year?

	Material JX	Material KZ
First cost, $	−205,000	−235,000
Maintenance cost, $/year	−29,000	−27,000
Salvage value, $	2,000	20,000
Life, years	2	4

5.14 Two processes can be used for producing a polymer that reduces friction loss in engines. Process K will have a first cost of $160,000, an operating cost of $7000 per quarter, and a salvage value of $40,000 after its 2-year life. Process L will have a first cost of $210,000, an operating cost of $5000 per quarter, and a $26,000 salvage value after its 4-year life. Which process should be selected on the basis of a present worth analysis at an interest rate of 8% per year, compounded quarterly?

5.15 Agrico-Eagle's Meadowbank gold mine in Nunavut has 3 options to supply safety equipment to mine workers. Two are vendors who sell the items, and a third will rent the equipment for $50,000 per year but for no more than 3 years per contract. The MARR is 10% per year. Determine which of the three options is cheaper over a study period of 3 years.

	Vendor A	Vendor B	Rental
Initial cost	$−75,000	$−125,000	$ 0
Annual maintenance cost, $/year	−27,000	−12,000	0
Annual rental cost, $/year	0	0	−50,000
Salvage value	0	30,000	0
Estimated life, years	2	3	Max. of 3

5.16 Two methods are under consideration for producing the case for a portable hazardous material photoionization monitor. A plastic case will require an initial investment of $75,000 and will have an annual operating cost of $27,000 with no salvage after 2 years. An aluminum case will require an investment of $125,000 and will have annual costs of $12,000. Some of the equipment can be sold for $30,000 after its 3-year life. At an interest rate of 10% per year, which case should be used on the basis of a present worth analysis?

5.17 Toyota Motor Corp. is considering three different plans for operation of their auto parts production plant in Simcoe, Ontario. Plan A would involve renewable 1-year contracts with payments of $1 million at the beginning of each year. Plan B would be a 2-year contract, and it would require four payments of $600,000 each, with the first one to be made now and the other three at 6-month intervals. Plan C would be a 3-year contract, and it would entail a payment of $1.5 million now and another payment of $0.5 million 2 years from now. Assuming that Toyota could renew any of the plans under the same conditions if it wants to do so, which plan is better on the basis of a present worth analysis at an interest rate of 6% per year, compounded semiannually?

Future Worth Comparison

5.18 The Citizens' Airshed Advisory Group of Vancouver Island has hired a consulting firm to monitor the air quality of a pulp mill that will soon be burning auto tires and railroad ties in its boiler furnance. A remotely located air sampling station can be powered by solar cells or by running an electric line to the site and using conventional power. Solar cells will cost $12,600 to install and will have a useful life of 4 years with no salvage value.

Annual costs for inspection, cleaning, etc., are expected to be $1400. A new power line will cost $11,000 to install, with power costs expected to be $800 per year. Since the air sampling project will end in 4 years, the salvage value of the line is considered to be zero. At an interest rate of 10% per year, which alternative should the consultant select on the basis of a future worth analysis?

5.19 Whirlpool Canada is proposing a 20% increase in clothes washer efficiency by 2015 and a 35% increase by 2018. The 20% increase is expected to add $100 to the current price of a washer, while the 35% increase will add $240 to the price. If the cost for energy is $80 per year with the 20% increase in efficiency and $65 per year with the 35% increase, which one of the two proposed standards is more economical on the basis of a future worth analysis at an interest rate of 10% per year? Assume a 15-year life for all washer models.

5.20 A small strip-mining coal company is trying to decide whether it should purchase or lease a new clamshell. If purchased, the shell will cost $150,000 and is expected to have a $65,000 salvage value in 6 years. Alternatively, the company can lease a clamshell for $30,000 per year, but the lease payment will have to be made at the *beginning* of each year. If the clamshell is purchased, it will be leased to other strip-mining companies whenever possible, an activity that is expected to yield revenues of $12,000 per year. If the company's minimum attractive rate of return is 15% per year, should the clamshell be purchased or leased on the basis of a future worth analysis?

5.21 Three types of drill bits can be used in a certain manufacturing operation. A high-speed steel (HSS) bit is the least expensive to buy, but it has a shorter life than either gold oxide or titanium nitride bits. The HSS bits will cost $3500 to buy and will last for 3 months under the conditions in which they will be used. The operating cost for these bits will be $2000 per month. The gold oxide bits will cost $6500 to buy and will last for 6 months with an operating cost of $1500 per month. The titanium nitride bits will cost $7000 to buy and will last 6 months with an operating cost of $1200 per month. At an interest rate of 12% per year, compounded monthly, which type of drill bit should be used on the basis of a future worth analysis?

Capitalized Costs

5.22 The cost of painting Vancouver's Burrard Bridge is $400,000. If the bridge is painted now and every 2 years hereafter, what is the capitalized cost of painting at an interest rate of 6% per year?

5.23 The cost of extending a certain road at Kluane National Park is $1.7 million. Resurfacing and other maintenance are expected to cost $350,000 every 3 years. What is the capitalized cost of the road at an interest rate of 6% per year?

5.24 Determine the capitalized cost of an expenditure of $200,000 at time 0, $25,000 in years 2 through 5, and $40,000 per year from year 6 on. Use an interest rate of 12% per year.

5.25 A city is planning to build a new football stadium costing $250 million. Annual upkeep is expected to amount to $800,000 per year. The artificial turf will have to be replaced every 10 years at a cost of $950,000. Painting every 5 years will cost $75,000. If the city expects to maintain the facility indefinitely, what will be its capitalized cost at an interest rate of 8% per year?

5.26 A certain manufacturing alternative has a first cost of $82,000, an annual maintenance cost of $9000, and a salvage value of $15,000 after its 4-year life. What is its capitalized cost at an interest rate of 12% per year?

5.27 If you want to be able to withdraw $80,000 per year forever beginning 30 years from now, how much will you have to have in your retirement account (that earns 8% per year interest) in (a) year 29 and (b) year 0?

5.28 What is the capitalized cost (absolute value) of the *difference* between the following two plans at an interest rate of 10% per year? Plan A will require an expenditure of $50,000 every 5 years forever (beginning in year 5). Plan B will require an expenditure of $100,000 every 10 years forever (beginning in year 10).

5.29 What is the capitalized cost of expenditures of $3,000,000 now, $50,000 in months 1 through 12, $100,000 in months 13 through 25, and $50,000 in months 26 through infinity if the interest rate is 12% per year, compounded monthly?

5.30 Compare the following alternatives on the basis of their capitalized cost at an interest rate of 10% per year.

	Petroleum-Based Feedstock	Inorganic-Based Feedstock
First cost, $	−250,000	−110,000
Annual operating cost, $/year	−130,000	−65,000
Annual revenues, $/year	400,000	270,000
Salvage value, $	50,000	20,000
Life, years	6	4

5.31 An alumna of the University of New Brunswick wanted to set up an endowment fund that would award scholarships to female engineering students totalling $100,000 per year forever. The first scholarships are to be granted *now* and continue each year forever. How much must the alumna donate now, if the endowment fund is expected to earn interest at a rate of 8% per year?

5.32 Two large-scale conduits are under consideration by a large municipal utility district (MUD). The first involves construction of a steel pipeline at a cost of $225 million. Portions of the pipeline will have to be replaced every 40 years at a cost of $50 million. The pumping and other operating costs are expected to be $10 million per year. Alternatively, a gravity flow canal can be constructed at a cost of $350 million. The M&O costs for the canal are expected to be $0.5 million per year. If both conduits are expected to last forever, which should be built at an interest rate of 10% per year?

5.33 Compare the alternatives shown below on the basis of their capitalized costs, using an interest rate 12% per year, compounded quarterly.

	Alternative E	Alternative F	Alternative G
First cost, $	−200,000	−300,000	−900,000
Quarterly income, $/quarter	30,000	10,000	40,000
Salvage value, $	50,000	70,000	100,000
Life, years	2	4	∞

Payback Analysis

5.34 What is meant by no-return payback or simple payback?

5.35 Explain why the alternative that recovers its initial investment at a specified rate of return in the shortest time is *not necessarily* the most economically attractive one.

5.36 Determine the payback period for an asset that has a first cost of $40,000, a salvage value of $8000 anytime within 10 years of its purchase, and generates income of $6000 per year. The required return is 8% per year.

5.37 Bombardier Transportation is outsourcing some back-office accounting functions such as general ledger, accounts receivable, cost accounting, and accounts payable to Cebu, Philippines. Fifteen Canadian jobs will be lost, but 30 jobs will be created in Cebu paying approximately 3 times the local wage. For a return of 12% per year on the shift offshore and the net cash flows (NCF) shown below, what is the payback period?

	Month						
	0	1	2	3	4	5	6
NCF, $1000 per month	−40	+5	+7	+9	+11	+13	+25

5.38 Accusoft Systems is offering business owners a software package that keeps track of many accounting functions from the company's bank transactions sales invoices. The site licence will cost $22,000 to install and will involve a quarterly fee of $2000. If a certain small company can save $3500 every quarter and have the security of managing its books in-house, how long will it take for the company to recover its investment at an interest rate of 4% per quarter?

5.39 Darnell Enterprises constructed an addition to its building at a cost of $70,000. Extra annual expenses are expected to be $1850, but extra income will be $14,000 per year. How long will it take for the company to recover its investment at an interest rate of 10% per year?

5.40 A new process for manufacturing laser levels will have a first cost of $35,000 with annual costs of $17,000. Extra income associated with the new process is expected to be $22,000 per year. What is the payback period at (*a*) $i = 0\%$ and (*b*) $i = 10\%$ per year?

5.41 A multinational engineering consulting firm that wants to provide resort accommodations to certain clients is considering the purchase of a three-bedroom lodge in Lillooet, British Columbia, that will cost $250,000. The property in that area is rapidly appreciating in value because of its proximity to 2010 Olympics venues. If the company spends an average of $500 per month for utilities and the investment increases at a rate of 2% per month, how long would it be before the company could sell the property for $100,000 more than it has invested in it?

5.42 A window frame manufacturer is searching for ways to improve revenue from its triple-insulated sliding windows. Alternative A is an increase in TV and radio marketing. A total of $300,000 spent now is expected to increase revenue by $60,000 per year. Alternative B requires the same investment for enhancements to the in-plant manufacturing process that will improve the temperature retention properties of the seals around each glass pane. New revenues start slowly for this alternative at an estimated $10,000 the first year, with growth of $15,000 per year as the improved product gains reputation among builders. The MARR is 8% per year, and the maximum evaluation period is 10 years for either alternative. Use both payback analysis and present worth analysis at 8% (for 10 years) to select the more economical alternative. State the reason(s) for any difference in the alternative chosen between the two analyses.

Life-Cycle Costs

5.43 A high-technology defence contractor has been asked by the Department of National Defence to estimate the life-cycle cost (LCC) for a proposed light-duty support vehicle. Its list of items included the following general categories: R&D costs (R&D), nonrecurring investment (NRI) costs, recurring investment (RI) costs, scheduled and unscheduled maintenance costs (Maint), equipment usage costs (Equip), and disposal costs (Disp). The costs (in millions) for the 20-year life cycle are as indicated. Calculate the LCC at an interest rate of 7% per year.

Year	R&D	NRI	RI	Maint	Equip	Disp
0	5.5	1.1				
1	3.5					
2	2.5					
3	0.5	5.2	1.3	0.6	1.5	
4		10.5	3.1	1.4	3.6	
5		10.5	4.2	1.6	5.3	
6–10			6.5	2.7	7.8	
11 on			2.2	3.5	8.5	
18–20						2.7

5.44 A manufacturing software engineer at a major aerospace corporation has been assigned the management responsibility of a project to design, build, test, and implement AREMSS, a new-generation automated scheduling system for routine and expedited maintenance. Reports on the disposition of each service will also be entered by field personnel, then filed and archived by the system. The system is expected to be widely used over time for commercial aircraft maintenance scheduling. Once it is fully implemented, enhancements will have to be made, but the system will be able to serve as a worldwide scheduler for up to 15,000 separate aircraft. The engineer, who must make a presentation next week of the best estimates of costs over a 20-year life period, has decided to use the life-cycle cost approach of cost estimations. Use the following information to determine the current LCC at 6% per year for the AREMSS scheduling system.

Cost Category	Cost in Year ($ millions)							
	1	2	3	4	5	6 on	10	18
Field study	0.5							
Design of system	2.1	1.2	0.5					
Software design		0.6	0.9					
Hardware								
purchases			5.1					
Beta testing		0.1	0.2					
User's manual								
development		0.1	0.1	0.2	0.2	0.06		
System implemen-								
tation				1.3	0.7			
Field hardware				0.4	6.0	2.9		
Training trainers				0.3	2.5	2.5	0.7	
Software upgrades						0.6	3.0	3.7

5.45 Suncor wants to build lodging for oil sands workers near Fort McMurray. Two proposals are being considered.

Proposal A involves an off-the-shelf design and standard-grade construction of walls, windows, doors, and other features. With this option, heating and cooling costs will be greater, maintenance costs will be higher, and replacement will be sooner than for proposal B. The initial cost for A will be $750,000. Heating and cooling costs will average $6000 per month, with maintenance costs averaging $2000 per month. Minor remodelling will be required in years 5, 10, and 15 at a cost of $150,000 each time in order to render the units usable for 20 years. They will have no salvage value.

Proposal B will include tailored design and construction costs of $1.1 million initially, with estimated heating and cooling costs of $3000 per month and maintenance costs of $1000 per month. There will be no salvage value at the end of the 20-year life.

Which proposal should be accepted on the basis of a life-cycle cost analysis, if the interest rate is 0.5% per month?

5.46 Winnipeg plans to develop a software system to assist in project selection during the next 10 years. A life-cycle cost approach has been used to categorize costs into development, programming, operating, and support costs for each alternative. There are three alternatives under consideration, identified as A (tailored system), B (adapted system), and C (current system). The costs are summarized below. Use a life-cycle cost approach to identify the best alternative at 8% per year.

Alternative	Cost Component	Cost
A	Development	$250,000 now, $150,000 years 1 through 4
	Programming	$45,000 now, $35,000 years 1, 2
	Operation	$50,000 years 1 through 10
	Support	$30,000 years 1 through 5
B	Development	$10,000 now
	Programming	$45,000 year 0, $30,000 years 1 through 3
	Operation	$80,000 years 1 through 10
	Support	$40,000 years 1 through 10
C	Operation	$175,000 years 1 through 10

Bonds

5.47 A mortgage bond with a face value of $10,000 has a bond interest rate of 6% per year payable quarterly. What are the amount and frequency of the interest payments?

5.48 What is the face value of a corporate bond that has a bond interest rate of 4% per year with semiannual interest payments of $800?

5.49 What is the bond interest rate on a $20,000 bond that has semiannual interest payments of $1500 and a 20-year maturity date?

5.50 What is the present worth of a $50,000 bond that has interest of 10% per year, payable quarterly? The bond matures in 20 years. The interest rate in the marketplace is 10% per year, compounded quarterly.

5.51 What is the present worth of a $50,000 municipal bond that has an interest rate of 4% per year, payable quarterly? The bond matures in 15 years, and the market interest rate is 8% per year, compounded quarterly.

5.52 BCE issued 1000 debenture bonds 3 years ago with a face value of $5000 each and a bond interest rate of 8% per year payable semiannually. The bonds have a maturity date of 20 years *from the date they were issued.* If the interest rate in the market place is 10% per year, compounded semiannually, what is the present worth of one bond to an investor who wishes to purchase it today?

5.53 Caboto Corp. needs to raise $200 million for plant expansion. The bonds will pay interest semiannually at a rate of 7% per year, and they will mature in 30 years. Brokerage fees associated with the sale of the bonds will be $1 million. If the interest rate in the marketplace rises to 8% per year, compounded semiannually, before the bonds are issued, what will the face value of the bonds have to be for the corporation to net $200 million?

5.54 An engineer planning for his retirement thinks that the interest rates in the marketplace will decrease before he retires. Therefore, he plans to invest in corporate bonds. He plans to buy a $50,000 bond that has a bond interest rate of 12% per year, payable quarterly with a maturity date 20 years from now.
   (a) How much should he be able to sell the bond for in 5 years if the market interest rate is 8% per year, compounded quarterly?
   (b) If he invested the interest he received at an interest rate of 12% per year, compounded quarterly, how much will he have (total) immediately after he sells the bond 5 years from now?

CASE STUDY

PAYBACK EVALUATION OF ULTRALOW-FLUSH TOILET PROGRAM

Introduction

In many cities water is being withdrawn from reservoirs and subsurface aquifers faster than it is being replaced. The attendant depletion of water supplies has forced some of these cities to take actions ranging from restrictive pricing policies to mandatory conservation measures in residential, commercial, and industrial establishments. Beginning in 2010, a city undertook a project to encourage installation of ultralow-flush toilets in existing houses. To evaluate the cost-effectiveness of the program, an economic analysis was conducted.

Background

The heart of the toilet replacement program involved a rebate of 75% of the cost of the fixture (up to $100 per unit), providing the toilet used no more than 6 litres of water per flush. There was no limit on the number of toilets any individual or business could have replaced.

Procedure

To evaluate the water savings achieved (if any) through the program, monthly water use records were searched for 325 of the household participants, representing a sample size of approximately 13%. Water consumption data were obtained for 12 months before and 12 months after installation of the ultralow-flush toilets. If the house changed ownership during the evaluation period, that account was not included in the evaluation. Since water consumption increases dramatically during the hot summer months for lawn watering, evaporative cooling, car washing, etc., only the winter months of December, January, and February were used to evaluate water consumption before and after installation of the toilet. Before any calculations were made, high-volume water users (usually businesses) were screened out by eliminating all records whose average monthly consumption exceeded 50 CCF (1 CCF = 100 cubic feet = 2831 litres). Additionally, accounts which had monthly averages of 2 CCF or less (either before or after installation) were also eliminated because it was believed that such low consumption rates probably represented an abnormal condition, such as a house for sale which was vacant during part of the study period. The 268 records that remained after the screening procedures were then used to quantify the effectiveness of the program.

Results

Water Consumption

Monthly consumption before and after installation of the ultralow-flush toilets was found to be 11.2 and 9.1 CCF, respectively, for an average reduction of 18.8%. When only the months of January and February were used in the before and after calculations, the respective values were 11.0 and 8.7 CCF, resulting in a water savings rate of 20.9%.

Economic Analysis

The following table shows some of the program totals through the first 1¾ years of the program.

Program Summary	
Number of households participating	2466
Number of toilets replaced	4096
Number of persons	7981
Average cost of toilet	$115.83
Average rebate	$76.12

The results in the previous section indicated monthly water savings of 2.1 CCF. For the average program participant, the payback period n_p in years with *no interest considered* is calculated using Equation [5.7].

$$n_p = \frac{\text{net cost of toilets} + \text{installation cost}}{\text{net annual savings for water and sewer charges}}$$

The lowest rate block for water charges is $0.76 per CCF. The sewer surcharge is $0.62 per CCF. Using these values and a $50 cost for installation, the payback period is

$$n_p = \frac{(115.83 - 76.12) + 50}{(2.1\,\text{CCF/month} \times 12\,\text{months}) \times (0.76 + 0.62)/\text{CCF}}$$

$$= 2.6 \text{ years}$$

Less expensive toilets or lower installation costs would reduce the payback period accordingly, while consideration of the time value of money would lengthen it.

From the standpoint of the utility which supplies water, the cost of the program must be compared against the marginal cost of water delivery and wastewater treatment. The marginal cost c may be represented as

$$c = \frac{\text{cost of rebates}}{\text{volume of water not delivered} + \text{volume of wastewater not treated}}$$

Theoretically, the reduction in water consumption would go on for an infinite period of time, since replacement will never be with a less efficient model. But for a worst-case condition, it is assumed the toilet would have a "productive" life of only 5 years, after which it would leak and not be repaired. The cost to the city for the water not delivered or wastewater not treated would be

$$c = \frac{\$76.12}{(2.1 + 2.1\,\text{CCF/month})(12\,\text{months})(5\,\text{years})}$$

$$= \frac{\$0.302}{\text{CCF}}$$

Thus, unless the city can deliver water and treat the resulting wastewater for less than $0.302 per CCF, the toilet replacement program would be considered economically attractive. For the city, the operating costs alone, that is, without the capital expense, for water and wastewater services that were not expended were about $0.83 per CCF, which far exceeds $0.302 per CCF. Therefore, the toilet replacement program was clearly very cost-effective.

Case Study Exercises

1. For an interest rate of 8% and a toilet life of 5 years, what would the participant's payback period be?

2. Is the participant's payback period more sensitive to the interest rate used or to the life of the toilet?

3. What would the cost to the city be if an interest rate of 6% per year were used with a toilet life of 5 years? Compare the cost in $/CCF to those determined at 0% interest.

4. From the city's standpoint, is the success of the program sensitive to (a) the percentage of toilet cost rebated, (b) the interest rate, if rates of 4% to 15% are used, or (c) the toilet life, if lives of 2 to 20 years are used?

5. What other factors might be important to (a) the participants and (b) the city in evaluating whether the program is a success?

CHAPTER 6

Annual Worth Analysis

In this chapter, we add to our repertoire of alternative comparison tools. In the last chapter we learned the PW method. Here we learn the equivalent annual worth, or AW, method. AW analysis is commonly considered the more desirable of the two methods because the AW value is easy to calculate; the measure of worth—AW in dollars per year—is understood by most individuals; and its assumptions are essentially identical to those of the PW method.

Annual worth is also known by other titles. Some are equivalent annual worth (EAW), equivalent annual cost (EAC), annual equivalent (AE), and EUAC (equivalent uniform annual cost). The resulting equivalent annual worth amount is the same for all name variations. The alternative selected by the AW method will always be the same as that selected by the PW method, and all other alternative evaluation methods, provided they are performed correctly.

In the case study, the estimates made when an AW analysis was performed are found to be substantially different after the equipment is installed. Spreadsheets, sensitivity analysis, and annual worth analysis work together to evaluate the situation.

LEARNING OBJECTIVES

Purpose: Make annual worth calculations and compare alternatives using the annual worth method.

By the end of this chapter you should be able to

One life cycle	**1.** Calculate AW for alternatives having different lives.
AW calculation	**2.** Calculate capital recovery (CR) and AW using two methods.
Alternative selection by AW	**3.** Select the best alternative on the basis of an AW analysis.
Permanent investment AW	**4.** Calculate the AW of a permanent investment.

6.1 ADVANTAGES AND USES OF ANNUAL WORTH ANALYSIS

For many engineering economic studies, the AW method is the best to use, when compared to PW, FW, and rate of return (next two chapters). Since the AW value is the equivalent uniform annual worth of all estimated receipts and disbursements during the life cycle of the project or alternative, AW is easy to understand by any individual acquainted with annual amounts, that is, dollars per year. The AW value, which has the same economic interpretation as *A* used thus far, is equivalent to the PW and FW values at the MARR for *n* years. All three can be easily determined from each other by the relation

$$AW = PW(A/P,i,n) = FW(A/F,i,n) \qquad [6.1]$$

The *n* in the factors is the number of years for equal-service comparison. This is the LCM or the stated study period of the PW or FW analysis.

When all cash flow estimates are converted to an AW value, this value applies for every year of the life cycle, and for *each additional life cycle*. In fact, a prime computational and interpretation advantage is that

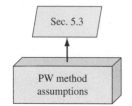

Sec. 5.3

PW method assumptions

> **The AW value has to be calculated for *only one life cycle*. Therefore, it is not necessary to use the LCM of lives, as it is for PW and FW analyses.**

Therefore, determining the AW over one life cycle of an alternative determines the AW for all future life cycles. As with the PW method, there are three fundamental assumptions of the AW method that should be understood.

> **When alternatives being compared have different lives, the AW method makes the assumptions that**
>
> 1. **The services provided are needed for at least the LCM of the lives of the alternatives.**
> 2. **The selected alternative will be repeated for succeeding life cycles in exactly the same manner as for the first life cycle.**
> 3. **All cash flows will have the same estimated values in every life cycle.**

In practice, no assumption is precisely correct. If, in a particular evaluation, the first two assumptions are not reasonable, a study period must be established for the analysis. Note that for assumption 1, the length of time may be the indefinite future (forever). In the third assumption, all cash flows are expected to change exactly with the inflation (or deflation) rate. If this is not a reasonable assumption, new cash flow estimates must be made for each life cycle, and, again, a study period must be used. AW analysis for a stated study period is discussed in Section 6.3.

EXAMPLE 6.1

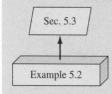

Sec. 5.3

Example 5.2

In Example 5.2 about office lease options, a PW analysis was performed over 18 years, the LCM of 6 and 9 years. Consider only location A, which has a 6-year life cycle. The diagram in Figure 6–1 shows the cash flows for all three life cycles (first cost $15,000; annual costs $3500; deposit return $1000). Demonstrate the equivalence at *i* = 15% of PW over three life cycles and AW over one cycle. In the previous example, present worth for location A was calculated as PW = $−45,036.

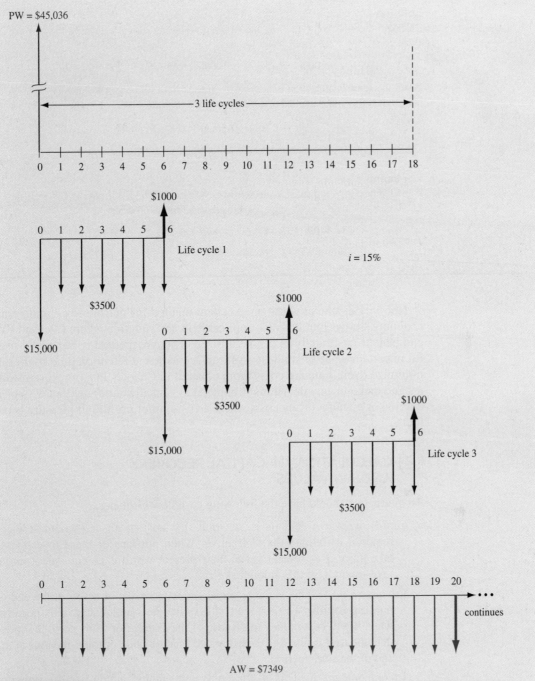

FIGURE 6–1
PW and AW values for three life cycles, Example 6.1.

Solution

Calculate the equivalent uniform annual worth value for all cash flows in the first life cycle.

$$AW = -15,000(A/P,15\%,6) + 1000(A/F,15\%,6) - 3500 = \$-7349$$

When the same computation is performed on each life cycle, the AW value is $\$-7349$. Now, Equation [6.1] is applied to the PW value for 18 years.

$$AW = -45,036(A/P,15\%,18) = \$-7349$$

The one-life-cycle AW value and the PW value based on 18 years are equal.

Comment

If the FW and AW equivalence relation is used, first find the FW from the PW over the LCM, then calculate the AW value. (There are small round-off errors.)

$$FW = PW(F/P,15\%,18) = -45,036(12.3755) = \$-557,343$$

$$AW = FW(A/F,15\%,18) = -557,343(0.01319) = \$-7351$$

Not only is annual worth an excellent method for performing engineering economy studies, but it is also applicable in any situation where PW (and FW and benefit-cost) analysis can be utilized. The AW method is especially useful in certain types of studies: asset replacement and retention time studies to minimize overall annual costs (both covered in Chapter 11), breakeven studies and make-or-buy decisions (Chapter 13), and all studies dealing with production or manufacturing costs where a cost/unit or profit/unit measure is the focus.

6.2 CALCULATION OF CAPITAL RECOVERY AND AW VALUES

An alternative should have the following cash flow estimates:

Initial investment P. This is the total first cost of all assets and services required to initiate the alternative. When portions of these investments take place over several years, their present worth is an equivalent initial investment. Use this amount as P.

Salvage value S. This is the terminal estimated value of assets at the end of their useful life. The S is zero if no salvage is anticipated; S is negative when it will cost money to dispose of the assets. For study periods shorter than the useful life, S is the estimated market value or trade-in value at the end of the study period.

Annual amount A. This is the equivalent annual amount (costs only for service alternatives; costs and receipts for revenue alternatives). Often this is the annual operating cost (AOC), so the estimate is already an equivalent A value.

The annual worth (AW) value for an alternative comprises two components: capital recovery for the initial investment P at a stated interest rate (usually the MARR) and the equivalent annual amount A. The symbol CR is used for the capital recovery component. In equation form,

$$AW = -CR - A \qquad [6.2]$$

Both CR and A have minus signs because they represent costs. The total annual amount A is determined from uniform recurring costs (and possibly receipts) and nonrecurring amounts. The P/A and P/F factors may be necessary to first obtain a present worth amount, then the A/P factor converts this amount to the A value in Equation [6.2]. (If the alternative is a revenue project, there will be positive cash flow estimates present in the calculation of the A value.)

The recovery of an amount of capital P committed to an asset, plus the time value of the capital at a particular interest rate, is a very fundamental principle of economic analysis. *Capital recovery is the equivalent annual cost of owning the asset plus the return on the initial investment.* The A/P factor is used to convert P to an equivalent annual cost. If there is some anticipated positive salvage value S at the end of the asset's useful life, its equivalent annual value is removed using the A/F factor. This action reduces the equivalent annual cost of owning the asset. Accordingly, CR is

$$CR = -[P(A/P,i,n) - S(A/F,i,n)] \qquad [6.3]$$

The computation of CR and AW is illustrated in Example 6.2.

EXAMPLE 6.2

Telesat's Anik-1 was the world's first domestic communications satellite when it was launched in 1972, bringing live broadcasts of *Hockey Night in Canada* to northern communities. Telstar 11N, the powerful new Ku band satellite, will connect North America, Europe, and Africa and serve growing demand for mobile broadband. Telesat is interested in a piece of Earth-based tracking equipment, which will require an investment of $13 million. Eight million dollars will be committed now and the remaining $5 million expended at the end of year 1 of the project. Annual operating costs for the system are expected to start the first year and continue at $0.9 million per year. The useful life of the tracker is 8 years with a salvage value of $0.5 million. Calculate the AW value for the system, if the corporate MARR is currently 12% per year.

Solution

The cash flows (Figure 6–2a) for the tracker system must be converted to an equivalent AW cash flow sequence over 8 years (Figure 6–2b). (All amounts are expressed in $1 million units.) The AOC is $A = \$-0.9$ per year, and the capital recovery is calculated by using Equation [6.3]. The present worth P in year 0 of the two separate investment amounts of $8 and $5 is determined *before* multiplying by the A/P factor.

$$CR = -\{[8.0 + 5.0(P/F,12\%,1)](A/P,12\%,8) - 0.5(A/F,12\%,8)\}$$
$$= -\{[12.46](0.2013) - 0.040\}$$
$$= \$-2.47$$

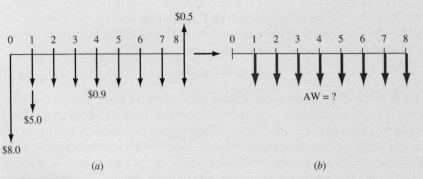

FIGURE 6–2

(a) Cash flow diagram for satellite tracker costs and (b) conversion to an equivalent AW (in $1 million), Example 6.2.

The correct interpretation of this result is very important to Telesat. It means that each and every year for 8 years, the equivalent total revenue from the tracker must be at least $2,470,000 *just to recover the initial present worth investment plus the required return of 12% per year.* This does not include the AOC of $0.9 million each year.

Since this amount, CR = $−2.47 million, is an *equivalent annual cost,* as indicated by the minus sign, total AW is found by Equation [6.2].

$$AW = -2.47 - 0.9 = \$-3.37 \text{ million per year}$$

This is the AW for all future life cycles of 8 years, provided the costs rise at the same rate as inflation, and the same costs and services are expected to apply for each succeeding life cycle.

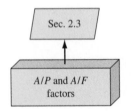

Sec. 2.3

A/P and A/F factors

There is a second, equally correct way to determine CR. Either method results in the same value. In Section 2.3, a relation between the A/P and A/F factors was stated as

$$(A/F,i,n) = (A/P,i,n) - i$$

Both factors are present in the CR Equation [6.3]. Substitute for the A/F factor to obtain

$$CR = -\{P(A/P,i,n) - S[(A/P,i,n) - i]\}$$
$$= -[(P - S)(A/P,i,n) + S(i)] \qquad [6.4]$$

There is a basic logic to this formula. Subtracting S from the initial investment P before applying the A/P factor recognizes that the salvage value will be recovered. This reduces CR, the annual cost of asset ownership. However, the fact that S is not recovered until year n of ownership is compensated for by charging the annual interest $S(i)$ against the CR.

In Example 6.2, the use of this second way to calculate CR results in the same value.

$$CR = -\{[8.0 + 5.0(P/F,12\%,1) - 0.5](A/P,12\%,8) + 0.5(0.12)\}$$
$$= -\{[12.46 - 0.5](0.2013) + 0.06\} = \$-2.47$$

Although either CR relation results in the same amount, it is better to consistently use the same method. The first method, Equation [6.3], will be used in this text.

For solution by computer, use the PMT function to determine CR only in a single spreadsheet cell. The general function PMT($i\%,n,P,F$) is rewritten using the initial investment as P and $-S$ for the salvage value. The format is

$$\text{PMT}(i\%,n,P,-S)$$

As an illustration, determine the CR only in Example 6.2 above. Since the initial investment is distributed over 2 years—$8 million in year 0 and $5 million in year 1—embed the PV function into PMT to find the equivalent P in year 0. The complete function for only the CR amount (in $1 million units) is PMT(12%,8,8 + *PV(12%,1,−5)*,−0.5), where the embedded PV function is in italic. The answer of $−2.47 (million) will be displayed in the spreadsheet cell.

6.3 EVALUATING ALTERNATIVES BY ANNUAL WORTH ANALYSIS

The annual worth method is typically the easiest of the evaluation techniques to perform, when the MARR is specified. The alternative selected has the lowest equivalent annual cost (service alternatives), or highest equivalent income (revenue alternatives). This means that the selection guidelines are the same as for the PW method, but using the AW value.

For mutually exclusive alternatives, calculate AW at the MARR.

One alternative: AW ≥ 0, MARR is met or exceeded.

Two or more alternatives: Choose the lowest-cost or highest-income (numerically largest) AW value.

If an assumption in Section 6.1 is not acceptable for an alternative, a study period analysis must be used. Then the cash flow estimates over the study period are converted to AW amounts. This is illustrated later in Example 6.4.

EXAMPLE 6.3

PizzaRush, which is located in the greater Toronto area, fares very well with its competition in offering fast delivery. Many students at the area universities and colleges work part-time delivering orders made via the Web at PizzaRush.com. The owner, a software engineering graduate of UT, plans to purchase and install five portable, in-car systems to increase delivery speed and accuracy. The systems provide a link between the Web order-placement software and the On-Star© system for satellite-generated directions to any address in the greater Toronto area. The expected result is faster, friendlier service to customers, and more income for PizzaRush.

Each system costs $4600, has a 5-year useful life, and may be salvaged for an estimated $300. Total operating cost for all systems is $650 for the first year, increasing by $50 per year thereafter. The MARR is 10%. Perform an annual worth evaluation for the owner that answers the following questions. Perform the solution by hand and by computer, as requested below.

(a) How much new annual income is necessary to recover the investment at the MARR of 10% per year? Generate this value by hand and by computer.

(b) The owner conservatively estimates increased income of $1200 per year for all five systems. Is this project financially viable at the MARR? Solve by hand and by computer.

(c) Based on the answer in part (b), use the computer to determine how much new income PizzaRush must have to economically justify the project. Operating costs remain as estimated.

Solution by Hand

(a and b) The CR and AW values will answer these two questions. Cash flow is presented in Figure 6–3 for all five systems. Use Equation [6.3] for the capital recovery at 10%.

$$CR = 5(4600)(A/P,10\%,5) - 5(300)(A/F,10\%,5)$$
$$= \$5822$$

The financial viability can be determined without calculating the AW value. The $1200 in new income is substantially lower than the CR of $5822, which does not yet include the annual costs. The purchase is clearly not economically justified. However, to complete the analysis, determine AW. The annual operating costs and incomes form an arithmetic gradient series with a base of $550 in year 1, decreasing by $50 per year for 5 years. The AW relation is

$$AW = -\text{capital recovery} + \text{equivalent net income}$$
$$= -5822 + 550 - 50(A/G,10\%,5)$$
$$= \$-5362$$

This is the equivalent 5-year net amount needed to return the investment and recover the estimated operating costs at a 10% per year return. This shows, once again, that the alternative is clearly not financially viable at MARR = 10%. Note that the estimated extra $1200 per year income, offset by the operating costs, has reduced the required annual amount from $5822 to $5362.

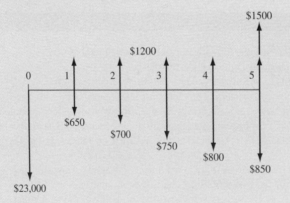

FIGURE 6–3
Cash flow diagram used to compute AW, Example 6.3.

Solution by Computer

The spreadsheet layout (Figure 6–4) shows the cash flows for the investment, the operating costs, and annual income in separate columns. The functions use global variable format for faster sensitivity analysis.

(*a* and *b*) The capital recovery value of $5822 is displayed in cell B7, which is determined by a PMT function with an embedded NPV function. Cells C7 and D7 also use the PMT function to find the annual equivalent for costs and incomes, again with an embedded NPV function.

  Cell F11 displays the final answer of AW = $−5362, which is the sum of all three AW components in row 7.

(*c*) To find the income (column D) necessary to justify the project, a value of AW = $0 must be displayed in cell F11. Other estimates remain the same. Because all the annual incomes in column D receive their value from cell B4, change the entry in B4 until F11 displays "$0". This occurs at $6562. (These amounts are not shown in B4 and F11 of Figure 6–4.) The owner of PizzaRush would have to increase the estimate of extra income for the new system from $1200 to $6562 per year to make a 10% return. This is a substantial increase.

	A	B	C	D	E	F	G
1							
2	MARR	10%			= −B3*PMT($B$2,5,NPV($B$2,B9:B13)+B8)		
3	# of systems	5					
4	Income/system	$ 1,200			= −PMT(10%, 5, NPV(10%,C9:C13)+C8)		
5			Annual	Annual			
6	Year	Investment	costs	income			
7	AW value	$ (5,822)	$ (741)	$ 1,200			
8	0	$ (4,600)	$ -	$ -			
9	1	$ -	$ (650)	$ 1,200	Total AW for	5	systems
10	2	$ -	$ (700)	$ 1,200			
11	3	$ -	$ (750)	$ 1,200		$ (5,362)	
12	4	$ -	$ (800)	$ 1,200			
13	5	$ 300	$ (850)	$ 1,200			
14					= SUM(B7:D7)		
15				= $B$4			
16							

FIGURE 6–4
Spreadsheet solution, Example 6.3(*a*) and (*b*).

EXAMPLE 6.4

In Example 5.12, PW analysis was performed (*a*) over the LCM of 24 years and (*b*) over a study period of 6 years. Compare the two plans for Lafarge Cement, under the same conditions, using the AW method. The MARR is 15%. Solve by hand and by computer.

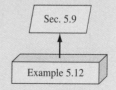

Sec. 5.9

Example 5.12

Solution by Hand

(*a*) Even though the two components of plan A, movers and pads, have different lives, the AW analysis is conducted for only one life cycle of each component. Each AW is made up of CR plus the annual operating cost. Use Equation [6.3] to find the CR amount.

$$AW_A = CR_{movers} + CR_{pad} + AOC_{movers} + AOC_{pad}$$

$$CR_{movers} = -90,000(A/P,15\%,8) + 10,000(A/F,15\%,8) = \$-19,328$$

$$CR_{pad} = -28,000(A/P,15\%,12) + 2000(A/F,15\%,12) = \$-5096$$

$$\text{Total } AOC_A = \$-12,000 - 300 = \$-12,300$$

The total AW for each plan is

$$AW_A = -19,328 - 5096 - 12,300 = \$-36,724$$

$$AW_B = CR_{conveyor} + AOC_{conveyor}$$

$$= -175,000(A/P,15\%,24) + 10,000(A/F,15\%,24) - 2500 = \$-29,646$$

Select plan B, the same decision as that for PW analysis.

(b) For the study period, perform the same analysis with $n = 6$ in all factors, after updating the salvage values to the residual values.

$$CR_{movers} = -90,000(A/P,15\%,6) + 40,000(A/F,15\%,6) = \$-19,212$$

$$CR_{pad} = -28,000(A/P,15\%,6) + 2000(A/F,15\%,6) = \$-7170$$

$$AW_A = -19,212 - 7170 - 12,300 = \$-38,682$$

$$AW_B = CR_{conveyor} + AOC_{conveyor}$$

$$= -175,000(A/P,15\%,6) + 25,000(A/F,15\%,6) - 2500$$

$$= \$-45,886$$

Now, select plan A for its lower AW of costs.

Comment

There is a fundamental relation between the PW and AW values of part (a). As stated by Equation [6.1], if you have the PW of a given plan, determine the AW by calculating $AW = PW(A/P,i,n)$; or if you have the AW, then $PW = AW(P/A,i,n)$. To obtain the correct value, the LCM must be used for all n values, because the PW method of evaluation must take place over an equal time period for each alternative to ensure an equal-service comparison. The PW values, with round-off considered, are the same as determined in Example 5.12, Figure 5–9.

$$PW_A = AW_A(P/A,15\%,24) = \$-236,275$$

$$PW_B = AW_B(P/A,15\%,24) = \$-190,736$$

Solution by Computer

E-SOLVE

(a) See Figure 6–5a. This is exactly the same format as that used for the PW evaluation over the LCM of 24 years (Figure 5–9), except only the *cash flows for one life cycle* are shown here, and the NPV functions at the head of each column are now *PMT functions with the NPV function embedded*. The cell tags detail two of the

PMT functions, where the initial minus sign ensures the result is a cost amount in the total AW for each plan (cells H19 and H22). (The bottom portion of the spreadsheet is not shown. Plan B continues through its entire life with the $10,000 salvage value in year 24, and the annual cost of $2500 continues through year 24.)

(a) AW comparison over one life cycle

MARR = 15%

= -PMT($B$3,8,NPV($B$3,B11:B34)+B10)

= -PMT($B$3,12, NPV($B$3,D11:D22)+D10)

	Plan A				Plan B		
	2 Movers		Pad		Conveyor		
Year	Investment	Annual CF	Investment	Annual CF	Investment	Annual CF	
AW values	$ (19,328)	$ (12,000)	$ (5,097)	$ (300)	$ (27,146)	$ (2,500)	
0	$ (90,000)	$ -	$ (28,000)	$ -	$ (175,000)	$ -	
1	$ -	$ (12,000)	$ -	$ (300)	$ -	$ (2,500)	
2	$ -	$ (12,000)	$ -	$ (300)	$ -	$ (2,500)	
3	$ -	$ (12,000)	$ -	$ (300)	$ -	$ (2,500)	
4	$ -	$ (12,000)	$ -	$ (300)	$ -	$ (2,500)	
5	$ -	$ (12,000)	$ -	$ (300)	$ -	$ (2,500)	
6	$ -	$ (12,000)	$ -	$ (300)	$ -	$ (2,500)	AW values for one life cycle:
7	$ -	$ (12,000)	$ -	$ (300)	$ -	$ (2,500)	
8	$ 10,000	$ (12,000)	$ -	$ (300)	$ -	$ (2,500)	AW A= AW mover + AW pad
9			$ -	$ (300)	$ -	$ (2,500)	$ (36,725)
10			$ -	$ (300)	$ -	$ (2,500)	
11			$ -	$ (300)	$ -	$ (2,500)	AW B = AW conveyor
12			$ 2,000	$ (300)	$ -	$ (2,500)	$ (29,646)
13					$ -	$ (2,500)	
14					$ -	$ (2,500)	
15					$ -	$ (2,500)	

(a)

AW comparison over study period of 6 years

MARR = 15%

= -PMT($B$3,6,NPV($B$3,D11:D16)+D10)

	Plan A				Plan B		
	2 Movers		Pad		Conveyor		
Year	Investment	Annual CF	Investment	Annual CF	Investment	Annual CF	
6-yr AW	$ (19,212)	$ (12,000)	$ (7,170)	$ (300)	$ (43,386)	$ (2,500)	
0	$ (90,000)	$ -	$ (28,000)	$ -	$ (175,000)	$ -	
1	$ -	$ (12,000)	$ -	$ (300)	$ -	$ (2,500)	
2	$ -	$ (12,000)	$ -	$ (300)	$ -	$ (2,500)	
3	$ -	$ (12,000)	$ -	$ (300)	$ -	$ (2,500)	
4	$ -	$ (12,000)	$ -	$ (300)	$ -	$ (2,500)	
5	$ -	$ (12,000)	$ -	$ (300)	$ -	$ (2,500)	
6	$ 40,000	$ (12,000)	$ 2,000	$ (300)	$ 25,000	$ (2,500)	

AW over 6 years

= SUM(B9:E9)

AW A = $ (38,682)
AW B = $ (45,886)

(b)

FIGURE 6-5

Spreadsheet solution using AW comparison of two alternatives: (a) one life cycle, (b) study period of 6 years, Example 6.4.

The resulting CR and AW values obtained here are the same as those for the solution by hand. Plan B is selected.

Plan A: $CR_{movers} = \$-19{,}328$ (in B8) $CR_{pad} = \$-5097$ (in D8)

$AW_A = \$-36{,}725$ (in H19)

Plan B: $CR_{conveyor} = \$-27{,}146$ (in F8) $AW_B = \$-29{,}646$ (in H22)

(b) In Figure 6–5b, the lives are shortened to the study period of 6 years. The estimated residual values in year 6 are entered (row 16 cells), and all AOC amounts beyond 6 years are deleted. When the *n* value in each PMT function is adjusted from 8, 12, or 24 years to 6 in every case, new CR values are displayed, and cells D20 and D21 display the new AW values. Now plan A is selected since it has a lower AW of costs. This is the same result as for the PW analysis in Figure 5–10 for Example 5.12(*b*).

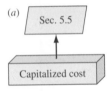

(a) Sec. 5.5 → Capitalized cost

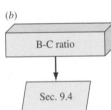

(b) B-C ratio → Sec. 9.4

If the projects are *independent*, the AW at the MARR is calculated. All projects with AW ≥ 0 are acceptable.

6.4 AW OF A PERMANENT INVESTMENT

This section discusses the annual worth equivalent of the capitalized cost. Evaluation of public sector projects, such as flood control dams, irrigation canals, bridges, or other large-scale projects, requires the comparison of alternatives that have such long lives that they may be considered infinite in economic analysis terms. For this type of analysis, the annual worth of the initial investment is the perpetual annual interest earned on the initial investment, that is, $A = Pi$. This is Equation [5.3]; however, the *A* value is also the capital recovery amount. (This same relation will be used again when benefit-cost ratios are discussed.)

Cash flows recurring at regular or irregular intervals are handled exactly as in conventional AW computations; they are converted to equivalent uniform annual amounts *A* for one cycle. This automatically annualizes them for each succeeding life cycle, as discussed in Section 6.1. Add all the *A* values to the CR amount to find total AW, as in Equation [6.2].

EXAMPLE 6.5

Spring and summer flooding of the Red River is increasingly submerging farmland and causing the closure of the Canadian–U.S. border crossing south of Winnipeg. The Province of Manitoba is considering three options to prevent future closures of Highway 75.

Proposal A requires improvements to the dike at Morris and to the banks of the Red River. The purchase of earthmoving and dredging equipment will cost $650,000, with a 10-year life and a $17,000 salvage value. Annual operating costs are estimated to total $50,000. The yearly cost of operations along the river bank between Morris and the border is expected to be $120,000.

Proposal B is to raise the portion of the highway in front of and over the dike at Morris. The initial cost will be $4 million and minor annual maintenance of the dike will cost $5000. In addition, highway resurfacing will have to be done every 5 years at a cost of $30,000.

Proposal C is to build a bypass of the highway in the area. Estimates are an initial cost of $6 million, annual maintenance of $3000, and a life of 50 years.

Compare the alternatives on the basis of annual worth using an interest rate of 5% per year.

Solution

Since this is an investment for a permanent project, compute the AW for one cycle of all recurring costs. For proposals A and C, the CR values are found using Equation [6.3], with $n_A = 10$ and $n_C = 50$, respectively. For proposal B, the CR is simply $P(i)$.

Proposal A	
CR of dredging equipment:	
$-650,000(A/P,5\%,10) + 17,000(A/F,5\%,10)$	$\$ -82,824$
Annual cost of dredging	$-50,000$
Annual cost of riverbank operations	$-120,000$
	$\$-252,824$
Proposal B	
CR of initial investment: $-4,000,000(0.05)$	$\$-200,000$
Annual maintenance cost	$-5,000$
Resurfacing cost: $-30,000(A/F,5\%,5)$	$-5,429$
	$-210,429$
Proposal C	
CR of bypass: $-6,000,000(A/P,5\%,50)$	$\$-328,680$
Annual maintenance cost	$-3,000$
	$\$-331,680$

Proposal B is selected, due to its lowest AW of costs.

Comment

Note the use of the A/F factor for the resurfacing cost in proposal B. The A/F factor is used instead of A/P, because the resurfacing cost begins in year 5, not year 0, and continues indefinitely at 5-year intervals.

If the 50-year life of proposal C is considered infinite, CR $= P(i) = \$-300,000$, instead of $\$-328,680$ for $n = 50$. This is a small economic difference. How long lives of 40 or more years are treated economically is a matter of "local" practice.

EXAMPLE 6.6

An engineer with Becker Consulting has just received a bonus of $10,000. If she deposits it now at an interest rate of 8% per year, how many years must the money accumulate before she can withdraw $2000 per year forever? Use a computer to find the answer.

Solution by Computer

Figure 6–6 presents the cash flow diagram. The first step is to find the total amount of money, call it P_n, that must be accumulated in year n, just 1 year prior to the first withdrawal of the perpetual $A = \$2000$ per year series. That is,

$$P_n = \frac{A}{i} = \frac{2000}{0.08} = \$25{,}000$$

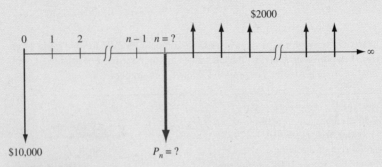

FIGURE 6–6

Diagram to determine n for a perpetual withdrawal, Example 6.6.

Use the NPER function in one cell to determine when the initial $10,000 deposit will accumulate to $25,000 (Figure 6–7, cell B4). The answer is 11.91 years. If the engineer leaves the money in for 12 years, and if 8% is earned every year, forever, the $2000 per year is ensured.

Figure 6–7 also presents a more general spreadsheet solution in cells B7 through B11. Cell B10 determines the amount to accumulate in order to receive any amount (cell B9) forever at 8% (cell B7), and B11 includes the NPER function developed in cell reference format for any interest rate, deposit, and accumulated amount.

	A	B	C	D	E
1					
2				= NPER(8%,, −10000, 25000)	
3					
4		11.91			
5					
6					
7	Interest rate	8%			
8	Amount deposited today	$10,000			
9	Amount to withdraw forever	$2,000	= B9/B7		
10	Amount to accumulate	$25,000			
11	Time required	11.91 years			
12			= NPER(B7, 0, −B8, B10)		

FIGURE 6–7

Two spreadsheet solutions to find an n value using the NPER function, Example 6.6.

CHAPTER SUMMARY

The annual worth method of comparing alternatives is often preferred to the present worth method, because the AW comparison is performed for only one life cycle. This is a distinct advantage when comparing different-life alternatives. AW for the first life cycle is the AW for the second, third, and all succeeding life cycles, under certain assumptions. When a study period is specified, the AW calculation is determined for that time period, regardless of the lives of the alternatives. As in the present worth method, the remaining value of an alternative at the end of the study period is recognized by estimating a market value.

For infinite-life alternatives, the initial cost is annualized simply by multiplying P by i. For finite-life alternatives, the AW through one life cycle is equal to the perpetual equivalent annual worth.

PROBLEMS

6.1 Seven years ago, a Nova Scotia logging contractor purchased a used Peterson 5000G wood chipper for $115,000 for biomass and custom chipping. Operating and maintenance costs averaged $9500 per year. A complete overhaul at the end of year 4 cost an additional $3200.

(a) Calculate the annual cost of the chipper at 7% per year.

(b) If the added revenue from using the chipper was at most $20,000 per year, was the purchase economically advantageous?

6.2 Assume that an alternative has a 3-year life and that you calculated its annual worth over its 3-year life cycle. If you were told to provide the annual worth of that alternative for a 4-year study period, would the annual worth value you calculated from the alternative's 3-year life cycle be a valid estimate of the annual worth over the 4-year study period? Why or why not?

6.3 Machine A has a 3-year life with no salvage value. Assume that you were told that the service provided by these machines would be needed for only 5 years. Alternative A would have to be repurchased and kept for only 2 years. What would its

salvage value have to be after the 2 years in order to make its annual worth the same as it is for its 3-year life cycle at an interest rate of 10% per year?

Year	Alternative A, $	Alternative B, $
0	−10,000	−20,000
1	−7,000	−5,000
2	−7,000	−5,000
3	−7,000	−5,000
4		−5,000
5		−5,000

Alternatives Comparison

6.4 Cameco Corporation's McArthur uranium mine in Saskatchewan wants to evaluate two alternative pumps to lift water away from its active mine system. Use AW method at 9% per year to select the better alternative.

	2-Cylinder Pump	3-Cylinder Pump
First cost, $	−250,000	−370,500
Annual operating cost, $/year	−40,000	−50,000
Life, years	3	5
Salvage value, $	20,000	20,000

6.5 A consulting engineering firm is considering two models of SUVs for the company principals. A GM model will have a first cost of $26,000, an operating cost of $2000, and a salvage value of $12,000 after 3 years. A Hyundai model will have a first cost of $29,000, an operating cost of $1200, and a $15,000 resale value after 3 years. At an interest rate of 15% per year, which model should the consulting firm buy? Conduct an annual worth analysis.

6.6 A large textile company is trying to decide which sludge dewatering process it should use ahead of its sludge drying operation. The costs associated with centrifuge and belt press systems are shown below. Compare them on the basis of their annual worths, using an interest rate of 10% per year.

	Centrifuge	Belt Press
First cost, $	−250,000	−170,000
Annual operating cost, $/year	−31,000	−35,000
Overhaul in year 2, $	—	−26,000
Salvage value, $	40,000	10,000
Life, years	6	4

6.7 A chemical engineer is considering two styles of pipes for moving distillate from a refinery to the tank farm. A small pipeline will cost less to purchase (including valves and other appurtenances) but will have a high head loss and, therefore, a higher pumping cost. The small pipeline will cost $1.7 million installed and will have an operating cost of $12,000 per month. A larger-diameter pipeline will cost $2.1 million installed, but its operating cost will be only $8000 per month. Which pipe size is more economical at an interest rate of 1% per month on the basis of an annual worth analysis? Assume the salvage value is 10% of the first cost for each pipeline at the end of the 10-year project period.

6.8 Polymer Molding, Inc., is considering two processes for manufacturing storm drains. Plan A involves conventional injection molding that will require making a steel mold at a cost of $2 million. The cost for inspecting, maintaining, and cleaning the molds is expected to be $5000 per month. Since the cost of materials for this plan is expected to be the same as for the other plan, this cost will not be included in the comparison. The salvage value for plan A is expected to be 10% of the first cost. Plan B involves using an innovative process known as virtual engineered composites wherein a floating mold uses an operating system that constantly adjusts the water pressure around the mold and the chemicals entering the process. The first cost to tool the floating mold is only $25,000, but because of the newness of the process, personnel and product-reject costs are expected to be higher than those for a conventional process. The company expects the operating costs to be $45,000 per month for the first 8 months and then to decrease to $10,000 per month thereafter. There will be no salvage value with this plan. At an interest rate of 12% per year, compounded monthly, which process should the company select on the basis of an annual worth analysis over a 3-year study period?

6.9 An industrial engineer is considering two robots for purchase by a fibre-optic manufacturing company. Robot X will have a first cost of $85,000, an annual maintenance and operation (M&O) cost of $30,000, and a $40,000 salvage value. Robot Y will have a first cost of $97,000, an annual M&O cost of $27,000, and a $48,000 salvage value. Which should be selected on the basis of an annual worth comparison at an interest rate of 12% per year? Use a 3-year study period.

6.10 Accurate airflow measurement requires straight unobstructed pipe for a minimum of 10 diameters upstream and 5 diameters downstream of the measuring device. In one particular application, physical constraints compromised the pipe layout, so the engineer was considering installing the airflow probes in an elbow, knowing that flow measurement would be less accurate but good enough for process control. This was plan A, which would be acceptable for only 2 years, after which a more accurate flow measurement system with the same costs as plan A will be available. This plan would have a first cost of $25,000 with annual maintenance estimated at $4000. Plan B involved installation of a recently designed submersible airflow probe. The stainless steel probe could be installed in a drop pipe with the transmitter located in a waterproof enclosure on the handrail. The cost of this system would be $88,000, but because it is accurate, it would not have to be replaced for at least 6 years. Its maintenance cost is estimated to be $1400 per year. Neither system will have a salvage value. At an interest rate of 12% per year, which one should be selected on the basis of an annual worth comparison?

6.11 A mechanical engineer is considering two types of pressure sensors for a low-pressure steam line. The costs are shown below. Which should be selected based on an annual worth comparison at an interest rate of 12% per year?

	Type X	Type Y
First cost,	$ -7,650	-12,900
Maintenance cost, $/year	-1,200	-900
Salvage value, $	0	2,000
Life, years	2	4

6.12 The machines shown below are under consideration for an improvement to an automated candy bar wrapping process.

Determine which should be selected on the basis of an annual worth analysis using an interest rate of 15% per year.

	Machine C	Machine D
First cost, $	-40,000	-65,000
Annual cost, $/year	-10,000	-12,000
Salvage value, $	12,000	25,000
Life, years	3	6

6.13 Two processes can be used for producing a polymer that reduces friction loss in engines. Process K will have a first cost of $160,000, an operating cost of $7000 per month, and a salvage value of $40,000 after its 2-year life. Process L will have a first cost of $210,000, an operating cost of $5000 per month, and a $26,000 salvage value after its 4-year life. Which process should be selected on the basis of an annual worth analysis at an interest rate of 12% per year, compounded monthly?

6.14 Two mutually exclusive projects have the estimated cash flows shown below. Use an annual worth analysis to determine which should be selected at an interest rate of 10% per year.

	Project Q	Project R
First cost, $	-42,000	-80,000
Annual cost, $/year	-6,000	-7,000 year 1, increasing by $1000 per year
Salvage value, $	0	4,000
Life, years	2	4

6.15 An environmental engineer is considering three methods for disposing of a nonhazardous chemical sludge: land application, fluidized-bed incineration, and private disposal contract. The details of each method are shown below. Determine which has the least cost on the basis of an annual worth comparison at 12% per year.

	Land Application	Incineration	Contract
First cost, $	−110,000	−800,000	0
Annual cost, $/year	−95,000	−60,000	−190,000
Salvage value, $	15,000	250,000	0
Life, years	3	6	2

6.16 The Ministry of Transport Ontario is trying to decide whether it should "hot-patch" a short section of an existing road or resurface it. If the hot-patch method is used, approximately 300 cubic metres of material would be required at a cost of $700 per cubic metre (in place). Additionally, the shoulders will have to be improved at the same time at a cost of $24,000. These improvements will last 2 years, at which time they will have to be redone. The annual cost of routine maintenance on the patched up road would be $5000. Alternatively, the road can be resurfaced at a cost of $850,000. This surface will last 10 years if the road is maintained at a cost of $2000 per year beginning 3 years from now. No matter which alternative is selected, the road will be completely rebuilt in 10 years. At an interest rate of 8% per year, which alternative should the Ministry select on the basis of an annual worth analysis?

Permanent Investments and Projects

6.17 The city of Victoria, B.C., is interested in having a wastewater heat recovery system for the downtown area included as part of the CRD's new sewage treatment project. The costs below compare the current schedule of upgrades and maintenance of existing buildings' heating systems (alternative A) to a new network of pipes to connect downtown buildings (alternative B). Recommend one of the two alternatives on the basis of an AW analysis at 10% per year compounded quarterly. Dollar values are in millions.

	Alternative A	Alternative B
First cost, $	−10	−50
Annual operating cost, $/year	−0.8	−0.6
Salvage value, $	0.7	0.2
Life, years	5	Almost permanent

6.18 How much must you deposit in your retirement account starting *now* and continuing each year through year 9 (i.e., 10 deposits) if you want to be able to withdraw $80,000 per year forever beginning 30 years from now? Assume the account earns interest at 10% per year.

6.19 What is the *difference* in annual worth between an investment of $100,000 per year for 100 years and an investment of $100,000 per year forever at an interest rate of 10% per year?

6.20 A stockbroker claims she can consistently earn 15% per year on an investor's money. If she invests $20,000 now, $40,000 two years from now, and $10,000 per year through year 11 starting 4 years from now, how much money can the client withdraw every year forever, beginning 12 years from now, if the stockbroker delivers what she said and the account earns 6% per year from year 12 forward? Disregard taxes.

6.21 Determine the perpetual equivalent annual worth (in years 1 through infinity) of an investment of $50,000 at time 0 and

$50,000 per year thereafter (forever) at an interest rate of 10% per year.

6.22 The cash flow associated with landscaping and maintaining a certain monument in Ottawa is $100,000 now and $50,000 every 5 years forever. Determine its perpetual equivalent annual worth (in years 1 through infinity) at an interest rate of 8% per year.

6.23 The cost associated with maintaining rural highways follows a predictable pattern. There are usually no costs for the first 3 years, but thereafter maintenance is required for restriping, weed control, light replacement, shoulder repairs, etc. For one section of a particular highway, these costs are projected to be $6000 in year 3, $7000 in year 4, and amounts increasing by $1000 per year through the highway's expected 30-year life. Assuming it is replaced with a similar roadway, what is its perpetual equivalent annual worth (in years 1 through infinity) at an interest rate of 8% per year?

6.24 A philanthropist working to set up a permanent endowment wants to deposit money each year, starting *now* and making 10 more (i.e., 11) deposits, so that money will be available for research related to kidney disease. If the size of the first deposit is $1 million and each

succeeding one is $100,000 larger than the previous one, how much will be available forever beginning in year 11, if the fund earns interest at a rate of 10% per year?

6.25 For the cash flow sequence shown below (in thousands of dollars), determine the amount of money that can be withdrawn annually for an infinite period of time, if the first withdrawal is to be made in year 10 and the interest rate is 12% per year.

Year	0	1	2	3	4	5	6
Deposit amount, $	100	90	80	70	60	50	40

6.26 A company that manufactures magnetic membrane switches is investigating three production options that have the estimated cash flows below. (*a*) Determine which option is preferable at an interest rate of 15% per year. (*b*) If the options are independent, determine which are economically acceptable. (All dollar values are in millions.)

	In-House	Licence	Contract
First cost, $	−30	−20	0
Annual cost, $/year	−5	−0.2	−2
Annual income, $/year	14	1.5	2.5
Salvage value, $	7	—	—
Life, years	10	∞	5

CASE STUDY

THE CHANGING SCENE OF AN ANNUAL WORTH ANALYSIS

Harry, owner of an automobile battery distributorship, performed an economic analysis 3 years ago when he decided to place surge protectors in-line for all his major pieces of testing equipment. The estimates used and the annual worth analysis at MAAR = 15% are summarized here. Two different manufacturers' protectors were compared.

	A	B	C	D	E	F	G	H	I
1									
2									
3	MARR =	15%							
4									
5			PowrUp			Lloyd's			
6		Investment	Annual	Repair	Investment	Annual	Repair		AW PowrUp
7	Year	and salvage	maint.	savings	and salvage	maint.	savings		$ 17,558
8	AW values	$ (6,642)	$ (800)	$ 25,000	$ (7,025)	$ (300)	$ 35,000		
9									AW Lloyd's
10	0	$ (26,000)	$ -	$ -	$ (36,000)	$ -	$ -		$ 27,675
11	1	$ -	$ (800)	$ 25,000	$ -	$ (300)	$ 35,000		
12	2	$ -	$ (800)	$ 25,000	$ -	$ (300)	$ 35,000		
13	3	$ -	$ (800)	$ 25,000	$ -	$ (300)	$ 35,000		
14	4	$ -	$ (800)	$ 25,000	$ -	$ (300)	$ 35,000		
15	5	$ -	$ (800)	$ 25,000	$ -	$ (300)	$ 35,000		
16	6	$ 2,000	$ (800)	$ 25,000	$ -	$ (300)	$ 35,000		
17	7				$ -	$ (300)	$ 35,000		
18	8				$ -	$ (300)	$ 35,000		
19	9				$ -	$ (300)	$ 35,000		
20	10				$ 3,000	$ (300)	$ 35,000		

FIGURE 6–8

AW analysis of two surge protector proposals, Case Study, Chapter 6.

	PowrUp	Lloyd's
Cost and installation	$−26,000	$−36,000
Annual maintenance cost	−800	−300
Salvage value	2000	3000
Equipment repair savings	25,000	35,000
Useful life, years	6	10

The spreadsheet in Figure 6–8 is the one Harry used to make the decision. Lloyd's was the clear choice due to its substantially large AW value. The Lloyd's protectors were installed.

During a quick review this last year (year 3 of operation), it was obvious the maintenance costs and repair savings have not followed (and will not follow) the estimates made 3 years ago. In fact, the maintenance contract cost (which includes quarterly inspection) is going from $300 to $1200 per year next year and will then increase 10% per year for the next 10 years. Also, the repair savings for the last 3 years were $35,000, $32,000, and $28,000, as best as Harry can determine. He believes savings will decrease by $2000 per year hereafter. Finally, these 3-year-old protectors are worth nothing on the market now, so the salvage in 7 years is zero, not $3000.

Case Study Exercises

1. Plot a graph of the newly estimated maintenance costs and repair savings projections, assuming the protectors last for 7 more years.

2. With these new estimates, what is the recalculated AW for the Lloyd's protectors? Use the old first cost and maintenance cost estimates for the first 3 years. If these estimates had been made 3 years ago, would Lloyd's still have been the economic choice?

3. How has the capital recovery amount changed for the Lloyd's protectors with these new estimates?

CHAPTER 7

Rate of Return Analysis: Single Alternative

Although the most commonly quoted measure of economic worth for a project or alternative is the rate of return (ROR), its meaning is easily misinterpreted, and the methods to determine ROR are often applied incorrectly. In this chapter, the procedures to correctly interpret and calculate the ROR of a cash flow series are explained, based on a PW or AW equation. The ROR is known by several other names: internal rate of return (IRR), return on investment (ROI), and profitability index (PI), to name three. ROI is often used when the time value of money is not considered, whereas IRR considers interest to be greater than zero. The determination of ROR is accomplished using a manual trial-and-error process or, more rapidly, using spreadsheet functions.

In some cases, more than one ROR value may satisfy the PW or AW equation. This chapter describes how to recognize this possibility and an approach to find the multiple values. Alternatively, one unique ROR value can be obtained by using a reinvestment rate that is established independently of the project cash flows.

Only one alternative is considered here; the next chapter applies these same principles to multiple alternatives.

The case study focuses on a cash flow series that has multiple rates of return.

LEARNING OBJECTIVES

Purpose: Understand the meaning of rate of return (ROR) and perform ROR calculations for one alternative.

Definition of ROR	By the end of this chapter you should be able to
	1. State the meaning of rate of return.
ROR using PW and AW	**2.** Calculate the rate of return using a present worth or annual worth equation.
Cautions about ROR	**3.** Outline the difficulties of using the ROR method, relative to PW and AW methods.
Multiple RORs	**4.** Determine the maximum number of possible ROR values and their values for a specific cash flow series.
Composite ROR	**5.** Calculate the composite rate of return using a stated reinvestment rate.

7.1 INTERPRETATION OF A RATE OF RETURN VALUE

From the perspective of someone who has borrowed money, the interest rate is applied to the *unpaid balance* so that the total loan amount and interest are paid in full exactly with the last loan payment. From the perspective of the lender, there is an *unrecovered balance* at each time period. The interest rate is the return on this unrecovered balance so that the total amount lent and interest are recovered exactly with the last receipt. *Rate of return* describes both of these perspectives.

> **Rate of return (ROR) is the rate paid on the unpaid balance of borrowed money, or the rate earned on the unrecovered balance of an investment, so that the final payment or receipt brings the balance to exactly zero with interest considered.**

The rate of return is expressed as a percent per period, for example, $i = 10\%$ per year. It is stated as a positive percentage; the fact that interest paid on a loan is actually a negative rate of return from the borrower's perspective is not considered. The numerical value of i can range from -100% to infinity, that is, $-100\% < i < \infty$. In terms of an investment, a return of $i = -100\%$ means the entire amount is lost.

The definition above does not state that the rate of return is on the initial amount of the investment; rather it is on the *unrecovered balance,* which changes each time period. The example below illustrates this difference.

EXAMPLE 7.1

Scotiabank lent a newly graduated engineer $1000 at $i = 10\%$ per year for 4 years to buy home office equipment. From the bank's perspective (the lender), the investment in this young engineer is expected to produce an equivalent net cash flow of $315.47 for each of 4 years.

$$A = \$1000(A/P,10\%,4) = \$315.47$$

This represents a 10% per year rate of return on the bank's unrecovered balance. Compute the amount of the unrecovered investment for each of the 4 years using (*a*) the rate of return on the unrecovered balance (the correct basis) and (*b*) the return on the initial $1000 investment. (*c*) Explain why all the initial $1000 amount is not recovered by the final payment in part (*b*).

Solution

(*a*) Table 7–1 shows the unrecovered balance at the end of each year in column 6 using the 10% rate on the *unrecovered balance at the beginning of the year.* After 4 years the total $1000 is recovered, and the balance in column 6 is exactly zero.

(*b*) Table 7–2 shows the unrecovered balance if the 10% return is always figured on the *initial $1000.* Column 6 in year 4 shows a remaining unrecovered amount of $138.12, because only $861.88 is recovered in the 4 years (column 5).

TABLE 7–1   Unrecovered Balances Using a Rate of Return of 10% on the Unrecovered Balance

(1)	(2)	(3) = 0.10 × (2)	(4)	(5) = (4) − (3)	(6) = (2) + (5)
Year	Beginning Unrecovered Balance	Interest on Unrecovered Balance	Cash Flow	Recovered Amount	Ending Unrecovered Balance
0	—	—	$−1,000.00	—	$−1,000.00
1	$−1,000.00	$100.00	+315.47	$215.47	−784.53
2	−784.53	78.45	+315.47	237.02	−547.51
3	−547.51	54.75	+315.47	260.72	−286.79
4	−286.79	28.68	+315.47	286.79	0
		$261.88		$1,000.00	

TABLE 7–2   Unrecovered Balances Using a 10% Return on the Initial Amount

(1)	(2)	(3) = 0.10 × (2)	(4)	(5) = (4) − (3)	(6) = (2) + (5)
Year	Beginning Unrecovered Balance	Interest on Initial Amount	Cash Flow	Recovered Amount	Ending Unrecovered Balance
0	—	—	$−1,000.00	—	$−1,000.00
1	$−1,000.00	$100	+315.47	$215.47	−784.53
2	−784.53	100	+315.47	215.47	−569.06
3	−569.06	100	+315.47	215.47	−353.59
4	−353.59	100	+315.47	215.47	−138.12
		$400		$861.88	

(c)   A total of $400 in interest must be earned if the 10% return each year is based on the initial amount of $1000. However, only $261.88 in interest must be earned if a 10% return on the unrecovered balance is used. There is more of the annual cash flow available to reduce the remaining loan when the rate is applied to the unrecovered balance as in part (a) and Table 7–1. Figure 7–1 illustrates the correct interpretation of rate of return in Table 7–1. Each year the $315.47 receipt represents 10% interest on the unrecovered balance in column 2 plus the recovered amount in column 5.

Because rate of return is the interest rate on the unrecovered balance, the computations in *Table 7–1 for part (a) present a correct interpretation of a 10% rate of return.* Clearly, an interest rate applied only to the principal represents a higher rate than is stated. In practice, a so-called add-on interest rate is frequently based on principal only, as in part (b). This is sometimes referred to as the *installment financing* problem.

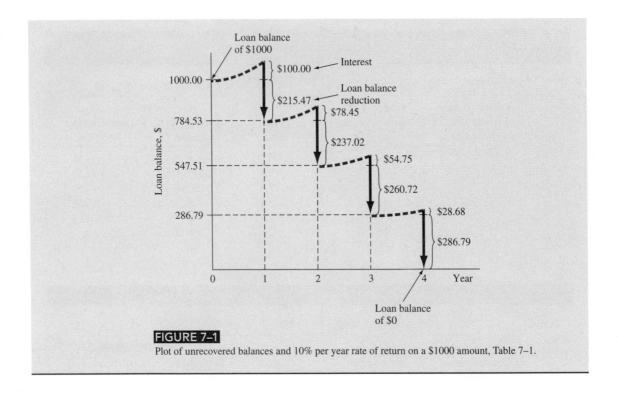

FIGURE 7–1

Plot of unrecovered balances and 10% per year rate of return on a $1000 amount, Table 7–1.

Installment financing can be discovered in many forms in everyday finances. One popular example is a "no-interest program" offered by retail stores on the sale of major appliances, audio and video equipment, furniture, and other consumer items. Many variations are possible, but in most cases, if the purchase is not paid for in full by the time the promotion is over, usually 6 months to 1 year later, *finance charges are assessed from the original date of purchase.* Further, the program's fine print may stipulate that the purchaser use a credit card issued by the retail company, which often has a higher interest rate than that of a regular credit card, for example, 24% per year compared to 18% per year. In all these types of programs, the one common theme is more interest paid over time by the consumer. Usually, the correct definition of *i* as interest on the unpaid balance does not apply directly; *i* has often been manipulated to the financial disadvantage of the purchaser.

7.2 RATE OF RETURN CALCULATION USING A PW OR AW EQUATION

To determine the rate of return of a cash flow series, set up the ROR equation using either PW or AW relations. The present worth of costs or disbursements PW_D is equated to the present worth of incomes or receipts PW_R. Equivalently, the two can be subtracted and set equal to zero. That is, solve for *i* using

$$PW_D = PW_R$$

$$0 = -PW_D + PW_R \qquad \text{[7.1]}$$

The annual worth approach utilizes the AW values in the same fashion to solve for i.

$$AW_D = AW_R$$

$$0 = -AW_D + AW_R \qquad [7.2]$$

The i value that makes these equations numerically correct is called i^*. It is the basis of the ROR relation. To determine if the alternative's cash flow series is viable, compare i^* with the established MARR.

If $i^* \geq$ MARR, accept the alternative as economically viable.

If $i^* <$ MARR, the alternative is not economically viable.

In Chapter 2 the method for calculating the rate of return on an investment was illustrated when only one engineering economy factor was involved. Here the present worth equation is the basis for calculating the rate of return when several factors are involved. Remember that the basis for engineering economy calculations is *equivalence* in PW, FW, or AW terms for a stated $i \geq 0\%$. In rate of return calculations, the objective is to *find the interest rate i^** at which the cash flows are equivalent. The calculations are the reverse of those made in previous chapters, where the interest rate was known. For example, if you deposit $1000 now and are promised payments of $500 three years from now and $1500 five years from now, the rate of return relation using PW factors is

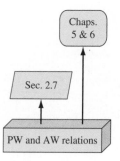

$$1000 = 500(P/F,i^*,3) + 1500(P/F,i^*,5) \qquad [7.3]$$

The value of i^* to make the equality correct is to be computed (see Figure 7–2). If the $1000 is moved to the right side of Equation [7.3], we have

$$0 = -1000 + 500(P/F,i^*,3) + 1500(P/F,i^*,5) \qquad [7.4]$$

which is the general form of Equation [7.1]. The equation is solved for i to obtain $i^* = 16.9\%$ by hand using trial and error or by computer using spreadsheet functions. The rate of return will always be greater than zero if the total amount of receipts is greater than the total amount of disbursements, when the time value of money is considered. Using $i^* = 16.9\%$, a graph similar to Figure 7–1 can be constructed. It will show that the unrecovered balances each year, starting with

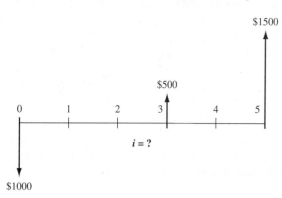

FIGURE 7–2

Cash flow for which a value of i is to be determined.

$-1000 in year 1, are exactly recovered by the $500 and $1500 receipts in years 3 and 5.

It should be evident that rate of return relations are merely a rearrangement of a present worth equation. That is, if the above interest rate is known to be 16.9%, and it is used to find the present worth of $500 three years from now and $1500 five years from now, the PW relation is

$$PW = 500(P/F,16.9\%,3) + 1500(P/F,16.9\%,5) = \$1000$$

This illustrates that rate of return and present worth equations are set up in exactly the same fashion. The only differences are what is given and what is sought.

There are two ways to determine i^* once the PW relation is established: solution via trial and error by hand and solution by spreadsheet function. The second is faster; the first helps in understanding how ROR computations work. We summarize both methods here and in Example 7.2.

i* Using Trial and Error by Hand   The general procedure of using a PW-based equation is

1. Draw a cash flow diagram.
2. Set up the rate of return equation in the form of Equation [7.1].
3. Select values of i by trial and error until the equation is balanced.

When the trial-and-error method is applied to determine i^*, it is advantageous in step 3 to get fairly close to the correct answer on the first trial. If the cash flows are combined in such a manner that the income and disbursements can be represented by a *single factor* such as P/F or P/A, it is possible to look up the interest rate (in the tables) corresponding to the value of that factor for n years. The problem, then, is to combine the cash flows into the format of only one of the factors. This may be done through the following procedure:

1. Convert all *disbursements* into either single amounts (P or F) or uniform amounts (A) by neglecting the time value of money. For example, if it is desired to convert an A to an F value, simply multiply the A by the number of years n. The scheme selected for movement of cash flows should be the one which minimizes the error caused by neglecting the time value of money. That is, if most of the cash flow is an A and a small amount is an F, convert the F to an A rather than the other way around.
2. Convert all *receipts* to either single or uniform values.
3. Having combined the disbursements and receipts so that a P/F, P/A, or A/F format applies, use the interest tables to find the approximate interest rate at which the P/F, P/A, or A/F value is satisfied. The rate obtained is a good estimate for the first trial.

It is important to recognize that this first-trial rate is only an *estimate* of the actual rate of return, because the time value of money is neglected. The procedure is illustrated in Example 7.2.

i* by Computer   The fastest way to determine an *i** value by computer, when there is a series of equal cash flows (*A* series), is to apply the RATE function. This is a powerful one-cell function, where it is acceptable to have a separate *P* value in year 0 and an *F* value in year *n*. The format is

RATE(*n,A,P,F*)

The *F* value does not include the series *A* amount.

When cash flows vary from year to year (period to period), the best way to find *i** is to enter the net cash flows into contiguous cells (including any $0 amounts) and apply the IRR function in any cell. The format is

IRR(first_cell:last_cell,guess)

where "guess" is the *i* value at which the computer starts searching for *i**.

The PW-based procedure for sensitivity analysis and a graphical estimation of the *i** value (or multiple *i** values, as discussed later) is as follows:

1. Draw the cash flow diagram.
2. Set up the ROR relation in the form of Equation [7.1].
3. Enter the cash flows onto the spreadsheet in contiguous cells.
4. Develop the IRR function to display *i**.
5. Use the NPV function to develop a chart of PW vs. *i* values. This graphically shows the *i** value at which PW = 0.

EXAMPLE 7.2

The Burg Khalifa in Dubai, UAE, is the world's tallest building. The HVAC engineer for a company involved in its construction has requested that $500,000 be spent on software and hardware to improve the efficiency of the environmental control systems. This is expected to save $10,000 per year for 10 years in energy costs and $700,000 at the end of 10 years in equipment refurbishment costs. Find the rate of return by hand and by computer.

Solution by Hand
Use the trial-and-error procedure based on a PW equation.

1. Figure 7–3 shows the cash flow diagram.
2. Use Equation [7.1] format for the ROR equation.

$$0 = -500{,}000 + 10{,}000(P/A,i^*,10) + 700{,}000(P/F,i^*,10) \qquad [7.5]$$

3. Use the estimation procedure to determine *i* for the first trial. All income will be regarded as a single *F* in year 10 so that the *P/F* factor can be used. The *P/F* factor is selected because most of the cash flow ($700,000) already fits this factor and errors created by neglecting the time value of the remaining money will be minimized. Only for the first estimate of *i*, define $P = \$500{,}000$, $n = 10$, and $F = 10(10{,}000) + 700{,}000 = \$800{,}000$. Now we can state that

$$500{,}000 = 800{,}000(P/F,i,10)$$

$$(P/F,i,10) = 0.625$$

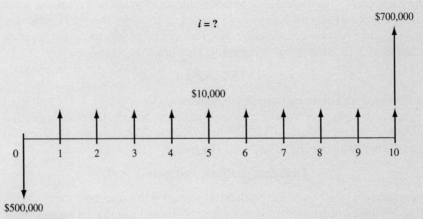

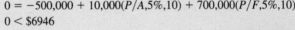

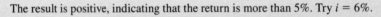

FIGURE 7–3
Cash flow diagram, Example 7.2.

The roughly estimated i is between 4% and 5%. Use 5% as the first trial because this approximate rate for the P/F factor is lower than the true value when the time value of money is considered. At $i = 5\%$, the ROR equation is

$$0 = -500{,}000 + 10{,}000(P/A,5\%,10) + 700{,}000(P/F,5\%,10)$$
$$0 < \$6946$$

The result is positive, indicating that the return is more than 5%. Try $i = 6\%$.

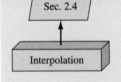

Sec. 2.4

Interpolation

$$0 = -500{,}000 + 10{,}000(P/A,6\%,10) + 700{,}000(P/F,6\%,10)$$
$$0 > \$-35{,}519$$

Since the interest rate of 6% is too high, linearly interpolate between 5% and 6%.

$$i^* = 5.00 + \frac{6946 - 0}{6946 - (-35{,}519)}(1.0)$$
$$= 5.00 + 0.16 = 5.16\%$$

Solution by Computer

Q-SOLVE

Enter the cash flows from Figure 7–3 into the RATE function. The entry RATE(10,10000, −500000,700000) displays $i^* = 5.16\%$. It is equally correct to use the IRR function. Figure 7–4, column B, shows the cash flows and IRR(B2:B12) function to obtain i^*.

For a more thorough analysis, use the i^* by computer procedure above.

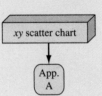

xy scatter chart

App. A

1, 2. The cash flow diagram and ROR relation are the same as in the by-hand solution.

3. Figure 7–4 shows the net cash flows in column B.

4. The IRR function in cell B14 displays $i^* = 5.16\%$.

5. In order to graphically observe i^*, column D displays PW for different i values (column C). The NPV function is used repeatedly to calculate PW for the Excel *xy* scatter chart of PW vs. i. The i^* is slightly less than 5.2%.

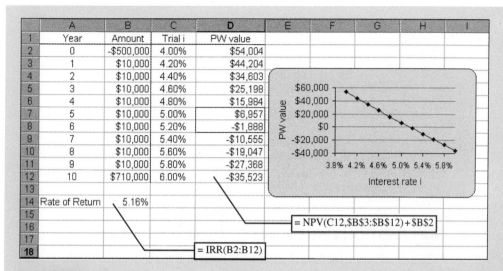

	A	B	C	D	E	F	G	H	I
1	Year	Amount	Trial i	PW value					
2	0	-$500,000	4.00%	$54,004					
3	1	$10,000	4.20%	$44,204					
4	2	$10,000	4.40%	$34,603					
5	3	$10,000	4.60%	$25,198					
6	4	$10,000	4.80%	$15,984					
7	5	$10,000	5.00%	$6,957					
8	6	$10,000	5.20%	-$1,888					
9	7	$10,000	5.40%	-$10,555					
10	8	$10,000	5.60%	-$19,047					
11	9	$10,000	5.80%	-$27,368					
12	10	$710,000	6.00%	-$35,523					
13									
14	Rate of Return		5.16%						
15									
16						= NPV(C12,$B$3:$B$12)+$B$2				
17									
18					= IRR(B2:B12)					

FIGURE 7–4

Spreadsheet solution for i^*, and a plot of PW vs. i values, Example 7.2.

As indicated in the cell D12 tag, $ signs are inserted into the NPV functions. This provides *absolute cell referencing*, which allows the NPV function to be correctly shifted from one cell to another (dragged with the mouse).

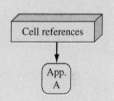

Cell references

App. A

Just as i^* can be found using a PW equation, it may equivalently be determined using an AW relation. This method is preferred when uniform annual cash flows are involved. Solution by hand is the same as the procedure for a PW-based relation, except Equation [7.2] is used.

The procedure for solution by computer is exactly the same as outlined above using the IRR function. Internally, IRR calculates the NPV function at different i values until NPV = 0 is obtained. (There is no equivalent way to utilize the PMT function, since it requires a fixed value of i to calculate an A value.)

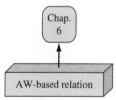

Chap. 6

AW-based relation

E-SOLVE

EXAMPLE 7.3

Use AW computations to find the rate of return for the cash flows in Example 7.2.

Solution
1. Figure 7–3 shows the cash flow diagram.
2. The AW relations for disbursements and receipts are formulated using Equation [7.2].

$$AW_D = -500,000(A/P,i,10)$$
$$AW_R = 10,000 + 700,000(A/F,i,10)$$
$$0 = -500,000(A/P,i^*,10) + 10,000 + 700,000(A/F,i^*,10)$$

3. Trial-and-error solution yields these results:

$$\text{At } i = 5\%, 0 < \$900$$
$$\text{At } i = 6\%, 0 > \$-4826$$

By interpolation, $i* = 5.16\%$, as before.

In closing, to determine $i*$ by hand, choose the PW, AW, or any other equivalence equation. It is generally better to consistently use one of the methods in order to avoid errors.

7.3 CAUTIONS WHEN USING THE ROR METHOD

The rate of return method is commonly used in engineering and business settings to evaluate one project, as discussed in this chapter, and to select one alternative from two or more, as explained in the next chapter.

When applied correctly, the ROR technique will always result in a good decision, indeed, the same one as with a PW or AW (or FW) analysis.

However, there are some assumptions and difficulties with ROR analysis that must be considered when calculating $i*$ and in interpreting its real-world meaning for a particular project. The summary provided below applies for solutions by hand and by computer.

- *Multiple i* values*. Depending upon the sequence of net cash flow disbursements and receipts, there may be more than one real-number root to the ROR equation, resulting in more than one $i*$ value. This difficulty is discussed in the next section.
- *Reinvestment at i**. Both the PW and AW methods assume that any net positive investment (i.e., net positive cash flows once the time value of money is considered) are reinvested at the MARR. But the ROR method assumes reinvestment at the $i*$ rate. When $i*$ is not close to the MARR (e.g., if $i*$ is substantially larger than MARR), this is an unrealistic assumption. In such cases, the $i*$ value is not a good basis for decision making. Though it is more involved computationally than PW or AW at the MARR, there is a procedure to use the ROR method and still obtain one unique $i*$ value. The concept of net positive investment and this method are discussed in Section 7.5.
- *Computational difficulty versus understanding*. Especially in obtaining a trial-and-error solution by hand for one or multiple $i*$ values, the computations rapidly become very involved. Spreadsheet solution is easier; however, there are no spreadsheet functions that offer the same level of understanding to the learner as that provided by hand solution of PW and AW relations.

- *Special procedure for multiple alternatives.* To correctly use the ROR method to choose from two or more mutually exclusive alternatives requires an analysis procedure significantly different from that used in PW and AW. Chapter 8 explains this procedure.

In conclusion, from an engineering economic study perspective, the annual worth or present worth method at a stated MARR should be used in lieu of the ROR method. However, there is a strong appeal for the ROR method because rate of return values are very commonly quoted. And it is easy to compare a proposed project's return with that of in-place projects.

When working with two or more alternatives, and when it is important to know the exact value of i^*, a good approach is to determine PW or AW at the MARR, then follow up with the specific i^* for the selected alternative.

As an illustration, if a project is evaluated at MARR $= 15\%$ and has PW < 0, there is no need to calculate i^*, because $i^* < 15\%$. However, if PW > 0, then calculate the exact i^* and report it along with the conclusion that the project is financially justified.

7.4 MULTIPLE RATE OF RETURN VALUES

In Section 7.2 a unique rate of return i^* was determined. In the cash flow series presented thus far, the algebraic signs on the *net cash flows* changed only once, usually from minus in year 0 to plus at some time during the series. This is called a *conventional (or simple) cash flow series*. However, for many series the net cash flows switch between positive and negative from one year to another, so there is more than one sign change. Such a series is called *nonconventional (nonsimple)*. As shown in the examples of Table 7–3, each series of positive or negative signs may be one or more in length. When there is more than one sign change in the net cash flows, it is possible that there will be multiple i^* values in the -100%

TABLE 7–3 Examples of Conventional and Nonconventional Net Cash Flow for a 6-Year Project

	Sign on Net Cash Flow							Number of Sign
Type of Series	0	1	2	3	4	5	6	Changes
Conventional	−	+	+	+	+	+	+	1
Conventional	−	−	−	+	+	+	+	1
Conventional	+	+	+	+	+	−	−	1
Nonconventional	−	+	+	+	−	−	−	2
Nonconventional	+	+	−	−	−	+	+	2
Nonconventional	−	+	−	−	+	+	+	3

to plus infinity range. There are two tests to perform in sequence on the nonconventional series to determine if there is one unique or multiple i^* values that are real numbers. The first test is the *(Descartes') rule of signs* which states that the total number of real-number roots is always less than or equal to the number of sign changes in the series. This rule is derived from the fact that the relation set up by Equation [7.1] or [7.2] to find i^* is an nth-order polynomial. (It is possible that imaginary values or infinity may also satisfy the equation.)

The second and more discriminating test determines if there is one, real-number, positive i^* value. This is the *cumulative cash flow sign test*, also known as *Norstrom's criterion*. It states that if there is only one sign change in a series of cumulative cash flows that starts negatively, there is one positive root to the polynomial relation. To perform this test, determine the series

$$S_t = \text{cumulative cash flows through period } t$$

Observe the sign of S_0 and count the sign changes in the series $S_0, S_1, \ldots, S_n$. Only if $S_0 < 0$ and signs change one time in the series is there a single, real-number, positive i^*.

With the results of these two tests, the ROR relation is solved for either the unique i^* or the multiple i^* values, using trial and error by hand, or by computer using an IRR function that incorporates the "guess" option. The development of the PW vs. i graph is recommended, especially when using a spreadsheet. Example 7.4 illustrates the tests and solution for i^* by hand and by computer.

EXAMPLE 7.4

The engineering design and testing group for Honda Motor Corp. does contract-based work for automobile manufacturers throughout the world. During the last 3 years, the net cash flows for contract payments have varied widely, as shown below, primarily due to a large manufacturer's inability to pay its contract fee.

Year	0	1	2	3
Cash flow ($1000)	+2000	−500	−8100	+6800

(a) Determine the maximum number of i^* values that may satisfy the ROR relation.

(b) Write the PW-based ROR relation and approximate the i^* value(s) by plotting PW vs. i by hand and by computer.

(c) Calculate the i^* values more exactly using the IRR function of the spreadsheet.

Solution by Hand

(a) Table 7–4 shows the annual cash flows and cumulative cash flows. Since there are two sign changes in the cash flow sequence, the rule of signs indicates a maximum of two real-number i^* values. The cumulative cash flow sequence starts with a positive number $S_0 = +2000$, indicating there is not just one positive root. The conclusion is that as many as two i^* values can be found.

(b) The PW relation is

$$PW = 2000 - 500(P/F,i,1) - 8100(P/F,i,2) + 6800(P/F,i,3)$$

TABLE 7–4   Cash Flow and Cumulative Cash Flow Sequences, Example 7.4

Year	Cash Flow ($1000)	Sequence Number	Cumulative Cash Flow ($1000)
0	+2000	S_0	+2000
1	−500	S_1	+1500
2	−8100	S_2	−6600
3	+6800	S_3	+200

Select values of i to find the two i^* values, and plot PW vs. i. The PW values are shown below and plotted in Figure 7–5 for i values of 0, 5, 10, 20, 30, 40, and 50%. The characteristic parabolic shape for a second-degree polynomial is obtained, with PW crossing the i axis at approximately $i_1^* = 8$ and $i_2^* = 41\%$.

$i\%$	0	5	10	20	30	40	50
PW ($1000)	+200	+51.44	−39.55	−106.13	−82.01	−11.83	+81.85

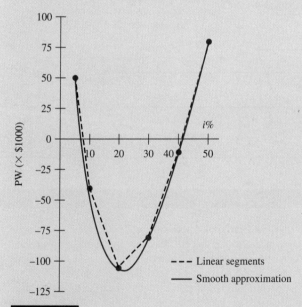

FIGURE 7–5

Present worth of cash flows at several interest rates, Example 7.4.

Solution by Computer

(a)   See Figure 7–6. The NPV function is used in column D to determine the PW value at several i values (column C), as indicated by the cell tag. The accompanying Excel xy scatter chart presents the PW vs. i graph. The i^* values cross the PW = 0 line at approximately 8% and 40%.

(b) Row 19 in Figure 7–6 contains the ROR values (including a negative value) entered as guess into the IRR function to find the $i*$ root of the polynomial that is closest to the guess value. Row 21 includes the two resulting $i*$ values: $i_1^* = 7.47\%$ and $i_2^* = 41.35\%$.

If "guess" is omitted from the IRR function, the entry IRR(B4:B7) will determine only the first value, 7.47%. As a check on the two $i*$ values, the NPV function can be set up to find PW at the two $i*$ values. Both NPV(7.47%,B5:B7)+B4 and NPV(41.35%,B5:B7)+B4 will display approximately $0.00.

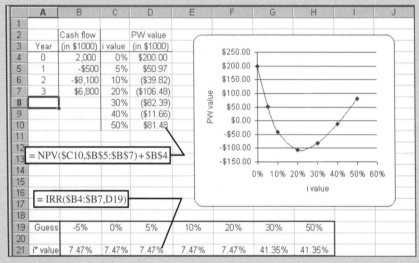

FIGURE 7–6

Spreadsheet showing PW vs. i graph and multiple $i*$ values, Example 7.4.

EXAMPLE 7.5

E-SOLVE

Researchers at Carleton University have developed new software for touch-screen technology that is attracting the attention of industry. If the SurfNet group was approached with the following 10-year licensing agreement, determine the number of $i*$ values; estimate them graphically and by the IRR function of a spreadsheet. Table 7–5 gives the estimated net cash flows from the perspective of SurfNet. The negative values in years 1, 2, and 4 reflect heavy marketing costs.

Solution by Computer

The rule of signs indicates a nonconventional net cash flow series with up to three roots. The cumulative net cash flow series starts negatively and has only one sign change in year 10, thus indicating that one unique positive root can be found. (Zero values in the cumulative cash flow series are neglected when applying Norstrom's criterion.) A PW-based ROR relation is used to find $i*$.

$$0 = -2000(P/F,i,1) - 2000(P/F,i,2) + \cdots + 100(P/F,i,10)$$

TABLE 7–5 Net Cash Flow Series and Cumulative Cash Flow Series, Example 7.5

	Cash Flow, $100			Cash Flow, $100	
Year	Net	Cumulative	Year	Net	Cumulative
1	−2000	−2000	6	+500	−900
2	−2000	−4000	7	+400	−500
3	+2500	−1500	8	+300	−200
4	−500	−2000	9	+500	0
5	+600	−4000	10	+100	+100

The PW of the right side is calculated for different values of i and plotted on the spreadsheet (Figure 7–7). The unique value $i^* = 0.77\%$ is obtained using the IRR function with the same "guess" values for i as in the PW vs. i graph.

Comment

Once the spreadsheet is set up as in Figure 7–7, the cash flows can be "tweaked" to perform sensitivity analysis on the i^* value(s). For example, if the cash flow in year 10 is changed only slightly from $+100 to $−100, the results displayed change across the spreadsheet to $i^* = -0.84\%$. Also, this simple change in cash flow substantially alters the cumulative cash flow sequence. Now $S_{10} = \$-100$, as can be confirmed in Table 7–5. There are now no sign changes in the cumulative cash flow sequence, so *no unique positive root* can be found. This is confirmed by the value $i^* = -0.84\%$. If other cash flows are altered, the two tests we have learned should be applied to determine whether multiple roots may now exist. This means that spreadsheet-based sensitivity analysis must be performed carefully when the ROR method is applied, because not all i^* values may be determined as cash flows are tweaked on the screen.

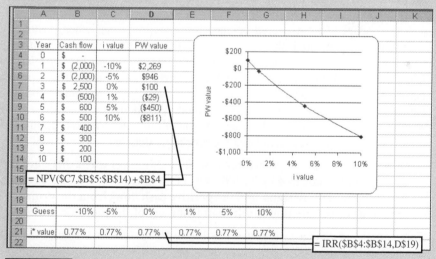

FIGURE 7–7

Spreadsheet solution to find i^*, Example 7.5.

In many cases some of the multiple $i*$ values will seem ridiculous because they are too large or too small (negative). For example, values of 10, 150, and 750% for a sequence with three sign changes are difficult to use in practical decision making. (Obviously, one advantage of the PW and AW methods for alternative analysis is that unrealistic rates do not enter into the analysis.) In determining which $i*$ value to select as *the* ROR value, it is common to neglect negative and large values or to simply never compute them. *Actually, the correct approach is to determine the unique composite rate of return,* as described in the next section.

If a standard spreadsheet system, such as Excel, is used, it will normally determine only one real-number root, unless different "guess" amounts are entered sequentially. This one $i*$ value determined from Excel is usually a realistically valued root, because the $i*$ which solves the PW relation is determined by the spreadsheet's built-in trial-and-error method. This method starts with a default value, commonly 10%, or with the user-supplied guess, as illustrated in the previous example.

7.5 COMPOSITE RATE OF RETURN: REMOVING MULTIPLE $i*$ VALUES

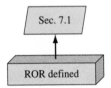

Sec. 7.1

ROR defined

The rates of return we have computed thus far are the rates that exactly balance plus and minus cash flows with the time value of money considered. Any method which accounts for the time value of money can be used in calculating this balancing rate, such as PW, AW, or FW. The interest rate obtained from these calculations is known as the *internal rate of return (IRR)*. Simply stated, the internal rate of return is the rate of return on the unrecovered balance of an investment, as defined earlier. The funds that remain unrecovered are still inside the investment, hence the name *internal rate of return*. The general terms rate of return and interest rate usually imply internal rate of return. The interest rates quoted or calculated in previous chapters are all internal rates.

The concept of unrecovered balance becomes important when positive net cash flows are generated (thrown off) before the end of a project. A positive net cash flow, once generated, becomes *released as external funds to the project* and is not considered further in an internal rate of return calculation. These positive net cash flows may cause a nonconventional cash flow series and multiple $i*$ values to develop. However, there is a method to explicitly consider these funds, as discussed below. Additionally, the dilemma of multiple $i*$ roots is eliminated.

It is important to understand that the procedure detailed below is used to

Determine the rate of return for cash flow estimates when there are multiple $i*$ values indicated by both the cash flow rule of signs and the cumulative cash flow rule of signs, and net positive cash flows from the project will earn at a stated rate that is different from any of the multiple $i*$ values.

For example, assume a cash flow series has two $i*$ values that balance the ROR equation—10% and 60% per year—and any cash released by the project is invested by the company at a rate of return of 25% per year. The procedure below will find a single unique rate of return for the cash flow series. However, if it is known that released cash will earn exactly 10%, the unique rate is 10%. The same statement can be made using the 60% rate.

As before, if the exact rate of return for a project's cash flow estimates is not needed, it is equally correct to use a PW or AW analysis at the MARR to determine if the project is financially viable. This is the normal mode of operation in an engineering economy study.

Consider the internal rate of return calculations for the following cash flows: $10,000 is invested at $t = 0$, $8000 is received in year 2, and $9000 is received in year 5. The PW equation to determine i^* is

$$0 = -10,000 + 8000(P/F,i,2) + 9000(P/F,i,5)$$
$$i^* = 16.815\%$$

If this rate is used for the unrecovered balances, the investment will be recovered exactly at the end of year 5. The procedure to verify this is identical to that used in Table 7–1, which describes how the ROR works to exactly remove the unrecovered balance with the final cash flow.

Unrecovered balance at end of year 2 immediately before $8000 receipt:

$$-10,000(F/P,16.815\%,2) = -10,000(1 + 0.16815)^2 = \$-13,646$$

Unrecovered balance at end of year 2 immediately after $8000 receipt:

$$-13,646 + 8000 = \$-5646$$

Unrecovered balance at end of year 5 immediately before $9000 receipt:

$$-5646(F/P,16.815\%,3) = \$-9000$$

Unrecovered balance at end of year 5 immediately after $9000 receipt:

$$\$-9000 + 9000 = \$0$$

In this calculation, no consideration is given to the $8000 available after year 2. What happens if funds released from a project *are* considered in calculating the overall rate of return of a project? After all, something must be done with the released funds. One possibility is to assume the money is reinvested at some stated rate. The ROR method assumes funds that are excess to a project earn at the i^* rate, but this may not be a realistic rate in everyday practice. Another approach is to simply assume that reinvestment occurs at the MARR. In addition to accounting for all the money released during the project period and reinvested at a realistic rate, the approach discussed below has the advantage of converting a nonconventional cash flow series (with multiple i^* values) to a conventional series with one root, which can be considered *the* rate of return for making a decision about the project.

The rate of earnings used for the released funds is called the *reinvestment rate* or *external rate of return* and is symbolized by c. (It is also sometimes referred to as the *auxiliary rate of return*.) This rate, established outside (external to) the cash flow estimates being evaluated, depends upon the market rate available for investments. If a company is making, say, 8% on its daily investments, then $c = 8\%$. It is common practice to set c equal to the MARR. The one interest rate that now satisfies the rate of return equation is called the *composite rate of return (CRR)* and is symbolized by i'. By definition,

The *composite rate of return i'* is the unique rate of return for a project that assumes that net positive cash flows, which represent money not immediately needed by the project, are reinvested at the reinvestment rate *c*.

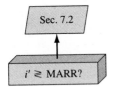

The term *composite* is used here because this rate is derived from another interest rate, namely the reinvestment rate *c*. If *c* happens to equal any one of the i^* values, then the composite rate i' will equal that i^* value. The CRR is also known by the term *return on invested capital (RIC)*. Once the unique i' is determined, it is compared to the MARR to decide on the project's financial viability, as outlined in Section 7.2.

The correct procedure to determine i' is called the *net-investment procedure*. The technique involves finding the future worth of the net investment amount 1 year in the future. Find the project's net-investment value F_t in year t from F_{t-1} by using the F/P factor for 1 year at the reinvestment rate *c* if the previous net investment F_{t-1} is positive (extra money generated by project), or at the CRR rate i' if F_{t-1} is negative (project used all available funds). To do this mathematically, for each year t set up the relation

$$F_t = F_{t-1}(1 + i) + C_t \qquad [7.6]$$

where $\quad t = 1, 2, \ldots, n$
$\quad\quad\quad n = $ total years in project
$\quad\quad\quad C_t = $ net cash flow in year t

$$i = \begin{cases} c & \text{if } F_{t-1} > 0 \quad \text{(net positive investment)} \\ i' & \text{if } F_{t-1} < 0 \quad \text{(net negative investment)} \end{cases}$$

Set the net-investment relation for year n equal to zero ($F_n = 0$) and solve for i'. The i' value obtained is unique for a stated reinvestment rate *c*.

The development of F_1 through F_3 for the cash flow series below, which is graphed in Figure 7–8*a*, is illustrated for a reinvestment rate of $c = $ MARR $= 15\%$.

Year	Cash Flow, $
0	50
1	−200
2	50
3	100

The net investment for year $t = 0$ is

$$F_0 = \$50$$

which is positive, so it returns $c = 15\%$ during the first year. By Equation [7.6], F_1 is

$$F_1 = 50(1 + 0.15) - 200 = \$-142.50$$

This result is shown in Figure 7–8*b*. Since the project net investment is now negative, the value F_1 earns interest at the composite rate i' for year 2. Therefore, for year 2,

$$F_2 = F_1(1 + i') + C_2 = -142.50(1 + i') + 50$$

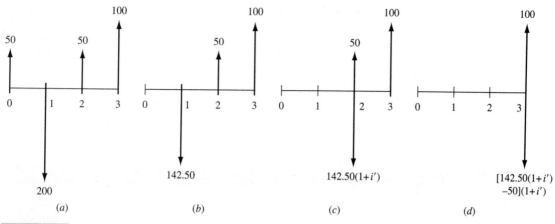

FIGURE 7–8
Cash flow series for which the composite rate of return i' is computed: (a) original form; equivalent form in (b) year 1, (c) year 2, and (d) year 3.

The i' value is to be determined (Figure 7–8c). Since F_2 will be negative for all $i' > 0$, use i' to set up F_3 as shown in Figure 7–8d.

$$F_3 = F_2(1 + i') + C_3 = [-142.50(1 + i') + 50](1 + i') + 100 \quad [7.7]$$

Setting Equation [7.7] equal to zero and solving for i' will result in the values of 3.13% and -168%, since Equation [7.7] is a quadratic relation (power 2 for i'). The value of $i' = 3.13\%$ is the correct i^* in the range -100% to ∞; therefore, it results in the unique composite rate of return i'. The procedure to find i' may be summarized as follows:

1. Draw a cash flow diagram of the original net cash flow series.
2. Develop the series of net investments using Equation [7.6] and the c value. The result is the F_n expression in terms of i'.
3. Set $F_n = 0$ and find the i' value to balance the equation.

Several comments are in order. If the reinvestment rate c is equal to the internal rate of return i^* (or one of the i^* values when there are multiple ones), the i' that is calculated will be exactly the same as i^*; that is, $c = i^* = i'$. The closer the c value is to i^*, the smaller the difference between the composite and internal rates. As mentioned earlier, it is correct to assume that $c =$ MARR, if all throw-off funds from the project can realistically earn at the MARR rate.

A summary of the relations between c, i, and i^* follows, and the relations are demonstrated in Example 7.6.

Relation Between Reinvestment Rate c and i^*	Relation Between CRR i and i^*
$c = i^*$	$i' = i^*$
$c < i^*$	$i' < i^*$
$c > i^*$	$i' > i^*$

Remember: This entire net-investment procedure is used when multiple i^* values are indicated. Multiple i^* values are present when a nonconventional cash flow series does not have one positive root, as determined by Norstrom's criterion. Additionally, none of the steps in this procedure are necessary if the present worth or annual worth method is used to evaluate a project at the MARR.

The net-investment procedure can also be applied when one internal rate of return (i^*) is present, but the stated reinvestment rate (c) is significantly different from i^*. The same relations between c, i^*, and i' stated above remain correct for this situation.

EXAMPLE 7.6

Compute the composite rate of return for the Honda Motor Corp. engineering group in Example 7.4 if the reinvestment rate is (*a*) 7.47% and (*b*) the corporate MARR of 20%. The multiple i^* values are determined in Figure 7–6.

Solution

(*a*) Use the net-investment procedure to determine i' for $c = 7.47\%$.

1. Figure 7–9 shows the original cash flow.
2. The first net-investment expression is $F_0 = \$+2000$. Since $F_0 > 0$, use $c = 7.47\%$ to write F_1 by Equation [7.6].

$$F_1 = 2000(1.0747) - 500 = \$1649.40$$

Since $F_1 > 0$, use $c = 7.47\%$ to determine F_2.

$$F_2 = 1649.40(1.0747) - 8100 = \$-6327.39$$

Figure 7–10 shows the equivalent cash flow at this time. Since $F_2 < 0$, use i' to express F_3.

$$F_3 = -6327.39(1 + i') + 6800$$

FIGURE 7–9
Original cash flow (in thousands), Example 7.6.

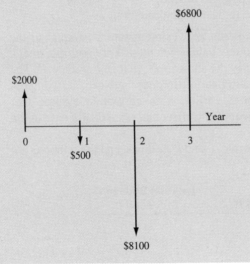

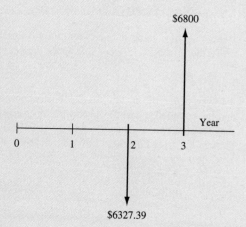

FIGURE 7–10
Equivalent cash flow (in thousands) of Figure 7–9 with reinvestment at $c = 7.47\%$.

3. Set $F_3 = 0$ and solve for i' directly.

$$-6327.39(1 + i') + 6800 = 0$$

$$1 + i' = \frac{6800}{6327.39} = 1.0747$$

$$i' = 7.47$$

The CRR is 7.47%, which is the same as c, the reinvestment rate, and the $i_1{}^*$ value determined in Example 7.4, Figure 7–6. Note that 41.35%, which is the second i^* value, no longer balances the rate of return equation. The equivalent future worth result for the cash flow in Figure 7–10, if i' were 41.35%, is

$$6327.39(F/P, 41.35\%, 1) = \$8943.77 \neq \$6800$$

(b) For MARR $= c = 20\%$, the net-investment series is

$$F_0 = +2000 \qquad\qquad (F_0 > 0, \text{ use } c)$$
$$F_1 = 2000(1.20) - 500 = \$1900 \qquad (F_1 > 0, \text{ use } c)$$
$$F_2 = 1900(1.20) - 8100 = \$-5820 \qquad (F_2 < 0, \text{ use } i')$$
$$F_3 = -5820(1 + i') + 6800$$

Set $F_3 = 0$ and solve for i' directly.

$$1 + i' = \frac{6800}{5820} = 1.1684$$

$$i' = 16.84\%$$

The CRR is $i' = 16.84\%$ at a reinvestment rate of 20%, which is a marked increase from $i' = 7.47\%$ at $c = 7.47\%$.

Note that since $i' < \text{MARR} = 20\%$, the project is not financially justified. This is verified by calculating PW $= \$-106$ at 20% for the original cash flows.

EXAMPLE 7.7

Determine the composite rate of return for the cash flows in Table 7–6 if the reinvestment rate is the MARR of 15% per year. Is the project justified?

Solution

A review of Table 7–6 indicates that the nonconventional cash flows have two sign changes and the cumulative cash flow sequence does not start with a negative value. There are a maximum of two i^* values. To find the one i' value, develop the net-investment series F_0 through F_{10} using Equation [7.6] and $c = 15\%$.

$$F_0 = 0$$

$$F_1 = \$200 \qquad\qquad (F_1 > 0, \text{use } c)$$

$$F_2 = 200(1.15) + 100 = \$330 \qquad\qquad (F_2 > 0, \text{use } c)$$

$$F_3 = 330(1.15) + 50 = \$429.50 \qquad\qquad (F_3 > 0, \text{use } c)$$

$$F_4 = 429.50(1.15) - 1800 = \$-1306.08 \qquad (F_4 < 0, \text{use } i')$$

$$F_5 = -1306.08(1 + i') + 600$$

Since we do not know if F_5 is greater than zero or less than zero, all remaining expressions use i'.

$$F_6 = F_5(1 + i') + 500 = [-1306.08(1 + i') + 600](1 + i') + 500$$

$$F_7 = F_6(1 + i') + 400$$

$$F_8 = F_7(1 + i') + 300$$

$$F_9 = F_8(1 + i') + 200$$

$$F_{10} = F_9(1 + i') + 100$$

TABLE 7–6 Cash Flow and Cumulative Cash Flow Sequences, Example 7.7

	Cash Flow, $100			Cash Flow, $100	
Year	Net	Cumulative	Year	Net	Cumulative
0	0	0	6	500	−350
1	200	+200	7	400	+50
2	100	+300	8	300	+350
3	50	+350	9	200	+550
4	−1800	−1450	10	100	+650
5	600	−850			

To find i', the expression $F_{10} = 0$ is solved by trial and error. Solution determines that $i' = 21.24\%$. Since $i' >$ MARR, the project is justified. In order to work more with this exercise and the net-investment procedure, do the case study in this chapter.

Comment
The two rates which balance the ROR equation are $i_1^* = 28.71\%$ and $i_2^* = 48.25\%$. If we rework this problem at either reinvestment rate, the i' value will be the same as this reinvestment rate; that is, if $c = 28.71\%$, then $i' = 28.71\%$.

There is a spreadsheet function called MIRR (modified IRR) which determines a unique interest rate when you input a reinvestment rate c for positive cash flows. However, the function does not implement the net-investment procedure for nonconventional cash flow series as discussed here, and the function requires that a finance rate for the funds used as the initial investment be supplied. So the formulas for MIRR and CRR computation are not the same. The MIRR will not produce exactly the same answer as Equation [7.6] unless all the rates happen to be the same and this value is one of the roots of the ROR relation.

CHAPTER SUMMARY

Rate of return, or interest rate, is a term used and understood by almost everybody. Most people, however, can have considerable difficulty in calculating a rate of return $i*$ correctly for any cash flow series. For some types of series, more than one ROR possibility exists. The maximum number of $i*$ values is equal to the number of changes in the signs of the net cash flow series (Descartes' rule of signs). Also, a single positive rate can be found if the cumulative net cash flow series starts negatively and has only one sign change (Norstrom's criterion).

For all cash flow series where there is an indication of multiple roots, a decision must be made about whether to calculate the multiple $i*$ internal rates, or the one composite rate of return using an externally determined reinvestment rate. This rate is commonly set at the MARR. While the internal rate is usually easier to calculate, the composite rate is the correct approach with two advantages: multiple rates of return are eliminated, and released project net cash flows are accounted for using a realistic reinvestment rate. However, the calculation of multiple $i*$ rates, or the composite rate of return, is often computationally involved.

If an exact ROR is not necessary, it is strongly recommended that the PW or AW method at the MARR be used to judge economic justification.

PROBLEMS

Understanding ROR

7.1 What does a rate of return of −100% mean?

7.2 A $10,000 loan amortized over 5 years at an interest rate of 10% per year would require payments of $2638 to completely repay the loan when interest is charged on the unrecovered balance. If interest is charged on the principal instead of the unrecovered balance, what will be the balance after 5 years if the same $2638 payments are made each year?

7.3 A-1 Mortgage makes loans with the interest paid on the loan principal rather than on the unpaid balance. For a 4-year loan of $10,000 at 10% per year, what annual payment would be required to repay the loan in 4 years if interest is charged on (*a*) the principal and (*b*) the unrecovered balance?

7.4 A small industrial contractor purchased a warehouse building for storing equipment and materials that are not immediately needed at construction job sites. The cost of the building was $100,000, and the contractor made an agreement with the seller to finance the purchase over a 5-year period. The agreement stated that monthly payments would be made based on a 30-year amortization, but the balance owed at the end of year 5 would be paid in a lump-sum balloon payment. What was the size of the balloon payment if the interest rate on the loan was 6% per year, compounded monthly?

Determination of ROR

7.5 What rate of return per month will an entrepreneur make over a 2½-year project period if he invested $150,000 to produce portable 12-volt air compressors? His estimated monthly costs are $27,000 with income of $33,000 per month.

7.6 Vale's workers at the Sudbury, Ontario, nickel mining operation were on strike for 12 months. If a contract between the company and the United Steelworkers Union called for the company to spend $100 million in capital investment to upgrade facilities and provide buyout packages for 400 workers, what rate of return will the company make over a 10-year study period? Assume that the average buyout package is $100,000, that the company is able to reduce costs by $20 million per year, and that all of the company's expenditures occur at time 0 and the savings begin 1 year later.

7.7 The Beaverhill Landfill was required to install a plastic liner to prevent leachate from migrating into the groundwater. The fill area was 50,000 square metres, and the installed liner cost was $8 per square metre. To recover the investment, the owner charged $10 for pickup loads, $25 for dump truck loads, and $70 for compactor truck loads. If the monthly distribution is 200 pickup loads, 50 dump truck loads, and 100 compactor truck loads, what rate of return will the landfill owner make on the investment if the fill area is adequate for 4 years?

7.8 Swagelok Enterprises is a manufacturer of miniature fittings and valves. Over a 5-year period, the costs associated with one product line were as follows: first cost of $30,000 and annual costs of $18,000. Annual revenue was $27,000, and the used equipment was salvaged for $4000. What rate of return did the company make on this product?

7.9 Barron Chemical uses a thermoplastic polymer to enhance the appearance of certain RV panels. The initial cost of one process was $130,000 with annual costs of $49,000 and revenues of $78,000 in year 1, increasing by $1000 per year. A salvage value of $23,000 was realized when the process was discontinued after 8 years. What rate of return did the company make on the process?

7.10 A graduate of Concordia University of Montreal who built a successful business wanted to start an endowment in her name that would provide scholarships to IE students. She wanted the scholarships to amount to $10,000 per year, and she wanted the first one to be given on the day she made the donation (i.e., at time 0). If she planned to donate $100,000, what rate of return would the university have to make in order to be able to award the $10,000 per year scholarships forever?

7.11 PPG manufactures an epoxy amine that is used to protect the contents of polyethylene terephthalate (PET) containers from reacting with oxygen. The cash flow (in millions) associated with the process is shown below. Determine the rate of return.

Year	Cost, $	Revenue, $
0	−10	—
1	−4	2
2	−4	3
3	−4	9
4	−3	9
5	−3	9
6	−3	9

7.12 An entrepreneurial mechanical engineer started a tire shredding business. The cost of the shredder was $220,000. She spent $15,000 to get 460-volt power to the site and another $76,000 in site preparation. Through contracts with tire dealers, she was paid $2 per tire and handled an average

of 12,000 tires per month for 3 years. The annual operating costs for labour, power, repairs, etc., amounted to $1.05 per tire. She also sold some of the tire chips to septic tank installers for use in drain fields. This endeavour netted $2000 per month. After 3 years, she sold the equipment for $100,000. What rate of return did she make (*a*) per month and (*b*) per year (nominal and effective)?

7.13 An Internet B to C company projected the following cash flows (in millions). What annual rate of return will be realized if the cash flows occur as projected?

Year	Expenses, $	Revenue, $
0	−40	—
1	−40	12
2	−43	15
3	−45	17
4	−46	51
5	−48	63
6–10	−50	80

7.14 Algoma Steel is considering a plan to build an 8-megawatt cogeneration plant to provide for part of its power needs. The cost of the plant is expected to be $41 million. The company consumes 55,000 megawatt-hours per year at a cost of $120 per megawatt-hour. (*a*) If Algoma will be able to produce power at one-half the cost that it now pays, what rate of return will it make on its investment if the power plant lasts 30 years? (*b*) If the company can sell an average of 12,000 megawatt-hours per year back to the utility at $90 per megawatt-hour, what rate of return will it make?

7.15 A new razor from Gillette called the M5Power emits pulses that cause the skin to prop up hair so that it can be cut off more easily. This might make the blades last longer because there would be less need to repeatedly shave over the same surface. The M5Power system (including batteries) sells for $14.99 at some stores. The blades cost $10.99 for a package of four. The more conventional M5Turbo blades cost $7.99 for a package of four. If the blades for the M5Power system last 2 months while the blades for the M5Turbo last only 1 month, what rate of return (*a*) per month and (*b*) per year (nominal and effective) will be made if a person purchases the M5Power system? Assume the person already has an M5Turbo razor but needs to purchase blades at time 0. Use a 1-year project period.

7.16 Techstreet.com is a small Web design business that provides services for two main types of websites: brochure sites and e-commerce sites. One package involves an up-front payment of $90,000 and monthly payments of 1.4¢ per "hit." A new CAD software company is considering the package. The company expects to have at least 6000 hits per month, and it hopes that 1.5% of the hits will result in a sale. If the average income from sales (after fees and expenses) is $150, what rate of return per month will the CAD software company realize if it uses the website for 2 years?

7.17 A plaintiff in a successful lawsuit was awarded a judgment of $4800 per month for 5 years. The plaintiff needs a fairly large sum of money now for an investment and has offered the defendant the opportunity to pay off the award in a lump-sum amount of $110,000. If the defendant accepts the offer and pays the $110,000 now, what rate of return will the defendant have made on the "investment"? Assume the next $4800 payment is due 1 month from now.

7.18 The Advanced Space Vision System developed for the Canadian Space Agency will allow improved use of the robotic arms of

Canadarm2. The vision system will enable greater efficiencies in moving equipment and supplies around the International Space Station, which CSA engineers estimate will result in savings in many projects. The cash flows for one project are shown below. Determine the rate of return per year.

Year t	Cost ($1000)	Savings ($1000)
0	−210	—
1	−150	—
2–5	—	$100 + 60(t − 2)$

7.19 ASM International, an Australian steel company, claims that a savings of 40% of the cost of stainless steel threaded bar can be achieved by replacing machined threads with precision weld depositions. A Canadian manufacturer of rock bolts and grout-in fittings plans to purchase the equipment. A mechanical engineer with the company has prepared the following cash flow estimates. Determine the expected rate of return per quarter and per year (nominal).

Quarter	Cost, $	Savings, $
0	−450,000	—
1	−50,000	10,000
2	−40,000	20,000
3	−30,000	30,000
4	−20,000	40,000
5	−10,000	50,000
6–12	—	80,000

7.20 An indium-gallium-arsenide-nitrogen alloy is said to have potential uses in electricity-generating solar cells. The new material is expected to have a longer life, and it is believed to have a 40% efficiency rate, which is nearly twice that of standard silicon solar cells. The useful life of a telecommunications satellite could be extended from 10 to 15 years by using the new solar cells. What rate of return could be realized if an extra investment now of $950,000 would result in extra revenues of $450,000 in year 11, $500,000 in year 12, and amounts increasing by $50,000 per year through year 15?

7.21 A permanent endowment at the University of British Colombia is to award scholarships to engineering students. The awards are to be made beginning 5 years after the $10 million lump-sum donation is made. If the interest from the endowment is to fund 100 students each year in the amount of $10,000 each, what annual rate of return must the endowment fund earn?

7.22 A charitable foundation received a donation from a wealthy building contractor in the amount of $5 million. It specifies that $200,000 is to be awarded each year for 5 years starting *now* (i.e., 6 awards) to a university engaged in research pertaining to the development of layered composite materials. Thereafter, grants equal to the amount of interest earned each year are to be made. If the size of the grants from year 6 into the indefinite future is expected to be $1,000,000 per year, what annual rate of return is the foundation earning?

Multiple ROR Values

7.23 What is the difference between a conventional and a nonconventional cash flow series?

7.24 What cash flows are associated with Descartes' rule of signs and Norstrom's criterion?

7.25 According to Descartes' rule of signs, how many possible $i*$ values are there for net cash flows that have the following signs?
(a) − − − + + + − +
(b) − − − − − − + + + + +
(c) + + + + − − − − − − + − + − − −

7.26 Montreal-based Dorel Industries Inc. makes car safety seats for children, furniture and bicycles. If a European distributor of their products had the net cash flows shown below, (a) determine the number of possible rate of return values and (b) find all rate of return values between −30 and 130%.

Year	Net Cash Flow, $
0	−17,000
1	−20,000
2	4,000
3	−11,000
4	32,000
5	47,000

7.27 The cash flow (in 1000s) associated with a new method of manufacturing box cutters is shown below for a 2-year period. (a) Use Descartes' rule to determine the maximum number of possible rate of return values. (b) Use Norstrom's criterion to determine if there is only one positive rate of return value.

Quarter	Expense, $	Revenue, $
0	−20	0
1	−20	5
2	−10	10
3	−10	25
4	−10	26
5	−10	20
6	−15	17
7	−12	15
8	−15	2

7.28 RKI Instruments manufactures a ventilation controller designed for monitoring and controlling carbon monoxide in parking garages, boiler rooms, tunnels, etc. The net cash flow associated with one phase of the operation is shown below. (a) How many possible rate of return values are there for this cash flow series? (b) Find all the rate of return values between 0% and 100%.

Year	Net Cash Flow, $
0	−30,000
1	20,000
2	15,000
3	−2,000

7.29 A manufacturer of heavy-tow carbon fibres (used for sporting goods, thermoplastic compounds, windmill blades, etc.) reported the net cash flows below. (*a*) Determine the number of possible rate of return values, and (*b*) find all rate of return values between −50% and 120%.

Year	Net Cash Flow, $
0	−17,000
1	20,000
2	−5,000
3	8,000

7.30 Arc-bot Technologies, manufacturers of six-axis, electric servo-driven robots, has experienced the cash flows below in a shipping department. (*a*) Determine the number of possible rate of return values. (*b*) Find all *i** values between 0% and 100%.

Year	Expense, $	Savings, $
0	−33,000	0
1	−15,000	18,000
2	−40,000	38,000
3	−20,000	55,000
4	−13,000	12,000

7.31 Five years ago, a company made a $5 million investment in a new high-temperature material. The product was not well accepted after the first year on the market. However, when it was reintroduced 4 years later, it did sell well during the year. Major

research funding to broaden the applications has cost $15 million in year 5. Determine the rate of return for these cash flows (shown below in $1000s).

Year	Net Cash Flow, $
0	−5,000
1	4,000
2	0
3	0
4	20,000
5	−15,000

Composite Rate of Return

7.32 What is meant by the term *reinvestment rate*?

7.33 Hydro One, Ontario's largest electricity transmission and distribution company, is installing smart meters in its customers' homes. Customers have been shown to conserve power and move consumption from peak to off-peak periods in response to "time of use" electricity pricing. The cash flow for the smart meters program is shown below. Calculate the composite rate of return using a reinvestment rate of 14% per year.

Year	Cash Flow, $ (thousands)
0	5000
1	−2000
2	−1500
3	−7000
4	4000

7.34 An engineer working for Imperial oil invested his bonus money each year in company shares. His bonus has been $5000 each year for the past 6 years (i.e., at the end of years 1 through 6). At the end of year 7, he *sold* $9000 worth of his shares to remodel his kitchen (he didn't purchase any shares that year). In years 8 through 10, he again invested his $5000 bonus. The engineer sold all his remaining shares for $50,000 immediately after the last invest-ment at the end of year 10. (*a*) Determine the number of possible rate of return val-ues in the net cash flow series. (*b*) Find the internal rate of return(s). (*c*) Determine the composite rate of return. Use a reinvest-ment rate of 20% per year.

7.35 A company that makes clutch disks for race cars had the cash flows shown below for one department. Calculate (*a*) the inter-nal rate of return and (*b*) the composite rate of return, using a reinvestment rate of 15% per year.

Year	Cash Flow, $1000
0	−65
1	30
2	84
3	−10
4	−12

7.36 For the cash flow series below, calculate the composite rate of return, using a rein-vestment rate of 14% per year.

Year	Cash Flow, $
0	3000
1	−2000
2	1000
3	−6000
4	3800

7.37 For the high-temperature material project in Problem 7.31, determine the composite rate of return if the reinvestment rate is 15% per year. The cash flows (repeated below) are in $1000 units.

Year	Cash Flow, $
0	−5,000
1	4,000
2	0
3	0
4	20,000
5	−15,000

EXTENDED EXERCISES

EXTENDED EXERCISE 1—THE COST OF A POOR CREDIT RATING

Two people each borrow $5000 at a 10% per year interest rate for 3 years. A portion of Charles's loan agreement states that interest "is paid at the rate of 10% compounded each year on the declining balance." Charles is told his annual payment will be $2010.57, due at the end of each year of the loan.

Jeremy currently has a slightly degraded credit rating, which the bank loan officer discovered. Jeremy has a habit of paying his bills late. The bank approved the loan, but a part of his loan agreement states that interest "is paid at a rate of 10% compounded each year on the original loan amount." Jeremy is told his annual payment will be $2166.67 due at the end of each year.

Questions

Answer the following by hand, by computer, or both.

1. Develop a table and a plot for Charles and for Jeremy of the unrecovered balances (total amount owed) just before each payment is due.
2. How much more total money and interest will Jeremy pay than Charles over the 3 years?

EXTENDED EXERCISE 2—WHEN IS IT BEST TO SELL A BUSINESS?

After Jeff finished medical school and Imelda completed a degree in engineering, the couple decided to put a substantial part of their savings into rental property. With a hefty bank loan and a cash down payment of $120,000 of their own funds, they were able to purchase six duplexes from a person exiting the residential rental business. Net cash flow on rental income after all expenses and taxes for the first 4 years was good: $25,000 at the end of the first year, increasing by $5000 each year thereafter. A business friend of Jeff's introduced him to a potential buyer for all properties with an estimated $225,000 net cash-out after the 4 years of ownership. But they did not sell. They wanted to stay in the business for a while longer, given the increasing net cash flows they had experienced thus far.

During year 5, an economic downturn reduced net cash flow to $35,000. In response, an extra $20,000 was spent in improvements and advertising in each of years 6 and 7, but the net cash flow continued to decrease by $10,000 per year through year 7. Jeff had another offer to sell in year 7 for only $60,000. This was considered too much of a loss, so they did not take advantage of the opportunity.

In the last 3 years, they have expended $20,000, $20,000, and $30,000 each year in improvements and advertising costs, but the net cash flow from the business has been only $15,000, $10,000, and $10,000 each year.

Imelda and Jeff want out, but they have no offer to buy at any price, and they have most of their savings committed to the rental property.

Questions

Determine the rate of return for the following:

1. At the end of year 4, first, if the $225,000 purchase offer had been accepted; second, without selling.
2. After 7 years, first, if the $60,000 "sacrifice" offer had been accepted; and, second, without selling.
3. Now, after 10 years, with no prospect of sale.
4. If the houses are sold and given to a charity, assume a net cash infusion to Jeff and Imelda of $25,000 after taxes at the end of this year. What is the rate of return over the 10 years of ownership?

CASE STUDY

BOB LEARNS ABOUT MULTIPLE RATES OF RETURN[1]

Background

When Bob began a summer internship with VAC, an electricity distribution company, he was given a project on the first day by his boss, Kathy. Homeworth, one of the major corporate customers, just placed a request for a lower rate per kilowatt-hour, once its minimum required usage is exceeded each month. Kathy has an internal report from the Customer Relations Department that itemizes the net cash flows below for the Homeworth account during the last 10 years.

Year	Cash Flow ($1000)
1998	$ 200
1999	100
2000	50
2001	−1800
2002	600
2003	500
2004	400
2005	300
2006	200
2007	100

The report also states that the annual rate of return is between 25 and 50%, but no further information is provided. This information is not detailed enough for Kathy to evaluate the company's request.

Over the next few hours, Bob and Kathy had a series of discussions as Bob worked to answer Kathy's increasingly more specific questions. The following is an abbreviated version of these conversations. Luckily, both Bob and Kathy took an engineering economy course during their undergraduate work, and their professors covered the method to find a unique rate of return for any cash flow series.

Development of the Situation

1. Kathy asked Bob to do a preliminary study to find the correct rate of return. She wanted only one number, not a range, and not two or three possible values. She did, however, have a passing interest in initially knowing the values of multiple rates, if they do exist, in order to determine if the report from customer relations was correct or just a "shot in the dark."

   Kathy told Bob that the MARR for the company is 15% per year for these major clients. She also explained that the 2001 negative cash flow

[1]Contributed Dr. Tep Sastri (former Associate Professor, Industrial Engineering, Texas A&M University).

was caused by an on-site equipment upgrade when Homeworth expanded its manufacturing capacity and increased power usage about 5-fold.

2. Once Bob had finished his initial analysis, Kathy told him that she had forgotten to tell him that the rate of return earned externally on the positive cash flows from these major clients is placed into a venture capital pool headquartered in Toronto. It has been making 35% per year for the last decade. She wanted to know if a unique return still existed and if the Homeworth account was financially viable at a MARR of 35%.

In response to this request, Bob developed the four-step procedure outlined below to closely estimate the composite rate of return i' for any reinvestment rate c and two multiple rates i_1^* and i_2^*.

He plans to apply this procedure to answer this latest question and show the results to Kathy.

Step 1.   Determine the i^* roots of the PW relation for the cash flow series.

Step 2.   For a given reinvestment rate c and the two i^* values from step 1, determine which of the following conditions applies:
(a)   If $c < i_1^*$, then $i' < i_1^*$.
(b)   If $c > i_2^*$, then $i' > i_2^*$.
(c)   If $i_1^* < c < i_2^*$, then i' can be less than c or greater than c, and $i_1^* < i' < i_2^*$.

Step 3.   Guess a starting value for i' according to the result from step 2. Apply the net-investment method from periods 1 to n. Repeat this step until F_n is close to 0. If this F_n is a small positive value, guess another i' that will result in a small negative F_n value, and vice versa.

Step 4.   Using the two F_n results from step 3, linearly interpolate i' such that the corresponding F_n is approximately zero. Of course, the final i' value can also be obtained directly in step 3, without interpolation.

3. Finally, Kathy asked Bob to reevaluate the cash flows for Homeworth at the MARR of 35%, but using a reinvestment rate of 45% to determine if the series is still justified.

Case Study Exercises

1, 2, and 3.   Answer the questions for Bob using spreadsheets.

4. If the i' approximating procedure Bob developed is not available, use the original cash flow data to apply the basic net-investment procedure, and answer Exercises 2 and 3, where c is 35% and 45%, respectively.

5. Kathy concluded from this exercise that any cash flow series is economically justified for any reinvestment rate that is larger than the MARR. Is this a correct conclusion? Explain why or why not.

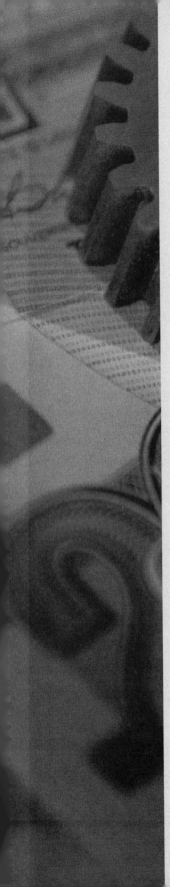

CHAPTER  8

Rate of Return Analysis: Multiple Alternatives

This chapter presents the methods by which two or more alternatives can be evaluated using a rate of return (ROR) comparison based on the methods of the previous chapter. The ROR evaluation correctly performed will result in the same selection as the PW, AW, and FW analyses, but the computational procedure is considerably different for ROR evaluations.

The first case study involves multiple options for a business owned for many years by one person. The second case explores nonconventional cash flow series with multiple rates of return and the use of the PW method in this situation.

LEARNING OBJECTIVES

Purpose: Select the best mutually exclusive alternative on the basis of rate of return analysis of incremental cash flows.

Why incremental analysis?	By the end of this chapter you should be able to
Incremental cash flows	**1.** State why an incremental analysis is necessary for comparing alternatives by the ROR method.
Interpretation	**2.** Prepare a tabulation of incremental cash flows for two alternatives.
Incremental ROR by PW	**3.** Interpret the meaning of ROR on the incremental initial investment.
Incremental ROR by AW	**4.** Select the better of two alternatives using incremental or breakeven ROR analysis based on present worth.
Multiple alternatives	**5.** Select the better of two alternatives using a ROR analysis based on annual worth.
Spreadsheets	**6.** Select the best of multiple alternatives using an incremental ROR analysis.
	7. Develop spreadsheets that include PW, AW, and ROR evaluation for multiple, different-life alternatives.

8.1 WHY INCREMENTAL ANALYSIS IS NECESSARY

When two or more mutually exclusive alternatives are evaluated, engineering economy can identify the one alternative that is the best economically. As we have learned, the PW, AW, and FW techniques can be used to do so. Now the procedure for using ROR to identify the best is presented.

Let's assume that a company uses a MARR of 16% per year, that the company has $90,000 available for investment, and that two alternatives (A and B) are being evaluated. Alternative A requires an investment of $50,000 and has an internal rate of return i_A^* of 35% per year. Alternative B requires $85,000 and has an i_B^* of 29% per year. Intuitively we may conclude that the better alternative is the one that has the larger return, A in this case. However, this is not necessarily so. While A has the higher projected return, it requires an initial investment that is much less than the total money available ($90,000). What happens to the investment capital that is left over? It is generally assumed that excess funds will be invested at the company's MARR, as we learned in the previous chapter. Using this assumption, it is possible to determine the consequences of the alternative investments. If alternative A is selected, $50,000 will return 35% per year. The $40,000 left over will be invested at the MARR of 16% per year. The rate of return on the total capital available, then, will be the weighted average. Thus, if alternative A is selected,

$$\text{Overall ROR}_A = \frac{50,000(0.35) + 40,000(0.16)}{90,000} = 26.6\%$$

If alternative B is selected, $85,000 will be invested at 29% per year, and the remaining $5000 will earn 16% per year. Now the weighted average is

$$\text{Overall ROR}_B = \frac{85,000(0.29) + 5000(0.16)}{90,000} = 28.3\%$$

These calculations show that even though the i^* for alternative A is higher, alternative B presents the better overall ROR for the $90,000. If either a PW or AW comparison is conducted using the MARR of 16% per year as i, alternative B will be chosen.

This simple example illustrates a major fact about the rate of return method for comparing alternatives:

> **Under some circumstances, project ROR values do not provide the same ranking of alternatives as do PW, AW, and FW analyses. This situation does not occur if we conduct an *incremental* cash flow ROR analysis (discussed in the next section).**

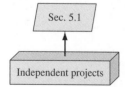

When independent projects are evaluated, no incremental analysis is necessary between projects. Each project is evaluated separately from others, and more than one can be selected. Therefore, the only comparison is with the do-nothing alternative for each project. The ROR can be used to accept or reject each independent project.

8.2 CALCULATION OF INCREMENTAL CASH FLOWS FOR ROR ANALYSIS

It is necessary to prepare an *incremental cash flow tabulation* between two alternatives in preparation for an incremental ROR analysis. A standardized format for the tabulation will simplify this process. The column headings are shown in Table 8–1. If the alternatives have *equal lives,* the year column will go from 0 to n. If the alternatives have *unequal lives,* the year column will go from 0 to the LCM (least common multiple) of the two lives. The use of the LCM is necessary because incremental ROR analysis requires equal-service comparison between alternatives. Therefore, all the assumptions and requirements developed earlier apply for any incremental ROR evaluation. When the LCM of lives is used, the salvage value and reinvestment in each alternative are shown at appropriate times. If a planning period is defined, the cash flow tabulation is for the specified period.

Only for the purpose of simplification, use the convention that between two alternatives, the one with the *larger initial investment* will be regarded as *alternative B.* Then, for each year in Table 8–1,

$$\text{Incremental cash flow} = \text{cash flow}_B - \text{cash flow}_A \qquad [8.1]$$

The initial investment and annual cash flows for each alternative (excluding the salvage value) occur in one of two patterns identified in Chapter 5:

Revenue alternative, where there are both negative and positive cash flows.
Service alternative, where all cash flow estimates are negative.

In either case, Equation [8.1] is used to determine the incremental cash flow series with the sign of each cash flow carefully determined. The next two examples illustrate incremental cash flow tabulation of service alternatives of equal and different lives. Later examples treat revenue alternatives.

Sec. 5.1

Revenue and service

TABLE 8–1 Format for Incremental Cash Flow Tabulation

Year	Cash Flow Alternative A (1)	Cash Flow Alternative B (2)	Incremental Cash Flow (3) = (2) − (1)
0			
1			
.			
.			
.			

EXAMPLE 8.1

A tool and die company in Calgary is considering the purchase of a drill press with fuzzy-logic software to improve accuracy and reduce tool wear. The company has the opportunity to buy a slightly used machine for $15,000 or a new one for $21,000.

Because the new machine is a more sophisticated model, its operating cost is expected to be $7000 per year, while the used machine is expected to require $8200 per year. Each machine is expected to have a 25-year life with a 5% salvage value. Tabulate the incremental cash flow.

Solution

Incremental cash flow is tabulated in Table 8–2. Using Equation [8.1], the subtraction performed is (new − used) since the new machine has a larger initial cost. The salvage values in year 25 are separated from ordinary cash flow for clarity. When disbursements are the same for a number of consecutive years, for hand solution only, it saves time to make a single cash flow listing, as is done for years 1 to 25. However, remember that several years were combined when performing the analysis. This approach cannot be used for spreadsheets.

TABLE 8–2   Cash Flow Tabulation for Example 8.1

Year	Cash Flow Used Press	Cash Flow New Press	Incremental Cash Flow (New − Used)
0	$ −15,000	$ −21,000	$ −6,000
1–25	−8,200	−7,000	+1,200
25	+750	+1,050	+300
Total	$−219,250	$−194,950	$+24,300

Comment

When the cash flow columns are subtracted, the difference between the totals of the two cash flow series should equal the total of the incremental cash flow column. This only provides a check of the addition and subtraction in preparing the tabulation. It is not a basis for selecting an alternative.

EXAMPLE 8.2

Maple Leaf Foods, Inc., has asked its lead process engineer to evaluate two different types of conveyors for the bacon curing line. Type A has an initial cost of $70,000 and a life of 8 years. Type B has an initial cost of $95,000 and a life expectancy of 12 years. The annual operating cost for type A is expected to be $9000, while the AOC for type B is expected to be $7000. If the salvage values are $5000 and $10,000 for type A and type B, respectively, tabulate the incremental cash flow using their LCM.

Solution

The LCM of 8 and 12 is 24 years. In the incremental cash flow tabulation for 24 years (Table 8–3) note that the reinvestment and salvage values are shown in years 8 and 16 for type A and in year 12 for type B.

TABLE 8–3 Incremental Cash Flow Tabulation, Example 8.2

Year	Cash Flow Type A	Cash Flow Type B	Incremental Cash Flow (B − A)
0	$−70,000	$−95,000	$−25,000
1–7	−9,000	−7,000	+2,000
8	−70,000 −9,000 +5,000	−7,000	+67,000
9–11	−9,000	−7,000	+2,000
12	−9,000	−95,000 −7,000 +10,000	−83,000
13–15	−9,000	−7,000	+2,000
16	−70,000 −9,000 +5,000	−7,000	+67,000
17–23	−9,000	−7,000	+2,000
24	−9,000 +5,000	−7,000 +10,000	+7,000
	$−411,000	$−338,000	$+73,000

The use of a spreadsheet to obtain incremental cash flows requires one entry for each year through the LCM for each alternative. Therefore, some combining of cash flows may be necessary before the entry is made for each alternative. The incremental cash flow column results from an application of Equation [8.1]. As an illustration, the first 8 years of the 24 years in Table 8–3 should appear as follows when entered onto a spreadsheet. The incremental values in column D are obtained using a subtraction relation, for example, C4−B4.

Column A Year	Column B Type A	Column C Type B	Column D Incremental
0	$−70,000	$−95,000	$−25,000
1	−9,000	−7,000	+2,000
2	−9,000	−7,000	+2,000
3	−9,000	−7,000	+2,000
4	−9,000	−7,000	+2,000
5	−9,000	−7,000	+2,000
6	−9,000	−7,000	+2,000
7	−9,000	−7,000	+2,000
8	−74,000	−7,000	+67,000
etc.			

8.3 INTERPRETATION OF RATE OF RETURN ON THE EXTRA INVESTMENT

The incremental cash flows in year 0 of Tables 8–2 and 8–3 reflect the *extra investment* or *cost* required if the alternative with the larger first cost is selected. This is important in an incremental ROR analysis in order to determine the ROR earned on the extra funds expended for the larger-investment alternative. If the incremental cash flows of the larger investment don't justify it, we must select the cheaper one. In Example 8.1 the new drill press requires an extra investment of $6000 (Table 8–2). If the new machine is purchased, there will be a "savings" of $1200 per year for 25 years, plus an extra $300 in year 25. The decision to buy the used or new machine can be made on the basis of the profitability of investing the extra $6000 in the new machine. If the equivalent worth of the savings is greater than the equivalent worth of the extra investment at the MARR, the extra investment should be made (i.e., the larger first-cost proposal should be accepted). On the other hand, if the extra investment is not justified by the savings, select the lower-investment proposal.

It is important to recognize that the rationale for making the selection decision is the same as if only *one alternative* were under consideration, that alternative being the one represented by the incremental cash flow series. When viewed in this manner, it is obvious that unless this investment yields a rate of return equal to or greater than the MARR, the extra investment should not be made. As further clarification of this extra-investment rationale, consider the following: The rate of return attainable through the incremental cash flow is an alternative to investing at the MARR. Section 8.1 states that any excess funds not invested in the alternative are assumed to be invested at the MARR. The conclusion is clear:

> **If the rate of return available through the incremental cash flow equals or exceeds the MARR, the alternative associated with the extra investment should be selected.**

Not only must the return on the extra investment meet or exceed the MARR, but also the return on the investment that is common to both alternatives must meet or exceed the MARR. Accordingly, before starting an incremental ROR analysis, it is advisable to determine the internal rate of return i^* for each alternative. (Of course, this is much easier with evaluation by computer than by hand.) This can be done only for revenue alternatives, because service alternatives have only cost (negative) cash flows and no i^* can be determined. The guideline is as follows:

> **For multiple revenue alternatives, calculate the internal rate of return i^* for each alternative, and eliminate all alternatives that have an $i^* <$ MARR. Compare the remaining alternatives incrementally.**

As an illustration, if the MARR $= 15\%$ and two alternatives have i^* values of 12 and 21%, the 12% alternative can be eliminated from further consideration. With only two alternatives, it is obvious that the second one is selected. If both alternatives have $i^* <$ MARR, no alternative is justified and the do-nothing

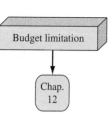

alternative is the best economically. When three or more alternatives are evaluated, it is usually worthwhile, but not required, to calculate $i*$ for each alternative for preliminary screening. Alternatives that cannot meet the MARR may be eliminated from further evaluation using this option. This option is especially useful when performing the analysis by computer. The IRR function applied to each alternative's cash flow estimates can quickly indicate unacceptable alternatives, as demonstrated later in Section 8.6.

When *independent projects* are evaluated, there is no comparison on the extra investment. The ROR value is used to accept all projects with $i* \geq$ MARR, assuming there is no budget limitation. For example, assume MARR = 10%, and three independent projects are available with ROR values of:

$$i_A^* = 12\% \quad i_B^* = 9\% \quad i_C^* = 23\%$$

Projects A and C are selected, but B is not because $i_B^* <$ MARR. Example 8.8 in Section 8.7 on spreadsheet applications illustrates selection from independent projects using ROR values.

8.4 RATE OF RETURN EVALUATION USING PW: INCREMENTAL AND BREAKEVEN

In this section we discuss the primary approach to making mutually exclusive alternative selections by the incremental ROR method. A PW-based relation like Equation [7.1] is developed for the incremental cash flows. Use hand or computer means to find Δi_{B-A}^*, the internal ROR for the series. Placing Δ (delta) before i_{B-A}^* distinguishes it from the ROR values i_A^* and i_B^*.

Since incremental ROR requires equal-service comparison, the LCM of lives must be used in the PW formulation. Because of the reinvestment requirement for PW analysis for different-life assets, the incremental cash flow series may contain several sign changes, indicating multiple $\Delta i*$ values. Though incorrect, this indication is usually neglected in actual practice. The correct approach is to establish the reinvestment rate c and follow the approach of Section 7.5. This means that the unique composite rate of return ($\Delta i'$) for the incremental cash flow series is determined. These three required elements—incremental cash flow series, LCM, and multiple roots—are the primary reasons that the ROR method is often applied incorrectly in engineering economy analyses of multiple alternatives. As stated earlier, it is always possible, and generally advisable, to use a PW or AW analysis *at an established MARR* in lieu of the ROR method when multiple rates are indicated.

The complete procedure by hand or computer for an incremental ROR analysis for two alternatives is as follows:

1. Order the alternatives by initial investment or cost, starting with the smaller one, called A. The one with the larger initial investment is in the column labelled B in Table 8–1.
2. Develop the cash flow and incremental cash flow series using the LCM of years, assuming reinvestment in alternatives.
3. Draw an incremental cash flow diagram, if needed.

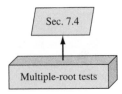

Sec. 7.4

Multiple-root tests

4. Count the number of sign changes in the incremental cash flow series to determine if multiple rates of return may be present. If necessary, use Norstrom's criterion on the cumulative incremental cash flow series to determine if a single positive root exists.
5. Set up the PW equation for the incremental cash flows in the form of Equation [7.1], and determine Δi^*_{B-A} using trial and error by hand or spreadsheet functions.
6. Select the economically better alternative as follows:

> **If $\Delta i^*_{B-A} <$ MARR, select alternative A.**
>
> **If $\Delta i^*_{B-A} \geq$ MARR, the extra investment is justified; select alternative B.**

> If the incremental i^* is exactly equal to or very near the MARR, noneconomic considerations will most likely be used to help in the selection of the "best" alternative.

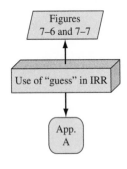

Figures
7–6 and 7–7

Use of "guess" in IRR

App.
A

In step 5, if trial and error is used to calculate the rate of return, time may be saved if the Δi^*_{B-A} value is bracketed, rather than approximated by a point value using linear interpolation, provided that a single ROR value is not needed. For example, if the MARR is 15% per year and you have established that Δi^*_{B-A} is in the 15 to 20% range, an exact value is not necessary to accept B since you already know that $\Delta i^*_{B-A} \geq$ MARR.

The IRR function on a spreadsheet will normally determine one Δi^* value. Multiple guess values can be input to find multiple roots in the range -100% to ∞ for a nonconventional series, as illustrated in Examples 7.4 and 7.5. If this is not the case, to be correct, the indication of multiple roots in step 4 requires that the net-investment procedure, Equation [7.6], be applied in step 5 to make $\Delta i' = \Delta i^*$. If one of these multiple roots is the same as the expected reinvestment rate c, this root can be used as the ROR value, and the net-investment procedure is not necessary. In this case only, $\Delta i' = \Delta i^*$, as concluded at the end of Section 7.5.

EXAMPLE 8.3

In 2010, Deutsche Telekom and France Telecom completed the merger of their British mobile phone units to create that country's biggest operator with a 37% market share and 28 million customers. As expected, some equipment incompatibilities had to be rectified. One item had two suppliers—a German firm (A) and a French firm (B). Approximately 3000 units of this equipment were needed. Estimates for vendors A and B are given for each unit, in Canadian funds.

	A	B
Initial cost, $	−8,000	−13,000
Annual costs, $	−3,500	−1,600
Salvage value, $	0	2,000
Life, years	10	5

TABLE 8–4 Incremental Cash Flow Tabulation, Example 8.3

Year	Cash Flow A (1)	Cash Flow B (2)	Incremental Cash Flow (3) = (2) − (1)
0	$-8,000	$-13,000	$-5,000
1–5	-3,500	-1,600	+1,900
5	—	$\begin{cases} +2,000 \\ -13,000 \end{cases}$	-11,000
6–10	-3,500	-1,600	+1,900
10	—	+2,000	+2,000
	$-43,000	$-38,000	$+5,000

Determine which vendor should be selected if the MARR is 15% per year. Show hand and computer solutions.

Solution by Hand
These are service alternatives, since all cash flows are costs. Use the procedure described above to determine Δi^*_{B-A}.

1. Alternatives A and B are correctly ordered with the higher first-cost alternative in column 2.
2. The cash flows for the LCM of 10 years are tabulated in Table 8–4.
3. The incremental cash flow diagram is shown in Figure 8–1.
4. There are three sign changes in the incremental cash flow series, indicating as many as three roots. There are also three sign changes in the cumulative incremental series, which starts negatively at $S_0 = \$-5000$ and continues to $S_{10} = \$+5000$, indicating that more than one positive root may exist.
5. The rate of return equation based on the PW of incremental cash flows is

$$0 = -5000 + 1900(P/A,\Delta i,10) - 11,000(P/F,\Delta i,5) + 2000(P/F,\Delta i,10) \qquad [8.2]$$

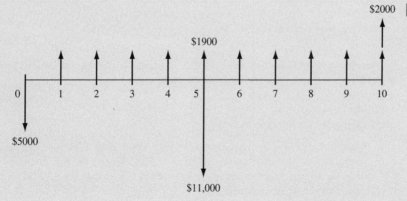

FIGURE 8–1
Diagram of incremental cash flows, Example 8.3.

Assume that the reinvestment rate is equal to the resulting Δi^*_{B-A} (or Δi^* for a shortened symbol). Solution of Equation [8.2] for the first root discovered results in Δi^* between 12 and 15%. By interpolation $\Delta i^* = 12.65\%$.

6. Since the rate of return of 12.65% on the extra investment is less than the 15% MARR, the lower-cost vendor A is selected. The extra investment of $5000 is not economically justified by the lower annual cost and higher salvage estimates.

Comment

In step 4, the presence of up to three i^* values is indicated. The preceding analysis finds one of the roots at 12.65%. When we state that the incremental ROR is 12.65%, we assume that any positive net-investments are reinvested at $c = 12.65\%$. If this is not a reasonable assumption, the net-investment procedure must be applied and an estimated reinvestment rate c must be used to find a different value $\Delta i'$ to compare with MARR = 15%.

		D15		= =IRR(D4:D14)					
	A	B	C	D	E	F	G	H
1	MARR =	15%						
2				Incremental				
3	Year	Vendor A	Vendor B	cash flow				
4	0	$ (8,000)	$ (13,000)	$ (5,000)				
5	1	$ (3,500)	$ (1,600)	$ 1,900				
6	2	$ (3,500)	$ (1,600)	$ 1,900				
7	3	$ (3,500)	$ (1,600)	$ 1,900				
8	4	$ (3,500)	$ (1,600)	$ 1,900				
9	5	$ (3,500)	$ (12,600)	$ (9,100)		= C10−B10		
10	6	$ (3,500)	$ (1,600)	$ 1,900				
11	7	$ (3,500)	$ (1,600)	$ 1,900				
12	8	$ (3,500)	$ (1,600)	$ 1,900				
13	9	$ (3,500)	$ (1,600)	$ 1,900		= IRR(D4:D14)		
14	10	$ (3,500)	$ 400	$ 3,900				
15	Incremental i*			12.65%				
16					= NPV($D$15,D5:D14)+D4			
17	PW @ inc i*			$0.00				
18	PW @ MARR			($438.91)				
19					= NPV($B$1,D5:D14)+D4			

FIGURE 8–2

Spreadsheet solution to find the incremental rate of return, Example 8.3.

The other two roots are very large positive and negative numbers, as the IRR function of Excel reveals. So they are not useful to the analysis.

Solution by Computer

Steps 1 through 4 are the same as above.

E-SOLVE

5. Figure 8–2 includes the incremental net cash flows from Table 8–4 calculated in column D. Cell D15 displays the Δi^* value of 12.65% using the IRR function.
6. Since the rate of return on the extra investment is less than the 15% MARR, the lower-cost vendor A is selected.

Comment
Once the spreadsheet is set up, there are a wide variety of analyses that can be performed. For example, cell D17 uses the NPV function to verify that the present worth is zero at the calculated Δi^*. Cell D18 is the PW at MARR = 15%, which is negative, thus indicating in yet another way that the extra investment does not return the MARR. Of course, any cash flow estimate and the MARR can be changed to determine what happens to Δi^*. A PW vs. Δi chart could easily be added, if two more columns are inserted, similar to those in Figures 7–6 and 7–7.

The rate of return determined for the incremental cash flow series can be interpreted as a *breakeven rate of return* value. If the incremental cash flow ROR (Δi^*) is greater than the MARR, the larger-investment alternative is selected. For example, if the PW vs. i graph for the incremental cash flows in Table 8–4 (and spreadsheet Figure 8–2) is plotted for various interest rates, the graph shown in Figure 8–3 is obtained. It shows the Δi^* breakeven at 12.65%. The conclusions are that

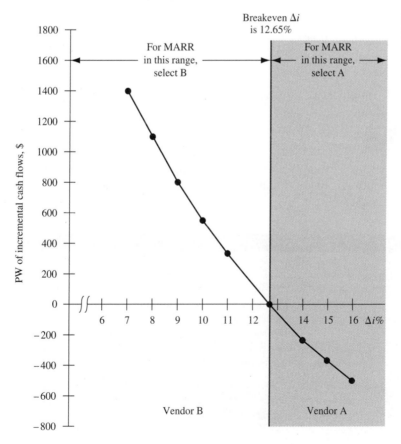

FIGURE 8–3
Plot of present worth of incremental cash flows for Example 8.3 at various Δi values.

FIGURE 8–4

Breakeven graph of
Example 8.3 cash flows
(not incremental).

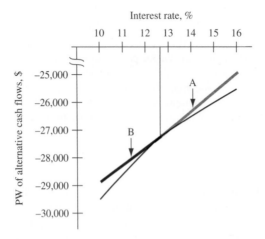

- For MARR < 12.65%, the extra investment for B is justified.
- For MARR > 12.65%, the opposite is true; the extra investment in B should not be made, and vendor A is selected.
- If MARR is exactly 12.65%, the alternatives are equally attractive.

Figure 8–4, which is a breakeven graph of PW vs. i for the cash flows (not incremental) of each alternative in Example 8.3, provides the same results. Since all net cash flows are negative (service alternatives), the PW values are negative. Now, the same conclusions are reached using the following logic:

- If MARR < 12.65%, select B since its PW of cost cash flows is smaller (numerically larger).
- If MARR > 12.65%, select A since now its PW of costs is smaller.
- If MARR is exactly 12.65%, either alternative is equally attractive.

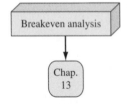

Breakeven analysis

Chap.
13

The next example illustrates incremental ROR evaluation and breakeven rate of return graphs for revenue alternatives. More of breakeven analysis is covered in Chapter 13.

EXAMPLE 8.4

E-SOLVE

Royal Bank of Canada uses a MARR of 30% on alternatives for its own business that are considered risky, that is, the response of the public to the service has not been well established by test marketing. Two alternative software systems and the marketing/delivery plans have been jointly developed by software engineers and the marketing department. They are for new online banking and loan services to passenger cruise ships and military vessels at sea internationally. For each system, startup, annual net income, and salvage value (i.e., sellout value to another financial corporation) estimates are summarized below.

(a) Perform the incremental ROR analysis by computer.
(b) Develop the PW vs. i graphs for each alternative and the increment. Which alternative, if either one, should be selected?

	System A	System B
Initial investment, $1000	−12,000	−18,000
Estimated net income, $1000 per year	5,000	7,000
Salvage value, $1000	2,500	3,000
Estimated competitive life, years	8	8

Solution by Computer

(a) Refer to Figure 8–5a. The IRR function is used in cells B13 and E13 to display i^* for each alternative. We use the i^* values as a preliminary screening tool only to determine which alternatives exceed the MARR. If none do, the DN alternative is indicated automatically. In both cases $i^* > 30\%$; they are both retained. The incremental cash flows are calculated (column G = column E − column B), and the IRR function results in $\Delta i^* = 29.41\%$. This value is slightly less than the MARR; alternative A is selected as the better economic choice.

(b) Figure 8–5b contains plots of PW vs. i for all three cash flow series between the interest rates of 25 and 42%. The bottom curve (incremental analysis) indicates the breakeven ROR at 29.41%, which is where the two alternative PW curves cross. The conclusion is again the same; with MARR = 30%, select alternative A because its PW value ($2930 in cell D5 of Figure 8–5a) is slightly larger than that for B ($2841 in F5).

Comment

With this spreadsheet format, both a PW analysis and an incremental ROR analysis have been accomplished with graphic backup to demonstrate the conclusion of the engineering economy analysis.

	A	B	C	D	E	F	G	H	I	J
1										
2	Year	Cash flow A	Rate, i	PW of A	Cash flow B	PW of B	Incr. CF	PW of Incr.		
3	0	$ (12,000)	25%	$ 5,064	$ (18,000)	$ 5,806	$ (6,000)	$ 742		
4	1	$ 5,000	28%	$ 3,726	$ 7,000	$ 3,947	$ 2,000	$ 221		
5	2	$ 5,000	30%	$ 2,930	$ 7,000	$ 2,841	$ 2,000	$ (89)		
6	3	$ 5,000	32%	$ 2,201	$ 7,000	$ 1,827	$ 2,000	$ (374)		
7	4	$ 5,000	34%	$ 1,532	$ 7,000	$ 896	$ 2,000	$ (635)		
8	5	$ 5,000	36%	$ 916	$ 7,000	$ 39	$ 2,000	$ (876)		
9	6	$ 5,000	38%	$ 348	$ 7,000	$ (751)	$ 2,000	$ (1,099)		
10	7	$ 5,000	40%	$ (178)	$ 7,000	$ (1,483)	$ 2,000	$ (1,305)		
11	8	$ 7,500	42%	$ (664)	10000	$ (2,160)	$ 2,500	$ (1,496)		
12										
13	i*	39.31%			36.10%		29.41%			
14										

= NPV($C11,$B$4:$B$11)+$B$3

= IRR(E3:E11)

= IRR(G3:G11)

= NPV($C11,$G$4:$G$11)+$G$3

(a)

FIGURE 8–5

Spreadsheet solution to compare two alternatives: (a) incremental ROR analysis, (b) PW vs. i graphs, Example 8.4.

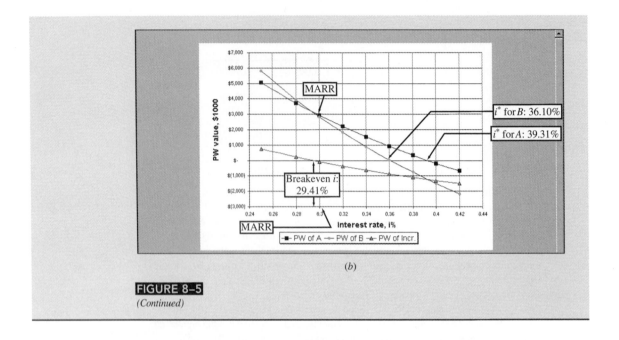

(b)

FIGURE 8–5

(Continued)

Figure 8–5*b* provides an excellent opportunity to see why the ROR method can result in selecting the wrong alternative when only *i** values are used to select between two alternatives. This is sometimes called the *ranking inconsistency problem* of the ROR method. *The inconsistency occurs when the MARR is set less than the breakeven rate between two revenue alternatives.* Since the MARR is established based on conditions of the economy and market, MARR is established external to any particular alternative evaluation. In Figure 8–5*b*, the breakeven rate is 29.41%, and the MARR is 30%. If the MARR were established lower than breakeven, say at 26%, the *incremental* ROR analysis results in correctly selecting B, because Δ*i** = 29.41%, which exceeds 26%. But if only the *i** values were used, system A would be wrongly chosen, because its *i** = 39.31%. This error occurs because the rate of return method assumes reinvestment at the alternative's ROR value (39.31%), while PW and AW analyses use the MARR as the reinvestment rate. The conclusion is simple:

If the ROR method is used to evaluate two or more alternatives, use the incremental cash flows and Δ*i** to make the decision between alternatives.

8.5 RATE OF RETURN EVALUATION USING AW

Comparing alternatives by the ROR method (correctly performed) always leads to the same selection as PW, AW, and FW analyses, whether the ROR is determined using a PW-based, an AW-based, or a FW-based relation. However, for the AW-based technique, there are two equivalent ways to perform the evaluation: using the *incremental cash flows* over the LCM of alternative lives, just as for the

PW-based relation (previous section), or finding the AW for each alternative's *actual cash flows* and setting the difference of the two equal to zero to find the Δi^* value. Of course, there is no difference between the two approaches if the alternative lives are equal. Both methods are summarized here.

Since the ROR method requires comparison for equal service, *the incremental cash flows must be evaluated over the LCM of lives.* When solving by hand for Δi^*, there may be no real computational advantage to using AW, as was found in Chapter 6. The same six-step procedure of the previous section (for PW-based calculation) is used, except in step 5 the AW-based relation is developed.

For comparison by computer with equal or unequal lives, the incremental cash flows must be calculated over the LCM of the two alternatives' lives. Then the IRR function is applied to find Δi^*. This is the same technique developed in the previous section and used in the spreadsheet in Figure 8–2. *Use of the IRR function in this manner is the correct way to use Excel spreadsheet functions to compare alternatives using the ROR method.*

The second AW-based method takes advantage of the AW technique's assumption that the equivalent AW value is the same for each year of the first and all succeeding life cycles. Whether the lives are equal or unequal, set up the *AW relation for the cash flows of each alternative,* form the relation below, and solve for i^*.

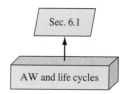

$$0 = AW_B - AW_A \qquad\qquad [8.3]$$

Equation [8.3] applies to solution by hand only, not solution by computer.

For both methods, all equivalent values are on an AW basis, so the i^* that results from Equation [8.3] is the same as the Δi^* found using the first approach. Example 8.5 illustrates ROR analysis using AW-based relations for unequal lives.

EXAMPLE 8.5

Compare the alternatives of vendors A and B for the mobile telephone merger in Example 8.3, using an AW-based incremental ROR method and the same MARR of 15% per year.

Solution
For reference, the PW-based ROR relation, Equation [8.2], for the incremental cash flow in Example 8.3 shows that vendor A should be selected with $\Delta i^* = 12.65\%$.

For the AW relation, there are two equivalent solution approaches. Write an AW-based relation on the *incremental* cash flow series over the *LCM of 10 years,* or write Equation [8.3] for the *two actual* cash flow series over *one life cycle* of each alternative.

For the incremental method, the AW equation is

$$0 = -5000(A/P,\Delta i,10) - 11{,}000(P/F,\Delta i,5)(A/P,\Delta i,10) + 2000(A/F,\Delta i,10) + 1900$$

It is easy to enter the incremental cash flows onto a spreadsheet, as in Figure 8–2, column D, and use the IRR(D4:D14) function to display $\Delta i^* = 12.65\%$.

For the second method, the ROR is found by Equation [8.3] using the respective lives of 10 years for A and 5 years for B.

$$AW_A = -8000(A/P,i,10) - 3500$$
$$AW_B = -13,000(A/P,i,5) + 2000(A/F,i,5) - 1600$$

Now develop $0 = AW_B - AW_A$.

$$0 = -13,000(A/P,i,5) + 2000(A/F,i,5) + 8000(A/P,i,10) + 1900$$

Solution again yields an interpolated value of $i* = 12.65\%$.

Comment

It is very important to remember that when an incremental ROR analysis using an AW-based equation is made on the *incremental cash flows,* the least common multiple of lives must be used.

8.6 INCREMENTAL ROR ANALYSIS OF MULTIPLE, MUTUALLY EXCLUSIVE ALTERNATIVES

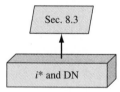

This section treats selection from multiple alternatives that are mutually exclusive, using the incremental ROR method. Acceptance of one alternative automatically precludes acceptance of any others. The analysis is based upon PW (or AW) relations for incremental cash flows between two alternatives at a time.

When the incremental ROR method is applied, the entire investment must return at least the MARR. When the $i*$ values on several alternatives exceed the MARR, incremental ROR evaluation is required. (For revenue alternatives, if not even one $i* \geq$ MARR, the do-nothing alternative is selected.) For all alternatives (revenue or service), the incremental investment must be separately justified. If the return on the extra investment equals or exceeds the MARR, then the extra investment should be made in order to maximize the total return on the money available, as discussed in Section 8.1.

Thus, for ROR analysis of multiple, mutually exclusive alternatives, the following criteria are used. Select the one alternative that

1. **Requires the *largest investment,* and**
2. **Indicates that the *extra investment over the best acceptable alternative is justified***

An important rule to apply when evaluating multiple alternatives by the incremental ROR method is that *an alternative should never be compared with one for which the incremental investment is not justified.*

The incremental ROR evaluation procedure for multiple, equal-life alternatives is summarized below. Step 2 applies only to revenue alternatives, because the first alternative is compared to DN only when revenue cash flows are estimated. The terms *defender* and *challenger* are dynamic in that they refer, respectively, to the alternative that is currently selected (the defender) and the one that is challenging it for acceptance based on Δi^*. In every pairwise evaluation, there is one of each. The steps for solution by hand or by computer are as follows:

1. Order the alternatives from *smallest to largest initial investment*. Record the annual cash flow estimates for each equal-life alternative.
2. *Revenue alternatives only:* Calculate i^* for the first alternative. In effect, this makes DN the defender and the first alternative the challenger. If $i^* <$ MARR, eliminate the alternative and go to the next one. Repeat this until $i^* \geq$ MARR for the first time, and define that alternative as the defender. The next alternative is now the challenger. Go to step 3. (*Note:* This is where solution by computer spreadsheet can be a quick assist. Calculate the i^* for all alternatives first, using the IRR function, and select as the defender the first one for which $i^* \geq$ MARR. Label it the defender and go to step 3.)
3. Determine the incremental cash flow between the challenger and defender, using the relation

$$\text{Incremental cash flow} = \text{challenger cash flow} - \text{defender cash flow}$$

    Set up the ROR relation.
4. Calculate Δi^* for the incremental cash flow series using a PW-, AW-, or FW-based equation. (PW is most commonly used.)
5. If $\Delta i^* \geq$ MARR, the challenger becomes the defender and the previous defender is eliminated. Conversely, if $\Delta i^* <$ MARR, the challenger is removed, and the defender remains against the next challenger.
6. Repeat steps 3 to 5 until only one alternative remains. It is the selected one.

Note that only two alternatives are compared at any one time. It is vital that the correct alternatives be compared, or the wrong alternative may be selected.

EXAMPLE 8.6

Ford's Essex Engine plant in Windsor, Ontario, wants to add a spare parts storage facility for its new fuel-efficient V-8 engines. A plant engineer has identified four different location options. Initial cost of earthwork and prefab building, and annual net cash flow estimates are detailed in Table 8–5. The annual net cash flow series vary due to differences in maintenance, labour costs, transportation charges, etc. If the MARR is 10%, use incremental ROR analysis to select the one economically best location.

TABLE 8–5   Estimates for Four Alternative Building Locations, Example 8.6

	A	B	C	D
Initial cost, $	−200,000	−275,000	−190,000	−350,000
Annual cash flow, $	+22,000	+35,000	+19,500	+42,000
Life, years	30	30	30	30

Solution

All sites have a 30-year life, and they are revenue alternatives. The procedure outlined above is applied.

1. The alternatives are ordered by increasing initial cost in Table 8–6.
2. Compare location C with the do-nothing alternative. The ROR relation includes only the P/A factor.

$$0 = -190,000 + 19,500(P/A,i^*,30)$$

Table 8–6, column 1, presents the calculated $(P/A,\Delta i^*,30)$ factor value of 9.7436 and $\Delta i_c^* = 9.63\%$. Since $9.63\% < 10\%$, location C is eliminated. Now the comparison is A to DN, and column 2 shows that $\Delta i_A^* = 10.49\%$. This eliminates the do-nothing alternative; the defender is now A and the challenger is B.

TABLE 8–6 Computation of Incremental Rate of Return for Four Alternatives, Example 8.6

	C (1)	A (2)	B (3)	D (4)
Initial cost, $	−190,000	−200,000	−275,000	−350,000
Cash flow, $	+19,500	+22,000	+35,000	+42,000
Alternatives compared	C to DN	A to DN	B to A	D to B
Incremental cost, $	−190,000	−200,000	−75,000	−75,000
Incremental cash flow, $	+19,500	+22,000	+13,000	+7,000
Calculated $(P/A,\Delta i^*,30)$	9.7436	9.0909	5.7692	10.7143
$\Delta i^*,\%$	9.63	10.49	17.28	8.55
Increment justified?	No	Yes	Yes	No
Alternative selected	DN	A	B	B

3. The incremental cash flow series, column 3, and Δi^* for *B-to-A comparison* is determined from

$$0 = -275,000 - (-200,000) + (35,000 - 22,000)(P/A,\Delta i^*,30)$$
$$= -75,000 + 13,000(P/A,\Delta i^*,30)$$

4. From the interest tables, look up the P/A factor at the MARR, which is $(P/A,10\%,30) = 9.4269$. Now, any P/A value greater than 9.4269 indicates that the Δi^* will be less than 10% and is unacceptable. The P/A factor is 5.7692, so B is acceptable. For reference purposes, $\Delta i^* = 17.28\%$.
5. Alternative B is justified incrementally (new defender), thereby eliminating A.
6. Comparison D-to-B (steps 3 and 4) results in the PW relation $0 = -75,000 + 7000(P/A, \Delta i^*,30)$ and a P/A value of 10.7143 ($\Delta i^* = 8.55\%$). Location D is eliminated, and only alternative B remains; it is selected.

Comment

An alternative must *always* be incrementally compared with an acceptable alternative, and the do-nothing alternative can end up being the only acceptable one. Since C was not justified in this example, location A was not compared with C. Thus, *if* the B-to-A comparison had not indicated that B was incrementally justified, then the D-to-A comparison would be correct instead of D-to-B.

To demonstrate how important it is to apply the ROR method correctly, consider the following. If the i^* of each alternative is computed initially, the results by ordered alternatives are

Location	C	A	B	D
i^*, %	9.63	10.49	12.35	11.56

Now apply *only* the first criterion stated earlier; that is, make the largest investment that has a MARR of 10% or more. Location D is selected. But, as shown above, this is the wrong selection, because the extra investment of $75,000 over location B will not earn the MARR. In fact, it will earn only 8.55%.

For service alternatives (costs only), the incremental cash flow is the difference between costs for two alternatives. There is no do-nothing alternative and no step 2 in the solution procedure. Therefore, the lowest-investment alternative is the initial defender against the next-lowest investment (challenger). This procedure is illustrated in Example 8.7 using a spreadsheet solution for equal-life service alternatives.

EXAMPLE 8.7

As the film of an oil spill from an at-sea tanker moves ashore, great losses occur for aquatic life as well as shoreline feeders and dwellers, such as birds. Environmental engineers and lawyers from several international petroleum corporations and transport companies—Exxon-Mobil, BP, Shell, and some transporters for OPEC producers—have developed a plan to strategically locate throughout the world newly developed equipment that is substantially more effective than manual procedures in cleaning crude oil residue from bird feathers. The Sierra Club, Greenpeace, and other international environmental interest groups are in favour of the initiative. Alternative machines from manufacturers in China, the United States, Germany, and Canada are available with the cost estimates in Table 8–7. Annual cost estimates are expected to be high to ensure readiness at any time. The company representatives have agreed to use the average of the corporate MARR values, which results in MARR = 13.5%. Use a computer and incremental ROR analysis to determine which manufacturer offers the best economic choice.

TABLE 8–7   Costs for Four Alternative Machines, Example 8.7

	Machine 1	Machine 2	Machine 3	Machine 4
First cost, $	−5,000	−6,500	−10,000	−15,000
Annual operating cost, $	−3,500	−3,200	−3,000	−1,400
Salvage value, $	+500	+900	+700	+1,000
Life, years	8	8	8	8

E-SOLVE

Solution by Computer

Follow the procedure for incremental ROR analysis outlined prior to Example 8.6. The spreadsheet in Figure 8–6 contains the complete solution.

1. The alternatives are already ordered by increasing first costs.
2. These are service alternatives, so there is no comparison to DN, since i^* values cannot be calculated.
3. Machine 2 is the first challenger to machine 1; the incremental cash flows for the 2-to-1 comparison are in column D.
4. The 2-to-1 comparison results in $\Delta i^* = 14.57\%$ in cell D17 by applying the IRR function.
5. This return exceeds MARR = 13.5%, so machine 2 is the new defender (cell D19).

The comparison continues for 3-to-2 in cell E17 where the return is very negative at $\Delta i^* = -18.77\%$; machine 2 is retained as the defender. Finally the 4-to-2 comparison has an incremental ROR of 13.60%, which is slightly larger than MARR = 13.5%. The conclusion is to purchase machine 4 because the extra investment is (marginally) justified.

Comment

As mentioned earlier, it is not possible to generate a PW vs. i graph for each service alternative because all cash flows are negative. However, it is possible to generate PW vs. i graphs for the incremental series in the same fashion as we have done previously. The curves will cross the PW = 0 line at the Δi^* values determined by the IRR functions.

The spreadsheet does not include logic to select the better alternative at each stage of the solution. This feature could be added at each comparison using the Excel IF-operator and the correct arithmetic operations for each incremental cash flow and Δi^* values. This is too time-consuming; it is faster for the analyst to make the decision and then develop the required functions for each comparison.

	A	B	C	D	E	F	G	H
1	MARR =	13.50%						
2								
3		Year	Machine 1	Machine 2	Machine 3	Machine 4		
4	Initial investment		-$5,000	-$6,500	-$10,000	-$15,000		
5	Annual cost		-$3,500	-$3,200	-$3,000	-$1,400		
6	Salvage value		$500	$900	$700	$1,000		
7	ROR comparison			2 to 1	3 to 2	4 to 2		= F4 – D4
8	Incremental investment	0		-$1,500	-$3,500	-$8,500		
9	Incremental cash flow	1		$300	$200	$1,800		
10		2		$300	$200	$1,800		= $F$5 – $D$5
11		3		$300	$200	$1,800		
12		4		$300	$200	$1,800		
13		5		$300	$200	$1,800		
14		6		$300	$200	$1,800		
15	= IRR(D8:D16)	7		$300	$200	$1,800		
16		8		$700	$0	$1,900		
17	Incremental i*			14.57%	-18.77%	13.60%		= IRR(F8:F16)
18	Increment justified?			Yes	No	Yes, barely		
19	Alternative selected			2	2	4		

FIGURE 8–6
Spreadsheet solution to select from four service alternatives, Example 8.7.

Selection from multiple, mutually exclusive alternatives with *unequal lives* using Δi^* values requires that the incremental cash flows be evaluated over the LCM of the two alternatives being compared. This is another application of the principle of equal-service comparison. The spreadsheet application in the next section illustrates the computations.

It is always possible to rely on PW or AW analysis of the incremental cash flows at the MARR to make the selection. In other words, don't find Δi^* for each pairwise comparison; find PW or AW at the MARR instead. However, it is still necessary to make the comparison over the LCM number of years for an incremental analysis to be performed correctly.

8.7 SPREADSHEET APPLICATION—PW, AW, AND ROR ANALYSES ALL IN ONE

The following spreadsheet example combines many of the economic analysis techniques we have learned so far—(internal) ROR analysis, incremental ROR analysis, PW analysis, and AW analysis. Now that the IRR, NPV, and PV functions are mastered, it is possible to perform a wide variety of evaluations for multiple alternatives on a single spreadsheet. To better understand how the functions are formatted and used, their formats must be developed by the reader, as there are no cell tags provided in this example. A nonconventional cash flow series for which multiple ROR values may be found, and selection from both mutually exclusive alternatives and independent projects, are included in this example.

EXAMPLE 8.8

In-flight telephones provided at airline passenger seats are an expected service by many customers. Air Canada knows it will have to replace 12,000 to 15,000 units in the next few years on its Boeing 767 aircraft. Four optional data-handling features which build upon one another are available from the manufacturer, but at an added cost per unit. Besides costing more, the higher-end options (e.g., satellite-based plug-in video service) are estimated to have longer lives before the next replacement is forced by new, advanced features expected by flyers. All four options are expected to boost annual revenues by varying amounts. Figure 8–7 spreadsheet rows 2 through 6 include all the estimates for the four options.

(a) Using MARR = 15%, perform ROR, PW, and AW evaluations to select the one level of options which is the most promising economically.

(b) If more than one level of options can be selected, consider the four that are described as independent projects. If no budget limitations are considered at this time, which options are acceptable if the MARR is increased to 20% when more than one option may be implemented?

Solution by Computer

(a) The spreadsheet (Figure 8–7) is divided into six sections:

E-SOLVE

Section 1 (rows 1, 2): MARR value and the alternative names (A through D) in increasing order of initial cost.

	A	B	C	D	E	F	G	H
1	MARR =	15%						
2	Alternative		A	B	C		D	
3	Initial cost		-$6,000	-$7,000	-$9,000		-$17,000	
4	Annual cash flow		$2,000	$3,000	$3,000		$3,500	
5	Salvage value		$0	$200	$300		$1,000	
6	Life	Year	3	4	6		12	
7	Incr. ROR comparison		Actual CF	Actual CF	Actual CF	C to B	Actual CF	D to C
8	Incremental investment	0	-6000	-7000	-9000	-$2,000	-17 000	-$8,000
9	Incremental cash flow	1	2000	3000	3000	$0	3500	$500
10	over the LCM	2	2000	3000	3000	$0	3500	$500
11		3	2000	3000	3000	$0	3500	$500
12		4		3200	3000	$6,800	3500	$500
13		5			3000	$0	3500	$500
14		6			3300	-$8,700	3500	$9,200
15		7				$0	3500	$500
16		8				$6,800	3500	$500
17		9				$0	3500	$500
18		10				$0	3500	$500
19		11				$0	3500	$500
20		12				$100	4500	$1,200
21	i*		0.00%	26.32%	24.68%		17.87%	
22	Retain or eliminate?		Eliminate	Retain	Retain		Retain	
23	Incremental i*					19.42%		11.23%
24	Increment justified?					Yes		No
25	Alternative selected					C		C
26	AW at MARR		($628)	$588	$656		$398	
27	PW at MARR		($3,403)	$3,188	$3,557		$2,159	
28	Alternative selected		No	No	Yes		No	
29	Alternative		A	B	C		D	

FIGURE 8–7

Spreadsheet analysis using ROR, PW, and AW methods for unequal-life, revenue alternatives, Example 8.8.

Section 2 (rows 3 to 6): Per-unit net cash flow estimates for each alternative. These are revenue alternatives with unequal lives.

Section 3 (rows 7 to 20): Actual and incremental cash flows are displayed here.

Section 4 (rows 21, 22): Because these are all revenue alternatives, i^* values are determined by the IRR function. If an alternative passes the MARR test ($i^* > 15\%$), it is retained and a column is added to the right of its actual cash flows so the incremental cash flows can be determined. Columns F and H were inserted to make space for the incremental evaluations. Alternative A does not pass the i^* test.

Section 5 (rows 23 to 25): The IRR functions display the Δi^* values in columns F and H. Comparison of C to B takes place over the LCM of 12 years. Since $\Delta i^*_{C-B} = 19.42\% > 15\%$, eliminate B; alternative C is the new defender and D is the next challenger. The final comparison of D to C over 12 years results in $\Delta i^*_{D-C} = 11.23\% < 15\%$, so D is eliminated. Alternative C is the chosen one.

Section 6 (rows 26 to 29): These include the AW and PW analyses. The AW value over the life of each alternative is calculated using the PMT function at the MARR with an embedded NPV function. Also, the PW value is determined from the AW value for 12 years using the PV function. For both measures, alternative C has the numerically largest value, as expected.

Conclusion: All methods result in the same, correct choice of alternative C.

(b) Since each option is independent of the others, and there is no budget limitation at this time, each i^* value in row 21 of Figure 8–7 is compared to MARR = 20%. This is a comparison of each option with the do-nothing alternative. Of the four, options B and C have $i^* > 20\%$. They are acceptable; the other two are not.

Comment

In part (*a*), we should have applied the two multiple-root sign tests to the incremental cash flow series for the C-to-B comparison. The series itself has three sign changes, and the cumulative cash flow series starts negatively and also has three sign changes. Therefore, up to three real-number roots may exist. The IRR function is applied in cell F23 to obtain $\Delta i^*_{C-B} = 19.42\%$ without using the net-investment procedure. This action assumes that the reinvestment assumption of 19.42% for positive net-investment cash flows is a reasonable one. If the MARR = 15%, or some other earning rate, were more appropriate, the net-investment procedure would have to be applied to determine the composite rate, which would be different from 19.42%. Depending upon the reinvestment rate chosen, alternative C may or may not be incrementally justified against B. Here, the assumption is made that the Δi^* value is reasonable, so C is justified.

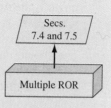

Secs. 7.4 and 7.5

Multiple ROR

CHAPTER SUMMARY

Just as present worth, annual worth, and future worth methods find the best alternative from among several, incremental rate of return calculations can be used for the same purpose. In using the ROR technique, it is necessary to consider the incremental cash flows when selecting between mutually exclusive alternatives. This was not necessary for the PW, AW, or FW methods. The incremental investment evaluation is conducted between only two alternatives at a time beginning with the lowest initial investment alternative. Once an alternative has been eliminated, it is not considered further.

If there is no budget limitation when independent projects are evaluated using the ROR method, the ROR value of each project is compared to the MARR. Any number, or none, of the projects can be accepted.

Rate of return values have a natural appeal to management, but the ROR analysis is often more difficult to set up and complete than the PW, AW, or FW analysis using an established MARR. Care must be taken to perform a ROR analysis correctly on the incremental cash flows; otherwise it may give incorrect results.

PROBLEMS

Understanding Incremental ROR

8.1 If alternative A has a rate of return of 10% and alternative B has a rate of return of 18%, what is known about the rate of return on the increment between A and B if the investment required in B is (*a*) larger than that required for A and (*b*) smaller than that required for A?

8.2 What is the overall rate of return on a $100,000 investment that returns 20% on the first $30,000 and 14% on the remaining $70,000?

8.3 Why is an incremental analysis necessary when you are conducting a rate of return analysis for service alternatives?

8.4 If all of the incremental cash flows are negative, what is known about the rate of return on the incremental investment?

8.5 Incremental cash flow is calculated as cash flow$_B$ – cash flow$_A$, where B represents the alternative with the larger initial investment. If the two cash flows were switched wherein B represents the one with the *smaller* initial investment, which alternative should be selected if the incremental rate of return is 20% per year and the company's MARR is 15% per year? Explain.

8.6 A food processing company is considering two types of moisture analyzers. The company expects an infrared model to yield a rate of return of 18% per year. A more expensive microwave model will yield a rate of return of 23% per year. If the company's MARR is 18% per year, can you determine which model(s) should be purchased solely on the basis of the rate of return information provided if (*a*) either one or both analyzers can be selected and (*b*) only one can be selected? Why or why not?

8.7 For each of the following scenarios, state whether an incremental investment analysis would be required to select an alternative and state why or why not. Assume that alternative Y requires a higher initial investment than alternative X and that the MARR is 20% per year.
   (*a*) X has a rate of return of 28% per year, and Y has a rate of return of 20% per year.
   (*b*) X has a rate of return of 18% per year, and Y has a rate of return of 23% per year.
   (*c*) X has a rate of return of 16% per year, and Y has a rate of return of 19% per year.
   (*d*) X has a rate of return of 30% per year, and Y has a rate of return of 26% per year.
   (*e*) X has a rate of return of 21% per year, and Y has a rate of return of 22% per year.

8.8 A small construction company has $100,000 set aside in a sinking fund to purchase new equipment. If $30,000 is invested at 30%, $20,000 at 25% and the remaining $50,000 at 20% per year, what is the overall rate of return on the entire $100,000?

8.9 A total of $50,000 was available for investing in a project to reduce insider theft in an appliance warehouse. Two alternatives identified as Y and Z were under consideration. The overall rate of return on the $50,000 was determined to be 40%, with the rate of return on the $20,000 increment between Y and Z at 15%. If Z is the higher first-cost alternative, (*a*) what is the size of the investment required in Y and (*b*) what is the rate of return on Y?

8.10 Prepare a tabulation of cash flow for the alternatives shown below.

	Machine A	Machine B
First cost, $	−15,000	−25,000
Annual operating cost, $/year	−1,600	−400
Salvage value, $	3,000	6,000
Life, years	3	6

8.11 A chemical company is considering two processes for making a cationic polymer. Process A will have a first cost of $100,000 and an annual operating cost of $60,000. Process B will have a first cost of $165,000. If both processes will be adequate for 4 years and the rate of return on the increment between the alternatives is 25%, what is the amount of the operating cost for process B?

Incremental ROR Comparison (two alternatives)

8.12 When the rate of return on the incremental cash flow between two alternatives is exactly equal to the MARR, which alternative should be selected—the one with the higher or lower initial investment? Why?

8.13 Fortress Paper of Vancouver is examining two processes for the manufacture of security paper used for banknotes. Process A incorporates new quantum dot technology in bills, while process B incorporates a transparent window. Determine which of the two processes should be selected by calculating the rate of return on the incremental investment. Assume the company's MARR is 21% per year.

	Process A	Process B
First cost, $	−50,000	−95,000
Annual cost, $/year	−100,000	−85,000
Salvage value, $	5,000	11,000
Life, years	3	6

8.14 A consulting engineering firm is trying to decide whether it should purchase Ford Explorers or Toyota 4Runners for company principals. The models under consideration would cost $29,000 for the Ford and $32,000 for the Toyota. The annual operating cost of the Explorer is expected to be $200 per year less than that of the 4Runner. The trade-in values after 3 years are estimated to be 50% of first cost for the Explorer and 60% for the Toyota. (*a*) What is the rate of return relative to that of Ford, if the Toyota is selected? (*b*) If the firm's MARR is 18% per year, which make of vehicle should it buy?

8.15 A plastics company is considering two injection molding processes. Process X will have a first cost of $600,000, annual costs of $200,000, and a salvage value of $100,000 after 5 years. Process Y will have a first cost of $800,000, annual costs of $150,000, and a salvage value of $230,000 after 5 years. (*a*) What is the rate of return on the increment of investment between the two? (*b*) Which process should the company select on the basis of a rate of return analysis, if the MARR is 20% per year?

8.16 A company that manufactures amplified pressure transducers is trying to decide between the machines shown below. Compare them on the basis of rate of return, and determine which should be selected if the company's MARR is 15% per year.

	Variable Speed	Dual Speed
First cost, $	−250,000	−225,000
Annual operating cost, $/year	−231,000	−235,000
Overhaul in year 3, $	—	−26,000
Overhaul in year 4, $	−39,000	—
Salvage value, $	50,000	10,000
Life, years	6	6

8.17 The manager of a canned food processing plant is trying to decide between two labelling machines. Determine which should be selected on the basis of rate of return with a MARR of 20% per year.

	Machine A	Machine B
First cost, $	−15,000	−25,000
Annual operating cost, $/year	−1,600	−400
Salvage value, $	3,000	4,000
Life, years	2	4

8.18 A solid waste recycling plant is considering two types of storage bins. Determine which should be selected on the basis of rate of return. Assume the MARR is 20% per year.

	Alternative P	Alternative Q
First cost, $	−18,000	−35,000
Annual operating cost, $/year	−4,000	−3,600
Salvage value, $	1,000	2,700
Life, years	3	6

8.19 The incremental cash flow between alternatives J and K is estimated below. If the MARR is 20% per year, which alternative should be selected on the basis of rate of return? Assume K requires the extra $90,000 initial investment.

Year	Incremental Cash Flow, $(K − J)
0	−90,000
1–3	+10,000
4–9	+20,000
10	+5,000

8.20 A chemical company is considering two processes for isolating DNA material. The incremental cash flow between two alternatives J and S is as shown. The company uses a MARR of 50% per year. The rate of return on the incremental cash flow below is less than 50%, but the company CEO prefers the more expensive process. The CEO believes she can negotiate the initial cost of the more expensive process downward. By how much would she have to reduce the first cost of S, the higher-cost alternative, for it to have an incremental rate of return of exactly 50%?

Year	Incremental Cash Flow, $(S − J)
0	−900,000
1	400,000
2	600,000
3	850,000

8.21 Alternative R has a first cost of $100,000, annual M&O costs of $50,000, and a $20,000 salvage value after 5 years. Alternative S has a first cost of $175,000 and a $40,000 salvage value after 5 years, but its annual M&O costs are not known. Determine the M&O costs for alternative S that would yield an incremental rate of return of 20% per year.

8.22 The incremental cash flows for alternatives M and N are shown below. Determine which should be selected, using an AW-based rate of return analysis. The MARR is 12% per year, and alternative N requires the larger initial investment.

Year	Incremental Cash Flow, $(N − M)
0	−22,000
1–8	+4,000
9	+12,000

8.23 Determine which of the two machines below should be selected, using an AW-based rate of return analysis, if the MARR is 18% per year.

	Semiautomatic	Automatic
First cost, $	−40,000	−90,000
Annual cost, $/year	−100,000	−95,000
Salvage value, $	5,000	7,000
Life, years	2	4

8.24 The incremental cash flows for alternatives X and Y are shown below. Calculate the incremental rate of return per month, and determine which should be selected, using an AW-based rate of return analysis. The MARR is 24% per year, compounded monthly, and alternative Y requires the larger initial investment.

Month	Incremental Cash Flow, $(Y − X)
0	−62,000
1–23	+4,000
24	+10,000

8.25 The incremental cash flow between alternatives Z1 and Z2 is shown below (Z2 has the higher initial cost). Use an AW-based rate of return equation to determine the incremental rate of return and which alternative should be selected, if the MARR is 17% per year. Let k = year 1 through 10.

Year	Incremental Cash Flow, $(Z2 − Z1)
0	−40,000
1–10	9000 − 500k

8.26 Two roadway designs are under consideration for access to a permanent suspension bridge. Design 1A will cost $3 million to build and $100,000 per year to maintain. Design 1B will cost $3.5 million to build and $40,000 per year to maintain. Use an AW-based rate of return equation to determine which design is preferred. Assume $n = 10$ years and the MARR is 6% per year.

8.27 A manufacturing company is in need of 3000 square metres for expansion because of a new 3-year contract it just won. The company is considering the purchase of land for $50,000 and erecting a temporary metal structure on it at a cost of $90 per square metre. At the end of the 3-year period, the company expects to be able to sell the land for $55,000 and the building for $60,000. Alternatively, the company can lease space for $3 per square metre *per month,* payable at the beginning of each year. Use an AW-based rate of return equation to determine which alternative is preferred. The MARR is 28% per year.

8.28 Four mutually exclusive *service* alternatives are under consideration for automating a manufacturing operation. The alternatives were ranked in order of increasing initial investment and then compared by incremental investment rate of return analysis. The rate of return on each increment of investment was less than the MARR. Which alternative should be selected?

Multiple-Alternative Comparison

8.29 Expansion plans at the pellet plant of Iron Ore Company of Canada in Labrador City involve a new conveyor system to remove bottlenecks in the existing ore delivery system. Which alternative system below is best, according to an incremental investment rate of return analysis? Assume a life of 20 years and a MARR of 25% per year.

Alternative	First Cost, $	Operating Cost, $/Year	Annual Income, $/Year
1	−40,000	−2,000	+4,000
2	−46,000	−1,000	+5,000
3	−61,000	−500	+8,000

8.30 A metal plating company is considering four different methods for recovering by-product heavy metals from a manufacturing site's liquid waste. The investment costs and incomes associated with each method have been estimated. All methods have an 8-year life. The MARR is 11% per year. (*a*) If the methods are independent, because they can be implemented at different plants, which ones are acceptable? (*b*) If the methods are mutually exclusive, determine which one method should be selected, using a ROR evaluation.

Method	First Cost, $	Salvage Value, $	Annual Income, $/Year
A	−30,000	+1,000	+4,000
B	−36,000	+2,000	+5,000
C	−41,000	+500	+8,000
D	−53,000	−2,000	+10,500

8.31 Mountain Pass Canning Company has determined that any one of five machines can be used in one phase of its canning operation. The costs of the machines are estimated below, and all machines have a 5-year life. If the minimum attractive rate of return is 20% per year, determine the one machine that should be selected on the basis of a rate of return analysis.

Machine	First Cost, $	Annual Operating Cost, $/Year
1	−31,000	−18,000
2	−28,000	−19,500
3	−34,500	−17,000
4	−48,000	−12,000
5	−41,000	−15,500

8.32 An independent dirt contractor is trying to determine which size dump truck to buy. The contractor knows that as the bed size increases, the net income increases, but he is uncertain whether the incremental expenditure required for the larger trucks is justified. The cash flows associated with each size truck are estimated below. The contractor's MARR is 18% per year, and all trucks are expected to have a useful life of 5 years. (*a*) Determine which size truck should be purchased. (*b*) If two trucks of different size are to be purchased, what should be the size of the second truck?

Truck Bed Size, Cubic Metres	Initial Investment, $	Annual Operating Cost, $/Year	Salvage Value, $	Annual Income, $/Year
8	−30,000	−14,000	+2,000	+26,500
10	−34,000	−15,500	+2,500	+30,000
15	−38,000	−18,000	+3,000	+33,500
20	−48,000	−21,000	+3,500	+40,500
25	−57,000	−26,000	+4,600	+49,000

8.33 An engineer at Anode Metals is considering the projects below, all of which can be considered to last indefinitely. If the company's MARR is 15% per year, determine which should be selected (*a*) if they are independent and (*b*) if they are mutually exclusive.

	First Cost, $	Annual Income, $/Year	Alternative's Rate of Return, %
A	−20,000	+3,000	15
B	−10,000	+2,000	20
C	−15,000	+2,800	18.7
D	−70,000	+10,000	14.3
E	−50,000	+6,000	12

8.34 Only one of four different machines is to be purchased for a certain production process. An engineer performed the following analyses to select the best machine. All machines are assumed to have a 10-year life. Which machine, if any, should the company select if its MARR is (*a*) 12% per year and (*b*) 20% per year?

	Machine			
	1	2	3	4
Initial cost, $	−44,000	−60,000	−72,000	−98,000
Annual cost, $/year	−70,000	−64,000	−61,000	−58,000
Annual savings, $/year	+80,000	+80,000	+80,000	+82,000
ROR, %	18.6	23.4	23.1	20.8
Machines compared		2 to 1	3 to 2	4 to 3
Incremental investment, $		−16,000	−12,000	−26,000
Incremental cash flow, $/year		+6,000	+3,000	+5,000
ROR on increment, %		35.7	21.4	14.1

8.35 The four alternatives described in the table below are being evaluated.

(a) If the proposals are independent, which should be selected when the MARR is 16% per year?

(b) If the proposals are mutually exclusive, which one should be sele-cted when the MARR is 9% per year?

(c) If the proposals are mutually exclusive, which one should be selected when the MARR is 12% per year?

Alternative	Initial Investment, $	Rate of Return, %	Incremental Rate of Return, %, When Compared with Alternative		
			A	B	C
A	−40,000	29			
B	−75,000	15	1		
C	−100,000	16	7	20	
D	−200,000	14	10	13	12

8.36 A rate of return analysis was initiated for the infinite-life alternatives below.

(a) Fill in the blanks in the incremental rate of return column on the incremental cash flow portion of the table.

(b) How much revenue is associated with each alternative?

(c) What alternative should be selected if they are mutually exclusive and the MARR is 16%?

(d) What alternative should be selected if they are mutually exclusive and the MARR is 11%?

(e) Select the two best alternatives at a MARR of 19%.

Alternative	Alternative's Investment, $	Alternative's Rate of Return, %	Incremental Rate of Return, %, on Incremental Cash Flow When Compared with Alternative			
			E	F	G	H
E	−20,000	20	—			
F	−30,000	35		—		
G	−50,000	25			—	11.7
H	−80,000	20			11.7	—

8.37 A rate of return analysis was initiated for the infinite-life alternatives below.

(a) Fill in the blanks in the alternative's rate of return column and incremental rate of return columns of the table.

(b) What alternative should be selected if they are independent and the MARR is 21% per year?

(c) What alternative should be selected if they are mutually exclusive and the MARR is 24% per year?

Alternative	Alternative's Investment, $	Alternative's Rate of Return, %	Incremental Rate of Return, %, on Incremental Cash Flow When Compared with Alternative			
			E	F	G	H
E	−10,000	25	—	20		
F	−25,000		20	—	4	
G	−30,000			4	—	
H	−60,000	30				—

EXTENDED EXERCISE

INCREMENTAL ROR ANALYSIS WHEN ESTIMATED ALTERNATIVE LIVES ARE UNCERTAIN

Make-to-Specs is a software system under development by ABC Corporation. It will be able to translate digital versions of three-dimensional computer models, containing a wide variety of part shapes with machined and highly finished (ultra-smooth) surfaces. The product of the system is the numerically controlled (NC) machine code for the part's manufacturing. Additionally, Make-to-Specs will build the code for super-fine finishing of surfaces with continuous control of the finishing machines. There are two alternative computers that can provide the server function for the software interfaces and shared database updates on the manufacturing floor while Make-to-Specs is operating in parallel mode. The server first cost and estimated contribution to annual net cash flow are summarized below.

	Server 1	Server 2
First cost, $	$100,000	$200,000
Net cash flow, $/year	$35,000	$50,000 year 1, plus $5000 per year for years 2, 3, and 4 (gradient)
		$70,000 maximum for years 5 on, even if the server is replaced
Life, years	3 or 4	5 or 8

The life estimates were developed by two different individuals: a design engineer and a manufacturing manager. They have asked that at this stage of the project, all analyses be performed using both life estimates for each system.

Questions

Use computer analysis to answer the following:

1. If the MARR = 12%, which server should be selected? Use the PW or AW method to make the selection.

2. Use incremental ROR analysis to decide between the servers at MARR = 12%.

3. Use any method of economic analysis to display on the spreadsheet the value of the incremental ROR between server 2 with a life estimate of 5 years and a life estimate of 8 years.

CASE STUDY 1

SO MANY OPTIONS. CAN A NEW ENGINEERING GRADUATE HELP HIS FATHER?[1]

Background

"I don't know whether to sell it, expand it, lease it, or what. But I don't think we can keep doing the same thing for many more years. What I really want to do is to keep it for 5 more years, then sell it for a bundle," Elmer Kettler said to his wife Janise, their son, John Kettler, and new daughter-in-law, Suzanne Gestory, as they were gathered around the dinner table. Elmer was sharing thoughts on EJK Wholesale Auto Parts, a company he has owned and operated for 25 years. The business has excellent contracts for parts supply with several national retailers operating in the area. Additionally, EJK operates a rebuild shop serving these same retailers for major automobile components, such as carburetors, transmissions, and air conditioning compressors.

At his home after dinner, John decided to help his father with an important and difficult decision: What to do with his business? John graduated just last year with an engineering degree, where he completed a course in engineering economy. Part of his job at Energcon Industries is to perform basic rate of return and present worth analyses on energy management proposals.

Options

Over the next few weeks, Mr. Kettler outlined five options, including his favourite of selling in 5 years. John summarized all the estimates over a 10-year horizon. The options and estimates were given to Elmer, and he agreed with them.

> Option 1: *Remove rebuild.* Stop operating the rebuild shop and concentrate on selling wholesale parts. The removal of the rebuild operations and the switch to an "all parts house" is expected to cost $750,000 in the first year. Overall revenues will drop to $1 million the first year with an expected 4% increase per year thereafter. Expenses are projected at $0.8 million the first year, increasing 6% per year thereafter.

> Option 2: *Contract rebuild operations.* To get the rebuild shop ready for an operations contractor to take over will cost $400,000 immediately. If expenses stay the same for 5 years, they will average $1.4 million per year, but

[1]Based upon a study by Mr. Alan C. Stewart, Consultant, Communications and High Tech Solutions Engineering, Accenture LLP.

they can be expected to rise to $2 million per year in year 6 and thereafter. Elmer thinks revenues under a contract arrangement can be $1.4 million the first year and rise 5% per year for the duration of a 10-year contract.

Option 3: *Maintain status quo and sell out after 5 years.* (Elmer's personal favourite.) There is no cost now, but the current trend of negative net profit will probably continue. Projections are $1.25 million per year for expenses and $1.15 million per year in revenue. Elmer had an appraisal last year, and the report indicated EJK Wholesale Auto Parts is worth a net $2 million. Elmer's wish is to sell out completely after 5 more years at this price, and to make a deal that the new owner pay $500,000 per year at the end of year 5 (sale time) and the same amount for the next 3 years.

Option 4: *Trade-out.* Elmer has a close friend in the antique auto parts business who is making a "killing," so he says, with e-commerce. Although the possibility is risky, it is enticing to Elmer to consider a whole new line of parts, but still in the basic business that he already understands. The trade-out would cost an estimated $1 million for Elmer immediately. The 10-year horizon of annual expenses and revenues is considerably higher than for his current business. Expenses are estimated at $3 million per year and revenues at $3.5 million each year.

Option 5: *Lease arrangement.* EJK could be leased to some turnkey company with Elmer remaining the owner and bearing part of the expenses for building, delivery trucks, insurance, etc. The first-cut estimates for this option are $1.5 million to get the business ready now, with annual expenses at $500,000 per year and revenues at $1 million per year for a 10-year contract.

Case Study Exercises

Help John with the analysis by doing the following:

1. Develop the actual cash flow series and incremental cash flow series (in $1000 units) for all five options in preparation for an incremental ROR analysis.

2. Discuss the possibility of multiple rate of return values for all the actual and incremental cash flow series. Find any multiple rates in the range of 0 to 100%.

3. If John's father insists that he make 25% per year or more on the selected option over the next 10 years, what should he do? Use all the methods of economic analysis you have learned so far (PW, AW, ROR) so John's father can understand the recommendation in one way or another.

4. Prepare plots of the PW vs. *i* for each of the five options. Estimate the breakeven rate of return between options.

5. What is the minimum amount that must be received in each of years 5 through 8 for option 3 (the one Elmer wants) to be best economically? Given this amount, what does the sale price have to be, assuming the same payment arrangement as presented in the description?

CASE STUDY 2

PW ANALYSIS WHEN MULTIPLE INTEREST RATES ARE PRESENT[2]

Background

Two engineering economy students, Jane and Bob, could not agree on what evaluation tool should be used to select one of the following investment plans. The cash flow series are identical except for their signs. They recall that a PW or AW equation should be set up to solve for a rate of return. It seems that the two investment plans should have identical ROR value(s). It may be that the two plans are equivalent and should both be acceptable.

Year	Plan A	Plan B
0	$+1900	$-1900
1	-500	+500
2	-8000	+8000
3	+6500	-6500
4	+400	-400

Up to this point in class, the professor has discussed the present worth and annual worth methods at a given MARR for evaluating alternatives. He explained the composite rate of return method during the last class. The two students remember that the professor said, "The calculation of the composite rate of return is often computationally involved. If an actual ROR is not necessary, it is strongly recommended that the PW or AW at MARR be used to decide on project acceptability."

Bob admitted that it is not very clear to him why the simplistic "PW at MARR" is strongly recommended. Bob is unsure how to determine if a rate of return is "not necessary." He said to Jane, "Since the composite ROR technique always yields a unique ROR value and every student has a calculator or a computer with a spreadsheet system on it, who cares about the computation problem? I would always perform the composite ROR method." Jane was more cautious and suggested that a good analysis starts with a simple, common-sense approach. She suggested that Bob inspect the cash flows and see if he could pick the better plan just through observation of the cash flows. Jane also proposed that they try every method they had learned so far. She said, "If we experiment with them, I think we may understand the real reason that the PW (or AW) at the MARR method is recommended over the composite rate of return method."

[2]Contributed by Dr. Tep Sastri (former Associate Professor, Industrial Engineering, Texas A&M University).

Case Study Exercises

Given their discussion, the following are some questions Jane and Bob need to answer. Help them develop the answers.

1. By simply inspecting the two cash flow patterns, determine which is the preferred plan. In other words, if someone is offering the two plans, which one do you think might obtain a higher rate of return?

2. Which plan is the better choice if the MARR is (*a*) 15% per year and (*b*) 50% per year? Two approaches should be taken here: First, evaluate the two options using PW analysis at the MARR, ignoring the multiple roots, whether they exist or not. Second, determine the internal rate of return of the two plans. Do the two cash flow series have the same ROR values?

3. Perform an incremental ROR analysis of the two plans. Are there still multiple roots to the incremental cash flow series that limit Bob's and Jane's ability to make a definitive choice? If so, what are they?

4. The students want to know if the composite ROR analysis will consistently yield a logical and unique decision as the MARR value changes. To answer this question, find out which plan should be accepted if any end-of-year released cash flows (excess project funds) earn at the following three reinvestment rates. The MARR rates change also.

   (*a*) Reinvestment rate is 15% per year; MARR is 15% per year.
   (*b*) Reinvestment is at 45% per year; MARR is 15% per year.
   (*c*) Reinvestment rate and MARR are both 50% per year.
   (*d*) Explain your findings about these three different rate combinations to Bob and Jane.

CHAPTER

Benefit-Cost Analysis and Public Sector Economics

The evaluation methods of previous chapters are usually applied to alternatives in the private sector, that is, for-profit and not-for-profit corporations and businesses. Customers, clients, and employees utilize the installed alternatives. This chapter introduces *public sector alternatives* and their economic consideration. Here the users (beneficiaries) are the citizens of government jurisdictions—federal, provincial or territorial, or municipal. Government sponsors provide the mechanisms to raise (investment) capital and operating funds for projects through taxes, user fees, bond issues, and loans. There are substantial differences in the characteristics of public and private sector alternatives and their economic evaluation, as outlined in the second section. Partnerships of the public and private sector have become increasingly common, especially for large infrastructure construction projects such as major highways, power generation plants, water resource developments, and the like. Government-provided incentives such as tax credits can also motivate industry to make changes in the public interest.

In order for public sector programs to reflect wider Canadian values, engineering economics requires a methodology for addressing conflicting objectives. Benefit-cost analysis (BCA) is a valuable framework to direct debate on the impacts of a project. There is always predictable disagreement among citizens (individuals and groups) about how the benefits of an alternative are defined and valued. The benefit-cost ratio (BCR) introduces objectivity into the economic analysis of public sector evaluation, reducing the effects of politics and special interests. BCA can provide compelling evidence to decision makers who wish to help communities develop while protecting vulnerable populations and the environment. The different formats of BCA, and associated disbenefits of an alternative, are discussed here. The BCA uses equivalency computations based on PW, AW, or FW values. Performed correctly, the method will always select the same alternative as PW, AW, and ROR analyses.

A public sector project to enhance freeway lighting is the subject of the case study.

LEARNING OBJECTIVES

Purpose: Understand public sector economics; evaluate a project and compare alternatives using the benefit-cost ratio method.

	By the end of this chapter you should be able to
Public sector	**1.** Identify fundamental differences between public and private sector economic alternatives.
Benefit-cost ratio for single project	**2.** Use the benefit-cost ratio to evaluate a single project.
Alternative selection	**3.** Select the better of two alternatives using the incremental benefit-cost ratio method.
Multiple alternatives	**4.** Select the best from multiple alternatives using the incremental benefit-cost method.

9.1 ENGINEERING ECONOMY IN THE PUBLIC SECTOR

We perform engineering design in a market economy in which prices are determined according to the relative demand and supply of goods. Individuals and companies make consumption choices on the basis of costs and their perception of the benefits accrued if they purchase them. When externalities exist that are not variables within the financial decision, the process fails.

For example, environmental externalities such as air, soil and water pollution, overuse of scarce resources such as oil and water, and sacrifices in bio-diversity from development are not adequately addressed in the market economy. Economic activities that result in these disbenefits cause an inefficient use of resources and lead to *market failure*. Since many of our environmental resources (ocean, lakes, aquifers, forests, fisheries) are available to everyone, a reduction in their quality occurs when they are overused. This can lead to degradation of the resources that we need for our quality of life. When an item approaches a critical level of scarcity, competition for it increases and can totally destroy the resource. This is referred to as the *tragedy of the commons*. It is the public sector that serves to resolve these negative externalities.

Discussions of Canadian values always include the virtue of fairness, which is reflected in our universal health care and social security systems and in our programs to help Canada's vulnerable populations and ecosystems. In the private sector, we take pride in our innovative contributions to emerging technologies such as in advanced materials processes, advanced manufacturing and processing, and biomedical engineering, and in information technologies. Our values are also expressed through Canadian industry, which shows prudence by addressing environmental assessment not as an annoyance but as a cogent design objective alongside the maximization of profit. In both sectors, the precautionary principle guides our strong commitment to attain sustainable development. This principal espouses short-term and long-term decision making that takes into account the possible consequences of irreversible changes to our economic and/or biophysical environment.

To illustrate, consider the environmental sphere. Similar analysis can address public programs in other jurisdictions. Interventions to protect the environment—improvements to technology, the minimization of waste, and the more efficient use of natural resources—are within the domain of engineering expertise. Engineers need to be active in the process of selecting the technologies that should be embraced for future research, development, and implementation and in designing incentives for their rapid diffusion. All engineering professional associations have codes, which state that our ethical concerns dictate that we design quality, high-value products and services that are in harmony with the safety, health, and welfare of the public. For instance, the ecology of the manufacturing process chosen as well as the operating efficiency designed into the product itself can reflect these goals. Benefit-cost analysis (BCA) is used to assess and select policies and interventions that provide support for sectors of the economy, which might otherwise be marginalized.

To prevent market failure, the Canadian government introduces incentives and regulations to influence companies and individuals in their decisions that impact society. Incentives are often through tax credits or subsidies to encourage the implementation of advanced technologies that increase production efficiency (less consumption of raw materials and energy) and decrease pollution. Fines are used to discourage noncompliance. Regulations are sometimes done in conjunction with tradable permits, such as greenhouse credits, to create an innovative market that provides flexibility in how companies and individuals respond. BCA is used to assist government decision makers in determining a best set of policy initiatives to balance the needs of the economy and the needs of the environment.

Consider the impacts of air pollution on citizens living in a region. If there are no incentives or regulations for industry to reduce their discharge of pollution, many will continue to maximize their profits by continuing the practice. However, the health and quality of life of the citizenry will suffer and their health care costs will increase. A systems perspective of the situation often demonstrates that government subsidies or tax deductions aimed at reducing the pollution (preventative health care) is far cheaper than dealing with its health consequences (curative health care). It is BCA that captures the economics of this policy and provides a structure for collaboration among the different levels of government and jurisdictions that share responsibility for Canada's decentralized federal government. Public sector economic studies require the consultation of complementary divisions of authority among the central government and the provinces and territories to form public policy. This level of independence is unique to Canada's parliamentary government.

Traditionally, the federal and/or provincial government compensates for market failure by providing goods and services, such as police and fire protection, education, infrastructure, and health care. In other situations, publicly owned firms called Crown corporations such as CBC, VIA Rail, and Canada Post provide services. Crown corporations also exist at the provincial level, especially for the provision of electric power and natural gas.

Public sector projects are rewarding and challenging, because they integrate the social affects of engineered systems into the design process. This provides another dimension to engineering decisions by adding the social context to the business frame of reference. With growing needs for technology policy analysis and the expansion of infrastructure, opportunities will continue to increase. Current literature confirms the need for engineers to participate in the decisions involving public and corporate policies that allocate scarce public resources to the competing demands of emerging technologies in the context of the greater good of society. Benefit-cost analysis assists decision makers by providing a systematic means to address conflicting perspectives in support of responsible interventions.

9.2) PUBLIC SECTOR PROJECTS

Public sector projects are owned, used, and financed by the citizenry of any government level, whereas projects in the private sector are owned by corporations, partnerships, and individuals. The products and services of private sector projects are used by individual customers and clients. Virtually all the examples in previous chapters have been from the private sector. Notable exceptions occur in Chapters 5 and 6 where capitalized cost was introduced as an extension to PW analysis for long-life alternatives and perpetual investments.

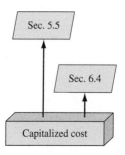

Public sector projects have a primary purpose to provide services to the citizenry for the public good at no profit. Areas such as health, safety, environment management, economic welfare, and utilities make up a majority of the alternatives that require engineering economic analysis. Some examples of public sector projects and concerns are

Hospitals and clinics	Transportation: highways, bridges,
Parks and recreation	waterways, ferry systems
Utilities: water, electricity,	Police and fire protection
gas, sewer, sanitation	Courts and prisons
Schools: primary, secondary,	Environmental impacts
colleges, universities	Job training
Economic development	Resource management
Convention centres	Emergency relief
Sports and arts centres	Codes and standards—
	workplace and environmental

There are significant differences in the characteristics of private and public sector alternatives.

Characteristic	Public Sector	Private Sector
Size of investment	Larger	Some large; more medium to small

Often alternatives developed to serve public needs require large initial investments, possibly distributed over several years. Modern highways, public transportation systems, airports, and flood control systems are examples.

Life estimates	Longer (30−50+ years)	Shorter (2−25 years)

The long lives of public projects often prompt the use of the capitalized cost method, where infinity is used for n and annual costs are calculated as $A = P(i)$. As n gets larger, especially over 30 years, the differences in calculated A values become small. For example, at $i = 7\%$, there will be a very small difference in 30 and 50 years, because $(A/P,7\%,30) = 0.08059$ and $(A/P,7\%,50) = 0.07246$.

Annual cash flow estimates	No profit; costs, benefits, and disbenefits, are estimated	Revenues contribute to profits; costs are estimated

Public sector projects do not have profits; they do have costs that are paid by the appropriate government entity, or sponsor; and they benefit the citizenry. Public sector projects often have undesirable consequences, as stated by some portion of the public. It is these consequences that can cause public controversy about the projects. The economic analysis should consider these consequences in monetary terms to the degree estimable. Often in private sector analysis, undesirable consequences are not considered, or they may be directly addressed as costs. To perform an analysis of public alternatives, the costs (initial and annual), the benefits, and the disbenefits, should be estimated as accurately as possible in monetary units.

Costs—estimated expenditures *to the government entity or sponsor* for construction, operation, and maintenance of the project, less any expected salvage value.

Benefits—advantages to be experienced *by the users, the public.*

Disbenefits—expected undesirable or negative consequences *to the users* if the alternative is implemented. Disbenefits may be indirect economic disadvantages of the alternative.

The following is important to realize:

It is difficult to estimate and agree upon the economic impact of benefits and disbenefits for a public sector alternative.

For example, assume a short bypass around a congested area in town is recommended. How much will it benefit a driver in *dollars per driving minute* to be able to bypass five traffic lights while averaging 50 kilometres per hour, as compared to currently driving through the lights averaging 30 kilometres per hour and stopping at an average of two lights for an average of 45 seconds each? The bases and standards for benefits estimation are always difficult to establish and verify. Relative to revenue cash flow estimates in the private sector, benefit estimates are much harder to make, and vary more widely around uncertain averages. And the disbenefits that accrue from an alternative are harder to estimate. In fact, the disbenefit itself may not be known at the time the evaluation is performed.

The methodology involved in BCA also provides insights for making decisions when monetary estimates are unavailable. BCA can be combined with utility theory, where non-monetary units are used to measure values such as the quality of life, the health of the environment, the cost of trauma, or the cost of time. Utility theory will be discussed in Chapter 17.

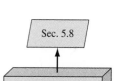

Characteristic	Public Sector	Private Sector
Funding	Taxes, fees, bonds, private funds	Stock, bonds, loans, individual owners

The capital used to finance public sector projects is commonly acquired from taxes, bonds, and fees. Taxes are collected from those who are the owners—the citizens (e.g., federal gasoline taxes for highways are paid by all gasoline users). This is also the case for fees, such as toll road fees for drivers. Federal, provincial, and municipal bonds can be issued to raise funds for capital projects. Private lenders can provide up-front financing. Also, private donors may provide funding for museums, memorials, parks, and garden areas through gifts.

Interest rate	Lower	Higher, based on market cost of capital

Because many of the financing methods for public sector projects are classi-fied as *low-interest,* the interest rate is virtually always lower than for private sector alternatives. The determination of the interest rate for public sector evalu-ation is as important as the determination of the MARR for a private sector anal-ysis. The public sector interest rate is identified as *i*; however, it is referred to as the *social discount rate,* to distinguish it from the private sector rate.

Characteristic	Public Sector	Private Sector
Alternative selection criteria	Multiple criteria	Primarily based on rate of return

Multiple categories of users, economic as well as noneconomic interests, and special-interest political and citizen groups make the selection of one alternative over another much more difficult in public sector economics. Seldom is it pos-sible to select an alternative on the sole basis of a criterion such as PW or ROR. It is important to describe and itemize the criteria and selection method prior to the analysis. This helps determine the perspective or viewpoint when the evalua-tion is performed. Viewpoint is discussed below.

Environment of the evaluation	Politically inclined	Primarily economic

There are often public meetings and debates associated with public sector projects to accommodate the various interests of citizens. Elected officials commonly assist with the selection, especially when pressure is brought to bear by voters, develop-ers, environmentalists, and others. The selection process is more complex than in private sector evaluation, where the decision is reduced to profit maximization.

The viewpoint of the public sector analysis must be determined before cost, benefit, and disbenefit estimates are made and before the evaluation is for-mulated and performed. There are several viewpoints for any situation, and the different perspectives may alter how a cash flow estimate is classified.

Some example perspectives are the citizen; the city tax base; number of stu-dents in the school district; creation and retention of jobs; economic develop-ment potential; a particular industry interest, such as agriculture, banking, or electronics manufacturing; and many others. In general, the viewpoint of the analysis should be as broadly defined as those who will bear the costs of the project and reap its benefits. Once established, the viewpoint assists in catego-rizing the costs, benefits, and disbenefits of each alternative, as illustrated in Example 9.1.

EXAMPLE 9.1

The Land Conservancy has recommended that the city of Dundee borrow $5 million for the purchase of greenbelt/floodplain land to preserve low-lying green areas and wildlife habitat on the east side of this rapidly expanding city of 62,000. The proposal is referred to as the Greenway Acquisition Initiative. Developers immediately opposed the proposal due to the reduction of available land for commercial development. The city engineer and economic development director have made the following preliminary estimates for some obvious areas, considering the Initiative's consequences in maintenance, parks, commercial development, and flooding over a projected 15-year planning horizon. The inaccuracy of these estimates is made very clear in the report to the Dundee City Council. The estimates are not yet classified as costs, benefits, or disbenefits. If the Greenway Acquisition Initiative is implemented, the estimates are as follows.

Economic Dimension	Estimate
1. Annual cost of $5 million over 15 years at 6% interest rate	$300,000 (years 1–14) $5,300,000 (year 15)
2. Annual maintenance, upkeep, and program management	$75,000 + 10% per year
3. Annual parks development budget	$500,000 (years 5–10)
4. Annual loss in commercial development	$2,000,000 (years 8–10)
5. Tax rebates not realized	$275,000 + 5% per year (years 8 on)
6. Annual municipal income from park use and regional sports events	$100,000 + 12% per year (years 6 on)
7. Savings in flood control projects	$300,000 (years 3–10) $1,400,000 (years 10–15)
8. Property damage (personal and city) not experienced due to flooding	$500,000 (years 10 and 15)

Identify three different viewpoints for the economic analysis of the proposal, and classify the estimates accordingly.

Solution
There are many perspectives to take; three are addressed here. The viewpoints and goals are identified and each estimate is classified as a cost, benefit, or disbenefit. (How the classification is made will vary depending upon who does the analysis. This solution offers only one logical answer.)

Viewpoint 1: Citizen of the city. Goal: Maximize the quality and wellness of citizens with family and neighbourhood as prime concerns.

        Costs: 1, 2, 3   Benefits: 6, 7, 8   Disbenefits: 4, 5

Viewpoint 2: City budget. Goal: Ensure the budget is balanced and of sufficient size to fund rapidly growing city services.

        Costs: 1, 2, 3, 5   Benefits: 6, 7, 8   Disbenefits: 4

Viewpoint 3: Economic development. Goal: Promote new commercial and industrial economic development for creation and retention of jobs.

        Costs: 1, 2, 3, 4, 5   Benefits: 6, 7, 8   Disbenefits: None

Classification of estimates 4 (loss of commercial development) and 5 (loss of tax rebates) changes depending upon the view taken for the economic analysis. If the analyst favours the economic development goals of the city, commercial development losses are considered real costs, whereas they are undesirable consequences (disbenefits) from the citizen and budget viewpoints. Also, the loss of tax rebates is interpreted as a real cost from the budget and economic development perspectives, but as a disbenefit from the citizen viewpoint.

Comment

Disbenefits may be included or disregarded in an analysis, as discussed in the next section. This decision can make a distinctive difference in the acceptance or rejection of a public sector alternative.

9.3 CANADIAN P3s

For the past 20 years, larger public sector projects have been developed increasingly often through public-private partnerships, "P3s." This is the trend in part because of the perceived greater efficiency of the private sector and in part because of the sizable cost to design, construct, and operate such projects. Full funding by the government unit may not be possible using traditional means of government financing—fees, taxes, and bonds. Some examples of the projects are as follows:

Project	Some Purposes of the Project
Bridges and tunnels	Speed traffic flows; reduce congestion; improve safety
Ports and harbours	Increase cargo capacity; support industrial development
Airports	Increase capacity; improve passenger safety; support development
Water resources	Treatment of drinking water; meet irrigation and industrial needs; improve wastewater treatment

In these joint ventures, the public sector (government) is responsible for the cost and service to the citizenry, and the private sector partner (corporation) is responsible for varying aspects of the projects as detailed below. The government unit cannot make a profit, but the corporation(s) involved can realize a reasonable profit; in fact the profit margin is usually written into the contract that governs the design, construction, operation, and ownership of the project.

In various countries, such construction projects have been designed for and financed by a government unit with a contractor doing the construction under either a lump-sum (*fixed-price*) contract or a cost reimbursement (*cost-plus*) contract that specifies the agreed upon margin of profit. In these cases, the contractor does not share the risk of the project's success with the government "owner." When a partnership of public and private interests is developed, the P3 is commonly contracted under an arrangement called *build-operate-transfer (BOT)*, which may also be referred to as BOOT, where the first O is for *own*. The BOT/BOOT-administered project may require that the contractor be responsible partially or completely for design and financing, and completely responsible for the construction (the build element), operation (operate), and maintenance activities for a specified number of years. After this time period, the owner becomes the government unit when the title of ownership is transferred (transfer) at no or very low cost. This arrangement may have several advantages, some of which are

- Efficient resource allocation of private enterprise
- Ability to acquire funds (loans) based on financial record of the government and corporate partners
- Environmental, liability, and safety issues addressed by the private sector, where there may be greater expertise
- Contracting corporation(s) able to realize a return on the investment during the operation phase

The Confederation Bridge linking Prince Edward Island and New Brunswick is an example of a BOOT-administered project. Many of the projects in international settings and in developing countries utilize the BOT/BOOT form of partnership. There are, of course, disadvantages to this arrangement. One risk is that the amount of financing committed to the project may not cover the actual build cost because it is considerably higher than estimated. A second risk is that a reasonable profit may not be realized by the private corporation due to low usage of the facility during the operate phase. To plan against such problems, the original contract may provide for special loans guaranteed by the government unit and special subsidies. The subsidy may cover costs plus (contractually agreed-to) profit if usage is lower than a specified level. The level used may be the breakeven point with the agreed-to profit margin considered.

A variation of the BOT/BOOT method is BOO (build-own-operate), where the transfer of ownership never takes place. This form of P3 may be used when the project has a relatively short life or the technology deployed is changing quickly.

There are controversial issues surrounding the growing use of P3 arrangements. In the future, if we continue the trend toward a less regulated environment, controls now existing on corporations may not be in place to guarantee the desired social benefit of a project. Other controversies centre on the higher costs to users that are often necessary to provide a profit for the corporations involved and the potential of decreased transparency in accounting and decision making.

Much of the current infrastructure boom in Canada is the work of a consortium of private lenders in collaboration with major construction companies and government deal-makers. Provincial agencies such as Infrastructure Alberta, Infrastructure Ontario, Infrastructure Quebec, and Partnerships BC manage most of the large privately financed contracts for public projects. They have been successful in getting government stimulus money into the economy and promoting the use of P3s. In British Columbia, any project seeking over $50 million in provincial funding has to demonstrate that the option of undertaking the project as a P3 has been considered. A new Crown corporation, P3 Canada, recently formed to facilitate broader use of P3s in infrastructure projects, will fund up to 25% of the projects it selects from a $1.2 billion fund. Their second call for project proposals in June 2010 resulted in 68 submissions.

In the quest for balanced budgets, the P3 is politically desirable, because the cost of the project does not appear in the government's budget and the debt does not appear on the government's books, or at least is transferred to some future time. Whether provincial governments should abandon their traditional role of advancing public funds to build new facilities in favour of private financing—a factor that pushes up overall costs as much as 10%—is open to debate. P3 proponents believe that the increased costs of financing and legal fees is balanced by the increased incentive industry partners have to get projects built on time and on budget to avoid facing additional interest costs. Nevertheless, the government or users still have to pay for the P3's construction and operation at a cost much higher than if the project had been publicly procured, as has been discovered by recent auditor-generals' reports in Nova Scotia, Ontario, and Quebec. P3 project evaluations demonstrate that P3s can be a valuable tool in the provision of certain infrastructure projects requiring extensive expertise provided the project has a good contract and management, and with the understanding that the transfer of risk between the public and private partners is a difficult process. The best known of Canada's P3s include the Air Canada privatization, the construction of the Confederation Bridge, and the privately operated Highway 407 Express Toll Road in Ontario, but now P3s have been used widely all over Canada.

Another controversial topic within the realm of public-private partnerships is the option of allowing private clinics to provide medical services within provincial health care systems. The generation of private investment capital for the acquisition of advanced diagnostic, procedural, and surgical devices and less-invasive procedures might be enhanced, but many concerns exist. A Harvard Medical School study published by the *New England Journal of Medicine* says Americans spend 300% more on administrative costs for their private health care system than Canadians spend on the universal single-payer Medicare system, and that plans with high administrative costs are inclined to be of mediocre clinical quality. Despite health care reforms, millions of Americans still lack adequate, affordable health insurance. On the other hand, many argue that shortages of expensive services can result from underfunding when taxpayers do not support tax increases and there are no opportunities to pay for premium services. Many also suggest that there is greater creativity, innovation, and cost-effective delivery of services due to the increased competition for the private partnership.

There are compelling arguments on both sides of the controversy from health economists and medical professionals, reflecting a variety of viewpoints in the debate concerning the role of private health care in Canada. An analysis involving opposing arguments and cross-national alternatives will help decision makers think critically about the issues and challenge conventional positions while avoiding misleading notions. Building a BCA provides a framework for assessing alternatives, in order to reach a consensus and move policies forward.

9.4 BENEFIT-COST PROCESS

The process involved in the BCA methodology creates an opportunity for learning about the system that is being analyzed. Even if the measurements are not available due to the lack of time, economic data, or forecasts, the exercise of identifying the benefits and costs of potential interventions will create surprising insights for decision makers.

Traditionally, First Nations decision makers focused on the impacts of their governing for six generations. This commitment to view the wider community context attempts to transform the social and economic fabric to improve the lives of our children's children's children's children's children.

Forecasts become less reliable the further into the future we attempt to make predictions. Many scientists are suggesting that our environment is healthy and adapting to human activity, while others are concerned that it is reaching a threshold of damage that has unpredictable negative consequences. Aboriginal pedagogy teaches us to seek wiser decisions by looking into the future even without hard numbers. When the benefits and costs are only known as variables, the BCA model can be the structure to articulate debates concerning decisions that affect the long term. Decisions must sometimes be made in the absence of complete information.

EXAMPLE 9.2

Harnessing wind power is becoming a more competitive means for the generation of electricity. Technological innovations are bringing the price of wind-generated electricity down to 6 cents per kilowatt-hour from the current 10 cents. The high price of oil, the diminishing reserves of Canadian natural gas, the lack of economically feasible hydroelectric sites, and the limits that will eventually be established for Canada's carbon emissions are all bringing wind power generation into the economic domain. Many Canadian companies are addressing their potential return on investment according to a 20-year life cycle in which most of the costs are up front. Since the economics of wind technology improve with large turbines, manufacturers in Europe are developing offshore wind turbines that have a blade span of 126 metres with the goal of producing electricity for 3 cents per kilowatt-hour by 2015. Currently Denmark satisfies 20% of its electricity requirements by wind generation. Germany produces 8%, and Canada 1.1% with 99 wind farms generating approximately 3250 megawatts of generating capacity. Quebec and Ontario are the provinces with bold targets and economic incentives to encourage development of large wind farms such as the Le Nordais farm in Gaspé, Quebec, that produces 100 MW for 16,000 homes. The provinces, by offering incentives for tax relief and development subsidies, establish requests-for-proposal from companies with the capacity to develop wind farms in remote areas within a few kilometres of existing transmission lines. Ontario is planning to quadruple wind power capacity with projects such as Kruger Energy's Chatham Wind Project on the shore of Lake Erie, in which 44 wind turbines of 2.3 megawatts each will provide enough electricity to power about 30,000 homes.

List some of the general categories of relevant benefits that are difficult to measure but important not to ignore in the decision-making process.

Solution

Benefits
- Use of renewable energy source; ecologically sustainable
- Less dependence on hydrocarbon fuels, and therefore less greenhouse gas emissions and less warming of the global climate
- Less risk from changing rainfall patterns and increasing storm damage along coasts due to warming of the global climate

- Increased safety in generation of energy
- Reduced costs of energy as technology evolves
- Wind industry job creation
- Less air pollution
- Less toxic heavy metal waste and less chlorinated chemicals compared to other energy sources
- Improved health of the citizenry
- Entrepreneurial opportunities as industry expands
- Less disturbance to the earth's large-scale bio-geo-chemical cycle
- Less regional conflict over scarce natural resources

Costs
- Lost opportunity for other public sector projects
- Noise
- Hazard to birds
- Aesthetics of pristine areas
- New transmission lines for connection to grid
- High cost if large turbines fail
- Petroleum industry loss of energy market share and concomitant loss of jobs
- Productivity fluctuates with wind speed, necessitating supplementary capacity
- Construction costs
- Operating and maintenance costs
- Administrative costs
- Disruption of existing oil economy during transition

The use of the BCA as a process contributes to policy debates concerning the controversial issues of our scientific and technological society. The affected citizenry is often engaged through public debates or hearings. By thinking ahead as to how the essence of their various perspectives will become input for a BCA, the facilitators can better capture the relevant tradeoffs inherent to the decision.

It is important for benefit-cost analyses to be performed in a consistent fashion. Various Canadian federal agencies provide guidelines to assist in the identification and rationalization of key assumptions and provide evaluation criteria. The guidelines, obtainable at ministry websites, will typically address how the public user benefits should be assessed. Valuations of the benefit from services, time reductions, improvements to safety, and reduction of risk can be found there as well as appropriate costs that should be included in a study.

Guidelines are available in the areas of transportations studies (Transport Canada), crime prevention, the Treasury Board, regulatory programs, the International Development Research Centre, economic development (Industry Canada), and Canadian health care. A Web search on "benefit-cost guide + Canada" will yield a current list of sites.

Each guideline suggests a range of MARR values to be used for the benefit-cost analysis. In Canada, this value is referred to as the *social discount rate*. It will change according to inflation rates and is related to both the government bond rate required to raise funds for the project and a lost opportunity interest rate reflecting the rate of return that taxpayers could be receiving on other projects. The guidelines suggest a MARR value and a range of values that are usually +2% and –2% in order to perform a sensitivity analysis. For example, if the suggested MARR is 10%, it is recommended that the benefit-cost analysis be performed for an 8% MARR, a 10% MARR, and a 12% MARR. If the decision to implement a particular alternative does not change on the basis of the results of the three analyses, the uncertainty concerning the best value of the social discount rate is not an issue. If it does change, further research should address the best MARR value to be used.

9.5 BENEFIT-COST ANALYSIS OF A SINGLE PROJECT

The benefit-cost ratio (BCR) is relied upon as a fundamental analysis method for public sector projects. There are several variations of the BCR; however, the fundamental approach is the same. All cost and benefit estimates must be converted to a common equivalent monetary unit (PW, AW, or FW) at the social discount rate (interest rate). The BCR is then calculated using one of these relations:

$$\text{BCR} \cong \frac{\text{PW of benefits}}{\text{PW of costs}} \cong \frac{\text{AW of benefits}}{\text{AW of costs}} \cong \frac{\text{FW of benefits}}{\text{FW of costs}} \qquad [9.1]$$

Slight differences in the ratios will occur due to rounding of the compound interest factors, but the final decisions will remain the same.

Present worth and annual worth equivalencies are more used than future worth values. The sign convention for BCA analysis is positive signs, so *costs are preceded by a + sign.* Salvage values, when they are estimated, are subtracted from costs. Disbenefits are considered in different ways depending upon the model used. Most commonly, disbenefits are subtracted from benefits and placed in the numerator. The different formats are discussed below.

The decision guideline is simple:

If BCR ≥ 1.0, accept the project as economically acceptable for the estimates and discount rate applied.

If BCR < 1.0, the project is not economically acceptable.

If the BCR value is exactly or very near 1.0, noneconomic factors will help make the decision for the "best" alternative.

The *conventional BCR,* probably the most widely used, is calculated as follows:

$$\text{BCR} = \frac{\text{benefits} - \text{disbenefits}}{\text{costs}} = \frac{B - D}{C} \qquad [9.2]$$

In Equation [9.2] disbenefits are subtracted from benefits, not added to costs. The BCR value could change considerably if disbenefits are regarded as costs. For example, if the numbers 10, 8, and 8 are used to represent the PW of benefits, disbenefits, and costs, respectively, the correct procedure results in BCR = (10 − 8)/8 = 0.25. The incorrect placement of disbenefits in the denominator results in BCR = 10/(8 + 8) = 0.625, which is more than twice the correct BCR value of 0.25. Clearly, then, the method by which disbenefits are handled affects the magnitude of the BCR. However, no matter whether disbenefits are (correctly) subtracted from the numerator or (incorrectly) added to costs in the denominator, a BCR of less than 1.0 by the first method will always yield a BCR less than 1.0 by the second method, and vice versa.

The *modified BCR* includes maintenance and operation (M&O) costs in the numerator and treats them in a manner similar to disbenefits. The denominator includes only the initial investment. Once all amounts are expressed in PW, AW, or FW terms, the modified BCR is calculated as

$$\text{Modified BCR (BCRM)} = \frac{\text{benefits} - \text{disbenefits} - \text{M\&O costs}}{\text{initial investment}} \qquad [9.3]$$

Salvage value is included in the denominator as a negative cost. The BCRM will obviously yield a different value than the conventional BCR method. However, as with disbenefits, *the modified procedure can change the magnitude of the ratio but not the decision to accept or reject the project.*

The *benefit and cost difference* measure of worth, which does not involve a ratio, is based on the difference between the PW, AW, or FW of benefits and costs, that is, $B - C$. If $(B - C) \geq 0$, the project is acceptable. This method has the advantage of eliminating the discrepancies noted above when disbenefits are regarded as costs, because B represents *net benefits*. Thus, for the numbers 10, 8, and 8 the same result is obtained regardless of how disbenefits are treated.

Subtracting disbenefits from benefits: $B - C = (10 - 8) - 8 = -6$

Adding disbenefits to costs: $B - C = 10 - (8 + 8) = -6$

Before calculating the BCR by any formula, check whether the alternative with the larger AW or PW of costs also yields a larger AW or PW of benefits. It is possible for one alternative with larger costs to generate lower benefits than other alternatives, thus making it unnecessary to further consider the larger-cost alternative.

EXAMPLE 9.3

The Millennium Foundation expects to award $15 million in grants to secondary schools to develop new ways to teach the fundamentals of engineering that prepare students for university-level material. The grants will extend over a 10-year period and will create an estimated savings of $1.5 million per year in faculty salaries and student-related expenses. The Foundation uses a rate of return of 6% per year on all grant awards.

This grants program will share Foundation funding with ongoing activities, so an estimated $200,000 per year will be removed from other program funding. To make this program successful, a $500,000 per year operating cost will be incurred from the regular M&O budget. Use BCA to determine if the grants program is economically justified.

Solution

Use annual worth as the common monetary equivalent. All three BCA models are used to evaluate the program.

AW of investment cost.	$15,000,000(A/P,6\%,10) = \$2,038,050$ per year
AW of benefit.	$1,500,000 per year
AW of disbenefit.	$200,000 per year
AW of M&O cost.	$500,000 per year

Use Equation [9.2] for conventional BCA, where M&O is placed in the denominator as an annual cost.

$$BCR = \frac{1,500,000 - 200,000}{2,038,050 + 500,000} = \frac{1,300,000}{2,538.050} = 0.51$$

The project is not justified, since BCR < 1.0.

By Equation [9.3] the modified BCR ratio treats the M&O cost as a reduction to benefits.

$$BCRM = \frac{1,500,000 - 200,000 - 500,000}{2,038,050} = 0.39$$

The project is also not justified by the modified BCA method, as expected.

For the $(B - C)$ model, B is the net benefit, and the annual M&O cost is included with costs.

$$B - C = (1,500,000 - 200,000) - (2,038,050 + 500,000) = \$-1.24 \text{ million}$$

Since $(B - C) < 0$, the program is not justified.

EXAMPLE 9.4

Aaron is a new project engineer with the Alberta Ministry of Transportation. Based on annual worth relations, Aaron performed the conventional BCA of the two separate proposals shown below.

Bypass proposal: New routing around part of Edmonton to improve safety and decrease average travel time.

Initial investment in present worth: $P = \$40$ million.
Annual maintenance: $1.5 million.
Annual benefits to public: $B = \$6.5$ million.
Expected life: 20 years.
Funding: Shared 50–50 federal and provincial funding; federally required 8% social
    discount rate applies.

Upgrade proposal: Widening of roadway through parts of Edmonton to alleviate traffic congestion and improve traffic safety.

Initial investment in present worth: $P = \$4$ million.
Annual maintenance: $150,000.

Annual benefits to public: $B = \$650{,}000$.

Expected life: 12 years.

Funding: 100% provincial funding required; 4% social discount rate applies.

Aaron used a hand solution for the conventional BCA in Equation [9.2] with AW values calculated at 8% per year for the bypass proposal and at 4% per year for the upgrade proposal.

Bypass proposal: AW of investment = $\$40{,}000{,}000(A/P,8\%,20) = \$4{,}074{,}000$ per year

$$BCR = \frac{6{,}500{,}000}{4{,}074{,}000 + 1{,}500{,}000} = 1.17$$

Upgrade proposal: AW of investment = $\$4{,}000{,}000(A/P,4\%,12) = \$426{,}200$ per year

$$BCR = \frac{650{,}000}{426{,}200 + 150{,}000} = 1.13$$

Both proposals are economically justified since $B/C > 1.0$.

(a) Perform the same analysis by computer, using a minimum number of computations.

(b) The social discount rate for the upgrade proposal is not certain, because the Province is thinking of asking for federal funds for it. Is the upgrade economically justified if the 8% social discount rate also applies to it?

Solution by Computer

(a) See Figure 9–1a. The BCR values of 1.17 and 1.13 are in B4 and D4 ($1 million units). The function PMT($i\%,n,-P$) plus the annual maintenance cost calculates the AW of costs in the denominator. See the cell tags.

(b) Cell F4 uses an i value of 8% in the PMT function. There is a real difference in the justification decision. At the 8% rate, the upgrade proposal is no longer justified.

Comment

Figure 9–1b presents a complete BCR spreadsheet solution. There are no differences in the conclusions from those in the Q-Solve spreadsheet, but the proposal estimates and BCR results are shown in detail on this spreadsheet. Also, additional sensitivity analysis is easily performed on this expanded version, because of the use of cell reference functions.

	B	C	D	E	F	G
1			**BCR for Upgrade**		**BCR for Upgrade**	
2	**BCR for Bypass**		**at 4%**		**at 8%**	
3						
4	1.17		1.13		0.95	
5						
6						
7		= 6.5/(1.5+PMT(8%,20, −40))			= 0.65/(0.15+PMT(8%,12, −4))	
8						

(a)

FIGURE 9–1

Spreadsheet for BCR of two proposals: (a) Q-Solve solution and (b) expanded solution, Example 9.4.

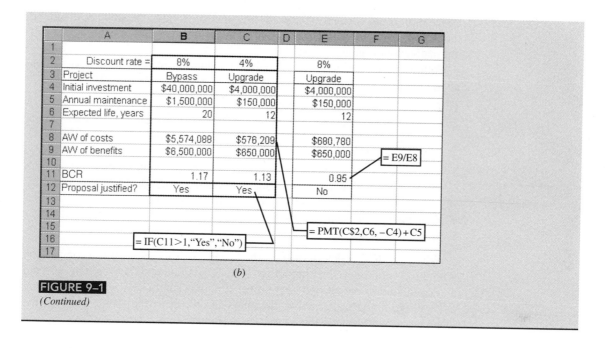

	A	B	C	D	E	F	G
1							
2	Discount rate =	8%	4%		8%		
3	Project	Bypass	Upgrade		Upgrade		
4	Initial investment	$40,000,000	$4,000,000		$4,000,000		
5	Annual maintenance	$1,500,000	$150,000		$150,000		
6	Expected life, years	20	12		12		
7							
8	AW of costs	$5,574,088	$576,209		$680,780		
9	AW of benefits	$6,500,000	$650,000		$650,000	= E9/E8	
10							
11	BCR	1.17	1.13		0.95		
12	Proposal justified?	Yes	Yes		No		
13							
14							
15						= PMT(C$2,C6, −C4)+C5	
16			= IF(C11>1,"Yes","No")				
17							

(b)

FIGURE 9–1

(Continued)

9.6 ALTERNATIVE SELECTION USING INCREMENTAL BENEFIT-COST ANALYSIS

The technique to compare two mutually exclusive alternatives using BCA is virtually the same as that for incremental ROR in Chapter 8. The incremental (conventional) BCR is determined using PW, AW, or FW calculations, and the extra-cost alternative is justified if this BCR is equal to or larger than 1.0. The selection rule is as follows:

If incremental BCR ≥ 1.0, choose the higher-cost alternative, because its extra cost is economically justified.

If incremental BCR < 1.0, choose the lower-cost alternative.

To perform a correct incremental BCA, it is required that each alternative be compared only with another alternative for which the incremental cost is already justified. This same rule was used previously in incremental ROR analysis.

There are several special considerations for BCA that make it slightly different from that for ROR analysis. As mentioned earlier, all costs have a positive sign in the BCR. Also, the *ordering of alternatives is done on the basis of total costs* in the denominator of the ratio. Thus, if two alternatives, A and B, have equal initial investments and lives, but B has a larger equivalent annual cost, then B must be incrementally justified against A. (This is illustrated in the next example.) If this

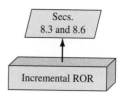

Secs.
8.3 and 8.6

Incremental ROR

convention is not correctly followed, it is possible to get a negative cost value in the denominator, which can incorrectly make BCR < 1 and reject a higher-cost alternative that is actually justified.

Follow these steps to correctly perform a conventional BCR analysis of two alternatives. Equivalent values can be expressed in PW, AW, or FW terms.

1. Determine the total equivalent costs for both alternatives.
2. Order the alternatives by total equivalent cost; smaller first, then larger. Calculate the incremental cost (ΔC) for the larger-cost alternative. This is the denominator in BCR.
3. Calculate the total equivalent benefits and any disbenefits estimated for both alternatives. Calculate the incremental benefits (ΔB) for the larger-cost alternative. (This is $\Delta(B - D)$ if disbenefits are considered.)
4. Calculate the incremental BCR using Equation [9.2], $(B - D)/C$.
5. Use the selection guideline to select the higher-cost alternative if $B/C \geq 1.0$.

When the BCR is determined for the lower-cost alternative, it is a comparison with the do-nothing (DN) alternative. If BCR < 1.0, then DN should be selected and compared to the second alternative. If neither alternative has an acceptable BCR value, the DN alternative must be selected. In public sector analysis, the DN alternative is usually the current condition.

EXAMPLE 9.5

The city of Rosemount has received designs for a new patient room wing to its hospital from two architectural consultants. One of the two designs must be accepted in order to announce it for construction bids. The costs and benefits are the same in most categories, but the city financial manager decided that the three estimates below should be considered to determine which design to recommend.

	Design A	Design B
Construction cost, $	10,000,000	15,000,000
Building maintenance cost, $/year	35,000	55,000
Patient usage cost, $/year	450,000	200,000

The patient usage cost is an estimate of the amount paid by patients to travel to a larger hospital 60 kilometres away for medical treatments and in-patient care. Since design B is almost 50% larger than A, it will accommodate more of the expected demand. The social discount rate is 5%, and the life of the building is estimated at 30 years.

(a) Use conventional BCR analysis to select design A or B.
(b) Once the two designs were publicized, a privately owned medical taxi service lodged a complaint that design A will reduce their income by an estimated $100,000 per year because of reduced demand for transportation between Rosemount and the larger hospital. The taxi service has decided that with design B, there will be no

change in their yearly income, since they anticipate more business from trips into Rosemount from neighbouring towns to use the new facilities. The city financial manager stated that this concern would be entered into the evaluation as a disbenefit of design A. Redo the BCA to determine if the economic decision is still the same as when the disbenefit was not considered.

Solution

(a) Since most of the cash flows are already annualized, the incremental BCR will use AW values. No disbenefit estimates are considered. Follow the steps of the procedure above:

1. The AW of costs is the sum of construction and maintenance costs.

    $$AW_A = 10,000,000(A/P,5\%,30) + 35,000 = \$685,500$$
    $$AW_B = 15,000,000(A/P,5\%,30) + 55,000 = \$1,030,750$$

2. Design B has the larger AW of costs, so it is the alternative to be incrementally justified. The incremental cost value is

    $$\Delta C = AW_B - AW_A = \$345,250 \text{ per year}$$

3. The AW of benefits is derived from the patient usage costs, since these are consequences to the public. The benefits for the BCA are not the costs themselves, but the *difference* if design B is selected. The lower usage cost each year is a positive benefit for design B.

    $$\Delta B = \text{usage}_A - \text{usage}_B = \$450,000 - \$200,000 = \$250,000 \text{ per year}$$

4. The incremental BCR is calculated by Equation [9.2].

    $$BCR = \frac{\$250,000}{\$345,250} = 0.72$$

5. The BCR is less than 1.0, indicating that the extra costs associated with design B are not justified. Therefore, design A is selected for the construction bid.

(b) The revenue loss estimates are considered disbenefits. Since the disbenefits of design B are \$100,000 less than those of A, this positive difference is added to the \$250,000 benefits of B to give it a total benefit of \$350,000. Now

$$BCR = \frac{\$350,000}{\$345,250} = 1.01$$

Design B is slightly favoured. In this case the inclusion of disbenefits has reversed the previous economic decision. This has probably made the situation more difficult politically. New disbenefits will surely be claimed in the near future by other special-interest groups.

Like other methods, BCA requires *equal-service comparison* of alternatives. Usually, the expected useful life of a public project is long (25 or 30 or more years), so alternatives generally have equal lives. However, when alternatives do have unequal lives, the use of PW to determine the equivalent costs and benefits requires that the LCM of lives be used. This is an excellent opportunity to use the AW equivalency of costs and benefits, if the implied assumption that the project could be repeated is reasonable. Therefore, use AW-based analysis for BCR when different-life alternatives are compared.

9.7 INCREMENTAL BENEFIT-COST ANALYSIS OF MULTIPLE, MUTUALLY EXCLUSIVE ALTERNATIVES

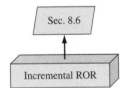

The procedure necessary to select one from three or more mutually exclusive alternatives using incremental BCA is essentially the same as that of the last section. The procedure also parallels that for incremental ROR analysis in Section 8.6. The selection guideline is as follows:

> **Choose the largest-cost alternative that is justified with an incremental BCR ≥ 1.0 when this selected alternative has been compared with another justified alternative.**

There are two types of benefit estimates—estimation of *direct benefits,* and implied benefits based on *usage cost* estimates. Example 9.5 is a good illustration of the second type of implied benefit estimation. *When direct benefits are estimated,* the BCR for each alternative may be calculated first as an initial screening mechanism to eliminate unacceptable alternatives. At least one alternative must have BCR ≥ 1.0 to perform the incremental BCA. If all alternatives are unacceptable, the DN alternative is indicated as the choice. (This is the same approach as that of step 2 for "revenue alternatives only" in the ROR procedure of Section 8.6. However, the term "revenue alternative" is not applicable to public sector projects.)

As in the previous section comparing two alternatives, selection from multiple alternatives by incremental BCR utilizes total equivalent costs to initially order alternatives from smallest to largest. Pairwise comparison is then undertaken. Also, remember that all costs are considered positive in BCA calculations. The terms *defender* and *challenger alternative* are used in this procedure, as in a ROR-based analysis. The procedure for incremental BCA of multiple alternatives is as follows:

1. Determine the total equivalent cost for all alternatives. (Use AW, PW, or FW equivalencies for equal lives; use AW for unequal lives.)
2. Order the alternatives by total equivalent cost, smallest first.
3. Determine the total equivalent benefits (and any disbenefits estimated) for each alternative.
4. *Direct benefits estimation only:* Calculate the BCR for the first ordered alternative. (In effect, this makes DN the defender and the first alternative the challenger.) If BCR < 1.0, eliminate the challenger, and go to

the next challenger. Repeat this until BCR ≥ 1.0. The defender is eliminated, and the next alternative is now the challenger. (For analysis by computer, determine the BCR for all alternatives initially and retain only acceptable ones.)

5. Calculate incremental costs (ΔC) and benefits (ΔB) using the relations

$$\Delta C = \text{challenger cost} - \text{defender cost} \qquad [9.4]$$

$$\Delta B = \text{challenger benefits} - \text{defender benefits} \qquad [9.5]$$

If relative *usage costs* are estimated for each alternative, rather than direct benefits, ΔB may be found using the relation

$$\Delta B = \text{defender usage costs} - \text{challenger usage costs} \qquad [9.6]$$

6. Calculate the incremental BCR for the first challenger compared to the defender.

$$\text{BCR} = \Delta B / \Delta C \qquad [9.7]$$

If incremental BCR ≥ 1.0 in Equation [9.7], the challenger becomes the defender and the previous defender is eliminated. Conversely, if incremental BCR < 1.0, remove the challenger and the defender remains against the next challenger.

7. Repeat steps 5 and 6 until only one alternative remains. It is the selected one.

In all the steps above, incremental disbenefits may be considered by replacing ΔB with $\Delta(B - D)$, as in the conventional BCR Equation [9.2].

EXAMPLE 9.6

A non-profit citizens' group on Salt Spring Island, B.C., is promoting the building of a recreation centre in Ganges. Four alternative proposals have been put together to take advantage of economic incentives that the Capital Regional District permits.

In-place economic incentive guidelines allow industry partners to receive up to $500,000 cash as a first-year incentive award and 10% of this amount each year for 8 years in property tax reduction. All the proposals meet the requirements for these two incentives. Each proposal includes a provision that residents of the island will benefit from reduced entrance (usage) fees when using the centre. This fee reduction will be in effect as long as the property tax reduction incentive continues. The citizens' group has estimated the annual total entrance fees with the reduction included for local residents, as well as the extra HST revenue expected for the four centre designs. These estimates and the costs for the initial incentive and annual 10% tax reduction are summarized in the top section of Table 9–1.

Utilize hand and computer analysis to perform an incremental BCA to determine which centre proposal is the best economically. The social discount rate used is 7% per year. Can the current incentive guidelines be used to accept the winning proposal?

TABLE 9–1 Estimates of Costs and Benefits, and the Incremental BCA for Four Recreation Centre Proposals, Example 9.6

	Proposal 1	Proposal 2	Proposal 3	Proposal 4
Initial incentive, $	250,000	350,000	500,000	800,000
Tax incentive cost, $/year	25,000	35,000	50,000	80,000
Resident entrance fees, $/year	500,000	450,000	425,000	250,000
Extra HST, $/year	310,000	320,000	320,000	340,000
Study period, years	8	8	8	8
AW of total costs, $	66,867	93,614	133,735	213,976
Alternatives compared		2-to-1	3-to-2	4-to-2
Incremental costs ΔC, $/year		26,747	40,120	120,360
Entrance fee reduction, $/year		50,000	25,000	200,000
Extra HST, $/year		10,000	0	20,000
Incremental benefits ΔB, $/year		60,000	25,000	220,000
Incremental BCR		2.24	0.62	1.83
Increment justified?		Yes	No	Yes
Alternative selected		2	2	4

Solution by Hand

The viewpoint taken for the economic analysis is that of a resident of the island. The first-year cash incentives and annual tax reduction incentives are real costs to the residents. Benefits are derived from two components: the decreased entrance fee estimates and the increased HST receipts. These will benefit each citizen indirectly through the increase in money available to those who use the centre and through the municipal budget where tax receipts are deposited. Since these benefits must be calculated indirectly from these two components, the initial proposal BCR values cannot be calculated to initially eliminate any proposals. A BCA incrementally comparing two alternatives at a time must be conducted.

Table 9–1 includes the results of applying the procedure above. Equivalent AW values are used for benefit and cost amounts per year. Since the benefits must be derived indirectly from the entrance fee estimates and HST receipts, step 4 is not used.

1. For each alternative, the capital recovery amount over 8 years is determined and added to the annual property tax incentive cost. For proposal 1,

$$AW \text{ of total costs} = \text{initial incentive}(A/P,7\%,8) + \text{tax cost}$$
$$= \$250,000(A/P,7\%,8) + 25,000 = \$66,867$$

2. The alternatives are ordered by the AW of total costs in Table 9–1.
3. The annual benefit of an alternative is the incremental benefit of the entrance fees and HST amounts. These are calculated in step 5.
4. This step is not used.

5. Table 9–1 shows incremental costs calculated by Equation [9.4]. For the 2-to-1 comparison,

$$\Delta C = \$93{,}614 - 66{,}867 = \$26{,}747$$

Incremental benefits for an alternative are the sum of the resident entrance fees compared to those of the next-lower-cost alternative, plus the increase in HST receipts over those of the next-lower-cost alternative. Thus, the benefits are determined incrementally for each pair of alternatives. For example, when proposal 2 is compared to proposal 1, the resident entrance fees decrease by $50,000 per year and the HST receipts increase by $10,000. Then the total benefit is the sum of these, that is, $\Delta B =$ $60,000 per year.

6. For the 2-to-1 comparison, Equation [9.7] results in

$$BCR = \$60{,}000/\$26{,}747 = 2.24$$

Alternative 2 is clearly incrementally justified. Alternative 1 is eliminated, and alternative 3 is the new challenger to defender 2.

7. This process is repeated for the 3-to-2 comparison, which has an incremental BCR of 0.62 because the incremental benefits are substantially less than the increase in costs. Therefore, proposal 3 is eliminated, and the 4-to-2 comparison results in

$$BCR = \$220{,}000/\$120{,}360 = 1.83$$

Since BCR > 1.0, proposal 4 is retained. Since proposal 4 is the one remaining alternative, it is selected.

The recommendation for proposal 4 requires an initial incentive of $800,000, which exceeds the $500,000 limit of the approved incentive limits. The citizens' group will have to request the municipality grant an exception to the guidelines. If the exception is not approved, proposal 2 is accepted.

Solution by Computer

Figure 9–2 presents a spreadsheet using the same calculations as those in Table 9–1. Row 8 cells include the function PMT(7%,8,−initial incentive) to calculate the capital recovery for each alternative, plus the annual tax cost. These AW of total cost values are used to order the alternatives for incremental comparison.

The cell tags for rows 10 through 13 detail the formulas for incremental costs and benefits used in the incremental BCR computation (row 14). Note the difference in row 11 and 12 formulas, which find the incremental benefits for entrance fees and HST, respectively. The order of the subtraction between columns in row 11 (e.g., =B5−C5, for the 2-to-1 comparison) must be correct to obtain the incremental entrance fees benefit. The IF operators in row 15 accept or reject the challenger, based upon the size of BCR. After the 3-to-2 comparison with BCR = 0.62 in cell D14, alternative 3 is eliminated. The final selection is alternative 4, as in the solution by hand.

	A	B	C	D	E	F	G
1	Discount rate =	7%					
2	Alternative	#1	#2	#3	#4		
3	Initial incentive, $	$ 250,000	$ 350,000	$ 500,000	$ 800,000		
4	Tax incentive cost, $/yr	$ 25,000	$ 35,000	$ 50,000	$ 80,000		
5	Resident entrance fees, $/yr	$ 500,000	$ 450,000	$ 425,000	$ 250,000		
6	Extra HST, $/yr	$ 310,000	$ 320,000	$ 320,000	$ 340,000		
7	Life	8	8	8	8		
8	AW of total costs	$ 66,867	$ 93,614	$ 133,734	$ 213,974		
9	Alternatives compared		2-to-1	3-to-2	4-to-2		
10	Incremental costs (delta C)		$ 26,747	$ 40,120	$ 120,360		
11	Entrance fees reduction, $/yr		50,000	25,000	200,000		
12	Extra HST, $/yr		10,000	-	20,000		
13	Incremental benefits (delta B)		$ 60,000	$ 25,000	$ 220,000		= E$13/E$10
14	Incremental BCR		2.24	0.62	1.83		
15	Increment justified?		Yes	No	Yes		
16	Alternative selected		#2	#2	#4		
17		= C$8 – B$8					
18	= PMT($B$1,C$7, –C3)+C4	= B$5 –C$5		= IF(E14 > 1,"Yes","No")			
19		= C$6 –B$6					
20							
21		= C$11+C$12					

FIGURE 9–2

Spreadsheet solution for an incremental BCA of four mutually exclusive alternatives, Example 9.6.

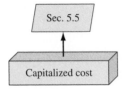

Sec. 5.5

Capitalized cost

When the lives of alternatives are so long that they can be considered infinite, the capitalized cost is used to calculate the equivalent PW or AW values for costs and benefits. Equation [5.3], $A = P(i)$, is used to determine the equivalent AW values in the incremental BCA.

If two or more *independent projects* are evaluated using BCA and there is no budget limitation, no incremental comparison is necessary. The only comparison is between each project separately with the do-nothing alternative. The project BCR values are calculated, and those with BCR $\geq$ 1.0 are accepted. This is the same procedure as that used to select from independent projects using the ROR method (Chapter 8). When a budget limitation is imposed, the capital budgeting procedure discussed in Chapter 12 must be applied.

EXAMPLE 9.7

The Saskatchewan Watershed Authority wants to construct a dam on a flood-prone river. The estimated construction cost and average annual dollar benefits are listed below. (a) If a 6% per year rate applies and dam life is infinite for analysis purposes, select the one best location using BCA. If no site is acceptable, other sites will be determined later. (b) If more than one dam site can be selected, which sites are acceptable, using the BCA?

Site	Construction Cost, $ Millions	Annual Benefits, $
A	6	350,000
B	8	420,000
C	3	125,000
D	10	400,000
E	5	350,000
F	11	700,000

Solution

(a) The capitalized cost $A = Pi$ is used to obtain AW values for annual capital recovery of the construction cost, as shown in the first row of Table 9–2. Since benefits are estimated directly, the site BCR can be used for initial screening. Only sites E and F have BCR > 1.0, so they are evaluated incrementally. The E-to-DN comparison is performed because it is not required that one site must be selected. The analysis between the mutually exclusive alternatives in the lower portion of Table 9–2 is based on Equation [9.7].

$$\text{Incremental BCR} = \frac{\Delta \text{ annual benefits}}{\Delta \text{ annual costs}}$$

Since only site E is incrementally justified, it is selected.

(b) The dam site proposals are now independent projects. The site BCR is used to select from none to all six sites. In Table 9–2, BCR > 1.0 for sites E and F only; they are acceptable, the rest are not.

TABLE 9–2   Use of Incremental BCR Analysis for Example 9.7 (values in $1000)

	C	E	A	B	D	F
Capital recovery cost, $	180	300	360	480	600	660
Annual benefits, $	125	350	350	420	400	700
Site BCR	0.69	1.17	0.97	0.88	0.67	1.06
Decision	No	Retain	No	No	No	Retain
Comparison		E-to-DN				F-to-E
Δ Annual cost, $		300				360
Δ Annual benefits, $		350				350
Δ BCR		1.17				0.97
Increment justified?		Yes				No
Site selected		E				E

Comment

In part (a), suppose that site G is added with a construction cost of $10 million and an annual benefit of $700,000. The site BCR is acceptable at BCR = 700/600 = 1.17. Now, incrementally compare G-to-E; the incremental BCR = 350/300 = 1.17, in favour of G. In this case, site F must be compared with G. Since the annual benefits are the same ($700,000), the BCR is zero and the added investment is not justified. Therefore, site G is chosen.

CHAPTER SUMMARY

Benefit-cost analysis is used primarily to evaluate projects and to select from alternatives in the public sector. When one is comparing mutually exclusive alternatives, the incremental BCR must be greater than or equal to 1.0 for the incremental equivalent total cost to be economically justified. The PW, AW, or FW of the initial costs and estimated benefits can be used to perform an incremental BCA. If alternative lives are unequal, the AW values should be used, provided the assumption of project repetition is not unreasonable. For independent projects, no incremental BCA is necessary. All projects with BCR ≥ 1.0 are selected provided there is no budget limitation.

Public sector economics are substantially different from those of the private sector. For public sector projects, the initial costs are usually large, the expected life is long (25, 35, or more years), and the sources for capital are usually a combination of taxes levied on the citizenry, user fees, bond issues, and private lenders. *It is very difficult to make accurate estimates of benefits for a public sector project.* The interest rates, called the social discount rates in the public sector, are lower than those for corporate capital financing. Although the social discount rate is as important to establish as the MARR, it can be difficult to establish, because various government agencies qualify for different rates. Standardized social discount rates are suggested for some federal agencies.

PROBLEMS

Public Sector Economics

9.1 State the difference between public and private sector alternatives with respect to the following characteristics.
   (a) Size of investment
   (b) Life of project
   (c) Funding
   (d) MARR

9.2 Indicate whether the following characteristics are primarily associated with public sector or private sector projects.
   (a) Profits
   (b) Taxes
   (c) Disbenefits
   (d) Infinite life
   (e) User fees
   (f) Corporate bonds

9.3 Identify each cash flow as a benefit, disbenefit, or cost.
   (a) $500,000 annual income from tourism created by a freshwater reservoir

   (b) $700,000 per year maintenance by container ship port authority
   (c) Expenditure of $45 million for tunnel construction on a provincial highway
   (d) Elimination of $1.3 million in salaries based on reduced international trade
   (e) Reduction of $375,000 per year in car accident repairs because of improved lighting
   (f) $700,000 per year loss of revenue by farmers because of highway right-of-way removal from the Agricultural Land Reserve

9.4 During its 20 years in business, Deware Construction Company has always developed its contracts under a fixed-fee or cost-plus arrangement. Now it has been offered an opportunity to participate in a project to provide cross-country highway transportation in an international setting, specifically, a country in Africa. If accepted, Deware will work as subcontractor to a larger

European corporation, and the BOT form of contracting will be used with the African country government. Describe for the president of Deware at least four of the significant differences that may be expected when the BOT format is utilized in lieu of its more traditional forms of contract making.

9.5 If a corporation accepts the BOT form of contracting, (*a*) identify two risks taken by a corporation and (*b*) state how these risks can be reduced by the government partner.

Project BCR Value

9.6 The estimated annual cash flows for a proposed city government project are costs of $450,000 per year, benefits of $600,000 per year, and disbenefits of $100,000 per year. Determine the (*a*) BCR and (*b*) value of B − C.

9.7 Use spreadsheet software such as Excel, PW analysis, and a discount rate of 5% per year to determine that the BCR value for the following estimates is 0.375, making the project not acceptable using the benefit/cost method. (*a*) Enter the values and equations on the spreadsheet so they may be changed for the purpose of sensitivity analysis.

First cost = $8 million
Annual cost = $800,000 per year
Benefit = $550,000 per year
Disbenefit = $100,000 per year

(*b*) Do the following sensitivity analysis by changing only two cells on your spreadsheet. Change the discount rate to 3% per year, and adjust the annual cost estimate until BCR = 1.023. This makes the project just acceptable using benefit-cost analysis.

9.8 Assume that 2.5% of the median household income is a reasonable amount to pay for safe drinking water. The median household income is $30,000 per year. For a regulation that would affect the health of people in 1%

of the households, what would the health benefits have to equal in dollars per household (for that 1% of the households) for the BCR to be equal to 1.0?

9.9 Use a spreadsheet to set up and solve Problem 9.8, and then apply the following changes. Observe the increases and decreases in the required economic value of the health benefits for each of these changes.
(*a*) Median income is $18,000 (poorer country), and percentage of household income is reduced to 2%.
(*b*) Median income is $30,000 and 2.5% is spent on safe water, but only 0.5% of the households are affected.
(*c*) What percentage of the households must be affected if the required health benefit and annual income both equal $18,000? Assume the 2.5% of income estimate is maintained.

9.10 The fire chief of a medium-size city has estimated that the initial cost of a new fire station will be $4 million. Annual upkeep costs are estimated at $300,000. Benefits to citizens of $550,000 per year and disbenefits of $90,000 per year have also been identified. Use a social discount rate of 4% per year to determine if the station is economically justified by (*a*) the conventional BCR and (*b*) the B − C difference.

9.11 As part of the rehabilitation of the downtown area, the Parks and Recreation Department is planning to develop a skateboard park and basketball courts. The initial cost is expected to be $150,000 for improvements which are expected to have a 20-year life. Annual maintenance costs are projected to be $12,000. The department expects 24,000 people per year to use the facilities an average of 2 hours each. The value of the recreation has been conservatively set at $0.50 per hour. At a social discount rate of 3% per year, what is the BCR for the project?

9.12 The City of Kingston, Ontario, is working on an On-Road Bikeway Implementation

Plan to build a more visible and connected cycling network. The City estimates that the cost of the second phase of dedicated bicycle pathways will be $2.3 million. Annual maintenance costs are estimated at $120,000. Benefits of $340,000 per year and disbenefits of $40,000 per year have also been identified. Using a discount rate of 6% per year, calculate (*a*) the conventional BCR and (*b*) the BCRM.

9.13 The BCR for a new flood control project along the banks of the Red River is required to be 1.3. If the benefit is estimated at $600,000 per year and the maintenance cost is expected to total $300,000 per year, what is the allowed maximum initial cost of the project? The social discount rate is 7% per year, and a project life of 50 years is expected. Solve in two ways: (*a*) by hand and (*b*) using a spreadsheet set up for sensitivity analysis.

9.14 Use the spreadsheet developed in Problem 9.13(*b*) to determine the BCR if the initial cost is actually $3.23 million and the social discount rate is now 5% per year.

9.15 The BCRM for a hospital heliport project is 1.7. If the initial cost is $1 million and the annual benefits are $150,000, what is the amount of the annual M&O costs used in the calculation, if a discount rate of 6% per year applies? The estimated life is 30 years.

9.16 Ontario is in the midst of a 15-year, $90 billion plan for renewing the Province's hospitals, roads, jails, and schools. Calculate the BCR for the cash flow estimates shown below at a discount rate of 8% per year for a health centre planned by Infrastructure Ontario.

Item	Cash Flow
PW of benefits, $	3,800,000
AW of disbenefits, $/year	65,000
First cost, $	1,200,000
M&O costs, $/year	300,000
Life of project, years	20

9.17 Hemisphere Corp. is considering a BOT contract to construct and operate a large dam with a hydroelectric power generation facility in a developing nation in the southern hemisphere. The initial cost of the dam is expected to be $30 million, and it is expected to cost $100,000 per year to operate and maintain. Benefits from flood control, agricultural development, tourism, etc., are expected to be $2.8 million per year. At an interest rate of 8% per year, should the dam be constructed on the basis of its conventional BCR? The dam is assumed to be a permanent asset for the country. (*a*) Solve by hand. (*b*) Using a spreadsheet, find the BCR with only a single cell computation.

9.18 Manitoba is considering the feasibility of constructing a small flood control dam. The initial cost of the project will be $2.2 million, with inspection and upkeep costs of $10,000 per year. In addition, minor reconstruction will be required every 15 years at a cost of $65,000. If flood damage will be reduced from the present cost of $90,000 per year to $10,000 annually, use BCA to determine if the dam should be constructed. Assume that the dam will be permanent and the interest rate is 12% per year.

9.19 A highway construction company is under contract to build a new roadway through a scenic area and two rural towns in Nova Scotia. The road is expected to cost $18 million, with annual upkeep estimated at $150,000 per year. Additional income from tourists of $900,000 per year is estimated. If the road is expected to have a useful commercial life of 20 years, use one spreadsheet to determine if the highway should be constructed at an interest rate of 6% per year by applying (*a*) the B − C method, (*b*) BCA, and (*c*) the modified BCA. (Additionally, if the instructor requests it: Set up the spreadsheet for sensitivity analysis and use the Excel IF operator to make the build–don't build decision in each part of the problem.)

9.20 Alberta is considering a project to extend irrigation canals. The initial cost of the project is expected to be $1.5 million, with annual maintenance costs of $25,000 per year. (*a*) If agricultural revenue is expected to be $175,000 per year, do a BCA to determine whether the project should be undertaken, using a 20-year study period and a discount rate of 6% per year. (*b*) Rework the problem, using the modified BCR.

9.21 (*a*) Set up the spreadsheet and (*b*) use hand calculations to calculate the BCR for Problem 9.20 if the canal must be dredged every 3 years at a cost of $60,000 and there is a $15,000 per year disbenefit associated with the project.

Alternative Comparison

9.22 Apply incremental BCA analysis at an interest rate of 8% per year to determine which alternative should be selected. Use a 20-year study period, and assume the damage costs might occur in year 6 of the study period.

	Alternative A	Alternative B
Initial cost, $	600,000	800,000
Annual M&O costs $/year	50,000	70,000
Potential damage costs $	950,000	250,000

9.23 Two routes are under consideration for a new highway segment. The long route would be 15 kilometres and would have an initial cost of $21 million. The short trans-mountain route would span 5 kilometres and would have an initial cost of $45 million. Maintenance costs are estimated at $40,000 per year for the long route and $15,000 per year for the short route. Additionally, a major overhaul and resurfacing will be required every 10 years at a cost of 10% of the first cost of each route. Regardless of which route is selected, the volume of traffic is expected to be 400,000 vehicles per year.

If the vehicle operating expense is assumed to be $0.35 per kilometre and the value of reduced travel time for the short route is estimated at $900,000 per year, determine which route should be selected, using a conventional BCA. Assume an infinite life for each road, an interest rate of 6% per year, and that one of the roads will be built.

9.24 A city engineer and economic development director are evaluating two sites for construction of a multipurpose sports arena. At the downtown site, the city already owns enough land for the arena. However, the land for construction of a parking garage will cost $1 million. The west side site is 30 kilometres from downtown, but the land will be donated by a developer who knows that an arena at this site will increase the value of the remainder of his land holdings by many times. The downtown site will have extra construction costs of about $10 million because of infrastructure relocations, the parking garage, and drainage improvements. However, because of its centralized location, there will be greater attendance at most of the events held there. This will result in more revenue to vendors and local merchants in the amount of $350,000 per year. Additionally, the average attendee will not have to travel as far, resulting in annual benefits of $400,000 per year. All other costs and revenues are expected to be the same at either site. If the city uses a social discount rate of 8% per year, where should the arena be constructed? One of the two sites must be selected.

9.25 A country with rapid economic expansion has contracted for an economic evaluation of possibly building a new container port to augment the current port. The west coast site has deeper water so the dredging cost is lower than that for the east coast site. Also, the redredging of the west site will be required only every 6 years while the east site must be reworked each 4 years. Redredging, which is expected to increase in cost by 10% each time, will not take place in the last year of a port's commercial life. Disbenefit estimates vary from west (fishing revenue loss) to east (fishing and resort revenue losses). Fees to shippers per 20-metre STD equivalent are expected to be higher at the west site due to greater difficulty in handling ships because of the ocean currents present in the area and a higher cost of labour in this area of the country. All estimates are summarized below in $1 million, except annual revenue and life. Use spreadsheet analysis and a social discount rate of 4% per year to determine if either port should be constructed. It is not necessary that the country build either port since one is already operating successfully.

	West Coast Site	East Coast Site
Initial cost, $:		
Year 0	21	8
Year 1	0	8
Dredging cost, $, year 0	5	12
Annual M&O, $/year	1.5	0.8
Recurring dredging cost, $	2 each 6 years with increase of 10% each time	1.2 each 4 years with increase of 10% each time
Annual disbenefits, $/year	4	7
Annual fees: Number of 20-metre STD at $/container	5 million/year at $2.50 each	8 million/year at $2 each
Commercial life, years	20	12

9.26 A privately owned utility is considering two programs to achieve water conservation. Program 1, which is expected to cost an average of $60 per household, would involve a rebate of 75% of the purchase and installation costs of an ultralow-flush toilet. This program is projected to achieve a 5% reduction in overall household water use over a 5-year evaluation period. This will benefit the citizenry to the extent of $1.25 per household per month. Program 2 would involve installing water meters. This is expected to cost $500 per household, but it will result in reduced water cost at an estimated $8 per household per month (on average). At a social discount rate of 0.5% per month, which program, if either, should the utility undertake? Use the BCA.

9.27 Solar and conventional alternatives are available for providing energy at a remote research site. The costs associated with each alternative are shown below. Use the BCA to determine which should be selected at a discount rate of 7% per year over a 5-year study period.

	Conventional	Solar
Initial cost, $	2,000,000	1,300,000
M&O cost, $/year	80,000	9,000
Salvage value, $	10,000	150,000

9.28 Prince Edward Island is considering two locations for a new provincial park. Location E would require an investment of $3 million and $50,000 per year in maintenance. Location W would cost $7 million to construct, but P.E.I. would receive an additional $25,000 per year in park use fees. The operating cost of location W will be $65,000 per year. The revenue to park concessionaires will be $500,000 per year at location E and $700,000 per year at location W. The disbenefits associated with each location are $30,000 per year for location E and $40,000 per year for location W. Use (*a*) BCA and (*b*) the modified BCA to determine which location, if either, should be selected, using an interest rate of 12% per year. Assume that the park will be maintained indefinitely.

9.29 Three engineers made the estimates shown below for two optional methods by which new construction technology would be implemented at a site for public housing. Either one of the two options or the current method may be selected. Set up a spreadsheet for benefit-cost sensitivity analysis, and determine if option 1, option 2, or the do-nothing option is selected by each of the three engineers. Use a life of 5 years and a social discount rate of 10% per year for all analyses.

	Engineer Aaron		Engineer Beatrix		Engineer Chen	
	Option 1	Option 2	Option 1	Option 2	Option 1	Option 2
Initial cost, $	50,000	90,000	75,000	90,000	60,000	70,000
Cost, $/year	3,000	4,000	3,800	3,000	6,000	3,000
Benefits, $/year	20,000	29,000	30,000	35,000	30,000	35,000
Disbenefits, $/year	500	1,500	1,000	0	5,000	1,000

Multiple Alternatives

9.30 One of four new techniques, or the current method, can be used to control mildly irritating chemical fume leakage into the surounding air from a mixing machine. The estimated costs and benefits (in the form of reduced employee health costs) are given below for each method. Assuming that all methods have a 10-year life with zero salvage value, determine which one should be selected, using a MARR of 15% per year and BCA.

	Technique			
	1	2	3	4
Installed cost, $	15,000	19,000	25,000	33,000
AOC, $/year	10,000	12,000	9,000	11,000
Benefits, $/year	15,000	20,000	19,000	22,000

9.31 Use a spreadsheet to perform a BCA for the techniques in Problem 9.30, assuming they are independent projects. The benefits are cumulative if more than one technique is used in addition to the current method.

9.32 The Selkrik Water Service Authority is considering four sizes of pipe for a new water line. The costs per kilometre ($/km) for each size are given in the table. Assuming that all pipes will last 15 years and the MARR is 8% per year, which size pipe should be purchased based on a BCA? Installation cost is considered a part of the initial cost.

	Pipe Size, Millimetres			
	130	150	200	230
Initial equipment cost, $/km	9,180	10,510	13,180	15,850
Installation cost, $/km	600	800	1,400	1,500
Usage cost, $/km per year	6,000	5,800	5,200	4,900

9.33 Over the last several months, seven different toll bridge designs have been proposed and estimates made to connect a resort island to the mainland of an Asian country.

Location	Construction Cost, $ Millions	Annual Excess Fees over Expenses, $100,000
A	14	4.0
B	8	6.1
C	22	10.8
D	9	8.0
E	12	7.5
F	6	3.9
G	18	9.3

A public-private partnership has been formed, and the national bank will be providing funding at a rate of 4% per year. Each bridge is expected to have a very long useful life. Use BCA to answer the following. Solution by spreadsheet or by hand is acceptable.

(a) If one bridge design must be selected, determine which one is the best economically.

(b) An international bank has offered to fund as many as two additional bridges, since it is estimated that the trafffic and trade between the island and mainland will increase significantly. Determine which are the three best designs economically, if there is no budget restraint for the purpose of this analysis.

9.34 A consulting engineer is evaluating four different projects for the Saskatchewan Energy Conservation & Development Authority. The present worths of the costs,

benefits, disbenefits, and cost savings are shown below. Assuming the interest rate is 10% per year compounded continuously, determine which of the projects, if any, should be selected if the projects are (a) independent, and (b) mutually exclusive.

	A	B	C	D
PW of costs, $	10,000	8,000	20,000	14,000
PW of benefits, $	15,000	11,000	25,000	42,000
PW of disbenefits, $	6,000	1,000	20,000	31,000
PW of cost savings, $	1,500	2,000	16,000	3,000

9.35 Three alternatives identified as X, Y, and Z were evaluated by BCA. The analyst, Joyce, calculated project BCR values of 0.92, 1.34, and 1.29. The alternatives are listed in order of increasing total equivalent costs. She isn't sure whether an incremental analysis is needed.

(a) What do you think? If no incremental analysis is needed, why not; if so, which alternatives must be compared incrementally?

(b) For what type of projects is incremental analysis never necessary? If incremental analysis necessary? If X, Y, and Z are all this type of project, which alternatives are selected for the BCR values calculated?

9.36 The four mutually exclusive alternatives below are being compared using the BCA. What alternative, if any, should be selected?

Alternative	Initial Investment, $ Millions	BCR	Incremental BCR When Compared with Alternative:			
			J	K	L	M
J	20	1.10	—			
K	25	0.96	0.40	—		
L	33	1.22	1.42	2.14	—	
M	45	0.89	0.72	0.80	0.08	—

9.37 The city of Oshawa is considering various proposals regarding the disposal of used tires. All the proposals involve shredding, but the charges for the service and handling of the tire shreds differ in each plan.

An incremental BCA was initiated, but the engineer conducting the study left recently. (*a*) Fill in the blanks in the incremental BCR portion of the table. (*b*) What alternative should be selected?

Alternative	Initial Investment, $ Millions	BCR	Incremental BCR When Compared with Alternative:			
			P	Q	R	S
P	10	1.1	—	2.83		
Q	40	2.4	2.83	—		
R	50	1.4			—	
S	80	1.5				—

EXTENDED EXERCISE

COSTS TO PROVIDE LADDER TRUCK SERVICE FOR FIRE PROTECTION

For many years, the city of Langford has paid a neighbouring city (Victoria) for the use of its ladder truck when needed. The charges for the last few years have been $1000 per event when the ladder truck is only dispatched to a site in Langford, and $3000 each time the truck is activated. There has been no annual fee charged. The newly hired fire chief in Victoria has presented a substantially higher cost to the Langford fire chief for the use of the ladder truck:

Annual flat fee $30,000 with 5 years' fees paid up front (now)

Dispatch fee $3000 per event

Activation fee $8000 per event

The Langford chief has developed an alternative to purchase a ladder truck, with the following cost estimates for the truck and the fire station addition to house it:

Truck:

Initial cost $850,000

Life   15 years

Cost per dispatch $2000 per event

Cost per activation $7000 per event

Building:

Initial cost $500,000

Life   50 years

The chief has also taken data from a study completed last year and updated it. The study estimated the insurance premium and property loss reductions that the citizenry experienced by having a ladder truck available. The past savings and current estimates, if Langford had its own truck for more rapid response, are as follows:

	Past Average	Estimate If Truck Is Owned
Insurance premium reduction, $/year	100,000	200,000
Property loss reduction, $/year	300,000	400,000

Additionally, the Langford chief obtained the average number of events for the last 3 years and estimated the future use of the ladder truck. He believes there has been a reluctance to call for the truck from Victoria in the past.

	Past Average	Estimate If Truck Is Owned
Number of dispatches per year	10	15
Number of activations per year	3	5

Either the new cost structure must be accepted, or a truck must be purchased. The option to have no ladder truck service is not acceptable. A social discount rate of 6% per year is used for all proposals.

Questions

Use a spreadsheet to do the following.

1. Perform an incremental BCR to determine if Langford should purchase a ladder truck.

2. Several of the new city council members are up in arms over the new annual fee and cost structure. However, they do not want to build more fire station capacity or own a ladder truck that will be used an average of only 20 times per year. They believe that Victoria can be convinced to reduce or remove the annual $30,000 fee. How much must the annual fee be reduced for the alternative to purchase the ladder truck to be rejected?

3. Another council member is willing to pay the annual fee, but wants to know how much the building cost can change from $500,000 to make the alternatives equally attractive. Find this first cost for the building.

4. Finally, a compromise proposal offered by Langford might be acceptable to Victoria. Reduce the annual fee by 50%, and reduce the per-event charges to the same amount that the Langford fire chief estimates it will cost if the truck is owned. Then Langford will possibly adjust (if it seems reasonable) the sum of the insurance premium reduction and property loss reduction estimates to just make the arrangement with Victoria more attractive than owning the truck. Find this sum (for the estimates of premium reduction and property loss reduction). Does this new sum seem reasonable relative to the previous estimates?

FREEWAY LIGHTING

Introduction

A number of studies have shown that a disproportionate number of freeway traffic accidents occur at night. There are a number of possible explanations for this, one of which might be poor visibility. In an effort to determine whether freeway lighting was economically beneficial for reducing nighttime accidents, data were collected regarding accident frequency rates on lighted and unlighted sections of certain freeways. This case study is an analysis of part of those data.

Background

A value may be placed on accidents depending on the severity of the crash. There are a number of crash categories, the most severe of which is fatal. The cost of a fatal accident is placed at $2.8 million. The most common type of accident is not fatal or injurious and involves only property damage. The cost of this type of accident is placed at $4500. The ideal way to determine whether lights reduce traffic accidents is through before-and-after studies on a given section of freeway. However, this type of information is not readily available, so other methods must be used. One such method compares night to day accident rates for lighted and unlighted freeways. If lights are beneficial, the ratio of night to day accidents will be lower on the lighted section than on the unlighted one. If there is a difference, the reduced accident rate can be translated into benefits which can be compared to the cost of lighting to determine its economic feasibility. This technique is used in the following analysis.

Economic Analysis

The results of one particular study conducted over a 5-year period are presented in the table below. For illustrative purposes, only the property damage category will be considered.

The ratios of night to day accidents involving property damage for the unlighted and lighted freeway sections are $199/379 = 0.525$ and $839/2069 = 0.406$, respectively. These results indicate that the lighting was beneficial. To quantify the benefit, the accident-rate ratio from the unlighted section will be applied to the lighted section. This will yield the number of accidents that were prevented. Thus, there would have been $(2069)(0.525) = 1086$ accidents instead of the 839 if there had not been lights on the freeway. This is a difference of 247 accidents. At a cost of $4500 per accident, this results in a net benefit of

$$B = (247)(\$4500) = \$1,111,500$$

To determine the cost of the lighting, it will be assumed that the light poles are centre poles 67 metres apart with 2 bulbs each. The bulb size is 400 watts, and the installation cost is $3500 per pole. Since these data were collected over 87.8 kilometres (54.5 miles) of lighted freeway, the installed cost of the lighting is

$$\text{Installation cost} = \$3500 \left(\frac{87.8}{0.067} \right)$$
$$= 3500(1310.4)$$
$$= \$4,586,400$$

The annual power cost based on 1310 poles is as follows:

$$\begin{aligned}
\text{Annual power cost} = \ &1310 \text{ poles}(2 \text{ bulbs/pole})(0.4 \text{ kilowatts/bulb}) \\
&\times (12 \text{ hours/day})(365 \text{ days/year}) \\
&\times (\$0.08/\text{kilowatt-hour}) \\
= \ &\$367,219 \text{ per year}
\end{aligned}$$

These data were collected over a 5-year period. Therefore, the annualized cost C at $i = 6\%$ per year is

$$\begin{aligned}
\text{Total annual cost} &= \$4,586,400(A/P,6\%,5) + 367,219 \\
&= \$1,456,030
\end{aligned}$$

Freeway Accident Rates, Lighted and Unlighted

Accident Type	Unlighted		Lighted	
	Day	Night	Day	Night
Fatal	3	5	4	7
Incapacitating	10	6	28	22
Evident	58	20	207	118
Possible	90	35	384	161
Property damage	379	199	2069	839
Totals	540	265	2697	1147

Source: Michael Griffin, "Comparison of the Safety of Lighting Options on Urban Freeways," *Public Roads*, 58 (Autumn 1994), pp. 8–15.

The BCR is

$$\text{BCR} = \frac{\$1,111,500}{\$1,456,030} = 0.76$$

Since BCR < 1, the lighting is not justified on the basis of property damage alone. To make a final determination about the economic viability of the lighting, the benefits associated with the other accident categories would obviously also have to be considered.

Case Study Exercises

1. What would the BCR be if the light poles were twice as far apart as assumed above?

2. What is the ratio of night to day accidents for fatalities?

3. What would the BCR be if the installation cost were only $2500 per pole?

4. How many accidents would be prevented on the unlighted portion of freeway if it were lighted? Consider the property damage category only.

5. Using only the category of property damage, what would the lighted night-to-day accident ratio have to be for the lighting to be economically justified?

CHAPTER  10

Making Choices: The Method, MARR, and Multiple Attributes

This chapter broadens the capabilities of an engineering economy study. Some of the fundamental elements specified previously are unspecified here. As a result, many of the textbook aspects apparent in previous chapters are removed, thus coming closer to treating the more complex, real-world situations in which professional practice and decision making occur.

In all the previous chapters, the method for evaluating a project or comparing alternatives has been stated, or was obvious from the context of the problem. Also, when any method was used, the MARR was stated. Finally, only one dimension or attribute—the economic one—has been the judgment basis for the economic viability of one project, or the selection basis from two or more alternatives. In this chapter, the determination of all three of these parameters—evaluation method, MARR, and attributes—is discussed. Guidelines and techniques to determine each are developed and illustrated.

The case study examines the best balance between debt and equity capital, using a MARR-based analysis.

LEARNING OBJECTIVES

Purpose: Choose an appropriate method and MARR to compare alternatives economically, and using multiple attributes.

By the end of this chapter you should be able to

Choose a method	**1.** Choose an appropriate method to compare mutually exclusive alternatives.
Cost of capital and MARR	**2.** Describe the cost of capital and its relation to the MARR, while considering reasons for MARR variation.
WACC	**3.** Understand the debt-to-equity mix and calculate the weighted average cost of capital (WACC).
Cost of debt capital	**4.** Estimate the cost of debt capital.
Cost of equity capital	**5.** Estimate the cost of equity capital, and explain how it compares to WACC and MARR.
High D-E mixes	**6.** Explain the relation of corporate risk to high debt-to-equity mixes.
Multiple attributes	**7.** Identify and develop weights for multiple attributes used in alternative selection.
Weighted attribute method	**8.** Use the weighted attribute method for multiple-attribute decision making.

10.1 COMPARING MUTUALLY EXCLUSIVE ALTERNATIVES BY DIFFERENT EVALUATION METHODS

In the previous five chapters, several equivalent evaluation techniques have been discussed. Any method—PW, AW, FW, ROR, or BCA—can be used to select one alternative from two or more and obtain the same, correct answer. Only one method is needed to perform the engineering economy analysis, because any method, correctly performed, will select the same alternative. Yet different information about an alternative is available with each different method. The selection of a method and its correct application can be confusing.

Table 10–1 gives a recommended evaluation method for different situations, if it is not specified by the instructor in a course or by corporate practice in professional work. The primary criteria for selecting a method are speed and ease of performing the analysis. Interpretation of the entries in each column follows.

Evaluation period: Most private sector alternatives (revenue and service) are compared over their equal or unequal estimated lives, or over a specific period of time. Public sector projects are commonly evaluated using BCA and usually have long lives that may be considered as infinite for economic computation purposes.

Type of alternatives: Private sector alternatives have cash flow estimates that are revenue-based (includes income and cost estimates) or service-based (cost estimates only). For service alternatives, the revenue cash flow series is assumed to be equal for all alternatives. Public sector projects are

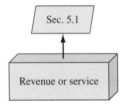

Sec. 5.1

Revenue or service

TABLE 10–1 Recommended Method to Compare Mutually Exclusive Alternatives, Provided the Method Is Not Preselected

Evaluation Period	Type of Alternatives	Recommended Method	Series to Evaluate
Equal lives of alternatives	Revenue or service	AW or PW	Cash flows
	Public sector	BCA, based on AW or PW	Incremental cash flows
Unequal lives of alternatives	Revenue or service	AW	Cash flows
	Public sector	BCA, based on AW	Incremental cash flows
Study period	Revenue or service	AW or PW	Updated cash flows
	Public sector	BCA, based on AW or PW	Updated incremental cash flows
Long to infinite	Revenue or service	AW or PW	Cash flows
	Public sector	BCA, based on AW	Incremental cash flows

normally service-based with the difference between costs and timing used to select one alternative over another.

Recommended method: Whether an analysis is performed by hand or by computer, the method(s) recommended in Table 10–1 will correctly select one alternative from two or more as rapidly as possible. Any other method can be applied subsequently to obtain additional information and, if needed, verification of the selection. For example, if lives are unequal and the rate of return is needed, it is best to first apply the AW method at the MARR and then determine the selected alternative's i^* using the same AW relation with i as the unknown.

Series to evaluate: The estimated cash flow series for one alternative and the incremental series between two alternatives are the only two options for present worth or annual worth evaluation. For spreadsheet analyses, this means that the NPV or PV functions (for present worth) or the PMT function (for annual worth) is applied. The word "updated" is added as a reminder that a study period analysis requires that cash flow estimates (especially salvage/market values) be reexamined and updated before the analysis is performed.

Once the evaluation method is selected, a specific procedure must be followed. These procedures were the primary topics of the last five chapters. Table 10–2 summarizes the important elements of the procedure for each method—PW, AW, ROR, and BCR. FW is included as an extension of PW. The meaning of the entries in Table 10–2 follows.

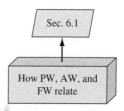

Equivalence relation: The basic equation written to perform any analysis is either a PW or an AW relation. The capitalized cost (CC) relation is a PW relation for infinite life, and the FW relation is likely determined from the PW equivalent value. Additionally, as we learned in Chapter 6, AW is simply PW times the A/P factor over the LCM of their lives.

Lives of alternatives and *time period for analysis:* The length of time for an evaluation (the n value) will always be one of the following: equal lives of the alternatives, LCM of unequal lives, specified study period, or infinity because the lives are so long.

> **PW analysis always requires the LCM of all alternatives.**
>
> **Incremental ROR and BCR methods require the LCM of the two alternatives being compared.**
>
> **The AW method allows analysis over the respective alternative lives.**

The one exception is for incremental ROR method for unequal-life alternatives using an AW relation for *incremental cash flows.* The LCM of the two alternatives compared must be used. This is equivalent to using an AW relation for the *actual cash flows* over the respective lives. Both approaches find the incremental rate of return Δi^*.

Series to evaluate: Either the estimated cash flow series or the incremental series is used to determine the PW value, the AW value, the i^* value, or the BCR.

TABLE 10–2 Characteristics of an Economic Analysis of Mutually Exclusive Alternatives Once the Evaluation Method Is Determined

Evaluation Method	Equivalence Relation	Lives of Alternatives	Time Period for Analysis	Series to Evaluate	Rate of Return; Interest Rate	Decision Guideline: Select*
Present worth	PW	Equal	Lives	Cash flows	MARR	Numerically largest PW
	PW	Unequal	LCM	Cash flows	MARR	Numerically largest PW
	PW	Study period	Study period	Updated cash flows	MARR	Numerically largest PW
	CC	Long to infinite	Infinity	Cash flows	MARR	Numerically largest CC
Future worth	FW	Same as present worth for equal lives, unequal lives, and study period				Numerically largest FW
Annual worth	AW	Equal or unequal	Lives	Cash flows	MARR	Numerically largest AW
	AW	Study period	Study period	Updated cash flows	MARR	Numerically largest AW
	AW	Long to infinite	Infinity	Cash flows	MARR	Numerically largest AW
Rate of return	PW or AW	Equal	Lives	Incremental cash flows	Find Δi^*	Last $\Delta i^* \geq$ MARR
	PW or AW	Unequal	LCM of pair	Incremental cash flows	Find Δi^*	Last $\Delta i^* \geq$ MARR
	AW	Unequal	Lives	Cash flows	Find Δi^*	Last $\Delta i^* \geq$ MARR
	PW or AW	Study period	Study period	Updated incremental cash flows	Find Δi^*	Last $\Delta i^* \geq$ MARR
Benefit-cost	PW	Equal or unequal	LCM of pairs	Incremental cash flows	Social discount rate	Last ΔBCR ≥ 1.0
	AW	Equal or unequal	Lives	Incremental cash flows	Social discount rate	Last ΔBCR ≥ 1.0
	AW or PW	Long to infinite	Infinity	Incremental cash flows	Social discount rate	Last ΔBCR ≥ 1.0

*Lowest equivalent cost or largest equivalent income.

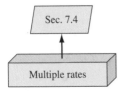

Sec. 7.4

Multiple rates

Rate of return (interest rate): The MARR value must be stated to complete the PW, FW, or AW method. This is also correct for the discount rate for public sector alternatives analyzed by the BCR. The ROR method requires that the incremental rate be found in order to select one alternative. It is here that the dilemma of multiple rates appears, if the sign tests indicate that a unique, real-number root does not necessarily exist for a nonconventional series.

Decision guideline: The selection of one alternative is accomplished using the general guideline in the rightmost column. Always select the alternative with the *numerically largest PW, FW, or AW value.* This is correct for both revenue and service alternatives. The incremental cash flow methods— ROR and BCR—require that the largest initial cost and incrementally justified alternative be selected, provided it is justified against an alternative that is itself justified. This means that the incremental i^* exceeds MARR, or the incremental BCR exceeds 1.0.

Table 10–2 is also printed on the inner-leaf sheet of the back cover of the text with references to the section(s) where the evaluation method is discussed.

10.2 MARR RELATIVE TO THE COST OF CAPITAL

The MARR value used in alternative evaluation is one of the most important parameters of a study. In Chapter 1 the MARR was described relative to the weighted costs of debt and equity capital. This section and the next four sections explain how to establish a MARR under varying conditions.

To form the basis for a realistic MARR, the cost of each type of capital financing is initially computed separately, and then the proportion from debt and equity sources is weighted to estimate the average interest rate paid for investment capital. This percentage is called the *cost of capital.* The MARR is then set relative to it. Additionally, the financial health of the corporation, the expected return on invested capital, and many other factors are considered when the MARR is established. If no specific MARR is established, the de facto MARR is set by the project's net cash flow estimates and the availability of capital funds. That is, in reality, the MARR is the *opportunity cost,* which is the i^* of the first project rejected due to the unavailability of funds.

Before we discuss cost of capital, the two primary sources of capital are reviewed.

Debt capital   represents borrowing from outside the company, with the principal repaid at a stated interest rate following a specified time schedule. Debt financing includes borrowing via *bonds, loans,* and *mortgages.* The lender does not share in the profits made using the debt funds, but there is risk in that the borrower could default on part of or all the borrowed funds. The amount of outstanding debt financing is indicated in the liabilities section of the corporate balance sheet.

Equity capital   is corporate money made up of the funds of owners and retained earnings. Owners' funds are further classified as common and preferred stock proceeds or owners' capital for a private (non-stock-issuing) company. Retained earnings are funds previously retained in the corporation for capital investment. The amount of equity is indicated in the net worth section of the corporate balance sheet.

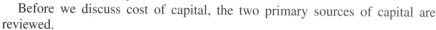

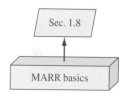

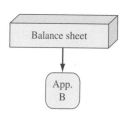

To illustrate the relation between cost of capital and MARR, assume a computer system project will be completely financed by a $5,000,000 bond issue (100% debt financing) and assume the dividend rate on the bonds is 8%. Therefore, the cost of debt capital is 8% as shown in Figure 10–1. This 8% is the minimum for MARR. Management may increase this MARR in increments that reflect its desire for added return and its perception of risk. For example, management may add an amount for all capital commitments in this area. Suppose this amount is 2%. This increases the expected return to 10% (Figure 10–1). Also, if the risk associated with the investment is considered substantial enough to warrant an additional 1% return requirement, the final MARR is 11%.

The recommended approach does not follow the logic presented above. Rather the cost of capital (8% here) should be the established MARR. Then the i^* value is determined from the estimated net cash flows. Using this approach, suppose the computer system is estimated to return 11%. Now, additional return requirements and risk factors are considered to determine if 3% above the MARR of 8% is sufficient to justify the capital investment. After these considerations, if the project is rejected, the effective MARR is now 11%. This is the opportunity cost discussed previously—the rejected project i^* has established the effective MARR for computer system alternatives at 11%, not 8%.

The setting of the MARR for an economy study is not an exact process. The debt and equity capital mix changes over time and between projects. Also, the MARR is not a fixed value established corporatewide. It is altered for different opportunities and types of projects. For example, a corporation may use a MARR of 10% for evaluating the purchase of assets (equipment, cars) and a MARR of 20% for expansion investments, such as purchasing smaller companies.

The effective MARR varies from one project to another and through time because of factors such as the following:

Project risk. Where there is greater risk (perceived or actual) associated with proposed projects, the tendency is to set a higher MARR. This is encouraged by the higher cost of debt capital for projects considered risky. This usually

FIGURE 10–1

A fundamental relation between cost of capital and MARR used in practice.

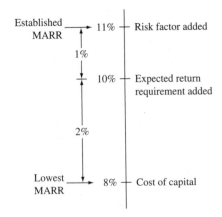

means that there is some concern that the project will not realize its projected revenue requirements.

Investment opportunity.   If management is determined to expand in a certain area, the MARR may be lowered to encourage investment with the hope of recovering lost revenue in other areas. This common reaction to investment opportunity can create havoc when the guidelines for setting on MARR are too strictly applied. Flexibility becomes very important.

Tax structure.   If corporate taxes are rising (due to increased profits, capital gains, local taxes, etc.), pressure to increase the MARR is present. Use of after-tax analysis may assist in eliminating this reason for a fluctuating MARR, since accompanying business expenses will tend to decrease taxes and after-tax costs.

Limited capital.   As debt and equity capital become limited, the MARR is increased. If the demand for limited capital exceeds supply, the MARR may tend to be set even higher. The opportunity cost has a large role in determining the MARR actually used.

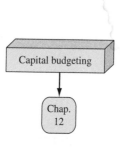

Market rates at other corporations.   If the MARR increases at other corporations, especially competitors, a company may alter its MARR upward in response. These variations are often based on changes in interest rates for loans, which directly impact the cost of capital.

If the details of after-tax analysis are not of interest, but the effects of income taxes are important, the MARR may be increased by incorporating an effective tax rate using the formula

$$\text{Before-tax MARR} = \frac{\text{after-tax MARR}}{1 - \text{tax rate}}$$

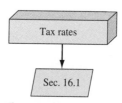

The total or effective tax rate, including federal, provincial, and local taxes, for most corporations is in the range of 13 to 45%. If an after-tax rate of return of 10% is required and the effective tax rate is 35%, the MARR for the before-tax economic analysis is $10\%/(1 - 0.35) = 15.4\%$.

EXAMPLE 10.1

Brother and sister twins Carl and Christy graduated several years ago from university. Carl, an architect, has worked in home design with Bulte Homes since graduation. Christy, a civil engineer, works with Butler Industries in structural components and analysis. They both reside in Edmonton. They have started a creative e-commerce network through which Alberta-based builders can buy their home plans and construction materials much more cheaply. Carl and Christy want to expand into a regional e-business corporation. They have gone to the HSBC Bank in Edmonton for a business development loan. Identify some factors that might cause the loan rate to vary when HSBC provides the quote. Also, indicate any impact on the established MARR when Carl and Christy make economic decisions for their business.

Solution

In all cases the direction of the loan rate and the MARR will be the same. Using the five factors mentioned above, some loan rate considerations are as follows:

Project risk: The loan rate may increase if there has been a noticeable downturn in housing starts, thus reducing the need for the e-commerce connection.

Investment opportunity: The rate could increase if other companies offering similar services have already applied for a loan at other HSBC branches regionally or nationwide.

Taxes: If the province increased the labour tax credit for the construction industry, the rate might be lowered slightly.

Capital limitation: Assume the computer equipment and software rights held by Carl and Christy were bought with their own funds and there are no outstanding loans. If additional equity capital is not available for this expansion, the rate for the loan (debt capital) should be lowered.

Market loan rates: The local HSBC branch probably obtains its development loan money from a large national pool. If market loan rates to this branch have increased, the rate for this loan will likely increase, because money is becoming "tighter."

10.3 DEBT-EQUITY MIX AND WEIGHTED AVERAGE COST OF CAPITAL

The *debt-to-equity (D-E) mix* identifies the percentages of debt and equity financing for a corporation. A company with a 40–60 D-E mix has 40% of its capital originating from debt capital sources (bonds, loans, and mortgages) and 60% derived from equity sources (stocks and retained earnings).

Most projects are funded with a combination of debt and equity capital made available specifically for the project or taken from a corporate *pool of capital*. The *weighted average cost of capital (WACC)* of the pool is estimated by the relative fractions from debt and equity sources. If known exactly, these fractions are used to estimate WACC; otherwise the historical fractions for each source are used in the relation

$$\text{WACC} = \text{(equity fraction)(cost of equity capital)} \\ + \text{(debt fraction)(cost of debt capital)} \qquad [10.1]$$

The two *cost* terms are expressed as percentage interest rates.

Since virtually all corporations have a mixture of capital sources, the WACC is a value between the debt and equity costs of capital. If the fraction of each type of equity financing—common stock, preferred stock, and retained earnings—is known, Equation [10.1] is expanded.

$$\text{WACC} = \text{(common stock fraction)(cost of common stock capital)} \\ + \text{(preferred stock fraction)(cost of preferred stock capital)} \\ + \text{(retained earnings fraction)(cost of retained earnings capital)} \\ + \text{(debt fraction)(cost of debt capital)} \qquad [10.2]$$

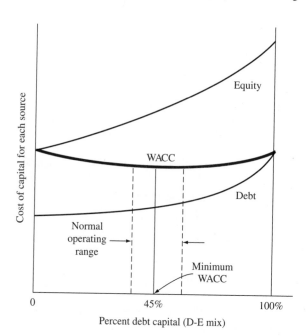

FIGURE 10–2
General shape of different cost of capital curves.

Figure 10–2 indicates the usual shape of cost of capital curves. If 100% of the capital is derived from equity or 100% is from debt sources, the WACC equals the cost of capital of that source of funds. There is virtually always a mixture of capital sources involved for any capitalization program. As an illustration only, Figure 10–2 indicates a minimum WACC at about 45% debt capital. Most firms operate over a range of D-E mixes. For example, a range of 30% to 50% debt financing for some companies may be very acceptable to lenders, with no increases in risk or MARR. However, another company may be considered "risky" with only 20% debt capital. It takes knowledge about management ability, current projects, and the economic health of the specific industry to determine a reasonable operating range of the D-E mix for a particular company.

EXAMPLE 10.2

A new program in genetics engineering at Gentex will require $10 million in capital. The chief financial officer (CFO) has estimated the following amounts of financing at the indicated interest rates:

Common stock sales	$5 million at 13.7%
Use of retained earnings	$2 million at 8.9%
Debt financing through bonds	$3 million at 7.5%

Historically, Gentex has financed projects using a D-E mix of 40% from debt sources costing 7.5%, and 60% from equity sources costing 10.0%.
(a) Compare the historical WACC value with that for this current genetics program.
(b) Determine the MARR if a return of 5% per year is required by Gentex.

Solution

(a) Equation [10.1] is used to estimate the historical WACC.

$$\text{WACC} = 0.6(10) + 0.4(7.5) = 9.0\%$$

For the current program, the equity financing comprises 50% common stock ($5 million out of $10 million) and 20% retained earnings, with the remaining 30% from debt sources. The program WACC by Equation [10.2] is higher than the historical average of 9%.

$$\text{WACC} = \text{stock portion} + \text{retained earnings portion} + \text{debt portion}$$

$$= 0.5(13.7) + 0.2(8.9) + 0.3(7.5) = 10.88\%$$

(b) The program should be evaluated using a MARR of $10.88 + 5.0 = 15.88\%$ per year.

The WACC value can be computed using before-tax or after-tax values for cost of capital. The after-tax method is the correct one since debt financing has a distinct tax advantage, as discussed in the next section. Approximations of after-tax or before-tax cost of capital are made using the effective tax rate T_e in the relation

$$\text{After-tax cost of debt} = (\text{before-tax cost})(1 - T_e) \qquad [10.3]$$

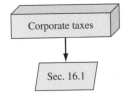

The effective tax rate is a combination of federal, provincial, and local tax rates. They are reduced to a single number T_e to simplify computations. Equation [10.3] may be used to approximate the cost of debt capital separately or inserted into Equation [10.1] for an after-tax WACC rate. Chapter 16 treats taxes and after-tax economic analysis in detail.

10.4 DETERMINATION OF THE COST OF DEBT CAPITAL

Debt financing includes borrowing, primarily via bonds and loans. In Canada, bond interest and loan interest payments are tax-deductible as a corporate expense. This reduces the taxable income base upon which taxes are calculated, with the end result of less taxes paid. The cost of debt capital is, therefore, reduced because there is an annual *tax savings* of the expense cash flow times the effective tax rate T_e. This tax savings is subtracted from the debt-capital expense cash flow in order to calculate the cost of debt capital. In formula form,

$$\textbf{Tax savings} = (\textbf{expenses})(\textbf{effective tax rate}) = \textbf{expenses}(T_e) \quad \textbf{[10.4]}$$

$$\textbf{Net cash flow} = \textbf{expenses} - \textbf{tax savings} = \textbf{expenses}(1 - T_e) \quad \textbf{[10.5]}$$

To find the cost of debt capital, develop a PW- or AW-based relation of the net cash flow (NCF) series with i^* as the unknown. Find i^* by hand through trial and error, or by the RATE or IRR functions on a computer spreadsheet. This is the cost of debt capital percentage used in the WACC computation in Equation [10.1].

EXAMPLE 10.3

CRX Corporation will generate $5 million in debt capital by issuing five thousand $1000 8% per year 10-year bonds. If the effective tax rate of the company is 50% and the bonds are discounted 2% for quick sale, compute the cost of debt capital (a) before taxes and (b) after taxes from the company perspective. Obtain the answers by hand and by computer.

Solution by Hand

(a) The annual bond dividend is $1000(0.08) = $80, and the 2% discounted sales price is $980 now. Using the company perspective, find the i^* in the PW relation

$$0 = 980 - 80(P/A,i^*,10) - 1000(P/F,i^*,10)$$

$$i^* = 8.3\%$$

The before-tax cost of debt capital is $i^* = 8.3\%$, which is slightly higher than the 8% bond interest rate, because of the 2% sales discount.

(b) With the allowance to reduce taxes by deducting the bond interest, Equation [10.4] shows a tax savings of $80(0.5) = $40 per year. The bond dividend amount for the PW relation is now $80 - $40 = $40. Solving for i^* after taxes reduces the cost of debt capital by nearly one-half, to 4.25%.

Solution by Computer

Figure 10–3 is a spreadsheet image for both before-tax (column B) and after-tax (column C) analysis using the IRR function. The after-tax net cash flow is calculated using Equation [10.5] with $T_e = 0.5$. See the cell tag.

Q-SOLVE

	A		B	C	D	E	F
1	**Bond face value**		**Before tax**	**After tax**			
2	$	1,000	cash flow	cash flow			
3	Year	0 $	980	$ 980			
4		1 $	(80)	$ (40)			
5		2 $	(80)	$ (40)			
6		3 $	(80)	$ (40)		= $B$4*(1−0.5)	
7	=−A2*0.08	4 $	(80)	$ (40)			
8		5 $	(80)	$ (40)			
9		6 $	(80)	$ (40)			
10		7 $	(80)	$ (40)			
11		8 $	(80)	$ (40)			
12		9 $	(80)	$ (40)			
13		10 $	(1,080)	$ (1,040)			
14							
15	Cost of debt capital		8.30%	4.25%			
16							
17						= IRR(C3:C13)	

FIGURE 10–3

Use of the IRR function to determine before-tax and after-tax cost of debt capital, Example 10.3.

EXAMPLE 10.4

The Imax Corporation will purchase a $20,000 10-year-life asset. Company managers have decided to put $10,000 down now and borrow $10,000 at an interest rate of 6%. The simplified loan repayment plan is $600 in interest each year, with the entire $10,000 principal paid in year 10. What is the after-tax cost of debt capital if the effective tax rate is 42%?

Solution

The after-tax net cash flow for interest on the $10,000 loan is an annual amount of $600(1 − 0.42) = 348 by Equation [10.5]. The loan repayment is $10,000 in year 10. PW is used to estimate a cost of debt capital of 3.48%.

$$0 = 10,000 - 348(P/A,i^*,10) - 10,000(P/F,i^*,10)$$

Comment

Note that the 6% annual interest on the $10,000 loan is not the WACC because 6% is paid only on the borrowed funds. Nor is 3.48% the WACC, since it is only the cost of debt capital.

10.5 DETERMINATION OF THE COST OF EQUITY CAPITAL AND THE MARR

Equity capital is usually obtained from the following sources:

Sale of preferred stock or shares

Sale of common stock or shares

Use of retained earnings

The cost of each type of financing is estimated separately and entered into the WACC computation. A summary of one commonly accepted way to estimate each source's cost of capital is presented here. There are additional methods for estimating the cost of equity capital via common shares. *There are no tax savings for equity capital, because dividends paid to shareholders are not tax-deductible.*

Issuance of *preferred shares* carries with it a commitment to pay a stated dividend annually. The cost of capital is the stated dividend percentage, for example, 10%, or the dividend amount divided by the price of the shares. A $20 dividend paid on a $200 share is a 10% cost of equity capital. Preferred shares may be sold at a discount to speed the sale, in which case the actual proceeds from the shares should be used as the denominator. For example, if a 10% dividend preferred share with a value of $200 is sold at a 5% discount for $190 per share, there is a cost of equity capital of ($20/$190) × 100% = 10.53%.

Estimating the cost of equity capital for *common shares* is more involved. The dividends paid are not a true indication of what the share issue will actually cost in the future. Usually a valuation of the common shares is used to estimate the cost. If R_e is the cost of equity capital (in decimal form),

$$R_e = \frac{\text{first-year dividend}}{\text{price of shares}} + \text{expected dividend growth rate}$$

$$R_e = \frac{DV_1}{P} + g \qquad\qquad\qquad \textbf{[10.6]}$$

The growth rate g is an estimate of the annual increase in returns that the shareholders receive. Stated another way, it is the compound growth rate on dividends that the company believes is required to attract shareholders. For example, assume a multinational corporation plans to raise capital through its Canadian subsidiary for a new plant in South America by selling $2,500,000 worth of common shares valued at $20 each. If a 5% or $1 dividend is planned for the first year and an appreciation of 4% per year is anticipated for future dividends, the cost of capital for this common share issue from Equation [10.6] is 9%.

$$R_e = \frac{1}{20} + 0.04 = 0.09$$

The *retained earnings* cost of equity capital is usually set equal to the common shares cost, since it is the shareholders who will realize any returns from projects in which retained earnings are invested.

Once the cost of capital for all planned equity sources is estimated, the WACC is calculated using Equation [10.2].

A second method used to estimate the cost of common share capital is the *capital asset pricing model (CAPM)*. Because of the fluctuations in share prices and the higher return demanded by some corporations' shares compared to others, this valuation technique is commonly applied. The cost of equity capital from common shares R_e, using CAPM, is

$$R_e = \textbf{risk-free return} + \textbf{premium above risk-free return}$$
$$= R_f + \beta(R_m - R_f) \qquad\qquad \textbf{[10.7]}$$

where β = volatility of a company's shares relative to other shares in the market ($\beta = 1.0$ is the norm)

R_m = return on shares in a defined market portfolio measured by a prescribed index

The term R_f is usually the quoted Government of Canada Treasury bill rate, since it is considered a "safe investment." The term $(R_m - R_f)$ is the premium paid above the safe or risk-free rate. The coefficient β (beta) indicates how the stock is expected to vary compared to a selected portfolio of stocks in the same general market area. If $\beta < 1.0$, the stock is less volatile, so the resulting premium can be smaller; when $\beta > 1.0$, larger price movements are expected, so the premium is increased.

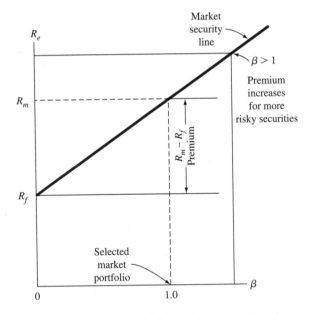

FIGURE 10–4

Expected return on common share issue using CAPM.

Security is a word which identifies a stock, bond, or any other instrument used to develop capital. To better understand how CAPM works, consider Figure 10–4. This is a plot of a market security line, which is a linear fit by regression analysis to indicate the expected return for different β values. When $\beta = 0$, the risk-free return R_f is acceptable (no premium). As β increases, the premium return requirement grows. Beta values are published periodically for most stock-issuing corporations. Once complete, this estimated cost of common stock equity capital can be included in the WACC computation in Equation [10.2].

EXAMPLE 10.5

The lead software engineer at SafeSoft, a food industry service corporation, has convinced the president to develop new software technology for the meat and food safety industry. It is envisioned that processes for prepared meats can be completed more safely and faster using this automated control software. A common share issue is a possibility to raise capital if the cost of equity capital is below 15%. SafeSoft, which has a historical beta value of 1.7, uses CAPM to determine the premium of its shares compared to other software corporations. The security market line indicates that a 5% premium above the risk-free rate is desirable. If Treasury bills are paying 4%, estimate the cost of common share capital.

Solution
The premium of 5% represents the term $R_m - R_f$ in Equation [10.7].

$$R_e = 4.0 + 1.7(5.0) = 12.5\%$$

Since this cost is lower than 15%, SafeSoft should issue common shares to finance this new venture.

In theory, a correctly performed engineering economy study uses a MARR equal to the cost of the capital committed to the specific alternatives in the study. Of course, such detail is not known. For a combination of debt and equity capital, the calculated WACC sets the minimum for the MARR. The most rational approach is to set MARR between the cost of equity capital and the corporation's WACC. The risks associated with an alternative should be treated separately from the MARR determination, as stated earlier. This supports the guideline that the MARR should not be arbitrarily increased to account for the various types of risk associated with the cash flow estimates. Unfortunately, the MARR is often set above the WACC because management does want to account for risk by increasing the MARR.

EXAMPLE 10.6

The Engineering Products Division of 4M Corporation has two mutually exclusive alternatives A and B with ROR values of $i_A^* = 9.2\%$ and $i_B^* = 5.9\%$. The financing scenario is yet unsettled, but it will be one of the following: plan 1—use all equity funds, which are currently earning 8% for the corporation; plan 2—use funds from the corporate capital pool, which is 25% debt capital costing 14.5% and the remainder from the same equity funds mentioned above. The cost of debt capital is currently high because the company has narrowly missed its projected revenue on common shares for the last two quarters, and banks have increased the borrowing rate for 4M. Make the economic decision on alternative A versus B under each financing scenario.

Solution

The capital is available for one of the two mutually exclusive alternatives. For plan 1, 100% equity, the financing is specifically known, so the cost of equity capital is the MARR, that is, 8%. Only alternative A is acceptable; alternative B is not since the estimated return of 5.9% does not exceed this MARR.

Under financing plan 2, with a D-E mix of 25–75,

$$WACC = 0.25(14.5) + 0.75(8.0) = 9.625\%$$

Now, neither alternative is acceptable, since both ROR values are less than MARR = WACC = 9.625%. The selected alternative should be to do nothing, unless one alternative absolutely must be selected, in which case noneconomic attributes must be considered.

10.6 EFFECT OF DEBT-EQUITY MIX ON INVESTMENT RISK

The D-E mix was introduced in Section 10.3. As the proportion of debt capital increases, the calculated cost of capital decreases due to the tax advantages of debt capital. *However, the leverage offered by larger debt capital percentages increases the riskiness of projects undertaken by the company.* When large debts are already present, additional financing using debt (or equity) sources gets more difficult to justify, and the corporation can be placed in a situation where it owns a smaller and smaller portion of itself. This is sometimes referred to as a *highly leveraged* corporation. Inability to obtain operating and investment capital means increased difficulty for the company and its projects. Thus, a reasonable balance between debt and equity financing is important for the financial health of a corporation. Example 10.7 illustrates the disadvantages of unbalanced D-E mixes.

EXAMPLE 10.7

Three manufacturing companies have the following debt and equity capital amounts and D-E mixes. Assume all equity capital is in the form of common shares.

| | Amount of Capital | | |
Company	Debt ($ in millions)	Equity ($ in millions)	D-E Mix (%–%)
A	10	40	20–80
B	20	20	50–50
C	40	10	80–20

Assume the annual revenue is $15 million for each one and that, after interest on debt is considered, the net incomes are $14.4, $13.4, and $10.0 million, respectively. Compute the return on common shares for each company, and comment on the return relative to the D-E mixes.

Solution
Divide the net income by the share (equity) amount to compute the common share return. In millions of dollars,

A: $\quad$ Return $= \dfrac{14.4}{40} = 0.36 \ (36\%)$

B: $\quad$ Return $= \dfrac{13.4}{20} = 0.67 \ (67\%)$

C: $\quad$ Return $= \dfrac{10.0}{10} = 1.00 \ (100\%)$

As expected, the return is by far the largest for highly leveraged C, where only 20% of the company is in the hands of the ownership. The return is excellent, but the risk associated with this firm is high compared to A, where the D-E mix is only 20% debt.

The use of large percentages of debt financing greatly *increases the risk* taken by lenders and share owners. Long-term confidence in the corporation diminishes, no matter how large the short-term return on shares.

The leverage of large D-E mixes does increase the return on *equity capital,* as shown in previous examples; but it can also work against the owners and investors. A small percentage decrease in asset value will more negatively affect a highly debt-leveraged investment compared to one with small leveraging. Example 10.8 illustrates this fact.

EXAMPLE 10.8

Two engineers place $10,000 each in different investments. Marylynn invests $10,000 in airline shares, and Carla leverages the $10,000 by purchasing a $100,000 residence to be used as rental property. Compute the resulting value of the $10,000 equity capital if there is a 5% decrease in the value of both the shares and the residence. Do the same for a 5% increase. Neglect any dividend, income, or tax considerations.

Solution

The airline share value decreases by 10,000(0.05) = $500, and the house value decreases by 100,000(0.05) = $5000. The effect is that a smaller amount of the $10,000 is returned, if the investment must be sold immediately.

Marylynn's loss: $\dfrac{500}{10,000} = 0.05$ (5%)

Carla's loss: $\dfrac{5000}{10,000} = 0.50$ (50%)

The 10-to-1 leveraging by Carla gives her a 50% decrease in the equity position, while Marylynn has only the 5% loss since there is no leveraging.

The opposite is correct for a 5% increase; Carla would benefit by a 50% gain on her $10,000, while Marylynn has only a 5% gain. The larger leverage is more risky. It offers a much *higher return for an increase* in the value of the investment and a much *larger loss for a decrease* in the value of the investment.

The same principles as discussed above for corporations are applicable to individuals. The person who is highly leveraged has large debts in terms of credit card balances, personal loans, and house mortgages. As an example, assume two engineers each have a take-home amount of $60,000 after all income tax, Canada pension plan, and insurance deductions from their annual salaries. Further, assume that the cost of the debt (money borrowed via credit cards and loans) averages 15% per year and that the current debt principal is being repaid in equal amounts over 20 years. If Jamal has a total debt of $25,000 and Barry owes $150,000, the remaining amount of the annual take-home pay may be calculated as follows:

Person	Total Debt, $	Cost of Debt at 15%, $	Repayment of Debt over 20-Year Period, $	Amount Remaining from $60,000, $
Jamal	25,000	3,750	1,250	55,000
Barry	150,000	22,500	7,500	30,000

Jamal has 91.7% of his base available while Barry has only 50% available.

10.7 MULTIPLE ATTRIBUTE ANALYSIS: IDENTIFICATION AND IMPORTANCE OF EACH ATTRIBUTE

In Chapter 1 the role and scope of engineering economy in decision making were outlined. The decision-making process explained in that chapter included the seven steps listed on the right side of Figure 10–5. Step 4 is to identify the

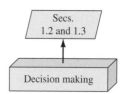

FIGURE 10–5

Expansion of the decision-making process to include multiple attributes.

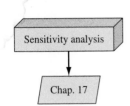

Sensitivity analysis

Chap. 17

Consider multiple attributes

Emphasis on one attribute

1. Understand the problem; define the objective.
2. Collect relevant information.
3. Define alternatives; make estimates.

4-1. Identify the attributes for decision making.
4-2. Determine the relative importance (weights) of attributes.
4-3. For each alternative, determine each attribute's value rating.

4. Identify the selection criteria (one or more attributes).

5. Evaluate each alternative using a multiple-attribute technique. Use sensitivity analysis for key attributes.

5. Evaluate each alternative; use sensitivity analysis.

6. Select the best alternative.
7. Implement the solution and monitor results.

one or multiple attributes upon which the selection criteria are based. In all prior evaluations in this text, only one attribute—the economic one—has been identified and used to select the best alternative. The criterion has been the maximization of the equivalent value of PW, AW, ROR, or the B-C ratio. As we are all aware, most evaluations do and should take into account multiple attributes in decision making. These are the factors labelled as noneconomic at the bottom of Figure 1–1, which describes the primary elements in performing an engineering economy study. However, these noneconomic dimensions tend to be intangible and often difficult, if not impossible, to quantify directly with economic and other scales. Nonetheless, among the many attributes that can be identified, there are key ones that must be considered in earnest before the alternative selection process is complete.

Multiple attributes enter into the decision-making process in many studies. Public sector projects are excellent examples of multiple-attribute problem solving. For example, the proposal to construct a dam to form a lake in a low-lying area or to widen the catch basin of a river usually has several purposes, such as flood control, drinking water, industrial use, commercial development, recreation, and nature conservation for fish, plants, and birds. High levels of complexity are introduced into the selection process by the multiple attributes thought to be important in selecting an alternative for the dam's location, design, and environmental impact.

The left side of Figure 10–5 expands steps 4 and 5 to consider multiple attributes. The discussion below concentrates on the expanded step 4, and the next section focuses on the evaluation measure and alternative selection of step 5.

4-1 Attribute Identification   Attributes to be considered in the evaluation methodology can be identified and defined by several methods, some much better than others depending upon the situation surrounding the study itself. To seek input from individuals other than the analyst is important; it helps focus the study on key attributes. The following is an incomplete listing of ways in which key attributes are identified.

- Comparison with similar studies that include multiple attributes
- Input from experts with relevant past experience
- Surveys of constituencies (customers, employees, managers) impacted by the alternatives
- Small group discussions using approaches such as focus groups, brainstorming, or nominal group technique
- The Delphi method, which is a progressive procedure to develop reasoned consensus from different perspectives and opinions

As an illustration, Air Canada has decided to purchase 18 more Boeing 777-300 ERs for overseas flights, primarily between the west coast and Asian cities, principally Hong Kong, Tokyo, and Shanghai. There are approximately 8000 options for each plane that must be decided upon by engineering, purchasing, maintenance, and marketing personnel at Air Canada before the order to Boeing is placed. Options range in scope from the material and colour of the plane's interior to the type of latching devices used on the engine cowlings, and in function from maximum engine thrust to pilot instrument design. An economic study based on the equivalent AW of the estimated passenger income per trip has determined that 150 of these options are clearly advantageous. But other noneconomic attributes are to be considered before some of the more expensive options are specified. A Delphi study was performed using input from 25 individuals. Concurrently, option choices for another, unidentified airline's recent order were shared with Air Canada personnel. From these two studies it was determined that there are 10 key attributes for options selection. Four of the most important attributes are

- *Repair time:* mean time to repair or replace (MTTR) if the option is or affects a flight-critical component.
- *Safety:* mean time to failure (MTTF) of flight-critical components.
- *Economic:* estimated extra revenue for the option. (Basically, this is the attribute evaluated by the economy study already performed.)
- *Crewmember needs:* some measure of the necessity and/or benefits of the option as judged by representative crewmembers—pilots and attendants.

The economic attribute of extra revenue may be considered an indirect measure of customer satisfaction, one that is more quantitative than customer opinion/ satisfaction survey results. Of course, many other attributes can be, and are, used. However, the point is that the economic study may directly address only one or a few of the key attributes vital to alternative decision making.

An attribute routinely identified by individuals and groups is *risk*. Actually, risk is not a stand-alone attribute, because it is a part of every attribute in one form or another. Considerations of variation, probabilistic estimates, etc., in the decision-making process are treated later in this text. Formalized sensitivity analysis, expected values, simulation, and decision trees are some of the techniques useful in handling the risk inherent in an attribute.

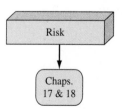

4-2 Importance (Weights) for the Attributes   Determination of the *extent of importance* for each attribute *i* results in a weight W_i that is incorporated into the final evaluation measure. The weight, a number between 0 and 1, is based upon the experienced opinion of one individual or a group of persons familiar with the attributes, and possibly the alternatives. If a group is utilized to determine the weights, there must be consensus among the members for each weight. Otherwise, some averaging technique must be applied to arrive at one weight value for each attribute.

Table 10–3 is a tabular layout of attributes and alternatives used to perform a multiple attribute evaluation. Weights W_i for each attribute are entered on the left side. The remainder of the table is discussed as we proceed through steps 4 and 5 of the expanded decision-making process.

Attribute weights are usually normalized such that their sum over all the alternatives is 1.0. This normalizing implies that each attribute's importance score is divided by the sum *S* over all attributes. Expressed in formula form, these two properties of weights for attribute *i* ($i = 1, 2, \ldots, m$) are

$$\text{Normalized weights: } \sum_{i=1}^{m} W_i = 1.0 \qquad [10.8]$$

$$\text{Weight calculation: } W_i = \frac{\text{importance score}_i}{\sum_{i=1}^{m} \text{importance score}_i} = \frac{\text{importance score}_i}{S} \qquad [10.9]$$

Of the many procedures developed to assign weights to an attribute, an analyst is likely to rely upon one which is relatively simple, such as equal weighting, rank order, or weighted rank order. Each is briefly presented below.

Equal Weighting   All attributes are considered to be of approximately the same importance, or there is no rationale to distinguish the more important from the less important attribute. This is the default approach. Each weight in Table 10–3 will be $1/m$, according to Equation [10.9]. Alternatively, the normalizing can be

TABLE 10–3   Tabular Layout of Attributes and Alternatives Used for Multiple-Attribute Evaluation

		Alternatives				
Attributes	Weights	1	2	3	$\cdots$	n
1	W_1					
2	W_2					
3	W_3		Value ratings V_{ij}			
.	.					
.	.					
.	.					
m	W_m					

omitted, in which case each weight is 1 and their sum is m. In this case, the final evaluation measure for an alternative will be the sum over all attributes.

Rank Order   The m attributes are placed (ranked) in order of increasing importance with a score of 1 assigned to the least important and m assigned to the most important. By Equation [10.9], the weights follow the pattern $1/S, 2/S, \ldots, m/S$. With this method, the difference in weights between attributes of increasing importance is constant.

Weighted Rank Order   The m attributes are again placed in the order of increasing importance. However, now differentiation between attributes is possible. The most important attribute is assigned a score, usually 100, and all other attributes are scored relative to it between 100 and 0. Now, define the score for each attribute as s_i, and Equation [10.9] takes the form

$$W_i = \frac{s_i}{\sum_{i=1}^{m} s_i} \qquad\qquad [10.10]$$

This is a very practical method to determine weights because one or more attributes can be heavily weighted if they are significantly more important than the remaining ones, and Equation [10.10] automatically normalizes the weights. For example, suppose the four key attributes in the previous aircraft purchase example are ordered: safety, repair time, crewmember needs, and economic. If repair time is only half as important as safety, and the last two attributes are each half as important as repair time, the scores and weights are as follows.

Attribute	Score	Weights
Safety	100	$100/200 = 0.50$
Repair time	50	$50/200 = 0.25$
Crewmember needs	25	$25/200 = 0.125$
Economic	25	$25/200 = 0.125$
Sum of scores and weights	200	1.000

There are other attribute weighting techniques, especially for group processes, such as utility functions, pairwise comparison, and others. These become increasingly sophisticated, but they are able to provide an advantage that these simple methods do not afford the analyst: *consistency of ranks and scores* between attributes and between individuals. If this consistency is important in that several decision makers with diverse opinions about attribute importance are involved in a study, a more sophisticated technique may be warranted. There is substantial literature on this topic.

4-3 Value Rating of Each Alternative, by Attribute   This is the final step prior to calculating the evaluation measure. Each alternative is awarded a value rating V_{ij} for each attribute i. These are the entries within the cells in Table 10–3. The ratings are appraisals by decision makers of how well an alternative will perform as each attribute is considered.

TABLE 10–4   Completed Layout for Four Attributes and Three Alternatives for Multiple-Attribute Evaluation

Attributes	Weights	Alternatives		
		1	2	3
Safety	0.50	6	4	8
Repair	0.25	9	3	1
Crew needs	0.125	5	6	6
Economic	0.125	5	9	7

The scale for the value rating can vary depending upon what is easiest to understand for those who do the valuation. A scale of 0 to 100 can be used for attribute importance scoring. However, the most popular is a scale of 4 or 5 gradations about the perceived ability of an alternative to accomplish the intent of the attribute. This is called a *Likert scale,* which can have descriptions for the gradations (e.g., very poor, poor, good, very good), or numbers assigned between 0 and 10, or -1 to $+1$, or -2 to $+2$. The last two scales can give a negative impact to the evaluation measure for poor alternatives. An example numerical scale of 0 to 10 is as follows:

If You Value the Alternative As:	Give It a Rating Between the Numbers:
Very poor	0–2
Poor	3–5
Good	6–8
Very good	9–10

It is preferable to have a Likert scale with four choices (an even number) so that the central tendency of "fair" is not overrated.

If we now build upon the aircraft purchase illustration to include value ratings, the cells are filled with ratings awarded by a decision maker. Table 10–4 includes example ratings V_{ij} and the weights W_i determined above. Initially, there will be one such table for each decision maker. Prior to calculating the final evaluation measure R_j, the ratings can be combined in some fashion; or a different R_j can be calculated using each decision maker's ratings. Determination of this evaluation measure is discussed below.

10.8   EVALUATION MEASURE FOR MULTIPLE ATTRIBUTES

The need for an evaluation measure that accommodates multiple attributes is indicated in step 5 of Figure 10–5. This measure should be a single-dimension number that effectively combines the different dimensions addressed by the attribute importance scores W_i and the alternative value ratings V_{ij}. The result is a formula to calculate an aggregated measure that can be used to select from two or more alternatives. The result is often referred to as a *rank-and-rate method.*

This reduction process removes much of the complexity of trying to balance the different attributes; however, it also eliminates much of the robust information captured by the process of ranking attributes for their importance and rating each alternative's performance against each attribute.

There are additive, multiplicative, and exponential measures, but by far the most commonly applied is the additive model. The most used additive model is the *weighted attribute method*. The evaluation measure, symbolized by R_j for each alternative j, is defined as

$$R_j = \sum_{j=1}^{n} W_i V_{ij}$$ [10.11]

The W_i numbers are the attribute importance weights, and V_{ij} is the value rating by attribute i for each alternative j. If the attributes are of equal weight (also called unweighted), all $W_i = 1/m$, as determined by Equation [10.9]. This means that W_i can be moved outside of the summation in the formula for R_j. (If an equal weight of $W_i = 1.0$ is used for all attributes, in lieu of $1/m$, then the R_j value is simply the sum of all ratings for the alternative.)

The selection guideline is as follows:

Choose the alternative with the largest R_j value. This measure assumes that increasing weights W_i mean more important attributes and increasing ratings V_{ij} mean better performance of an alternative.

Sensitivity analysis for any score, weight, or value rating is used to determine sensitivity of the decision to it.

EXAMPLE 10.9

An interactive regional dispatching and scheduling system for trains has been in place for several years at MB+O Railroad. Management and dispatchers alike agree it is time for an updated software system, and possibly new hardware. Discussions have led to three alternatives:

1. Purchase new hardware and develop new customized software in-house.
2. Lease new hardware and use an outside contractor for software services.
3. Develop new software using an outside contractor, and upgrade specific hardware components for the new software.

Six attributes for alternative comparison have been defined using a Delphi process involving decision makers from dispatching, field operations, and train engineering.

1. Initial investment requirement
2. Annual cost of hardware and software maintenance
3. Response time to "collision conditions"
4. User interface for dispatching
5. On-train software interface
6. Software system interface with other company dispatching systems

TABLE 10–5	Attribute Scores and Alternative Ratings for Multiple-Attribute Evaluation, Example 10.9			

		Value Ratings (0 to 100), V_{ij}		
Attribute i	Importance Score	Alternative 1	Alternative 2	Alternative 3
1	50	75	50	100
2	100	60	75	100
3	100	50	100	20
4	80	100	90	40
5	50	85	100	10
6	70	100	100	75
Total	450			

Attribute scores developed by the decision makers are shown in Table 10–5, using a weighted rank-order procedure with scores between 0 and 100. Attributes 2 and 3 are considered equally the most important attributes; a score of 100 is assigned to them. Once each alternative had been detailed enough to judge the capabilities from the system specifications, a three-person group placed value ratings on the three alternatives, again using a rating scale of 0 to 100 (Table 10–5). As an example, for alternative 3, the economics are excellent (scores of 100 for both attributes 1 and 2), but the on-train software interface is considered very poor, thus the low rating of 10. Use these scores and ratings to determine which alternative is the best to pursue.

Solution

Table 10–6 includes the normalized weights for each attribute determined by Equation [10.9]; the total is 1.0, as required. The evaluation measure R_j for the weighted attribute method is obtained by applying Equation [10.11] in each alternative column. For alternative 1,

$$R_1 = 0.11(75) + 0.22(60) + \cdots + 0.16(100) = 75.9$$

TABLE 10–6	Results for the Weighted-Attribute Method, Example 10.9			

		$R_j = W_i V_{ij}$		
Attribute i	Normalized Weight W_i	Alternative 1	Alternative 2	Alternative 3
1	0.11	8.3	5.5	11.0
2	0.22	13.2	16.5	22.0
3	0.22	11.0	22.0	4.4
4	0.18	18.0	16.2	7.2
5	0.11	9.4	11.0	1.1
6	0.16	16.0	16.0	12.0
Totals	1.00	75.9	87.2	57.7

When the totals are reviewed for the largest measure, alternative 2 is the best choice at $R_2 = 87.2$. Further detailing of this alternative should be recommended to management.

Comment
Any economic measure can be incorporated into a multiple-attribute evaluation using this method. All measures of worth—PW, AW, ROR, BCA—can be included; however, their impact on the final selection will vary relative to the importance placed on the noneconomic attributes.

CHAPTER SUMMARY

The best method to economically evaluate and compare mutually exclusive alternatives is usually either the AW or PW method at the stated MARR. The choice depends, in part, upon the equal lives or unequal lives of the alternatives, and the pattern of the estimated cash flows, as summarized in Table 10–1. Public sector projects are best compared using BCA, but the economic equivalency is still AW- or PW-based. Once the evaluation method is selected, Table 10–2 (also printed at the rear of the text with section references) can be used to determine the elements and decision guideline that must be implemented to correctly perform the study. If the estimated ROR for the selected alternative is needed, it is advisable to determine i^* by using the IRR function on a spreadsheet after the AW or PW method has indicated the best alternative.

The interest rate at which the MARR is established depends principally upon the cost of capital and the mix between debt and equity financing. The MARR should be set equal to the weighted average cost of capital (WACC). Risk, profit, and other factors can be considered after the AW, PW, or ROR analysis is completed and prior to final alternative selection.

If multiple attributes, which include more than the economic dimension of a study, are to be considered in making the alternative decision, first the attributes must be identified and their relative importance assessed. Then each alternative can be value-rated for each attribute. The evaluation measure is determined using a model such as the weighted attribute method, where the measure is calculated by Equation [10.11]. The largest value indicates the best alternative.

PROBLEMS

Choosing the Evaluation Method

10.1 When two or more alternatives are compared using the PW, AW, or BCA, there are three circumstances for which the length of time of the evaluation period is the same for all alternatives. List these three circumstances.

10.2 For what evaluation methods is it mandatory that an incremental cash flow series analysis be performed to ensure that the correct alternative is selected?

10.3 Explain what is meant by the decision guideline to choose the "numerically largest value" when selecting the one best mutually exclusive alternative from two or more alternatives.

10.4 For the following situation, (*a*) determine which evaluation method is probably the easiest and fastest to apply by hand and by computer in order to select from the five alternatives and (*b*) answer the two questions, using your chosen evaluation method.

An independent dirt contractor must determine which size dump truck to buy. The cash flows estimated with each size truck bed are tabulated. The MARR is 18% per year, and all alternatives are expected to have a useful life of 8 years. (1) What size truck bed should be purchased? (2) If two trucks are to be purchased, what should be the size of the second truck?

Truck Bed Size, Cubic Metres	Initial Investment, $	AOC, $/Year	Salvage Value, $	Annual Revenue, $/Year
8	−10,000	−4,000	+2,000	+6,500
10	−14,000	−5,500	+2,500	+10,000
15	−18,000	−7,000	+3,000	+14,000
20	−24,000	−11,000	+3,500	+20,500
25	−33,000	−16,000	+6,000	+26,500

10.5 Read Problem 9.26. (*a*) Determine which evaluation method is probably the easiest and fastest to apply by hand and by computer in order to select from the two alternatives. (*b*) If the evaluation method you chose is different from that used in Chapter 9, solve the problem using your chosen evaluation method.

10.6 For what type of alternatives should the capitalized cost method be used for comparison? Give several examples of these types of projects.

Working with MARR

10.7 After 15 years of employment in the airline industry, John started his own consulting company to use physical and computer simulation in the analysis of commercial airport accidents on runways. He estimates his average cost of new capital at 8% per year for physical simulation projects, that is, where he physically reconstructs the accident using scale versions of planes, buildings, vehicles, etc. He has established 12% per year as his MARR.

(*a*) What (net) rate of return on capital investments for physical simulation does he expect?

(*b*) John was recently offered an international project that he considers risky in that the information available is sketchy and the airport personnel do not appear to be willing to cooperate on the investigation. John considers this risk to be economically worth at least an added 5% return on his money. What is the recommended MARR in this situation, based upon what you have learned in this chapter? How should John consider the required return and perceived risk factors when evaluating this project opportunity?

10.8 State whether each of the following involves debt financing or equity financing.

(*a*) A bond issue for $3,500,000 by a city-owned utility

(*b*) An initial public offering (IPO) of $35,000,000 in common shares for a dot-com company

(c) $25,000 taken from your retirement account to pay cash for a new car

(d) A homeowner's equity loan for $25,000

10.9 Explain how the opportunity cost sets the effective MARR when, because of limited capital, only one alternative can be selected from two or more.

10.10 An engineering manager at Cenovus Energy wants to complete an alternative evaluation study. If all projects have to clear their average (pooled) cost by at least 4%, determine the minimum MARR.

Funds Source	Amount, $	Average Cost, $
Retained earnings	4 million	7.4
Stock sales	6 million	4.8
Long-term loans	5 million	9.8
Budgeted funds for project	15 million	

10.11 The initial investment and incremental ROR values for four mutually exclusive alternatives are indicated below. Select the best alternative if a maximum of (a) $300,000, (b) $400,000, and (c) $700,000 in capital funds is available and the MARR is the cost of capital, which is estimated at 9% per year. (d) What is the de facto MARR for these alternatives if no specific MARR is stated, the available capital is $400,000, and the opportunity cost interpretation is applied?

Alternative	Initial Investment, $	Incremental Rate of Return, %	Alternative Rate of Return, %
1	−100,000	8.8 for 1 to DN	8.8
2	−250,000	12.5 for 2 to DN	12.5
3	−400,000	11.3 for 3 to 2	14.0
4	−550,000	8.1 for 4 to 3	10.0

10.12 State the recommended approach in establishing the MARR when other factors, such as alternative risk, taxes, and market fluctuations are considered in addition to the cost of capital.

10.13 A partnership of four engineers operates a duplex rental business. Five years ago they purchased a block of duplexes, using a MARR of 14% per year. The estimated return at that time for the duplexes was 15% per year, but the investment was considered very risky due to the poor rental business economy in the city and state overall. Nonetheless, the purchase was made with 100% equity financing at a cost of 10% per year. Fortunately, the return has averaged 18% per year over the 5 years. Another purchase opportunity for more duplexes has now presented itself, but a loan at 8% per year would have to be taken to make the investment. (a) If the economy for rental property has not changed significantly, is there likely to be a tendency to now make the MARR higher than, lower than, or the same as that used previously? Why? (b) What is the recommended way to consider the rental business economy risk now that debt capital would be involved?

D-E Mix and WACC

10.14 A new cross-country, transmountain range natural gas pipeline needs to be built at an estimated first cost of $200,000,000. The consortium of cooperating companies has not fully decided the financial arrangements of this adventurous project. The WACC for similar projects has averaged 10% per year.

(a) Two financing alternatives have been identified. The first requires an investment of 60% equity funds at 12% and a loan for the balance at an interest rate of 9% per year. The second alternative requires only 20% equity funds and the balance obtained by a massive international loan estimated to carry an interest cost of 12.5% per year, which is, in part, based on the geographic location of the pipeline. Which financing plan will result in the smaller average cost of capital?

(b) If the consortium CFOs have decided that the WACC must not exceed the 5-year historical average of 10% per year, what is the maximum loan interest acceptable for each financing alternative?

10.15 A couple is planning ahead for their child's college education. They can fund part or all of the expected $100,000 tuition cost from their own funds or borrow all or part of it. The expected return for their own funds is 8% per year, but the loan is expected to have higher interest rates as the amount of the loan increases. Use a spreadsheet generated plot of the WACC curve and the estimated loan interest rates below to determine the best D-E mix for the couple.

Loan Amount, $	Estimated Interest Rate, % per Year
10,000	7.0
25,000	7.5
50,000	9.0
60,000	10.0
75,000	12.0
100,000	18.0

10.16 Tiffany Baking Co. wants to arrange for $50 million in capital for manufacturing a new consumer product. The current financing plan is 60% equity capital and 40% debt financing. Compute the WACC for the following financing scenario.

Equity capital. 60%, or $35 million, via common shares sales for 40% of this amount that will pay dividends at a rate of 5% per year, and the remaining 60% from retained earnings, which currently earn 9% per year.

Debt capital. 40%, or $15 million, obtained through two sources— bank loans for $10 million borrowed at 8% per year, and the remainder in convertible bonds at an estimated 10% per year bond interest rate.

10.17 The possible D-E mixes and costs of debt and equity capital for a new project are summarized below. Use the data (a) to plot the curves for debt, equity, and weighted average costs of capital and (b) to determine what mix of debt and equity capital will result in the lowest WACC.

	Debt Capital		Equity Capital	
Plan	Percentage	Rate, %	Percentage	Rate, %
1	100	14.5		
2	70	13.0	30	7.8
3	65	12.0	35	7.8
4	50	11.5	50	7.9
5	35	9.9	65	9.8
6	20	12.4	80	12.5
7			100	12.5

10.18 For Problem 10.17, use a spreadsheet to (a) determine the best D-E mix and (b) determine the best D-E mix if the cost of debt capital increases by 10% per year.

10.19 Brantford Industries, Ltd., is considering two plans to buy out a rival firm. Plan A requires 50% equity funds from Brantford retained earnings that currently earn 9% per year, with the balance borrowed externally at 6%, based on the company's excellent stock rating. Plan B requires only 20% equity funds, with the balance borrowed at a higher rate of 8% per year.

(a) Which plan has the lower average cost of capital?

(b) If the current corporate WACC of 8.2% will not be exceeded, what is the maximum cost of debt capital allowed for each plan? Are those rates higher or lower than the current estimates?

10.20 A public corporation in which you own common shares reported a WACC of 10.7% for the year in its annual report to shareholders. The common shares that you own have averaged a total return of 6% per year over the last 3 years. The annual report also mentions that projects within the corporation are 80% funded by its own capital. Estimate the company's cost of debt capital. Does this seem like a reasonable rate for borrowed funds?

10.21 To understand the advantage of debt capital from a tax perspective, determine the before-tax and after-tax weighted average costs of capital if a project is funded 40%–60% with debt capital borrowed at 9% per year. Assume that corporate equity funds earn 12% per year and that the effective tax rate is 35% for the year.

Cost of Debt Capital

10.22 Bristol Myers Squibb, an international pharmaceutical company, is initiating a new project for which it requires $2.5 million in debt capital. The current plan is to sell 20-year bonds that pay 4.2% per year, payable quarterly, at a 3% discount on the face value. BMS has an effective tax rate of 35% per year. Determine (a) the total face value of the bonds required to obtain $2.5 million and (b) the effective annual after-tax cost of debt capital.

10.23 The Sullivans' plan to purchase a refurbished condo in their parents' hometown for investment purposes. The negotiated $200,000 purchase price will be financed with 20% of their savings which consistently make 6.5% per year after all relevant income taxes are paid. Eighty percent will be borrowed at 9% per year for 15 years with the principal repaid in equal annual installments. If their effective tax rate is 22% per year, based only on these data, answer the following. (*Note*: The 9% rate on the loan is a before-tax rate.)

(a) What is the Sullivans' annual loan payment for each of the 15 years?

(b) What is the net present worth difference between the $200,000 now and the PW of the cost of the 80–20 D-E mix series of cash flows necessary to finance the purchase? What does this number mean?

(c) What is the Sullivans' after-tax WACC for this purchase?

10.24 An engineer is working on a design project for a plastics manufacturing company that has an after-tax cost of equity capital of 6% per year for retained earnings that may be used to 100% equity finance the project. An alternative financing strategy is to issue $4 million worth of 10-year bonds that will pay 8% per year interest on a quarterly basis. If the effective tax rate is 40%, which funding source has the lower cost of capital?

10.25 Bowden Gas Processors expects to borrow $800,000 for field engineering improvements. Two methods of debt financing are possible—borrow it all from a bank or issue debenture bonds. The company will pay an effective 8% compounded per year for 8 years to the bank. The principal on the loan will be reduced uniformly over the 8 years, with the remainder of each annual payment going toward interest. The bond issue will be 800 10-year bonds of $1000 each that require a 6% per year interest payment.

(a) Which method of financing is cheaper after an effective tax rate of 40% is considered?

(b) What is the cheaper method using a before-tax analysis?

Cost of Equity Capital

10.26 Common shares issued by Henry Harmon Builders paid shareholders $0.93 per share on an average price of $18.80 last year. The company expects to grow the dividend rate at a maximum of 1.5% per year. The stock volatility of 1.19 is somewhat higher than that of other public firms in the construction industry, and other stocks in this market are paying an average of 4.95% per year dividend. Treasury bills are returning 4.5%. Determine the company's cost of equity capital last year, using (a) the dividend method and (b) the CAPM.

10.27 Wholesome Chickens expects to use a D-E mix of 60%–40% to finance a $10 million effort for improved equipment, engineering, and quality control. After-tax cost of debt capital for loans is known to be 9.5% per year. However, obtaining sufficient equity capital will require the sale of common shares, as well as the commitment of corporate retained earnings. Use the following information to determine the WACC for the implementation of the plan.

Common shares: 100,000

Anticipated price = $32 per share

Initial dividend = $1.10 per share

Dividend growth per share = 2% annually

Retained earnings: same cost of capital as for common shares

10.28 An engineering graduate plans to purchase a new car. He has not decided how to pay the purchase price of $28,000 for the model he has selected. He has the total available in a savings account, so paying cash is an option; however, this would deplete virtually all his savings. These funds return an average of 6% per year, compounded every 6 months. Perform a before-tax analysis to determine which of the three financing plans below has the lowest WACC.

Plan 1: D-E is 50%–50%. Use $14,000 from the savings account and borrow $14,000 at a rate of 7% per year, compounded monthly. The difference between the payments and the savings would be deposited at 6% per year, compounded semi-annually.

Plan 2: 100% equity. Take $28,000 from savings now.

Plan 3: 100% debt. Borrow $28,000 now from the credit union at an effective rate of 0.75% per month, and repay the loan at $581.28 per month for 60 months.

10.29 Three projects have been identified. Capital will be developed 70% from debt sources at an average rate of 7.0% per year and 30% from equity sources at 10.34% per year. Set the MARR equal to WACC and make the economic decision, if the projects are (a) independent and (b) mutually exclusive.

Project	Initial Investment, $	Annual Net Cash Flow, $/Year	Salvage Value, $	Life, Years
1	−25,000	6,000	4,000	4
2	−30,000	9,000	−1,000	4
3	−50,000	15,000	20,000	4

10.30 The federal government imposes requirements upon industry in many areas, such as employee safety, pollution control, environmental protection, and noise control. One view of these regulations is that their compliance tends to decrease the return on investment and/or increase the cost of capital to the corporation. In many cases the economics of these regulated compliances cannot be evaluated as regular engineering economy alternatives. Use your knowledge of engineering economic analysis to explain how an engineer might economically evaluate alternatives that define the ways in which the company will comply with imposed regulations.

Different D-E Mixes

10.31 Why is it financially unhealthy for an individual to maintain a large percentage of debt financing over a long period of time, that is, to be highly debt-leveraged?

10.32 Fairmont Industries primarily relies on 100% equity financing to fund projects. A good opportunity is available that will require $250,000 in capital. The Fairmont owner can supply the money from personal investments that currently earn an average of 8.5% per year. The annual net cash flow from the project is estimated at $30,000 for the next 15 years. Alternatively, 60% of the required amount can be borrowed for 15 years at 9% per year. If the MARR is the WACC, determine which plan, if either, is better. This is a before-tax analysis.

10.33 Cott Corp. has different methods by which a $600,000 project can be funded, using debt and equity capital. A net cash flow of $90,000 per year is estimated for 7 years.

Type of Financing	Financing Plan, %			Cost per Year, %
	1	2	3	
Debt	20	50	60	10
Equity	80	50	40	7.5

Determine the rate of return for each plan, and identify the ones that are economically acceptable if (a) MARR equals the cost of equity capital, (b) MARR equals the WACC, or (c) MARR is halfway between the cost of equity capital and the WACC.

10.34 Mosaic Software has an opportunity to invest $10,000,000 in a new engineering remote-control system for offshore drilling platforms. Financing for Mosaic will be split between common share sales ($5,000,000) and a loan with an 8% per year interest rate. Mosaic's share of the annual net cash flow is estimated to be $2.0 million for each of the next 6 years. Mosaic is about to initiate CAPM as its common share evaluation model. Recent analysis shows that it has a volatility rating of 1.05 and is paying a premium of 5% common share dividend. Treasury bills are currently paying 4% per year. Is the venture financially attractive if the MARR equals (a) the cost of equity capital and (b) the WACC?

10.35 Draw the general shape of the three cost of capital curves (debt, equity, and WACC), using the form of Figure 10–2. Draw them under the condition that a high D-E mix has been present for some time for the corporation. Explain via your graph and words the movement of the minimum WACC point under historically high leveraged D-E mixes. *Hint:* High D-E mixes cause the debt cost to increase substantially. This makes it harder to obtain equity funds, so the cost of equity capital also increases.

10.36 In a leveraged buyout of one company by another, the purchasing company usually obtains borrowed money and inserts as little of its own equity funds as possible into the purchase. Explain some circumstances under which such a buy-out may put the purchasing company at economic risk.

Multiple-Attribute Evaluation

10.37 A committee of four people submitted the following statements about the attributes to be used in a weighted attribute method. Use the statements to determine the normalized weights if scores are assigned between 0 and 10.

Attribute	Comment
1. Flexibility	The most important factor
2. Safety	50% as important as uptime
3. Uptime	One-half as important as flexibility
4. Speed	As important as uptime
5. Rate of return	Twice as important as safety

10.38 Different types and capacities of crawler hoes are being considered for use in a major excavation on a pipe-laying project. Several supervisors on similar projects of the past have identified some of the attributes and their views of the importance of an attribute. The information has been shared with you. Determine the weighted rank order, using a 0 to 100 scale and the normalized weights.

Attribute	Comment
1. Truck versus hoe loading height	Vitally important factor
2. Type of topsoil	Usually only 10% of the problem
3. Type of soil below topsoil	One-half as important as matching trenching and laying speeds
4. Hoe cycle time	About 75% as important as soil type below topsoil
5. Match hoe trenching speed to pipe-laying speed	As important as attribute number one

10.39 You graduated 2 years ago, and you plan to purchase a new car. For three different models you have evaluated the initial cost and estimated annual costs for fuel and maintenance. You also evaluated the styling of each car in your role as a young engineering professional. List some additional factors (tangible and intangible) that might be used in your version of the weighted attribute method.

10.40 (*Note to instructor:* This and the next two problems may be assigned as a progressive exercise.) John, who works at Advent Electronics, has decided to use the weighted attribute method to compare three systems for manufacturing capacitors. The vice-president and her assistant have evaluated each of three attributes in terms of importance to them, and John has placed an evaluation from 0 to 100 on each alternative for the three attributes. John's *ratings* are as follows:

	Alternatives		
Attribute	1	2	3
Economic return > MARR	50	70	100
High throughput	100	60	30
Low scrap rate	100	40	50

Use the *weights* below to evaluate the alternatives. Are the results the same for the two persons' weights? Why?

Importance Score	VP	Assistant VP
Economic return > MARR	20	100
High throughput	80	80
Low scrap rate	100	20

10.41 In Problem 10.40 the vice-president and assistant vice-president are not consistent in their weights of the three attributes.

Assume you are a consultant asked to assist John.

(a) What are some conclusions you can draw about the weighted attribute method as an alternative selection method, given the alternative ratings and results in Problem 10.40?

(b) Use the new alternative ratings below that you have developed yourself to select an alternative. Using the same scores as the vice-president and her assistant given in Problem 10.40, comment on any differences in the alternative selected.

(c) What do your new alternative ratings tell you about the selections based on the importance scores of the vice-president and assistant vice-president?

Attribute	Alternatives		
	1	2	3
Economic return > MARR	30	40	100
High throughput	70	100	70
Low scrap rate	100	80	90

10.42 The capacitor division discussed in Problems 10.40 and 10.41 has just been fined $1 million for environmental pollution due to the poor quality of its discharge water. Also, John has become the vice-president, and there is no longer an assistant vice-president. John always agreed with the importance scores of the former assistant vice-president and the alternative ratings he developed earlier (those present initially in Problem 10.40). If he adds his own importance score of 80 to the new factor of environmental cleanliness and awards alternatives 1, 2, and 3 ratings of 80, 50, and 20, respectively, for this new factor,

redo the evaluation to select the best alternative.

10.43 For Example 10.9, use an equal weighting of 1 for each attribute to choose the alternative. Did the weighting of attributes change the selected alternative?

10.44 The Athlete's Shop has evaluated two proposals for weightlifting and exercise equipment. A present worth analysis at $i = 15\%$ of estimated incomes and costs resulted in $PW_A = \$420,500$ and $PW_B = \$392,800$. In addition to this economic measure, three attributes were independently assigned a relative importance score from 0 to 100 by the shop manager and the lead trainer.

Attribute	Importance Score	
	Manager	Trainer
Economics	100	80
Durability	35	10
Flexibility	20	100
Maintainability	20	10

Separately, you have used the four attributes to rate the two equipment proposals on a scale of 0.0 to 1.0. The economic attribute was rated using the PW values.

Attribute	Proposal A	Proposal B
Economics	1.00	0.90
Durability	0.35	1.00
Flexibility	1.00	0.90
Maintainability	0.25	1.00

Select the better proposal, using each of the following methods.

(a) Present worth

(b) Weighted evaluations of the manager

(c) Weighted evaluations of the lead trainer

EXTENDED EXERCISE

EMPHASIZING THE RIGHT THINGS

The City of Vancouver is looking at proposals to stem increasing crime rates in a downtown neighbourhood. In phase I of the effort, the police chief has made and preliminarily examined four proposals of ways in which police surveillance and protection may be provided in the target residential areas. In brief, they are putting additional officers in cars, on bicycles, on foot, or on horseback. Each alternative has been evaluated separately to estimate annual costs. Putting six new officers on bicycles is clearly the least expensive option at an estimated $700,000 per year. The next best is on foot, with 10 new officers at $925,000 per year. The other alternatives will cost slightly more than the "on foot" option.

Before entering phase II, which is a 3-month pilot study to test one or two of these approaches in the neighbourhoods, a committee of five members (comprising police staff and citizen-residents) has been asked to help determine and prioritize attributes that are important in this decision to them, as representatives of the residents and police officers. The five attributes agreed upon after 2 months of discussion are listed below, followed by each committee member's ordering of the attributes from the most important (a score of 1) to the least important (a score of 5).

	Committee Member					
Attribute	1	2	3	4	5	Sum
A. Ability to get "close" to the citizenry	4	5	3	4	5	21
B. Annual cost	3	4	1	2	4	14
C. Response time upon call or dispatch	2	2	5	1	1	11
D. Number of blocks in coverage area	1	1	2	3	2	9
E. Safety of officers	5	3	4	5	3	20
Totals	15	15	15	15	15	75

Questions

1. Develop weights that can be used in the weighted attribute method for each attribute. The committee members have agreed that the simple average of their five ordered-attribute scores can be considered the indicator of how important each attribute is to them as a group.

2. One committee member recommended, and obtained committee approval for, reducing the attributes considered in the final selection to only those that were listed as number 1 by one or more committee members. Select these attributes and recalculate the weights as requested in question 1.

3. A crime prevention analyst in the Police Department applied the weighted attribute method to the ordered attributes in question 1. The R_j values

obtained using Equation [10.11] are listed below. Which two options should the police chief select for the pilot study?

Alternative	Car	Bicycles	Foot	Horse
R_j	62.5	50.5	47.2	35.4

CASE STUDY

WHICH WAY TO GO—DEBT OR EQUITY FINANCING?

The Opportunity

Sobeys Inc. is considering extending its online catering service in Nova Scotia and New Brunswick. To deliver meals and serving personnel, it is about to purchase 200 vehicles for $1.5 million. Each van is expected to be used for 10 years and have a $1000 salvage value.

A feasibility study completed last year indicated that the business venture could realize an estimated annual net cash flow of $300,000 before taxes. After-tax considerations would have to take into account the effective tax rate of 35% paid by Sobeys.

An engineer with Sobeys' Distribution Division has worked with the corporate finance office to determine how to best develop the $1.5 million capital needed for the purchase of vans. There are two viable financing plans.

The Financing Options

Plan A is debt financing for 50% of the capital ($750,000) with the 8% per year compound interest loan repaid over 10 years with uniform year-end payments. (A simplifying assumption that $75,000 of the principal is repaid with each annual payment can be made.)

Plan B is 100% equity capital raised from the sale of $15 per share common stock. The financial manager informed the engineer that stock is paying $0.50 per share in dividends and that this dividend rate has been increasing at an average of 5% each year. This dividend pattern is expected to continue, based on the current financial environment.

Case Study Exercises

1. What values of MARR should the engineer use to determine the better financing plan?

2. The engineer must make a recommendation on the financing plan by the end of the day. He does not know how to consider all the tax angles for the debt financing in plan A. However, he does have a handbook that gives these relations for equity and debt capital about taxes and cash flows:

   Equity capital. No income tax advantages:

   After-tax net cash flow
   = (before-tax net cash flow)(1 − tax rate)

   Debt capital. Income tax advantage comes from interest paid on loans:

   After-tax net cash flow
   = before-tax net cash flow − loan principal
   − loan interest − taxes

   Taxes
   = (taxable income)(tax rate)

   Taxable income
   = net cash flow − loan interest

   He decides to forget any other tax consequences and use this information to prepare a recommendation. Is A or B the better plan?

3. The division manager would like to know how much the WACC varies for different D-E mixes, especially about 15% to 20% on either side of the 50% debt financing option in plan A. Plot the WACC curve and compare its shape with that of Figure 10–2.

LEVEL ③

Making Decisions on Real-World Projects

The chapters in this Level extend the use of economic evaluation tools into real-world situations. A large percentage of economic evaluations involve other than selection from new assets or projects. Probably the most commonly performed evaluation is that of replacing or retaining an in-place asset. *Replacement analysis* applies the evaluation tools to make the correct economic choice.

Often the evaluation involves choosing from *independent projects* under the restriction of limited capital investment. This requires a special technique that is based on the previous chapters.

Future estimates are certainly not exact. Therefore, an alternative should not be selected on the basis of fixed estimates only. *Breakeven analysis* assists in the evaluation process of a range of estimates for P, A, F, i, or n, and operating variables such as production level, workforce size, design cost, raw material cost, and sales price. Spreadsheets speed up this important, but often detailed, analysis tool.

Important note: **If asset depreciation and taxes are to be considered by an *after-tax analysis*, Chapters 15 and 16 should be covered before or in conjunction with these chapters. See the Preface for options.**

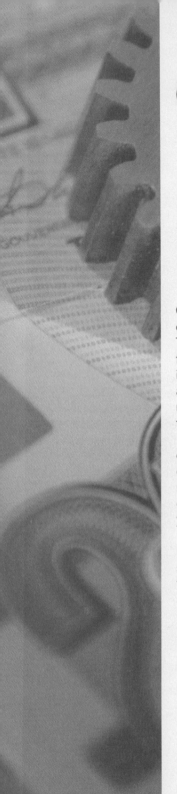

CHAPTER 11

Replacement and Retention Decisions

One of the most commonly performed engineering economy studies is that of replacement or retention of an asset or system that is currently installed. This differs from previous studies where all the alternatives are new. The fundamental question answered by a replacement study about a currently installed asset or system is, *Should it be replaced now or later?* When an asset is currently in use and its function is needed in the future, it will be replaced at some time. So, in reality, a replacement study answers the question of *when*, not *if*, to replace.

A replacement study is usually designed to first make the economic decision to retain or replace *now*. If the decision is to replace, the study is complete. If the decision is to retain, the cost estimates and decision will be revisited each year to ensure that the decision to retain is still economically correct. This chapter explains how to perform the initial year and follow-on year replacement studies.

A replacement study is an application of the AW method of comparing unequal-life alternatives, first introduced in Chapter 6. In a replacement study with no specified study period, the AW values are determined by a technique of cost evaluation called the *economic service life (ESL)* analysis. If a study period is specified, the replacement study procedure is different from that used when no study period is set. All these procedures are covered in this chapter.

The case study is a real-world replacement analysis involving in-place equipment and possible replacement by upgraded equipment.

If asset depreciation and taxes are to be considered in an *after-tax replacement analysis*, Chapters 15 and 16 should be covered before or in conjunction with this chapter. After-tax replacement analysis is included in Section 16.5.

LEARNING OBJECTIVES

Purpose: Perform a replacement study between an in-place asset or system and a new one that might replace it.

By the end of this chapter you should be able to

Basics	1. Identify and apply the fundamentals and terms for a replacement study.
Economic service life	2. Determine the economic service life of an asset that minimizes the total AW of costs.
Replacement study	3. Perform a replacement study between the defender and the best challenger.
Additional considerations	4. Address several aspects of a replacement study that may be experienced.
Study period	5. Perform a replacement study over a specified number of years.

11.1 BASICS OF THE REPLACEMENT STUDY

The need for a replacement study can develop from several sources:

Reduced performance. Because of physical deterioration, the ability to perform at an expected level of *reliability* (being available and performing correctly when needed) or *productivity* (performing at a given level of quality and quantity) is not present. This usually results in increased costs of operation, higher scrap and rework costs, lost sales, reduced quality, diminished safety, and larger maintenance expenses.

Altered requirements. New requirements of accuracy, speed, or other specifications cannot be met by the existing equipment or system. Often the choice is between complete replacement or enhancement through retrofitting or augmentation.

Obsolescence. International competition and rapidly changing technology make currently used systems and assets perform acceptably but less productively than equipment coming available. The ever-decreasing development cycle time to bring new products to market is often the reason for premature replacement studies, that is, studies performed before the estimated useful or economic life is reached.

Replacement studies use some terminology that is new, yet closely related to terms in previous chapters.

Defender and *challenger* are the names for two mutually exclusive alternatives. The defender is the currently installed asset, and the challenger is the potential replacement. A replacement study compares these two alternatives. The challenger is the "best" challenger because it has been selected as the one best challenger to possibly replace the defender. (This is the same terminology used earlier for incremental ROR and BCA of two new alternatives.)

AW values are used as the primary economic measure of comparison between the defender and challenger. The terms *EUAC* (*equivalent uniform annual cost*) or *AE* (*annual equivalent*) may be used in lieu of *AW*, because often only costs are included in the evaluation; revenues generated by the defender or challenger are assumed to be equal. Since the equivalence calculations for EUAC are exactly the same as for AW, we use the term AW. Therefore, all values will be negative when only costs are involved. Salvage value, of course, is an exception; it is a cash inflow and carries a plus sign.

Economic service life (ESL) for an alternative is the *number of years* at which the lowest AW of cost occurs. The equivalency calculations to determine ESL establish the life n for the best challenger, and it also establishes the lowest cost life for the defender in a replacement study. (The next section of this chapter explains how to find the ESL by hand and by computer for any new or currently installed asset.)

Defender first cost is the initial investment amount P used for the defender. The *current market value* (MV) is the correct estimate to use for P for the defender in a replacement study. The fair market value may be obtained from professional appraisers, resellers, or liquidators who know the value of used assets. The estimated salvage value at the end of 1 year becomes the market value at the beginning of the next year, provided the estimates remain correct as the years pass. It is incorrect to use the following as MV for the defender first cost: trade-in value that *does not represent a fair market value,* or the depreciated book value taken from accounting records. If the defender must be upgraded or augmented to make it equivalent to the challenger (in speed, capacity, etc.), this cost is added to the MV to obtain the estimate of defender first cost. In the case of asset augmentation for the defender alternative, this separate asset and its estimates are included along with the installed asset estimates to form the complete defender alternative. This alternative is then compared with the challenger via a replacement study.

Challenger first cost is the amount of capital that must be recovered (amortized) when replacing a defender with a challenger. This amount is almost always equal to P, the first cost of the challenger. On occasion, an unrealistically high trade-in value may be offered for the defender compared to its fair market value. In this event, the *net* cash flow required for the challenger is reduced, and this fact should be considered in the analysis. The correct amount to recover and use in the economic analysis for the challenger is its first cost minus the difference between the trade-in value (TIV) and market value (MV) of the defender. In equation form, this is $P - (TIV - MV)$. This amount represents the actual cost to the company because it includes both the opportunity cost (i.e., market value of the defender) and the out-of-pocket cost (i.e., first cost − trade-in) to acquire the challenger. Of course, when the trade-in and market values are the same, the challenger P value is used in all computations.

The challenger first cost is the estimated initial investment necessary to acquire and install it. Sometimes, an analyst or manager will attempt to *increase* this first cost by an amount equal to the *unrecovered capital* remaining in the defender as shown on the accounting records for the asset. This is observed most often when the defender is working well and in the early stages of its life, but technological obsolescence, or some other reason, has forced consideration of a replacement. This unrecovered capital amount is referred to as a *sunk cost.* A sunk cost must not be added to the challenger's first cost, because it will make the challenger appear to be more costly than it is.

> **Sunk costs are capital losses and cannot be recovered in a replacement study. Sunk costs are correctly handled in the corporation's income statement and by tax law allowances.**

A replacement study is performed most objectively if the analyst takes the *viewpoint of a consultant* to the company or unit using the defender. In this way, the perspective taken is that neither alternative is currently owned, and the services provided by the defender could be purchased now with an "investment" that is equal to its first cost (market value). This is indeed correct because the market value will be a forgone opportunity of cash inflow if the question

"Replace now?" is answered with a no. Therefore, the consultant's viewpoint is a convenient way to allow the economic evaluation to be performed without bias for either alternative. This approach is also referred to as the *outsider's viewpoint.*

As mentioned in the introduction, a replacement study is an application of the annual worth method. As such, the fundamental assumptions for a replacement study parallel those of an AW analysis. If the *planning horizon is unlimited,* that is, a study period is not specified, the assumptions are as follows:

1. The services provided are needed for the indefinite future.
2. The challenger is the best challenger available now and in the future to replace the defender. When this challenger replaces the defender (now or later), it will be repeated for succeeding life cycles.
3. Cost estimates for every life cycle of the challenger will be the same.

As expected, none of these assumptions is precisely correct. We discussed this previously for the AW method (and the PW method). When the intent of one or more of the assumptions becomes incorrect, the estimates for the alternatives must be updated and a new replacement study conducted. The replacement procedure discussed in Section 11.3 explains how to do this. When the *planning horizon is limited to a specified study period, the assumptions above do not hold.* The procedure of Section 11.5 discusses how to perform the replacement study in this case.

EXAMPLE 11.1

ADM, a large agricultural products corporation, purchased a state-of-the-art ground-levelling system for field preparation 3 years ago for $120,000. When purchased, it had an expected service life of 10 years, an estimated salvage of $25,000 after 10 years, and annual operating cost (AOC) $30,000. Current account book value is $80,000. The system is deteriorating rapidly; 3 more years of use and then salvaging it for $10,000 on the international used farm equipment network are now the expectations. The AOC is averaging $30,000.

A substantially improved, laser-guided model is offered today for $100,000 with a trade-in of $70,000 for the current system. The price goes up next week to $110,000 with a trade-in of $70,000. The ADM engineer estimates the laser-guided system to have a useful life of 10 years, a salvage of $20,000, and an AOC of $20,000. A $70,000 market value appraisal of the current system was made today.

If no further analysis is made on the estimates, state the correct values to include if the replacement study is performed today.

Solution

Take the consultant's viewpoint and use the most current estimates.

Defender	Challenger
$P = MV = \$-70{,}000$	$P = \$-100{,}000$
$AOC = \$-30{,}000$	$AOC = \$-20{,}000$
$S = \$10{,}000$	$S = \$20{,}000$
$n = 3$ years	$n = 10$ years

The defender's original cost, AOC, and salvage estimates, as well as its current book value, are all *irrelevant* to the replacement study. *Only the most current estimates should be used.* From the consultant's perspective, the services that the defender can provide could be obtained at a cost equal to the defender market value of $70,000. Therefore, this is the first cost of the defender for the study. The other values are as shown.

11.2) ECONOMIC SERVICE LIFE

Until now the estimated life *n* of an alternative or asset has been stated. In reality, the best life estimate to use in the economic analysis is not known initially. When a replacement study or an analysis between new alternatives is performed, the best value for *n* should be determined using current cost estimates. The best life estimate is called the *economic service life.*

> **The economic service life (ESL) is the number of years *n* at which the equivalent uniform annual worth (AW) of costs is the minimum, considering the most current cost estimates over all possible years that the asset may provide a needed service.**

The ESL is also referred to as the economic life or minimum cost life. Once determined, the ESL should be the estimated life for the asset used in an engineering economy study, if only economics are considered. When *n* years have passed, the ESL indicates that the asset should be replaced to minimize overall costs. To perform a replacement study correctly, it is important that the ESL of the challenger and ESL of the defender be determined, since their *n* values are usually not preestablished.

The ESL is determined by calculating the total AW of costs if the asset is in service 1 year, 2 years, 3 years, and so on, up to the last year the asset is considered useful. Total AW of costs is the sum of capital recovery (CR), which is the AW of the initial investment and any salvage value, and the AW of the estimated annual operating cost (AOC), that is,

$$\textbf{Total AW} = -\textbf{capital recovery} - \textbf{AW of annual operating costs}$$

$$= -\textbf{CR} - \textbf{AW of AOC} \qquad \textbf{[11.1]}$$

The ESL is the n value for the smallest total AW of costs. (*Remember:* These AW values are *cost* estimates, so the AW values are negative numbers. Therefore, -200 is a lower cost than -500.) Figure 11–1 shows the characteristic shape of a total AW of cost curve. The CR component of total AW decreases, while the AOC component increases, thus forming the concave shape. The two AW components are calculated as follows.

Decreasing cost of capital recovery. The capital recovery is the AW of investment; it decreases with each year of ownership. Capital recovery is calculated by Equation [6.3], which is repeated here. The salvage value *S*,

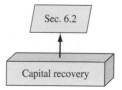

Sec. 6.2

Capital recovery

FIGURE 11–1

Annual worth curves of cost elements that determine the economic service life.

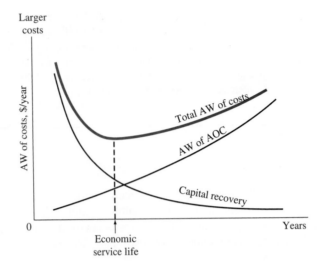

which usually decreases with time, is the estimated market value (MV) in that year.

$$\text{Capital recovery} = -P(A/P,i,n) + S(A/F,i,n) \qquad [11.2]$$

Increasing cost of AW of AOC. Since the AOC estimates usually increase over the years, the AW of AOC increases. To calculate the AW of the AOC series for 1, 2, 3, . . . years, determine the present worth of each AOC value with the P/F factor, then redistribute this P value over the years of ownership, using the A/P factor.

The complete equation for total AW of costs over k years is

$$\text{Total AW}_K = -P(A/P,i,k) + S_K(A/F,i,k)$$
$$- \left[\sum_{j=1}^{j=k} \text{AOC}_j(P/F,i,j) \right](A/P,i,k) \qquad [11.3]$$

where
P = initial investment or current market value
S_k = salvage value or market value after k years
AOC_j = annual operating cost for year j (j = 1 to k)

The current MV is used for P when the asset is the defender, and the estimated future MV values are substituted for the S values in years 1, 2, 3, ...

 To determine ESL by computer, the PMT function (with embedded NPV functions as needed) is used repeatedly for each year to calculate capital recovery and the AW of AOC. Their sum is the total AW for k years of ownership. The PMT function formats for the capital recovery and AOC components for each year k are as follows:

Capital recovery for the challenger: PMT($i\%$,years,P,−MV_in_year_k)

Capital recovery for the defender: PMT($i\%$,years,current_MV,−MV_in_year_k)

AW of AOC: −PMT($i\%$,years,NPV($i\%$, year_1_AOC:year_k_AOC) + 0)

When the spreadsheet is developed, it is recommended that the PMT functions in year 1 be developed using cell-reference format, then drag down the function through each column. A final column summing the two PMT results displays total AW. Augmenting the table with an Excel *xy* scatter plot graphically displays the cost curves in the general form of Figure 11–1, and the ESL is easily identified. Example 11.2 illustrates ESL determination by hand and by computer.

EXAMPLE 11.2

A 3-year-old manufacturing process asset is being considered for early replacement. Its current market value is $13,000. Estimated future market values and annual operating costs for the next 5 years are given in Table 11–1, columns 2 and 3. What is the economic service life of this defender if the interest rate is 10% per year? Solve by hand and by computer.

TABLE 11–1   Computation of Economic Service Life

Year j (1)	MV_j (2)	AOC_j (3)	Capital Recovery (4)	AW of AOC (5)	Total AW_k (6) = (4) + (5)
1	$9000	$-2500	$-5300	$-2500	$-7800
2	8000	-2700	-3681	-2595	-6276
3	6000	-3000	-3415	-2717	-6132
4	2000	-3500	-3670	-2886	-6556
5	0	-4500	-3429	-3150	-6579

Solution by Hand

Equation [11.3] is used to calculate total AW_k for $k = 1, 2, \ldots, 5$. Table 11–1, column 4, shows the capital recovery for the $13,000 current market value ($j = 0$) plus 10% return. Column 5 gives the equivalent AW of AOC for k years. As an illustration, the computation of total AW for $k = 3$ from Equation [11.3] is

$$\text{Total } AW_3 = -P(A/P,i,3) + MV_3(A/F,i,3) - [\text{PW of } AOC_1, AOC_2, \text{ and } AOC_3](A/P,i,3)$$

$$= -13{,}000(A/P,10\%,3) + 6000(A/F,10\%,3) - [2500(P/F,10\%,1)$$

$$+ 2700(P/F,10\%,2) + 3000(P/F,10\%,3)](A/P,10\%,3)$$

$$= -3415 - 2717 = \$-6132$$

A similar computation is performed for each year 1 through 5. The lowest equivalent cost (numerically largest AW value) occurs at $k = 3$. Therefore, the defender ESL is $n = 3$ years, and the AW value is -6132. In the replacement study, this AW will be compared with the best challenger AW determined by a similar ESL analysis.

Solution by Computer

See Figure 11–2 for the spreadsheet and chart for this example. (This format is a template for any ESL analysis; simply change the estimates and add rows for more years.) Contents of columns D and E are briefly described below. The PMT functions apply the formats for the defender as described above. Cell tags show detailed cell-reference format for year 5. The $ symbols are included for absolute cell referencing, needed when the entry is dragged down through the column.

E-SOLVE

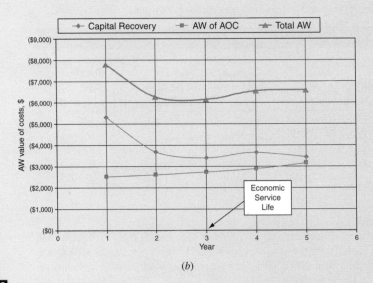

	A	B	C	D	E	F	G	H	I
1	Interest rate	10%							
2	First cost	$ 13,000							
3		Market							
4	Year	Value	AOC	Capital Recovery	AW of AOC	Total AW			
5	1	$9,000	-$2,500	($5,300)	($2,500)	($7,800)		=E7+D7	
6	2	$8,000	-$2,700	($3,681)	($2,595)	($6,276)			
7	3	$6,000	-$3,000	($3,415)	($2,718)	($6,132)	ESL		
8	4	$2,000	-$3,500	($3,670)	($2,886)	($6,556)			
9	5	$0	-$4,500	($3,429)	($3,150)	($6,580)			
10	= PMT($B$1,$A9,$B$2, –$B9)					= –PMT($B$1,$A9,NPV($B$1,$C$5:$C9)+0)			
11									

(a)

(b)

FIGURE 11–2

(a) Spreadsheet determination of the economic service life (ESL) and (b) plot of total AW and cost components, Example 11.2.

Column D: Capital recovery is the AW of the $13,000 investment (cell B2) in year 0 for each year 1 through 5 with the estimated MV in that year. For example, in actual numbers, the cell-reference PMT function in year 5 shown on the spreadsheet reads PMT(10%,5,13000,−0), resulting in $−3429. This series is plotted in Figure 11–2b as the middle curve, labelled "Capital Recovery" in the legend.

Column E: The NPV function embedded in the PMT function obtains the present worth in year 0 of all AOC estimates through year k. Then PMT calculates the AW of AOC over the k years. For example, in year 5, the PMT in numbers is −PMT(10%,5,NPV(10%,C5:C9)+0). The 0 is the AOC in year 0; it is optional. The graph plots the AW of AOC curve, which constantly increases in cost because the AOC estimates increase each year.

Comment
The *capital recovery curve* in Figure 11–2b (middle curve) is not a true concave shape
because the estimated market value changes each year. If the same MV were estimated for
each year, the curve would look like Figure 11–1. When several total AW values are
approximately equal, the curve will be flat over several periods. This indicates that the ESL
is relatively insensitive to costs.

It is reasonable to ask about the difference between the ESL analysis above
and the AW analyses performed in previous chapters. Previously we had an
estimated life of n years with associated other estimates: first cost in year 0, possibly a salvage value in year n, and an AOC that remained constant or varied each
year. For all previous analyses, the calculation of AW using these estimates determined the AW over n years. This is also the economic service life when n is fixed.
In all previous cases, there were no year-by-year MV estimates applicable over
the years. Therefore, we can conclude the following:

**When the expected life n is known for the challenger or defender, deter-
mine its AW over n years, using the first cost or current market value,
estimated salvage value after n years, and AOC estimates. This AW value
is the correct one to use in the replacement study.**

It is not difficult to estimate a series of market/salvage values for a new or current asset. For example, an asset with a first cost of P can lose market value at
20% per year, so the market value series for years 0, 1, 2, . . . is P, $0.8P$,
$0.64P$, . . . , respectively. If it is reasonable to predict the MV series on a year-by-
year basis, it can be combined with the AOC estimates to produce what is called
the *marginal costs* for the asset.

**Marginal costs (MC) are year-by-year estimates of the costs to own and
operate an asset for that year.**

There are three components to each annual marginal cost estimate:

- Cost of ownership (loss in market value is the best estimate of this cost)
- Forgone interest on the market value at the beginning of the year
- AOC for each year

Once the marginal costs are estimated for each year, their equivalent AW value
can be calculated. The sum of the AW values of the first two of these components
is identical to the capital recovery amount. Now, it should be clear that the total
AW of all three marginal cost components over k years is the same value as the
total annual worth for k years calculated in Equation [11.3]. That is, the following relation is

$$\text{AW of marginal costs} = \text{total AW of costs} \qquad [11.4]$$

Therefore, there is no need to perform a separate, detailed marginal cost analysis when yearly market values are estimated. The ESL analysis presented in Example 11.2 is sufficient in that it results in the same numerical values. This is demonstrated in Example 11.3 using the data of Example 11.2.

EXAMPLE 11.3

An engineer has determined that a 3-year-old manufacturing process asset has a market value of $13,000 now, and the estimated salvage/market values and AOC values shown in Table 11–1 (repeated in Figure 11–3, columns B and E). Determine the AW of the marginal values by computer, and compare it with the total AW values in Figure 11–2. Use the marginal cost series to determine the correct values for n and AW if the asset is the defender in a replacement study.

	A	B	C	D	E	F	G	H
1	Interest rate	10%						
2	Current MV	$ 13,000						
3								
4			Loss in MV	Lost Interest	Estimated	Marginal Cost	AW of	
5	Year	MV	for Year	on MV for Year	AOC	for the Year	Marginal Cost	
6	1	$9,000	-$4,000	-$1,300	-$2,500	-$7,800	($7,800)	
7	2	$8,000	-$1,000	-$900	-$2,700	-$4,600	($6,278)	
8	3	$6,000	-$2,000	-$800	-$3,000	-$5,800	($6,132)	
9	4	$2,000	-$4,000	-$600	-$3,500	-$8,100	($6,556)	
10	5	$0	-$2,000	-$200	-$4,500	-$6,700	($6,580)	
11								
12		= B8–B7		= –$B$1*$B7				
13						= $C8+$D8+$E8		
14								
15				= –PMT($B$1,$A8,NPV($B$1,$F$6:$F8)+0)				
16								

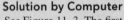

FIGURE 11–3

Calculation of AW of marginal cost series, Example 11.3.

Solution by Computer

E-SOLVE

See Figure 11–3. The first marginal cost component is the loss in MV by year (column C). The 10% interest on the MV (column D) is the second component, the forgone interest on the MV. Their sum is the year-by-year capital recovery amount. Based on the description above, the marginal cost for each year is the sum of columns C, D, and E, as shown in the spreadsheet cell tags. The series AW of marginal cost values in column G is identical to those determined for total AW of costs using the ESL analysis in Figure 11–2a. The correct values for a replacement study are $n = 3$ years and AW = $-6132, the same as for the ESL analysis in the previous example.

Now it is possible to draw two specific conclusions about the n and AW values to be used in a replacement study. These conclusions are based on the extent to which detailed annual estimates are made for the market value.

1. **Year-by-year market value estimates are made.** Use them to perform an ESL analysis, and determine the *n* value with the lowest total AW of costs. These are the best *n* and AW values for the replacement study.
2. **Yearly market value estimates are not made.** Here the only estimate available is market value (salvage value) in year *n*. Use it to calculate the AW over *n* years. These are the *n* and AW values to use; however, they may not be the "best" values in that they may not represent the best equivalent total AW of cost value.

Upon completion of the ESL analysis, the replacement study procedure in the next section is applied using the following values:

Challenger alternative (C): AW_C for n_C years

Defender alternative (D): AW_D for n_D years

11.3 PERFORMING A REPLACEMENT STUDY

Replacement studies are performed in one of two ways: without a study period specified or with one defined. Figure 11–4 gives an overview of the approach taken for each situation. The procedure discussed in this section applies when no study period (planning horizon) is specified. If a specific number of years is identified for the replacement study, for example, over the next 5 years, with no continuation considered after this time period in the economic analysis, the procedure in Section 11.5 is applied.

A replacement study determines when a challenger replaces the in-place defender. The complete study is finished if the challenger (C) is selected to replace the defender (D) now. However, if the defender is retained now, the study may extend over a number of years equal to the life of the defender n_D, after which a challenger replaces the defender. Use the annual worth and life values

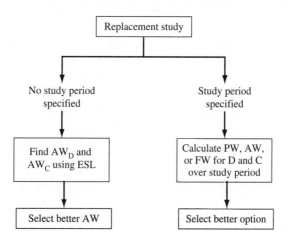

FIGURE 11–4

Overview of replacement study approaches.

for C and D determined in the ESL analysis to apply the following replacement study procedure. This assumes the services provided by the defender could be obtained at the AW_D amount.

New replacement study:

1. On the basis of the better AW_C or AW_D value, select the challenger alternative (C) or defender alternative (D). When the challenger is selected, replace the defender now, and expect to keep the challenger for n_C years. This replacement study is complete. If the defender is selected, plan to retain it for up to n_D more years. Next year, perform the following steps.

One-year-later analysis:

2. Are all estimates still current for both alternatives, especially first cost, market value, and AOC? If no, proceed to step 3. If yes and this is year n_D, replace the defender. If this is not year n_D, retain the defender for another year and repeat this same step. This step may be repeated several times.
3. Whenever the estimates have changed, update them and determine new AW_C and AW_D values. Initiate a new replacement study (step 1).

If the defender is selected initially (step 1), estimates may need updating after 1 year of retention (step 2). Possibly there is a new best challenger to compare with D. Either significant changes in defender estimates or availability of a new challenger indicates that a new replacement study is to be performed. In actuality, a replacement study can be performed each year to determine the advisability of replacing or retaining any defender, provided a competitive challenger is available.

Example 11.4 below illustrates the application of ESL analysis for a challenger and defender, followed by the use of the replacement study procedure. The planning horizon is unspecified in this example.

EXAMPLE 11.4

Two years ago, Toshiba Electronics made a $15 million investment in new assembly line machinery. It purchased approximately 200 units at $70,000 each and placed them in plants in 10 different countries. The equipment sorts, tests, and performs insertion-order kitting on electronic components in preparation for special-purpose printed circuit boards. This year, new international industry standards will require a $16,000 retro-fit on each unit, in addition to the expected operating cost. Due to the new standards, coupled with rapidly changing technology, a new system is challenging the retention of these 2-year-old machines. The chief engineer at Toshiba realizes that the economics must be considered, so he has asked that a replacement study be performed this year and each year in the future, if need be. At $i = 10\%$ and with the estimates below, do the following:

(a) Determine the AW values and economic service lives necessary to perform the replacement study by hand.
(b) Perform the replacement study now by computer.

> *Challenger:* First cost: $50,000
> Future market values: decreasing by 20% per year
> Estimated retention period: no more than 5 years
> AOC estimates: $5000 in year 1 with increases of $2000 per year thereafter
>
> *Defender:* Current international market value: $15,000
> Future market values: decreasing by 20% per year
> Estimated retention period: no more than 3 more years
> AOC estimates: $4000 next year, increasing by $4000 per year thereafter, plus the $16,000 retro-fit next year

(c) After 1 year, it is time to perform the follow-up analysis. The challenger is making large inroads to the market for electronic components assembly equipment, especially with the new international standards features built in. The expected market value for the defender is still $12,000 this year, but it is expected to drop to virtually nothing in the future—$2000 next year on the worldwide market and zero after that. Also, this prematurely outdated equipment is more costly to keep serviced, so the estimated AOC next year has been increased from $8000 to $12,000 and to $16,000 two years out. Perform the follow-up replacement study analysis by computer.

Solution by Hand

(a) The results of the ESL analysis, shown in Table 11–2, include all the MV and AOC estimates for the challenger in part (a) of the table. Note that $P = \$50,000$ is also

TABLE 11–2 Economic Service Life (ESL) Analysis of (a) Challenger and (b) Defender Costs, Example 11.4

(a) Challenger

Challenger Year k	Market Value	AOC	Total AW If Owned k Years	
0	$50,000	—	—	
1	40,000	$ −5,000	$−20,000	
2	32,000	−7,000	−19,524	
3	25,600	−9,000	−19,245	
4	20,480	−11,000	−19,123	ESL
5	16,384	−13,000	−19,126	

(b) Defender

Defender Year k	Market Value	AOC	Total AW If Retained k Years	
0	$15,000	—	—	
1	12,000	$−20,000	$−24,500	
2	9,600	−8,000	−18,357	
3	7,680	−12,000	−17,307	ESL

the MV in year 0. The total AW of costs is for each year, should the challenger be placed into service for that number of years. As an example, the year $k = 4$ amount of $\$-19,123$ is determined using Equation [11.3]. The A/G factor is applied in lieu of the P/F and A/P factors to find the AW of the arithmetic gradient series in the AOC.

$$\text{Total AW}_4 = -50,000(A/P,10\%,4) + 20,480(A/F,10\%,4)$$
$$-[5000 + 2000(A/G,10\%,4)]$$

$$= \$-19,123$$

The defender costs are analyzed in the same way in Table 11–2b up to the maximum retention period of 3 years.

The lowest AW cost (numerically largest) values for the replacement study are

Challenger: $\text{AW}_\text{C} = \$-19,123$ for $n_\text{C} = 4$ years

Defender: $\text{AW}_\text{D} = \$-17,307$ for $n_\text{D} = 3$ years

If plotted, the challenger total AW of cost curve (Table 11–2a) would be relatively flat after 2 years; there is virtually no difference in the total AW for years 4 and 5. For the defender, note that the AOC values change substantially over the 3 years, and they do not constantly increase or decrease.

Parts (b) and (c) are solved below by computer.

E-SOLVE

Solution by Computer

(a) Figure 11–5 includes the complete spreadsheet and total AW of cost graph for the challenger and defender. (The tables were generated by initially copying the spreadsheet developed in Figure 11–2a as a template. All the PMT functions in columns D and E, and summing function in column F, are identical. The first cost, market value, and AOC amounts are changed for this example.) Some critical functions are detailed in the cell tags. The *xy* charts show the total AW of cost curves. The AW and ESL values are the same as in the hand solution.

Since it is very easy to add years to an ESL analysis, years 5 through 10 are appended to the challenger analysis in spreadsheet rows 10 to 14. Note that the total AW curve has a relatively flat bottom, and it returns to the early-life AW cost level (about $\$-20,000$) after some number of years, 10 here. This is a classically shaped AW curve developed from constantly decreasing market values and constantly increasing AOC values. (Use of this tabular format and these functions is also recommended for an analysis where all the components of total AW need to be displayed.)

(b) To perform the replacement study now, apply only the first step of the procedure. Select the defender because it has the better AW of costs ($\$-17,307$), and expect to retain it for 3 more years. Prepare to perform the one-year-later analysis 1 year from now.

(c) One year later, the situation has changed significantly for the equipment Toshiba retained last year. Apply the steps for the one-year-later analysis (the last two steps of the replacement study procedure):

2. After 1 year of defender retention, the challenger estimates are still reasonable, but the defender market value and AOC estimates are substantially different. Go to step 3 to perform a new ESL analysis for the defender.

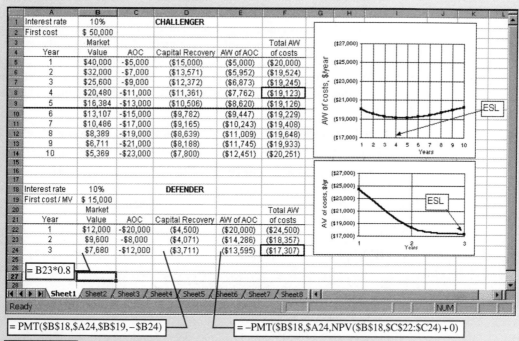

FIGURE 11–5

Economic service life (ESL) for the challenger and defender using a spreadsheet, Example 11.4. (The tabular format and functions are the same as in Figure 11–2a.)

3. The defender estimates in Table 11–2b are updated below, and new AW values are calculated using Equation [11.3]. There is now a maximum of 2 more years of retention, 1 year less than the 3 years determined last year.

Year k	Market Value	AOC	Total AW If Retained k More Years
0	$12,000	—	—
1	2,000	$-12,000	$-23,200
2	0	-16,000	-20,819

The AW and n values for the new replacement study are as follows:

Challenger: Unchanged at $AW_C = \$-19{,}123$ for $n_C = 4$ years

Defender: New $AW_D = \$-20{,}819$ for $n_D = 2$ more years

Now select the challenger on the basis of its favourable AW value. Therefore, replace the defender now, not 2 years from now. Expect to keep the challenger for 4 years, or until a better challenger appears on the scene.

Often it is helpful to know the minimum market value of the defender necessary to make the challenger economically attractive. If a realizable market value (trade-in) of at least this amount can be obtained, from an economic perspective the challenger should be selected immediately. This is a *breakeven value* between AW_C and AW_D; it is referred to as the *replacement value (RV)*. Set up the relation $AW_C = AW_D$ with the market value for the defender substituted as RV, which is the unknown. The AW_C is known, so RV can be determined. The selection guideline is as follows:

If the actual market trade-in exceeds the breakeven replacement value, the challenger is the better alternative, and should replace the defender now.

For Example 11.4*b*, $AW_C = \$-19,123$, and the defender was selected. Therefore, RV should be larger than the estimated defender market value of $15,000. Equation [11.3] is set up for 3 years of defender retention and equated to $\$-19,123$.

$$-RV(A/P,10\%,3) + 0.8^3RV(A/F,10\%,3) - [20,000(P/F,10\%,1)$$

$$+ 8,000(P/F,10\%,2) + 12,000(P/F,10\%,3)](A/P,10\%,3) = \$-19,123 \quad [11.5]$$

$$RV = \$22,341$$

Any market trade-in value above this amount is an economic indication to replace now with the challenger.

If the spreadsheet in Figure 11–5 has been developed for the ESL analysis, Excel's SOLVER (which is on the Tools toolbar) can find RV rapidly. It is important to understand what SOLVER does from an engineering economy perspective, so Equation [11.5] should be set up and understood. Cell F24 in Figure 11–5 is the "target cell" to equal $\$-19,123$ (the best AW_C in F8). This is how Excel sets up a spreadsheet equivalent of Equation [11.4]. SOLVER returns the RV value of $22,341 in cell B19 with a new estimated market value of $11,438 in year 3. Reflecting on the solution to Example 11.4(*b*), the current market value is $15,000, which is less than RV = $22,341. The defender is selected over the challenger. Use Appendix A or the Excel online help function to learn how to use SOLVER in an efficient way.

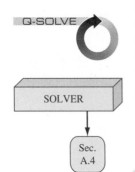

11.4 ADDITIONAL CONSIDERATIONS IN A REPLACEMENT STUDY

There are several additional aspects of a replacement study that may be introduced. Three of these are identified and discussed in turn.

- Future-year replacement decisions at the time of the initial replacement study
- Opportunity cost versus cash flow approaches to alternative comparison
- Anticipation of improved future challengers

In most cases when management initiates a replacement study, the question is best framed as, "Replace now, 1 year from now, 2 years from now, etc.?" The procedure above does answer this question provided the estimates for C and D do not change as each year passes. In other words, *at the time it is performed, step*

1 of the procedure does answer the replacement question for multiple years. It is only when estimates change over time that the decision to retain the defender may be prematurely reversed in favour of the then-best challenger, that is, prior to n_D years.

The first costs (P values) for the challenger and defender have been correctly taken as the initial investment for the challenger C and current market value for the defender D. This is called the *opportunity cost approach* because it recognizes that a cash inflow of funds equal to the market value is forgone if the defender is selected. This approach, also called the conventional approach, is correct for every replacement study. A second approach, called the *cash flow approach,* recognizes that when C is selected, the market value cash inflow for the defender is received and, in effect, immediately reduces the capital needed to invest in the challenger. Use of the cash-flow approach is strongly discouraged for at least two reasons: possible violation of the equal-service assumption and incorrect capital recovery value for C. As we are aware, all economic evaluations must compare alternatives with equal service. Therefore, the cash flow approach can work only when challenger and defender lives are exactly equal. This is commonly not the case; in fact, the ESL analysis and replacement study procedure are designed to compare two mutually exclusive, *unequal-life* alternatives via the annual worth method. If this equal-service comparison reason is not enough to avoid the cash flow approach, consider what happens to the challenger's capital recovery amount when its first cost is decreased by the market value of the defender. The capital recovery (CR) terms in Equation [11.3] will decrease, resulting in a falsely low value of CR for the challenger, were it selected. From the vantage point of the economic study itself, the decision for C or D will not change; but when C is selected and implemented, this CR value is not reliable. The conclusion is simple: *Use the initial investment of C and the MV of D as the first costs in the ESL analysis and in the replacement study.*

A basic premise of a replacement study is that some challenger will replace the defender at a future time, provided the service continues to be needed and a worthy challenger is available. The expectation of ever-improving challengers can offer strong encouragement to retain the defender until some situational elements—technology, costs, market fluctuations, contract negotiations, etc.—stabilize. This was the case in the previous example of the electronics assembly equipment. A large expenditure on equipment when the standards changed soon after purchase forced an early replacement consideration and a large loss of invested capital. The replacement study is no substitute for forecasting challenger availability. *It is important to understand trends, new advances, and competitive pressures that can complement the economic outcome of a good replacement study.* It is often better to compare a challenger with an augmented defender in the replacement study. Adding needed features to a currently installed defender may prolong its useful life and productivity until challenger choices are more appealing.

It is possible that a significant tax impact may occur when a defender is traded early in its expected life. If taxes should be considered, proceed now, or after the next section, to Chapter 16 and the after-tax replacement analysis in Section 16.5.

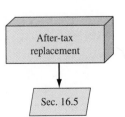

11.5 REPLACEMENT STUDY OVER A SPECIFIED STUDY PERIOD

When the time period for the replacement study is limited to a specified study period or planning horizon, for example, 6 years, the determinations of AW values for the challenger and for the remaining life of the defender are usually not based on the economic service life. What happens to the alternatives after the study period is not considered in the replacement analysis. Therefore, the services are not needed beyond the study period. In fact, a study period of fixed duration does not comply with the three assumptions stated in Section 11.1—service needed for indefinite future, best challenger available now, and estimates will be identical for future life cycles.

When performing a replacement study over a fixed study period, it is crucial that the estimates used to determine the AW values be accurate and used in the study. This is especially important for the defender. Failure to do the following violates the assumption of equal-service comparison.

When the defender's remaining life is shorter than the study period, the cost of providing the defender's services from the end of its expected remaining life to the end of the study period must be estimated as accurately as possible and included in the replacement study.

The right branch of Figure 11–4 presents an overview of the replacement study procedure for a stated study period.

1. *Succession options and AW values.* Develop all the viable ways to use the defender and challenger during the study period. There may be only one option or many options; the longer the study period, the more complex this analysis becomes. The AW_D and AW_C values are used to build the equivalent cash flow series for each option.
2. *Selection of the best option.* The PW or AW for each option is calculated over the study period. Select the option with the lowest cost, or highest income if revenues are estimated. (As before, the best option will have the numerically largest PW or AW value.)

The following three examples use this procedure and illustrate the importance of making cost estimates for the defender alternative when its remaining life is less than the study period.

EXAMPLE 11.5

Claudia works with Bombardier Inc. at the company's mass-transit railcar plant in La Pocatière, Quebec. She is considering the acquisition of a circuit diagnostics system for a new contract with New Jersey's transit authority to provide 100 commuter railcars. The current system was purchased 7 years ago on an earlier contract. It has no capital recovery costs remaining, and the following are reliable estimates: current market value = $70,000, remaining life of 3 more years, no salvage value, and AOC = $30,000 per year. The only options for this system are to replace it now or retain it for the full 3 additional years.

Claudia has found that there is only one good challenger system. Its cost estimates are: first cost of $750,000, life of 10 years, $S = 0$, and AOC = $50,000 per year.

Realizing the importance of accurate defender alternative cost estimates, Claudia asked the division chief what system would be a logical follow-on to the current one 3 years hence. The chief predicted Bombardier would purchase the very system she had identified as the challenger, because it is the best on the market. The company would keep it for the entire 10 additional years for use on an extension of this contract for up to 79 additional rail-cars or some other application that could recover the remaining 3 years of invested capital. Claudia interpreted the response to mean that the last 3 years would also be capital recovery years, but on some project other than this one. Claudia's estimate of the first cost of this same system 3 years from now is $900,000. Additionally, the $50,000 per year AOC is the best estimate at this time.

The division chief mentioned any study had to be conducted using the interest rate of 10%. Perform a replacement study for a contract period of 10 years.

Solution

The study period is fixed at 10 years, so the intent of the replacement study assumptions is not present. This means the defender follow-on estimates are very important to the analysis. Further, any analyses to determine the ESL values are unnecessary and incorrect since alternative lives are already set and no projected annual market values are available. The first step of the replacement study procedure is to define the options. Since the defender will be replaced now or in 3 years, there are only two options:

1. Challenger for all 10 years
2. Defender for 3 years, followed by challenger for 7 years

The AW values for C and D are calculated. For option 1, the challenger is used for all 10 years. Equation [11.3] is applied using the following estimates:

Challenger: $P = \$750,000$ AOC = $50,000

                    $n = 10$ years $S = 0$

$$AW_C = -750,000(A/P,10\%,10) - 50,000 = \$-172,063$$

The second option has more complex cost estimates. The AW for the in-place system is calculated over the first 3 years. *Added to this is the capital recovery for the defender, follow-on, for the next 7 years. However, in this case, the CR amount is determined over its full 10-year life.* (It is not unusual for the recovery of invested capital to be moved between projects, especially for contract work.) Refer to the AW components as AW_{DC} (subscript DC for defender, current) and AW_{DF} (subscript DF for "defender, follow-on"). The final cash flow diagrams are shown in Figure 11–6.

Defender, current: Market value = $70,000   AOC = $30,000

                    $n = 3$ years $S = 0$

$$AW_{DC} = [-70,000 - 30,000(P/A,10\%,3)](A/P,10\%,10) = \$-23,534$$

Defender, follow-on: $P = \$900,000$, $n = 10$ years for capital recovery calculation only, AOC = $50,000 for years 4 through 10, $S = 0$

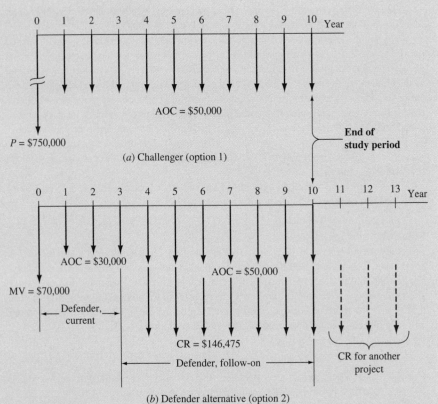

FIGURE 11–6
Cash flow diagrams for a 10-year period replacement study, Example 11.5.

The CR and AW for all 10 years are

$$CR_{DF} = -900,000(A/P,10\%,10) = \$-146,475 \qquad [11.6]$$

$$AW_{DF} = (-146,475 - 50,000)(F/A,10\%,7)(A/F,10\%,10) = \$-116,966$$

Total AW_D for the defender is the sum of the two annual worth values above. This is the AW for option 2.

$$AW_D = AW_{DC} + AW_{DF} = -23,534 - 116,966 = \$-140,500$$

Option 2 has a lower cost ($\$-140,500$ versus $\$-172,063$). Retain the defender now and expect to purchase the follow-on system 3 years hence.

Comment

The capital recovery cost for the defender, follow-on, will be borne by some yet-to-be-identified project for years 11 through 13. If this assumption were not made, its capital recovery cost would be calculated over 7 years, not 10, in Equation [11.6], increasing CR to $\$-184,869$. This raises the annual worth to $AW_D = \$-163,357$. The defender alternative (option 1) is still selected.

EXAMPLE 11.6

Three years ago Ottawa's Macdonald-Cartier International Airport purchased a new firetruck. Because of flight increases, new firefighting capacity is needed once again. An additional truck of the same capacity can be purchased now, or a double-capacity truck can replace the current truck. Estimates are presented below. Compare the options at 12% per year using (*a*) a 12-year study period and (*b*) a 9-year study period.

	Presently Owned	New Purchase	Double Capacity
First cost P, $	−151,000 (3 years ago)	−175,000	−190,000
AOC, $	−1,500	−1,500	−2,500
Market value, $	70,000	—	—
Salvage value, $	10% of P	12% of P	10% of P
Life, years	12	12	12

Solution

Identify option 1 as retention of the presently owned truck and augmentation with a new same-capacity vehicle. Define option 2 as replacement with the double-capacity truck.

	Option 1		Option 2
	Presently Owned	Augmentation	Double Capacity
P, $	−70,000	−175,000	−190,000
AOC, $	−1,500	−1,500	−2,500
S, $	15,100	21,000	19,000
n, years	9	12	12

(*a*) For a full-life 12-year study period of option 1,

$$AW_1 = \text{(AW of presently owned)} + \text{(AW of augmentation)}$$

$$= [-70,000(A/P,12\%,9) + 15,100(A/F,12\%,9) - 1500]$$
$$+ [-175,000(A/P,12\%,12) + 21,000(A/F,12\%,12) - 1500]$$

$$= -13,616 - 28,882$$

$$= \$-42,498$$

This computation assumes the equivalent services provided by the current firetruck can be purchased at $-13,616 per year for years 10 through 12.

$$AW_2 = -190,000(A/P,12\%,12) + 19,000(A/F,12\%,12) - 2500$$

$$= \$-32,386$$

Replace now with the double-capacity truck (option 2) at an advantage of $10,112 per year.

(*b*) The analysis for an abbreviated 9-year study period is identical, except that $n = 9$ in each factor; that is, 3 fewer years are allowed for the augmentation and double-capacity trucks to recover the capital investment plus a 12% per year return. The salvage values remain the same since they are quoted as a percentage of P for all years.

$$AW_1 = \$-46,539 \qquad AW_2 = \$-36,873$$

Option 2 is again selected; however, now the economic advantage is smaller. If the study period were abbreviated more severely, at some point the decision should reverse. If this example were solved by computer, the *n* values in the PMT functions could be decreased to determine if and when the decision reverses from option 2 to 1.

An engineering decision may be subject to other considerations that may overrule the purely economic calculations. For example, having additional trucks improves reliability. If one breaks down, the airport still has adequate fire service. Additional trucks also improves their capacity to fight multiple fires at the same time.

If there are several options for the number of years that the defender may be retained before replacement with the challenger, the first step of the replacement study—succession options and AW values—must include all the viable options. For example, if the study period is 5 years, and the defender will remain in service 1 year, or 2 years, or 3 years, cost estimates must be made to determine AW values for each defender retention period. In this case, there are four options; call them W, X, Y, and Z.

Option	Defender Retained	Challenger Serves
W	3 years	2 years
X	2	3
Y	1	4
Z	0	5

The respective AW values for defender retention and challenger use define the cash flows for each option. Example 11.7 illustrates the procedure.

EXAMPLE 11.7

Amoco Canada has oil field equipment placed into service 5 years ago for which a replacement study has been requested. Due to its special purpose, it has been decided that the current equipment will have to serve for either 2, 3, or 4 more years before replacement. The equipment has a current market value of $100,000, which is expected to decrease by $25,000 per year. The AOC is constant now, and is expected to remain so, at $25,000 per year. The replacement challenger is a fixed-price contract to provide the same services at $60,000 per year for a minimum of 2 years and a maximum of 5 years. Use MARR of 12% per year to perform a replacement study over a 6-year period to determine when to sell the current equipment and purchase the contract services.

Solution
Since the defender will be retained for 2, 3, or 4 years, there are three viable options (X, Y, and Z).

Option	Defender Retained	Challenger Serves
X	2 years	4 years
Y	3	3
Z	4	2

The defender annual worth values are identified with subscripts D2, D3, and D4 for the number of years retained.

$$AW_{D2} = -100,000(A/P,12\%,2) + 50,000(A/F,12\%,2) - 25,000 = \$-60,585$$

$$AW_{D3} = -100,000(A/P,12\%,3) + 25,000(A/F,12\%,3) - 25,000 = \$-59,226$$

$$AW_{D4} = -100,000(A/P,12\%,4) - 25,000 = \$-57,923$$

For all options, the challenger has an annual worth of

$$AW_C = \$-60,000$$

Table 11–3 presents the cash flows and PW values for each option over the 6-year study period. A sample PW computation for option Y is

$$PW_Y = -59,226(P/A,12\%,3) - 60,000(F/A,12\%,3)(P/F,12\%,6) = \$-244,817$$

Option Z has the lowest-cost PW value ($-240,369$). Keep the defender all 4 years, then replace it. Obviously, the same answer will result if the annual worth, or future worth, of each option is calculated at the MARR.

TABLE 11–3 Equivalent Cash Flows and PW Values for a 6-Year Study Period Replacement Analysis, Example 11.7

Option	Time in Service, Years Defender	Time in Service, Years Challenger	AW Cash Flows for Each Option, $/Year 1	2	3	4	5	6	Option PW, $
X	2	4	−60,585	−60,585	−60,000	−60,000	−60,000	−60,000	−247,666
Y	3	3	−59,226	−59,226	−59,226	−60,000	−60,000	−60,000	−244,817
Z	4	2	−57,923	−57,923	−57,923	−57,923	−60,000	−60,000	−240,369

Comment

If the study period is long enough, it is possible that the ESL of the challenger should be determined and its AW value used in developing the options and cash flow series. An option may include more than one life cycle of the challenger for its ESL period. Partial life cycles of the challenger can be included. Regardless, any years beyond the study period must be disregarded for the replacement study, or treated explicitly, in order to ensure that equal-service comparison is maintained, especially if PW is used to select the best option.

CHAPTER SUMMARY

It is important in a replacement study to compare the best challenger with the defender. *Best (economic) challenger is described as the one with the lowest annual worth (AW) of costs for some period of years.* If the expected remaining life of the defender and the estimated life of the challenger are specified, the AW values over these years are determined and the replacement study proceeds. However, if reasonable estimates of the expected market value (MV) and AOC for each year of ownership can be made, these year-by-year (marginal) costs help determine the best challenger.

The economic service life (ESL) analysis is designed to determine the best challenger's years of service and the resulting lowest total AW of costs. The resulting n_C and AW_C values are used in the replacement study procedure. The same analysis can be performed for the ESL of the defender.

Replacement studies in which no study period (planning horizon) is specified utilize the annual worth method of comparing two unequal-life alternatives. The better AW value determines how long the defender is retained before replacement.

When a study period is specified for the replacement study, it is vital that market value and cost estimates for the defender be as accurate as possible. When the defender's remaining life is shorter than the study period, it is critical that the cost for continuing service be estimated carefully. All the viable options for using the defender and challenger are enumerated, and their AW equivalent cash flows are determined. For each option, the PW or AW value is used to select the best option. This option determines how long the defender is retained before replacement.

PROBLEMS

Foundations of Replacement

11.1 Identify the basic assumptions made specifically about the challenger alternative when a replacement study is performed.

11.2 In a replacement analysis, what numerical value should be used as the first cost for the defender? How is this value best obtained?

11.3 Why is it important to take a consultant's viewpoint in a replacement analysis?

11.4 Chris is tired of driving the old used car she bought 2 years ago for $18,000. She estimates it is worth about $8000 now. A car salesman gave her this deal: "Look, I'll give you $10,000 in trade for this year's model. This is $2000 more than you expect, and it is $3000 more than the *Black Book* wholesale value for your car. Our sales price for your new car is only $28,000, which is $6000 less than the manufacturer's sticker price of $34,000. Considering the extra $3000 on the trade-in and the $6000 reduction from sticker, you are paying $9000 less for the new car. So, I am giving you a great deal, and you get $2000 more for your old clunker than you estimated it was worth. So, let's trade now. Okay?" If Chris were to perform a replacement study at this moment, what is the correct first cost for (*a*) the defender and (*b*) the challenger?

11.5 New microelectronics testing equipment was purchased 2 years ago by Mytesmall Industries at a cost of $600,000. At that time, it was expected to be used for 5 years and then traded or sold for its salvage value of $75,000. Expanded business in newly developed international markets is forcing the decision to trade now for a new unit at a cost of $800,000. The current equipment could be retained, if necessary, for another 2 years, at which time it would have a $5000 estimated market value. The current unit is appraised at $350,000 on the international market, and if it is used for another 2 years, it will have M&O costs (exclusive of operator costs) of $125,000 per year. Determine the values of P, n, S, and AOC for this defender if a replacement analysis were performed today.

11.6 Buffett Enterprises installed a new fire monitoring and control system for its manufacturing process lines exactly 2 years ago for $ 450,000 with an expected life of 5 years. The market value was described then by the relation $400,000 - 50,000k^{1.4}$, where k was the years from time of purchase. Previous experience with fire monitoring equipment indicated that its annual operating costs follow the relation $10,000 + 100k^3$. If the relations are correct over time, determine the values of P, S, and AOC for this defender if a replacement analysis is performed (a) now with a study period of 3 years specified and (b) 2 years from now with no study period identified.

11.7 A machine purchased 1 year ago for $85,000 costs more to operate than anticipated. When purchased, the machine was expected to be used for 10 years with annual maintenance costs of $22,000 and a $10,000 salvage value.

However, last year, it cost the company $35,000 to maintain it, and these costs are expected to escalate to $36,500 this year and increase by $1500 each year thereafter. The salvage value is now estimated to be $85,000 - $10,000k$, where k is the number of years since the machine was purchased. It is now estimated that this machine will be useful for a maximum of 5 more years. Determine the values of P, AOC, n, and S for a replacement study performed now.

Economic Service Life

11.8 Halcrow, Inc., expects to replace a downtime tracking system currently installed on CNC machines. The challenger system has a first cost of $70,000, an estimated annual operating cost of $20,000, a maximum useful life of 5 years, and a $10,000 salvage value anytime it is replaced. At an interest rate of 10% per year, determine its economic service life and corresponding AW value. Work this problem using a hand calculator.

11.9 Use a spreadsheet to work Problem 11.8 and plot the total AW curve and its components, (a) using the estimates originally made and (b) using new, more precise estimates, namely, an expected maximum life of 10 years, an AOC that will increase by 15% per year from the initial estimate of $20,000, and a salvage value that is expected to decrease by $1000 per year from the $10,000 estimated for the first year.

11.10 Eli Lilly Canada wants to purchase an Intelligent Devices RFID tracking system for temperature-controlled packaging, shipping, and distribution of pharmaceuticals at a cost of $345,000. The operating cost is expected to be $148,000 per year for the first 3 years and $210,000 for the next 3 years. The salvage value of the equipment is expected to be $140,000 for the first 3 years, but no significant amount after that. At an interest rate of 10% per year, determine the economic service life of the equipment and the associated annual worth.

11.11 An asset with a first cost of $250,000 is expected to have a maximum useful life of 10 years and a market value that decreases $25,000 each year. The annual operating cost is expected to be constant at $25,000 per year for 5 years and to increase at a substantial 25% per year thereafter. The interest rate is a low 4% per year, because the company, Toronto Hydro Energy Services Inc., is wholly owned by the city of Toronto and enjoys public project interest rates on its loans. (*a*) Verify that the ESL is 5 years. Is the ESL sensitive to the changing market value and AOC estimates? (*b*) The engineer doing a replacement analysis determines that this asset should have an ESL of 10 years when it is pitted against any challenger. If the estimated AOC series has proved to be correct, determine the minimum market value that will make ESL equal 10 years. Solve by hand or spreadsheet as instructed.

11.12 PCL Constructors Inc. is considering the purchase of an excavator with a first cost of $70,000 that can be used for a maximum of 6 years. The equation $S = 70,000(1 - 0.15)^n$ describes the salvage value of the excavator, which decreases by 15% per year, where n is the number of years after purchase. The operating cost will be constant at $75,000 per year. At an interest rate of 12% per year, determine the economic service life of the excavator and the associated AW value.

11.13 (*a*) Set up a general (cell reference format) spreadsheet that will indicate the ESL and associated AW value for any challenger asset that has a maximum useful life of 10 years. The relation for AW should be a single-cell formula to calculate AW for each year of ownership, using all the necessary estimates.

(*b*) Use your spreadsheet to find the ESL and AW values for the estimates tabulated. Assume $i = 10\%$ per year.

Year	Estimated Market Value, $	Estimated AOC, $
0	80,000	0
1	60,000	60,000
2	50,000	65,000
3	40,000	70,000
4	30,000	75,000
5	20,000	80,000

11.14 A piece of equipment has a first cost of $150,000, a maximum useful life of 7 years, and a salvage value described by $S = 120,000 - 20,000k$, where k is the number of years since it was purchased. The salvage value does not go below zero. The AOC series is estimated using $AOC = 60,000 + 10,000k$. The interest rate is 15% per year. Determine the economic service life (*a*) by hand solution, using regular AW computations, and (*b*) by computer, using annual marginal cost estimates.

11.15 Determine the economic service life and corresponding AW for a machine that has the following cash flow estimates. Use an interest rate of 14% per year and hand solution.

Year	Salvage Value, $	Operating Cost, $
0	100,000	—
1	75,000	−28,000
2	60,000	−31,000
3	50,000	−34,000
4	40,000	−34,000
5	25,000	−34,000
6	15,000	−45,000
7	0	−49,000

11.16 Use the annual marginal costs to find the economic service life for Problem 11.15 on a spreadsheet. Assume the salvage values are the best estimates of future market value. Develop an Excel chart of annual marginal costs (MC) and AW of MC over the 7 years.

Replacement Study

11.17 During a 3-year period Shanna, a project manager with Sherholme Medical Devices, performed replacement studies on microwave-based cancer detection equipment used in the diagnostic labs. She tabulated the ESL and AW values each year.

(*a*) What decision should be made each year?

(*b*) From the data, describe what changes took place in the defender and challenger over the 3 years.

	Maximum Life, Years	ESL, Years	AW, $/Year
	First Year 200X		
Defender	3	3	−10,000
Challenger 1	10	5	−15,000
	Second Year 200X + 1		
Defender	2	1	−14,000
Challenger 1	10	5	−15,000
	Third Year 200X + 2		
Defender	1	1	−14,000
Challenger 2	5	3	−9,000

11.18 A consulting engineer at Aerospatial estimated AW values for a presently owned, highly accurate steel rivet inserter based on company records of similar equipment.

If Retained This Number of Years	AW Value, $/Year
1	−62,000
2	−50,000
3	−47,000
4	−53,000
5	−70,000

A challenger has ESL = 2 years and $AW_C = \$-49,000$ per year. If the consultant must recommend a replace/retain decision today, should the company purchase the challenger? The MARR is 15% per year.

11.19 If a replacement study is performed and the defender is selected for retention for n_D years, explain what should be done 1 year later if a new challenger is identified.

11.20 BioHealth, a biodevice systems leasing company, is considering a new equipment purchase to replace a currently owned asset that was purchased 2 years ago for $250,000. It is appraised at a current market value of only $50,000. An upgrade is possible for $200,000 now that would be adequate for another 3 years of lease rights, after which the entire system could be sold on the international circuit for an estimated $40,000. The challenger can be purchased at a cost of $300,000, has an expected life of 10 years, and has a $50,000 salvage value. Determine whether the company should upgrade or replace at a MARR of 12% per year. Assume the AOC estimates are the same for both alternatives.

11.21 For the estimates in Problem 11.20, use a spreadsheet-based analysis to determine the maximum first cost for the augmentation of the current system that will make the defender and challenger break even. Is this a maximum or minimum for the upgrade, if the current system is to be retained?

11.22 A lumber company that cuts fine woods for cabinetry is evaluating whether it should retain the current bleaching system or replace it with a new one. The relevant costs for each system are known or estimated. Use an interest rate of 10% per year to (a) perform the replacement analysis and (b) determine the minimum resale price needed to make the challenger replacement choice now. Is this a reasonable amount to expect for the current system?

	Current System	New System
First cost 7 years ago, $	−450,000	
First cost, $		−700,000
Remaining life, years	5	10
Current market value, $	50,000	
AOC, $ per year	−160,000	−150,000
Future salvage, $	0	50,000

11.23 Five years ago, the Warm Bay Port Authority purchased several containerized transport vehicles for $350,000 each. Last year a replacement study was performed with the decision to retain the vehicles for 2 more years. However, this year the situation has changed in that each transport vehicle is estimated to have a value of only $8000 now. If they are kept in service, upgrading at a cost of $50,000 will make them useful for up to 2 more years. Operating cost is expected to be $10,000 the first year and $15,000 the second year, with no salvage value at all. Alternatively, the company can purchase a new vehicle with an ESL of 7 years, no salvage value, and an equivalent annual cost of $−55,540 per year. The MARR is 10% per year. If the budget to upgrade the current vehicles is available this year, use these estimates to determine (a) when the company should replace the upgraded vehicles and (b) the minimum future salvage value of a new vehicle necessary to indicate that purchasing now is economically advantageous to upgrading.

11.24 Annabelle went to work this month for Blackcat Ltd. She was asked to verify the results of a replacement study that concluded in favour of the challenger, a new piece of heavy-duty metal forming equipment for the manufacture of bulldozer blades, scraper blades, and bucket edges for loaders and excavators. At first she concurred because the numerical results were in favour of this challenger.

	Challenger	Defender
Life, years	4	6 more
AW, $ per year	−80,000	−130,000

Curious about past decisions of this same kind, she learned that similar replacement analyses had been performed three previous times every 2 years for the same category of equipment. The decision was consistently to replace with the then-current challenger. During her study, Annabelle concluded that the ESL values were not determined prior to comparing AW values in the analyses made 6, 4, and 2 years ago. She reconstructed as best as possible the analyses for estimated life, ESL, and associated AW values as tabulated. All cost amounts are rounded and in

$1000-per-year units. Determine the two sets of replacement study conclusions (i.e., life-based and ESL-based), and decide if Annabelle is correct in her initial conclusion that were the ESL and AW values calculated, the pattern of replacement decisions would have been significantly different.

11.26 What is meant by the opportunity cost approach in a replacement study?

11.27 Why is it suggested that the cash flow approach not be used when one is performing a replacement study?

11.28 Two years ago, Geo-Sphere Spatial, Inc. (GSSI) purchased a new GPS

Study Performed This Many Years Ago	Defender				Challenger			
	Life, Years	AW, $/Year	ESL, Years	AW, $/Year	Life, Years	AW, $/Year	ESL, Years	AW, $/Year
6	5	−140	2	−100	8	−130	7	−80
4	6	−130	5	−80	5	−120	3	−90
2	3	−140	3	−80	8	−130	8	−120
Now	6	−130	1	−100	4	−80	3 or 4	−80

11.25 Herald Richter and Associates 5 years ago purchased for $45,000 a microwave signal graphical plotter for corrosion detection in concrete structures. It is expected to have the market values and annual operating costs shown for the rest of its useful life of up to 3 years. It could be traded now at an appraised market value of $8000.

Year	Market Value at End of Year, $	AOC, $
1	6000	−50,000
2	4000	−53,000
3	1000	−60,000

A replacement plotter with new Internet-based, digital technology costing $125,000 has an estimated $10,000 salvage value after its 5-year life and an AOC of $31,000 per year. At an interest rate of 15% per year, determine how many more years Richter should retain the present plotter. Solve (*a*) by hand and (*b*) using a spreadsheet.

tracker system for $1,500,000. The estimated salvage value was $50,000 after 9 years. Currently the expected remaining life is 7 years with an AOC of $75,000 per year. A French corporation, La Aramis, has developed a challenger that costs $400,000 and has an estimated 12-year life, $35,000 salvage value, and AOC of $50,000 per year. If the MARR = 12% per year, use a spreadsheet or hand solution (as instructed) to (*a*) find the minimum trade-in value necessary now to make the challenger economically advantageous and (*b*) determine the number of years to retain the defender to just break even if the trade-in offer is $150,000. Assume the $50,000 salvage value can be realized for all retention periods up to 7 years.

11.29 Montreal Tool & Gauge, which supplies parts to aerospace and automotive customers, purchased a CNC lathe 10 years ago for $75,000. The lathe can be used for 3 more years with an annual operating cost of $63,000 and a salvage value of $25,000. A challenger will cost $130,000 with an economic service life of 6 years and an operating cost of $32,000 per year. Its salvage value will be $45,000. On the basis of these estimates, and using an interest rate of 12% per year, what market value for the existing asset will render the challenger equally attractive?

11.30 Three years ago, Mercy Hospital significantly improved its hyperbaric oxygen (HBO) therapy equipment for advanced treatment of problem wounds, chronic bone infections, and radiation injury. The equipment cost $275,000 then and can be used for up to 3 years more. If the HBO system is replaced now, the hospital can realize $20,000. If retained, the market values and operating costs tabulated are estimated. A new system, made of a composite material, is cheaper to purchase initially at $150,000 and cheaper to operate during its initial years. It has a maximum life of 6 years, but market values and AOC change significantly after 3 years of use due to the projected deterioration of the composite material used in construction. Additionally, a recurring cost of $40,000 per year to inspect and rework the composite material is anticipated after 4 years of use. Market values, operating cost, and material rework estimates are tabulated. On the basis of these estimates and $i = 15\%$ per year, what are the ESL and AW values for the defender and challenger, and in what year should the current HBO system be replaced? Work this problem by hand. (See Problems 11.31 and 11.33 for more questions using these estimates.)

| | Current HBO System | | Proposed HBO System | | |
| | Market | | Market | | Material |
Year	Value, $	AOC, $	Value, $	AOC, $	Rework, $
1	10,000	−50,000	65,000	−10,000	
2	6,000	−60,000	45,000	−14,000	
3	2,000	−70,000	25,000	−18,000	
4			5,000	−22,000	
5			0	−26,000	−40,000
6			0	−30,000	−40,000

11.31 Refer to the estimates of Problem 11.30.
(a) Work the problem, using a spreadsheet.
(b) Use Excel's SOLVER to determine the maximum allowed rework cost of the challenger's composite material in years 5 and 6 such that the challenger's AW value for 6 years will exactly equal the defender's AW value at its ESL. Explain the impact of this lower rework cost on the conclusion of the replacement study.

Replacement Study over a Study Period

11.32 Consider two replacement studies to be performed using the same defenders and challengers and the same estimated costs. For the first study, no study period is specified; for the second, a study period of 5 years is specified.

(a) State the difference in the fundamental assumptions of the two replacement studies.

(b) Describe the differences in the procedures followed in performing the replacement studies for the conditions.

11.33 Reread the situation and estimates explained in Problem 11.30. (a) Perform the replacement study for a fixed study period of 5 years. (b) If, in lieu of the challenger purchase, a full-service contract for hyperbaric oxygen therapy were offered to Mercy Hospital for a total of $85,000 per year if contracted for 4 or 5 years or $100,000 for a 3-year or less contract, which option or combination is economically the best between the defender and the contract?

11.34 A mining engineer determined that the equivalent annual worth of an existing impact crusher over its remaining useful life of 3 years will be $–70,000 per year. It can be replaced now or later with a machine that will have an AW of $–80,000 if it is kept for 2 years or less, $–68,000 if it is kept between 3 and 4 years, and $–75,000 if it is kept for 5 to 10 years. When should the mining company replace the crusher if a 3-year study period and an interest rate of 15% per year are used?

11.35 Use a spreadsheet to perform a replacement analysis for the following situation. An engineer estimates that the equivalent annual worth of an existing machine over its remaining useful life of 3 years is $–90,000 per year. It can be replaced now or after 3 years with a machine that will have an AW of $–90,000 per year if kept for 5 years or less and $–110,000 per year if kept for 6 to 8 years.

(a) Perform the analysis to determine the AW values for study periods

of length 5 through 8 years at an interest rate of 10% per year. Select the study period with the lowest AW value. How many years are the defender and challenger used?

(b) Can the PW values be used to select the best study period length and decide to retain or replace the defender? Why or why not?

11.36 Christie Brown and Co. currently employs staff to operate the equipment used to sterilize much of the mixing, baking, and packaging facilities in a large cookie and cracker manufacturing plant. The plant manager, who is dedicated to cutting costs but not sacrificing quality and cleanliness, has the projected data were the current system retained for up to its maximum expected life of 5 years. A contract company has proposed a turnkey sanitation system for $5.0 million per year if Christie signs on for 4 to 10 years and $5.5 million per year for a smaller number of years.

(a) At an MARR = 8% per year, perform a replacement study for the plant manager with a fixed planning horizon of 5 years, when it is anticipated that the plant will be shut down due to age of the facility and projected technological obsolescence. As you perform the study, take into account the fact that regardless of the number of years that the current sanitation system is retained, a one-time close-down cost will be incurred for personnel and equipment during the last year of operation.

(b) What is the percentage change in AW amount each year of the 5-year study period? If the decision to retain the current sanitation system is made, what is the economic disadvantage in AW amount compared to that of the best economic retention period?

Current Sanitation System Estimates

Years Retained	AW, $/Year	Close-Down Expense Last Year of Retention, $
0		−3,000,000
1	−2,300,000	−2,500,000
2	−2,300,000	−2,000,000
3	−3,000,000	−1,000,000
4	−3,000,000	−1,000,000
5	−3,500,000	−500,000

11.37 A machine purchased 3 years ago for $140,000 is now too slow to satisfy increased demand. It can be upgraded now for $70,000 or sold to a smaller company for $40,000. The current machine will have an annual operating cost of $85,000 per year and a $30,000 salvage value in 3 years. If upgraded, that machine will be retained for only 3 more years, then replaced with one to be used in the manufacture of several other product lines.

The replacement machine, which will serve the company now and for at least 8 years, will cost $220,000. Its salvage value will be $50,000 for years 1 through 5, $20,000 in year 6, and $10,000 thereafter. It will have an estimated operating cost of $65,000 per year. The company asks you to perform an economic analysis at 15% per year using a 3-year planning horizon. Should it replace the presently owned machine now, or 3 years from now? What are the AW values?

EXTENDED EXERCISE

ECONOMIC SERVICE LIFE UNDER VARYING CONDITIONS

New pumper system equipment is under consideration by a chemical processing plant. One crucial pump moves highly corrosive liquids from specially lined tanks on barges into storage and preliminary refining facilities dockside. Because of the variable quality of the raw chemical and the high pressures imposed on the pump chassis and impellers, a close log is maintained on the number of hours per year that the pump operates. Safety records and pump component deterioration are considered critical control points for this system. As currently planned, rebuild and M&O cost estimates are increased accordingly when cumulative operating time reaches the 6000-hour mark. Estimates made for this pump are as follows:

First cost: $−800,000

Rebuild cost: $−150,000 whenever 6000 cumulative hours are logged. Each rework will cost 20% more than the previous one. A maximum of 3 rebuilds is allowed.

M&O costs: $25,000 for each year 1 through 4

$40,000 per year starting the year after the first rebuild, plus 15% per year thereafter

MARR: 10% per year

Based on previous logbook data, the current estimates for number of operating hours per year are as follows:

Year	Hours per Year
1	500
2	1500
3 on	2000

Questions

1. Determine the economic service life of the pump.

2. The plant superintendent told the new engineer on the job that only one rebuild should be planned for, because these types of pumps usually have their minimum cost life before the second rebuild. Determine a market value for this pump that will force the ESL to be 6 years.

3. The plant superintendent also told the safety engineer that they should not plan for a rebuild after 6000 hours, because the pump will be replaced after a total of 10,000 hours of operation. The safety engineer wants to know what the base AOC in year 1 can be to make the ESL 6 years. The engineer assumes now that the 15% growth rate applies from year 1 forward. How does this base AOC value compare with the rebuild cost after 6000 hours?

CASE STUDY

REPLACEMENT ANALYSIS FOR QUARRY EQUIPMENT

Equipment used to move raw material from the quarry to the rock crushers was purchased 3 years ago by Archer Cement Ltd. When purchased, the equipment had $P = \$85,000$, $n = 10$ years, $S = \$5000$, with an annual capacity of 180,000 tonnes. Additional equipment with a capacity of 240,000 tonnes per year is now needed. Such equipment can be purchased for $P = \$70,000$, $n = 10$ years, $S = \$8000$.

However, a consultant has pointed out that the company can construct conveyor equipment to move the material from the quarry. This will cost an estimated $115,000 with a life of 15 years and no significant salvage value. It will carry 400,000 tonnes per year. The company needs some way to move material to the conveyor in the quarry. The presently owned equipment can be used, but it will have excess capacity. If new smaller-capacity equipment is purchased, there is a $15,000 market value for the currently used equipment. The smaller-capacity equipment will require a capital outlay of $40,000 with an estimated life of $n = 12$ years and $S = \$3500$. The capacity is 400,000 tonnes per year over this short distance. Monthly operating, maintenance, and insurance costs will average $0.01 per tonne-kilometre for the movers. Corresponding costs for the conveyor are expected to be $0.0075 per tonne.

The company wants to make 12% per year on this investment. Records show that the equipment must move raw material an average of 2.4 kilometres from the quarry to the crusher pad. The conveyor will be placed to reduce this distance to 0.75 kilometre.

Case Study Exercises

1. You have been asked to determine if the old equipment should be augmented with new equipment or if the conveyor equipment should be considered as a replacement. If replacement is more economical, which method of moving the material in the quarry should be used?

2. Because of new safety regulations, the control of dust in the quarry and at the crusher site has become a real problem and implies that new capital must be invested to improve the environment for employees, or else large fines may be imposed. Archer's president has obtained an initial quote from a subcontractor which would take over the entire raw material movement operation being evaluated here for a base annual amount of $21,000 and a variable cost of 1 cent per metric ton moved. The 10 employees in the quarry operation would be employed elsewhere in the company with no financial impact upon the estimates for this evaluation. Should this offer be seriously considered if the best estimate is that 380,000 tonnes per year would be moved by the subcontractor? Identify any additional assumptions necessary to adequately address this new question posed by the president.

CHAPTER

Selection from Independent Projects Under Budget Limitation

In most of the previous economic comparisons, the alternatives have been mutually exclusive; only one could be selected. If the projects are not mutually exclusive, they are categorized as independent of each other, as discussed at the beginning of Chapter 5. Now we learn techniques to select from several independent projects. It is possible to select any number of projects from none (do nothing) to all viable projects.

There is virtually always some upper limit on the amount of capital available for investment in new projects. This limit is considered as each independent project is economically evaluated. The technique applied is called the *capital budgeting method,* also referred to as capital rationing. It determines the economically best rationing of initial investment capital among independent projects. The capital budgeting method is an application of the present worth method.

The case study takes a look at the project selection dilemmas of an engineering professional society striving to serve its membership with a limited budget in a technologically changing world.

LEARNING OBJECTIVES

Purpose: Select from several independent projects when there is a capital investment limit.

By the end of this chapter you should be able to

Capital rationing	**1.** Explain the logic used to ration capital among independent projects.
Projects with equal lives	**2.** Use PW analysis to select from several equal-life independent projects.
Projects with unequal lives	**3.** Use PW analysis to select from several unequal-life independent projects.
Linear program model	**4.** Solve the capital budgeting problem using linear programming by hand and by computer.
Simplex algorithm	**5.** Use the simplex algorithm to solve large linear programming tradeoff problems.

12.1 AN OVERVIEW OF CAPITAL RATIONING AMONG PROJECTS

...ually exclusive
and independent

Investment capital is a scarce resource for all corporations; thus there is usually always a limited amount to be distributed among competing investment opportunities. When a corporation has several options for placing investment capital, a "reject or accept" decision must be made for each project. Effectively, each option is independent of other options, so the evaluation is performed on a project-by-project basis. Selection of one project does not impact the selection decision for any other project. This is the fundamental difference between mutually exclusive alternatives and independent projects.

The term *project* is used to identify each independent option. We use the term *bundle* to identify a collection of independent projects. The term mutually exclusive alternative continues to identify a project when only one may be selected from several.

There are two exceptions to purely independent projects: A *contingent project* is one that has a condition placed upon its acceptance or rejection. Two examples of contingent projects A and B are as follows: A cannot be accepted unless B is accepted; and A can be accepted in lieu of B, but both are not needed. A *dependent project* is one that must be accepted or rejected based on the decision about another project(s). For example, B must be accepted if both A and C are accepted. In practice, these complicating conditions can be bypassed by forming packages of related projects that are economically evaluated themselves as independent projects with the remaining, unconditioned projects.

The *capital budgeting* problem has the following characteristics:

1. Several independent projects are identified, and net cash flow estimates are available.
2. Each project is either selected entirely or not selected; that is, partial investment in a project is not possible.
3. A stated budgetary constraint restricts the total amount available for investment. Budget constraints may be present for the first year only or for several years. This investment limit is identified by the symbol b.
4. The objective is to maximize the return on the investments using a measure of worth, usually the PW value.

By nature, independent projects are usually quite different from one another. For example, in the public sector, a city government may develop several projects to choose from: drainage, city park, street widening, and an upgraded public bus system. In the private sector, sample projects may be: a new warehousing facility, expanded product base, improved quality program, upgraded information system, or acquisition of another firm. The typical capital budgeting problem is illustrated in Figure 12–1. For each independent project there is an initial investment, project life, and estimated net cash flows that can include a salvage value.

Present worth analysis is the recommended method to select projects. The selection guideline is as follows:

Accept projects with the best PW values determined at the MARR over the project life, provided the investment capital limit is not exceeded.

FIGURE 12–1
Basic characteristics
of a capital budgeting
problem.

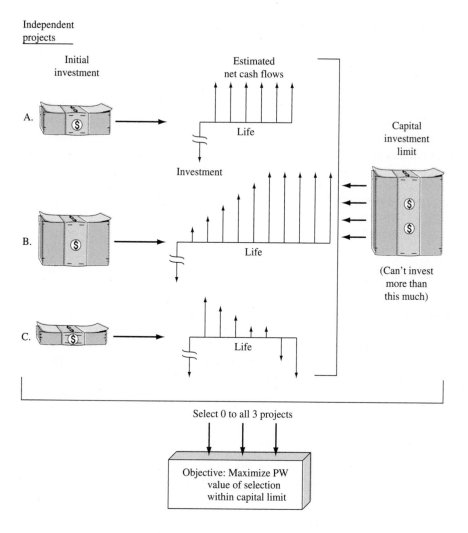

Independent
projects

Initial
investment

Estimated
net cash flows

A.

Life

Investment

Capital
investment
limit

B.

Life

(Can't invest
more than
this much)

C.

Life

Select 0 to all 3 projects

Objective: Maximize PW
value of selection
within capital limit

This guideline is no different from that used for selection in previous chapters for independent projects. As before, each project is compared with the do-nothing project; that is, incremental analysis between projects is not necessary. The primary difference now is that the amount of money available to invest is limited. Therefore, a specific solution procedure that incorporates this constraint is needed.

Previously, PW analysis required the assumption of equal service between alternatives. This assumption is not valid for capital rationing, because there is no life cycle of a project beyond its estimated life. Yet, the selection guideline is based on the *PW over the respective life of each independent project.* This means there is an implied reinvestment assumption, as follows:

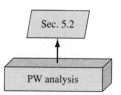

All positive net cash flows of a project are reinvested at the MARR from the time they are realized until the end of the longest-lived project.

This fundamental assumption is demonstrated to be correct at the end of Section 12.3, which treats PW-based capital rationing for unequal-life projects.

Another dilemma of capital rationing among independent projects concerns the flexibility of the capital investment limit b. The limit may marginally disallow an acceptable project that is next in line for acceptance. For example, assume project A has a positive PW value at the MARR. If A will cause the capital limit of $5,000,000 to be exceeded by only $1000, should A be included in the PW analysis? Commonly, a capital investment limit is somewhat flexible, so project A should be included. In the examples here, we will not exceed a stated investment limit.

It is possible to use a ROR analysis to select from independent projects. As we have learned in previous chapters, the ROR technique may not select the same projects as a PW analysis unless incremental ROR analysis is performed over the LCM of lives. The same is true in the case of capital rationing. Therefore, we recommend the PW method for capital rationing among independent projects.

12.2 CAPITAL RATIONING USING PW ANALYSIS OF EQUAL-LIFE PROJECTS

To select from projects that have the same expected life while investing no more than the limit b, first formulate all *mutually exclusive bundles*—one project at a time, two at a time, etc. Each feasible bundle must have a total investment that does not exceed b. One of these bundles is the do-nothing (DN) project. The total number of bundles for m projects is calculated using the relation 2^m. The number increases rapidly with m. For $m = 4$, there are $2^4 = 16$ bundles, and for $m = 6$, $2^6 = 64$ bundles. Then the PW of each bundle is determined at the MARR. The bundle with the largest PW value is selected.

To illustrate the development of mutually exclusive bundles, consider these four projects with equal lives.

Project	Initial Investment
A	$-10,000
B	-5,000
C	-8,000
D	-15,000

If the investment limit is $b = \$25,000$, of the 16 bundles there are 12 feasible ones to evaluate. The bundles ABD, ACD, BCD, and ABCD have investment totals that exceed $25,000. The viable bundles are shown below.

Projects	Total Initial Investment	Projects	Total Initial Investment
A	$-10,000	AD	$-25,000
B	-5,000	BC	-13,000
C	-8,000	BD	-20,000
D	-15,000	CD	-23,000
AB	-15,000	ABC	-23,000
AC	-18,000	Do nothing	0

The procedure to solve a capital budgeting problem using PW analysis is as follows:

1. Develop all mutually exclusive bundles with a total initial investment that does not exceed the capital limit b.
2. Sum the net cash flows NCF_{jt} for all projects in each bundle j and each year t from 1 to the expected project life n_j. Refer to the initial investment of bundle j at time $t = 0$ as NCF_{j0}.
3. Compute the present worth value PW_j for each bundle at the MARR.

$$PW_j = PW \text{ of bundle net cash flows} - \text{initial investment}$$

$$PW_j = \sum_{t=1}^{t=n_j} NCF_{jt}(P/F,i,t) - NCF_{j0} \qquad [12.1]$$

4. Select the bundle with the (numerically) largest PW_j value.

Selecting the maximum PW_j means that this bundle produces a return larger than any other bundle. Any bundle with $PW_j < 0$ is discarded, because it does not produce a return of MARR.

EXAMPLE 12.1

The projects review committee of Research in Motion Ltd. has $20 million to allocate next year to new product development. Any or all of five projects in Table 12–1 may be accepted. All amounts are in $1000 units. Each project has an expected life of 9 years. Select the project if a 15% return is expected.

TABLE 12–1   Five Equal-Life Independent Projects ($1000 units)

Project	Initial Investment	Annual Net Cash Flow	Project Life, Years
A	$-10,000	$2,870	9
B	-15,000	2,930	9
C	-8,000	2,680	9
D	-6,000	2,540	9
E	-21,000	9,500	9

Solution

Use the procedure above with $b = \$20,000$ to select one bundle that maximizes present worth. Remember the units are in $1000.

1. There are $2^5 = 32$ possible bundles. The eight bundles which require no more than $20,000 initial investments are described in columns 2 and 3 of Table 12–2. The $21,000 investment for E eliminates it from all bundles.

TABLE 12–2 Summary of Present Worth Analysis of Equal-Life Independent Projects ($1000 units)

Bundle j (1)	Projects Included (2)	Initial Investment NCF_{j0} (3)	Annual Net Cash Flow NCF_j (4)	Present Worth PW_j (5)
1	A	$-10,000	$2,870	$ +3,694
2	B	-15,000	2,930	-1,019
3	C	-8,000	2,680	+4,788
4	D	-6,000	2,540	+6,120
5	AC	-18,000	5,550	+8,482
6	AD	-16,000	5,410	+9,814
7	CD	-14,000	5,220	+10,908
8	Do nothing	0	0	0

2. The bundle net cash flows, column 4, are the sum of individual project net cash flows.

3. Use Equation [12.1] to compute the present worth for each bundle. Since the annual NCF and life estimates are the same for a bundle, PW_j reduces to

$$PW_j = NCF_j(P/A,15\%,9) - NCF_{j0}$$

4. Column 5 of Table 12–2 summarizes the PW_j values at $i = 15\%$. Bundle 2 does not return 15%, since $PW_2 < 0$. The largest is $PW_7 = \$10,908$; therefore, invest $14 million in C and D. This leaves $6 million uncommitted.

Comment

This analysis assumes that the $6 million not used in this initial investment will return the MARR by placing it in some other, unspecified investment opportunity. The return on bundle 7 exceeds 15% per year. The actual rate of return, using the relation $0 = -14,000 + 5220(P/A,i^*,9)$ is $i^* = 34.8\%$, which significantly exceeds MARR = 15%.

12.3 CAPITAL RATIONING USING PW ANALYSIS OF UNEQUAL-LIFE PROJECTS

Usually independent projects do not have the same expected life. As stated in Section 12.1, the PW method for solution of the capital budgeting problem assumes that each project will last for the period of the longest-lived project n_L. *Additionally, reinvestment of any positive net cash flows is assumed to be at the MARR from the time they are realized until the end of the longest-lived project,* *that is, from year n_j through year n_L.* Therefore, the use of the least common multiple of lives is not necessary, and it is correct to use Equation [12.1] to select bundles of unequal-life projects by PW analysis using the procedure of the previous section.

EXAMPLE 12.2

For a MARR = 15% per year and b = $20,000, select from the following independent projects. Solve by hand and by computer.

Project	Initial Investment	Annual Net Cash Flow	Project Life, Years
A	$ −8,000	$3,870	6
B	−15,000	2,930	9
C	−8,000	2,680	5
D	−8,000	2,540	4

Solution by Hand
The unequal-life values make the net cash flows vary over a bundle's life, but the selection procedure is the same as above. Of the $2^4 = 16$ bundles, 8 are economically feasible. Their PW values by Equation [12.1] are summarized in Table 12–3. As an illustration, for bundle 7:

$$PW_7 = -16,000 + 5220(P/A,15\%,4) + 2680(P/F,15\%,5) = \$235$$

Select bundle 5 (projects A and C) for a $16,000 investment.

TABLE 12–3   Present Worth Analysis for Unequal-Life Independent Projects, Example 12.2

Bundle j (1)	Project (2)	Initial Investment, NCF_{j0} (3)	Net Cash Flows Year t (4)	Net Cash Flows NCF_{jt} (5)	Present Worth PW_j (6)
1	A	$ −8,000	1–6	$3,870	$+6,646
2	B	−15,000	1–9	2,930	−1,019
3	C	−8,000	1–5	2,680	+984
4	D	−8,000	1–4	2,540	−748
5	AC	−16,000	1–5	6,550	+7,630
			6	3,870	
6	AD	−16,000	1–4	6,410	+5,898
			5–6	3,870	
7	CD	−16,000	1–4	5,220	+235
			5	2,680	
8	Do nothing	0		0	0

E-SOLVE

Solution by Computer

Figure 12–2 presents a spreadsheet with the same information as in Table 12–3. It is necessary to initially develop the mutually exclusive bundles and total net cash flows each year. Bundle 5 (projects A and C) has the largest PW value (row 16 cells). The NPV function is used to determine PW for each bundle j over its respective life, using the format NPV(MARR,NCF_year_1:NCF_year_n_j)+investment.

	A	B	C	D	E	F	G	H	I	J
1	MARR =	15%								
2										
3	Bundle	1	2	3	4	5	6	7	8	
4	Projects	A	B	C	D	AC	AD	CD	Do nothing	
5	Year				Net cash flows, NCF(j,t)					
6	0	-$8,000	-$15,000	-$8,000	-$8,000	-$16,000	-$16,000	-$16,000	0	
7	1	$3,870	$2,930	$2,680	$2,540	$6,550	$6,410	$5,220	0	
8	2	$3,870	$2,930	$2,680	$2,540	$6,550	$6,410	$5,220	0	
9	3	$3,870	$2,930	$2,680	$2,540	$6,550	$6,410	$5,220	0	
10	4	$3,870	$2,930	$2,680	$2,540	$6,550	$6,410	$5,220	0	
11	5	$3,870	$2,930	$2,680		$6,550	$3,870	$2,680	0	
12	6	$3,870	$2,930			$3,870	$3,870		0	
13	7		$2,930					= D7+E7	0	
14	8		$2,930						0	
15	9		$2,930						0	
16	PW Value	$6,646	-$1,019	$984	-$748	$7,630	$5,898	$235	$0	
17										
18			= NPV($B$1,C7:C15)+C6					= NPV($B$1,H7:H15)+H6		
19										

FIGURE 12–2

Spreadsheet analysis to select from independent projects of unequal life using the PW method of capital rationing, Example 12.2.

It is important to understand why solution of the capital budgeting problem by PW evaluation using Equation [12.1] is correct. The following logic verifies the assumption of reinvestment at the MARR for all net positive cash flows when project lives are unequal. Refer to Figure 12–3, which uses the general layout of a two-project bundle. Assume each project has the same net cash flow each year. The P/A factor is used for PW computation. Define n_L as the life of the longer lived project. At the end of the shorter-lived project, the bundle has a total future worth of $NCF_j(F/A,MARR,n_j)$ as determined for each project. Now, assume reinvestment at the MARR from year n_{j+1} through year n_L (a total of $n_L - n_j$ years). The assumption of the return at the MARR is important; this PW approach does not necessarily select the correct projects if the return is not at the MARR. The results are the two future worth arrows in year n_L in Figure 12–3. Finally, compute the bundle PW value in the initial year. This is the bundle PW $= PW_A + PW_B$. In general form, the bundle j present worth is

$$PW_j = NCF_j(F/A,MARR,n_j)(F/P,MARR,n_L - n_j)(P/F,MARR,n_L) \quad [12.2]$$

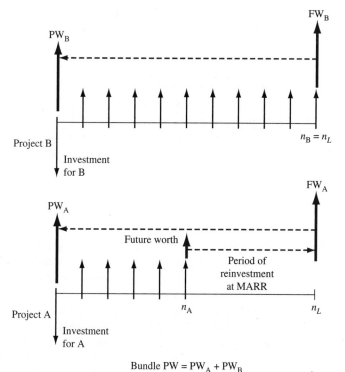

FIGURE 12–3
Representative cash flows used to compute PW for a bundle of two independent unequal-life projects by Equation [12.1].

Substitute the symbol i for the MARR, and use the factor formulas to simplify.

$$PW_j = NCF_j \frac{(1+i)^{n_j}-1}{i}(1+i)^{n_L-n_j}\frac{1}{(1+i)^{n_L}}$$

$$= NCF_j\left[\frac{(1+i)^{n_j}-1}{i(1+i)^{n_j}}\right] \qquad [12.3]$$

$$= NCF_j(P/A,i,n_j)$$

Since the bracketed expression in Equation [12.3] is the $(P/A,i,n_j)$ factor, computation of PW_j for n_j years assumes reinvestment at the MARR of all positive net cash flows until the longest-lived project is completed in year n_L.

To demonstrate numerically, consider bundle $j = 7$ in Example 12.2. The evaluation is in Table 12–3, and the net cash flow is pictured in Figure 12–4. At 15% the future worth in year 9, life of B, the longest-lived project of the four, is

$$FW = 5220(F/A,15\%,4)(F/P,15\%,5) + 2680(F/P,15\%,4) = \$57,111$$

The present worth at the initial investment time is

$$PW = -16,000 + 57,111(P/F,15\%,9) = \$235$$

FIGURE 12–4

Initial investment and cash flows for bundle 7, projects C and D, Example 12.2.

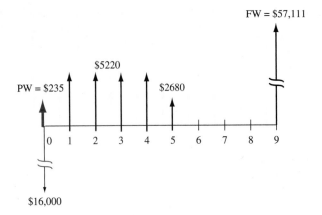

The PW value is the same as PW_7 in Table 12–3 and Figure 12–2. This demonstrates the reinvestment assumption for positive net cash flows. If this assumption is not realistic, the PW analysis must be conducted using the *LCM of all project lives.*

Project selection can also be accomplished using the *incremental rate of return* procedure. Once all viable, mutually exclusive bundles are developed, they are ordered by increasing initial investment. Determine the incremental rate of return on the first bundle relative to the do-nothing bundle, and the return for each incremental investment and incremental net cash flow sequence on all other bundles. If any bundle has an incremental return less than the MARR, it is removed. The last justified increment indicates the best bundle. This approach results in the same answer as the PW procedure. There are a number of incorrect ways to apply the rate of return method, but the procedure of incremental analysis on mutually exclusive bundles ensures a correct result, as in previous applications of incremental rate of return.

12.4 CAPITAL BUDGETING PROBLEM FORMULATION USING LINEAR PROGRAMMING

The capital budgeting problem can be stated in the form of the linear programming model. The problem is formulated using the integer linear programming (ILP) model, which means simply that all relations are linear and that the variable x can take on only integer values. In this case, the variables can only take on the values 0 or 1, which makes it a special case called the 0-or-1 ILP model. The formulation in words follows.

Maximize: Sum of PW of net cash flows of independent projects.

Constraints:

- Capital investment constraint is that the sum of initial investments must not exceed a specified limit.
- Each project is completely selected or not selected.

For the math formulation, define b as the capital investment limit, and let x_k ($k = 1$ to m projects) be the variables to be determined. If $x_k = 1$, project k is completely selected; if $x_k = 0$, project k is not selected. Note that the subscript k represents each *independent project,* not a mutually exclusive bundle.

If the sum of PW of the net cash flows is Z, the math programming formulation is

Maximize:

$$\sum_{k=1}^{k=4} PW_k x_k = Z$$

Constraints:

$$\sum_{k=1}^{k=4} NCF_{k0} x_k \leq b \qquad [12.4]$$

$$x_k = 0 \text{ or } 1 \qquad \text{for } k = 1, 2, \ldots, m$$

The PW_k of each project is calculated using Equation [12.1] at MARR $= i$.

$$PW_k = \text{PW of project net cash flows for } n_k \text{ years}$$

$$= \sum_{t=1}^{t=n_k} NCF_{kt}(P/F, i, t) - NCF_{k0} \qquad [12.5]$$

Computer solution is accomplished by a linear programming software package which treats the ILP model. Also, Excel and its optimizing tool SOLVER can be used to develop the formulation and select the projects, as illustrated in Example 12.3.

EXAMPLE 12.3

Review Example 12.2. (*a*) Formulate the capital budgeting problem using the math programming model presented in Equation [12.4], and insert the solution into the model to verify that it does indeed maximize present worth. (*b*) Set up and solve the problem using Excel.

Solution
(*a*) Define the subscript $k = 1$ through 4 for the four projects, which are relabelled as 1, 2, 3, and 4. The capital investment limit is $b = \$20,000$ in Equation [12.4].

Maximize:

$$\sum_{k=1}^{k=4} PW_k x_k = Z$$

Constraints:

$$\sum_{k=1}^{k=4} NCF_{k0} x_k \leq 20,000$$

$$x_k = 0 \text{ or } 1 \qquad \text{for } k = 1 \text{ through } 4$$

Calculate the PW_k for the estimated net cash flows using $i = 15\%$ and Equation [12.5].

Project k	Net Cash Flow NCF_{kt}	Life n_k	Factor $(P/A,15\%,n_k)$	Initial Investment NCF_{k0}	Project PW_k
1	$3,870	6	3.7845	$-8,000	$+6,646
2	2,930	9	4.7716	-15,000	-1,019
3	2,680	5	3.3522	-8,000	+984
4	2,540	4	2.8550	-8,000	-748

Now, substitute the PW_k values into the model, and put the initial investments in the budget constraint. Plus signs are used for all values in the capital investment constraint. We have the complete 0-or-1 ILP formulation.

Maximize: $6646x_1 - 1019x_2 + 984x_3 - 748x_4 = Z$

Constraints: $8000x_1 + 15{,}000x_2 + 8000x_3 + 8000x_4 < 20{,}000$

$x_1, x_2, x_3,$ and $x_4 = 0$ or 1

Solution to select projects 1 and 3 is written:

$$x_1 = 1 \qquad x_2 = 0 \qquad x_3 = 1 \qquad x_4 = 0$$

for a PW value of $7630.

E-SOLVE

(b) Figure 12–5 presents a spreadsheet template developed to select from six or fewer independent projects with 12 years or less of net cash flow estimates per project. The spreadsheet template can be expanded in either direction if needed. Figure 12–6 shows the SOLVER parameters set to solve this example for four projects and an investment limit of $20,000. The descriptions below and the cell tags identify the contents of the rows and cells in Figure 12–5, and their linkage to SOLVER parameters.

Rows 4 and 5: Projects are identified by numbers in order to distinguish them from spreadsheet column letters. Cell I5 is the expression for Z, the sum of the PW values for the projects. This is the target cell for SOLVER to maximize (see Figure 12–6).

Rows 6 to 18: These are initial investments and net cash flow estimates for each project. Zero values that occur after the life of a project need not be entered; however, any $0 estimates that occur during a project's life must be entered.

Row 19: The entry in each cell is 1 for a selected project and 0 if not selected. These are the changing cells for SOLVER. Since each entry must be 0 or 1, a binary constraint is placed on all row 19 cells in SOLVER, as shown in Figure 12–6. When a problem is to be solved, it is best to initialize the spreadsheet with 0s for all projects. SOLVER will find the solution to maximize Z.

Row 20: The NPV function is used to find the PW for each net cash flow series. The cell tags, which detail the NPV functions, are set for any project with a life up to 12 years at the MARR entered in cell B1.

Row 21: The contribution to the Z function occurs when a project is selected. Where row 19 has a 0 entry for a project, no contribution is made.

Row 22: This row shows the initial investment for the selected projects. Cell I22 is the total investment. This cell has the budget limitation placed on it by the constraint in SOLVER. In this example, the constraint is I22 $< =$ $20,000.

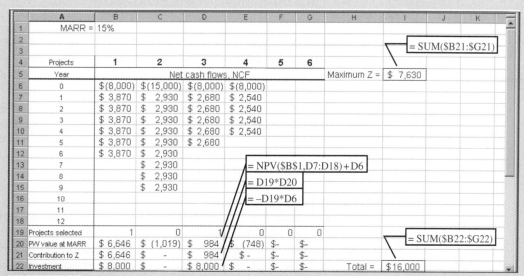

FIGURE 12–5

Excel spreadsheet configured to solve a capital budgeting problem, Example 12.3.

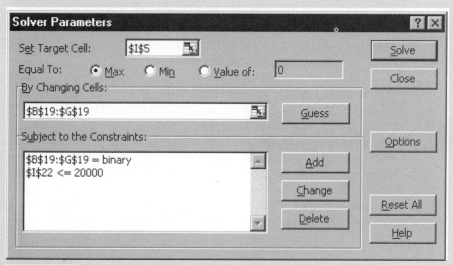

FIGURE 12–6

SOLVER parameters set to solve the capital budgeting problem in Example 12.3.

To use the spreadsheet to solve the example, set all values in row 19 to 0, set up the SOLVER parameters as described above, and click on Solve. (Since this is a linear model, the SOLVER options choice "Assume Linear Model" may be checked, if desired.) If needed, further directions on saving the solution, making changes, etc., are available in Appendix A, Section A.4, and on the Excel help function.

For this problem, the selection is projects 1 and 3 (cells B19 and D19) with $Z = \$7630$, the same as determined previously. Sensitivity analysis can now be performed on any estimates made for the projects.

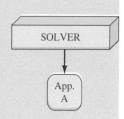

12.5 LINEAR PROGRAMMING WITH RELAXED ASSUMPTIONS

The capital rationing constraints that were established in Section 12.1 can be relaxed. In the private sector, engineering economic studies are often performed to assess the optimal mix of products to be manufactured that will maximize the profit of a corporation. In the public sector, subsidies to various government jurisdictions can be mixed to provide a fair set of services to the various needs of the population. When the requirement of having results expressed as integers is relaxed, linear programming (LP) models will determine the optimal mix of budgets to optimize the overall allocation of capital.

Typical applications are the following:

- Given a factory that produces several products and has a limited capacity in labour hours and machining equipment, find the product mix that makes the best use of the labour and equipment available.
- Given a processing plant that produces several products and has a limited supply of raw materials or inputs, find the optimal allocation of inputs to products that will yield the maximum profit.
- Given an advertising budget and various media, maximize product exposure to the consumer.
- Given a set of manufacturing or agricultural production centres with several distribution centres located in various geographical locations, where each factory has a defined capacity and each warehouse needs a certain quantity, allocate the product centre's outputs to the distribution centres in a manner that minimizes the transportation costs.
- Given a public agency responsible for several services and products but constrained in its monetary, time, and personnel resources, select the mix of services that optimally uses the limited inputs.
- Given a limited budget, find the optimum combination of programs within a jurisdiction such as education where various educational structures can be used in combination to deliver the program. The goal may range from the desire to increase the public's quality of life to that of increasing their efficiency and productivity. The need is to maximize the community's exposure to the educational program by selecting an optimum combination of project alternatives.

Engineering economic projects frequently lend themselves to the framework of linear programming when they involve numerous and discrete alternatives and have resource limitations comprising inequality constraints. As in other analysis techniques, the principal purpose of modelling is to illuminate the consequences and impacts of various alternative policies and to provide evidence for decision making. Much can be learned even from very aggregated models designed to answer specific questions of policy, since the exercise forces quantitative consistency in planning decisions and helps to view the problems from a new perspective.

The graphical method for solving LP problems involves the following steps:

- Formulate the problem with an objective equation (maximizing service or profit or minimizing cost), and a set of constraints (limits to available resources and budget).
- Graph each constraint. The intersection of these lines will establish the feasible solution region.
- Assign an arbitrary value to the objective function and graph this straight-line equation. The slope of this line represents an iso-profit line, on which the profit is the same at each point. Parallel lines (with the same slope) indicate other objective functions that have different values. Since the objective is to maximize the value of the equation, movement away from the origin provides the best set of operating characteristics.
- Move this line parallel to itself until the last point of the feasible region is touched.
- Determine the optimal solution by solving the two constraint equations (with two unknowns), which determine the optimal point on the graph.
- Substitute these values back into the objective function to determine the optimal value of the objective function.

EXAMPLE 12.4

Engineers Without Borders Canada (EWB) has 28 university chapters and more than 50,000 members across the country. Chapters are able to send volunteers to developing communities for four-month Junior Fellowship Programme work terms in which they interact with local partners to help alleviate poverty through access to technology. A principal goal is to build capacity within these communities so the local entrepreneurs can take over the management, maintenance, and expansion of the projects. James Orbinski, past president of Médecins Sans Frontiéres, and His Excellency John Ralston Saul are on its advisory board.

A simplified problem situation allows an illustration of a development policy analysis example and the mechanics of linear programming with its graphical solution. Consider the choices involved in the planting of crops to feed people and livestock in Ethiopia. The community's well-being is best served by producing a combination of both. The total amounts to be planted are constrained by agricultural inputs, which limit the expansion of production. In this example, there are limited supplies of arable land, water, and animal and tractor power. Labour, fertilizer, and seed are available in sufficient quantities.

The initial decision is that of choosing a level of production for rice, beans, and cassava as food crops on the one hand, and maize for livestock feed on the other. The objective is to select the production levels that will optimize the community's well-being, considering such factors as quality of life, health, security in the supply of basic needs, and purchasing power. For simplicity, this example will assume monetary units for these concerns, because the production of these crops supply some of the community's basic needs and can supply additional money to them through the exportation of the surplus. The expression of these terms in the framework of utility analysis is another option, which we explore in Chapter 17 of this text.

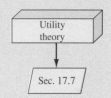

The required data are summarized as follows (all numbers $\times 10^3$):

Maximum available arable land = 96 hectares/season

Maximum available irrigation and water supplies = 220 cubic metres

Maximum available animal and tractor power = 15 hours of planting and harvesting/period

| | Resources Consumed | | | |
	Land	Water	Power	Contribution to Objective
Food crop (x_1)	8	10	1	$8
Livestock feed (x_2)	5	17	1	$6

Define x_1 to be the level of food crops to be farmed and x_2 to be the level of livestock feed to produce. The objective is to maximize the productivity of the inputs with respect to their influence on the community's quality of life expressed in terms of the yield that can be anticipated for various planting levels and its monetary return.

Data indicate that each tonne of food crop will contribute $8 of profit to the objective and each tonne of livestock feed will contribute $6 of profit. Therefore, the objective function is:

$$Z_0 = 8x_1 + 6x_2$$

where

Z_0 = profit ($)

x_1 = amount of food crops produced (tonnes)

x_2 = amount of livestock feed produced (tonnes)

The project is limited by the supply of land, water, and power services available. These limitations are written as "less than or equal to" constraints as follows:

$8x_1 + 5x_2 \leq 96$	for arable land
$10x_1 + 17x_2 \leq 220$	for irrigation and water supplies
$x_1 + x_2 \leq 15$	for animal and tractor power services
$x_1, x_2 \geq 0$	for nonnegativity of production

The first equation represents the facts that each tonne of food crop consumes 8 hectares of land per season and that each tonne of livestock feed consumes 5 hectares of land. The total amount of land as a resource that is available per season is 96 hectares. All 96 hectares or less can be used, but not more. The model uses this equation to ascertain that the land constraint will not be violated. Every unit (tonne) of x_1 depletes 8 units (hectares) from the 96 for further exploitation, and every unit of x_2 removes 5 units from the 96 until they are all used. The other constraints have similar explanations.

To summarize our equations we have the following set of linear equations:

Maximize:	$Z_0 = 8x_1 + 6x_2$
Subject to:	$8x_1 + 5x_2 \leq 96$
	$10x_1 + 17x_2 \leq 220$
	$x_1 + x_2 \leq 15$
	$x_1, x_2 \geq 0$

This set of equations can be solved graphically by plotting the constraint lines, shading the feasible region defined by those lines, and finally calculating the optimum point determined by the slope of the objective function. Refer to Figure 12–7, where the arable land constraint is plotted. Since the equation is of a less-than-or-equal-to constraint, the shaded area illustrated defines the feasible solution space. Any combination of x_1 and x_2 within this triangle will not violate the limited supply of land. The water supply and power service equations are plotted in similar fashion to yield Figure 12–8, which defines the total solution space. The solution will be a member of the polygon whose sides are these constraint lines and the x_1 and x_2 axis, which force the solution quantities to be nonnegative.

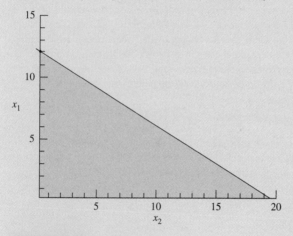

FIGURE 12-7

Plot of arable land constraint, Example 12.4.

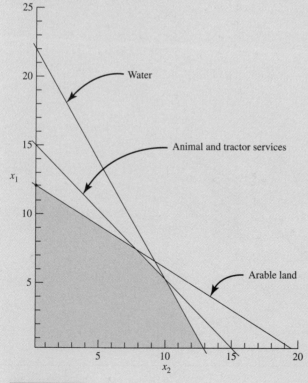

FIGURE 12-8

Plot of solution space, Example 12.4.

The objective function is to maximize the value of the equation

$$Z_0 = 8x_1 + 6x_2$$

This line has no single distinct solution, but indicates that the slope of the equation defines a set of iso-profit lines; in this case the slope is $-3/4$. The value of the equation is equivalent for any solution point lying on the same line. It does not matter where operations occur on the line; the objective is to move away from the origin as far as possible to the point that has the higher iso-profit value and remains feasible. Progressing away from the origin, the last of these parallel lines that can be drawn coincides with the point A at

$$Z_0 = 8(7) + 6(8) = 104 \text{ units of profit}$$

This is the optimum solution.

As can be seen from Figure 12–9, the optimum will occur at a corner of the polygon whenever the slope of the objective is not the same as the slope of one of the binding constraint equations. If the slopes happen to be the same, the corner point will still be an optimum, but now the whole line will provide the same optimum. Therefore, it would not be a distinct solution.

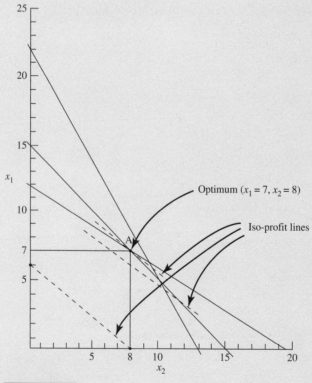

FIGURE 12–9

Plot of iso-profit lines and constraints, Example 12.4.

12.6 THE SIMPLEX ALGORITHM

The graphical solution is convenient when the choice involves the distribution of scarce resources between two items. If there exist three alternatives to allocate resources, the graph would become three-dimensional; if four alternatives, four-dimensional. To overcome the limitation this poses, a computational scheme is introduced. The simplex algorithm is a series of matrix row procedures designed to search for a solution through a very similar approach to that of the graphical method. A corner of the feasible polygon is assessed and then the algorithm makes a decision to stop or to move on to another corner if the optimum has not been attained. The approach uses the Gaussian elimination process of linear algebra for the transformations. An initial corner that represents a feasible solution must first be known before beginning the process. This is taken as the origin, since it is known as a corner and it is also feasible.

The simplex algorithm requires that the equations be expressed in a standard form, which is then translated into a tableau. The standard form does not allow for inequality expressions, so a slack variable is introduced into the constraint equations to account for unused portions of the available resources. When the process is initiated at the origin, all the resources are ignored and the values of the slack variables are equal to their capacity. For the EWB agricultural example of Section 12.5, the arable land constraint of 96 hectares becomes

$$8x_1 + 5x_2 + S_A = 96$$

where

$\qquad S_A =$ the unused portion of arable land available

In the initial iteration $S_A = 96$ since $x_1, x_2 = 0$.

Similarly, the other two constraints become

$$10x_1 + 17x_2 + S_W$$
$$x_1 + x_2 = S_T$$

where

$\qquad S_W =$ the unused portion of water resources

$\qquad S_T =$ the unused portion of tractor and animal services

Each slack variable appears in an augmented objective function with coefficients of zero, since they do not contribute to the realization of the objective. The new objective function is then written as:

$$\text{Maximize: } Z_0 = 8x_1 + 6x_2 + 0S_A + 0S_W + 0S_T$$

The simplex tableau provides a column for each variable and a row for each constraint. The nonnegativity constraints are implicit to the tableau but, as Table 12–4 illustrates, all other equations are entered.

The coefficients are entered directly into the table using zeros whenever a particular variable does not exist in one of the equations. The variable C_j in the

TABLE 12–4 Initial Simplex Tableau, Example 12.4

Maximize: $Z_0 = 8x_1 + 6x_2 + 0S_A + 0S_B + 0S_T$

Subject to: $8x_1 + 5x_2 + S_A = 96$

$10x_1 + 17x_2 + S_W = 220$

$x_1 + x_2 + S_T = 15$

C_j	Basic Variables	8 x_1	6 x_2	0 S_A	0 S_W	0 S_T	Current Values
0	S_A	8	5	1	0	0	96
0	S_W	10	17	0	1	0	220
0	S_T	1	1	0	0	1	15
	Z_j						0
	$C_j - Z_j$						

corner signifies the objective function coefficients. The row labelled Z_j represents opportunity costs and the row below it labelled $C_j - Z_j$ represents a simplex criterion to ascertain the computations required for the next iteration. The Current Values column presents the level of the basic variables. The basic variables are those that are currently part of the solution. The nonzero variables at the origin are the slack variables. As can be seen from the table, there are always exactly three nonzero variables, so each iteration essentially substitutes a new variable for one of the basic variables and eliminates the old one from the next solution. Initially, the current values of the slack or basic variables are the values that the constraint equations are equivalent to in the equations. The value at the intersection of the current value column and the Z_j row is the total value of the objective function for the iteration. Initially this is zero at the origin.

To complete the first iteration, test the solution for optimality by calculating the Z_j row. The operation required for each column is to sum the products of the C_j column value multiplied by the constraint coefficient that corresponds to both that row and the column being analyzed. Table 12–5 illustrates the calculations. Since all of the C_j values are zero, the Z_j values are also zero. Future iterations are more interesting. The Z_j value can be interpreted as the opportunity cost of a variable. It indicates the economic penalty of introducing a particular variable or investment.

The $C_j - Z_j$ row is calculated by subtracting the top C_j row from the Z_j row just computed. This is illustrated in the x_1 column where $C_j = 8$ and $Z_j = 0$. The $C_j - Z_j$ is then $8 - 0$ or 8. This row provides an indication of the marginal contribution or

TABLE 12-5   Calculating the Z_j Row, Example 12.4

C_j Basic Variables	8 x_1	6 x_2	0 S_A	0 S_W	0 S_T	Current Values
0 S_A	8 $()\times() = 0$	5	1	0	0	96
0 S_W	10 $()\times() = 0$	17	0	1	0	220
0 S_T	1 $()\times() = 0$ $\Sigma = 0$	1	0	0	1	15
Z_j	0 $()-() = 8$	0	0	0	0	0
$C_j - Z_j$	8	6	0	0	0	

Calculations

$Z_1 = (0 \times 8) + (0 \times 10) + (0 \times 1) = 0$, as illustrated in column x_1
$Z_2 = (0 \times 5) + (0 \times 17) + (0 \times 1) = 0$
$Z_3 = (0 \times 1) + (0 \times 0) + (0 \times 0) = 0$
$Z_4 = (0 \times 0) + (0 \times 1) + (0 \times 0) = 0$
$Z_5 = (0 \times 0) + (0 \times 0) + (0 \times 1) = 0$

The "Current Values" column has the same algebraic calculations performed to it such that
Z_6 = objective function value = $(0 \times 96) + (0 \times 220) + (0 \times 15) = 0$.

net impact a variable will have on the objective function by subtracting its cost per unit from its opportunity cost per unit.

There are three criteria to apply in preparation for the next iteration. The first involves testing for optimality; the second and third criteria determine the incoming and outgoing variables. Moving from the origin as the first intersection to a second intersection or potential solution, one variable goes out of solution (set equal to zero) and another that was previously equal to zero takes on a value and comes into solution. Referring to Figure 12–9, this implies movement along an axis until intersecting a constraint line. This point represents an intersection where the slack variable associated with that constraint is now zero and, hence, leaves the basic solution. The variable represented by the axis being traversed is now taking on a value and is, therefore, the incoming variable. Continue to allow for these intersection changes as long as the objective function value can be increased through the substitution. A substitution will increase the objective function value whenever a potential incoming variable's computed marginal contribution is greater than zero. These values were calculated and recorded as the $C_j - Z_j$ row.

The three criteria are as follows:

- *Criterion 1.* When all $C_j - Z_j$ values (the simplex criterion row) are negative or zero, an optimum has been reached. If criterion 1 is not satisfied, apply criterions 2 and 3 to identify substitutions for the next iteration.
- *Criterion 2.* Take the most positive element in the $C_j - Z_j$ simplex criterion row; this is associated with the variable coming into the substitution of the pivot column.

- *Criterion 3.* Take the smallest ratio of the figures from the current values column divided by their respective pivot column values; this identifies the pivot row.

Substitute the variable into the solution which has the greatest marginal contribution by taking the most positive $C_j - Z_j$ value for criterion 2. It thereby increases the objective function at the most rapid rate possible. Table 12–6 illustrates the ratios discussed in criterion 3.

Applying criterion 2 to the agricultural decision being discussed specifies that x_1 will be the incoming variable because its $C_j - Z_j$ value of 8 is the most positive element in the simplex criterion row. Criterion 3 instructs that the current value column should be divided by the respective values in this new column. As done in Table 12–5, circle the column. By dividing these two columns, the process is identifying which constraint line will become binding on the solution space first. Referring back to Figure 12–9, it can be seen that as x_1 is substituted in one unit at a time, the solution moves up the ordinate axis labelled x_1 until intersecting the polygonal solution space when $x_1 = 12$. This point corresponds to the constraint line S_A for exhausting the available arable land. Continuing past this corner would intersect the S_T constraint for tractor services at point 15 and S_W for water at point 22. These correspond to the three ratios calculated in Table 12–6, where the only feasible point is the smallest one, since this defines the feasible solution space boundary. Any point lying outside this line violates the arable land constraint. Circle the entire row defined by that ratio, as this is the pivot row. If any of the ratios computed are negative, they are ignored since this implies that the basic variable increases for the incoming variable and will not create a binding constraint.

The element, which is a member of both the pivot column and the pivot row, becomes the pivot element. To substitute the new variable x_1 into the solution and delete S_A from the solution (since that resource is now used to its capacity), use

TABLE 12–6 Criterion 3 Ratios, Example 12.4

C_j Basic Variables	8 x_1	6 x_2	0 S_A	0 S_W	0 S_T	Current Values	Ratios
0 S_A	8	5	1	0	0	96	$\frac{96}{8} = 12$
		Pivot element			Smallest ratio		
0 S_W	10	17	0	1	0	220	$\frac{220}{10} = 22$
0 S_T	1	1	0	0	1	15	$\frac{15}{1} = 15$
Z_j	0	0	0	0	0	0	
$C_j - Z_j$	8	6	0	0	0		

Most positive element

TABLE 12–7   The Second Iteration, Example 12.4

C_j Basic Variables	8 x_1	6 x_2	0 S_A	0 S_W	0 S_T	Current Values	Ratios
8 x_1	$\frac{8}{8}=1$	$\frac{5}{8}=0.625$	$\frac{1}{8}=0.125$	0	0	$\frac{96}{8}=12$	19.2
0 S_W	0	10.75	−1.25	1	0	100	9.30
0 S_A	0	0.375	−0.125	0	1	3	8.0
Z_j	8	5	1	0	0	96	
$C_j = Z_j$	0	1	−1	0	0		

linear algebra. Initially, dividing the pivot element into each of the pivot row coefficients including itself and the current value modifies the pivot row. Table 12–7 illustrates this exercise. In this table, depicting the second iteration, note that the basic variable column now has x_1 included since it is now in the solution set. When bringing across the x_1, bring with it the corresponding value of C_j, which in this case is 8. It is this row that has been divided by the pivot element of 8.

To eliminate the coefficient of the incoming variable from the other equations, subtract from these equations the appropriate multiples of the equation that contain the pivot element. In the tableau for the next iteration, the old pivot column should display all zeros except for the pivot element, which will be 1, as just calculated. This will be accomplished by subtracting the other old rows from the new pivot row in such a way that the element in the pivot column will become 0. To do this, multiply the entire row by the inverse of that element, making the new element equal to unity. Then when it is subtracted it will yield 1. These steps are all computations associated with the transformations of linear algebra for the inverse elimination process.

To revise the S_W row, multiply the entire new x_1 row by the pivot column element, which is equal to 10, to attain

	x_1	x_2	S_A	S_W	S_T	Current Value
x_1	10×1 $= 10$	10×0.625 $= 6.25$	10×0.125 $= 1.25$	$10 \times 0 = 0$	$10 \times 0 = 0$	10×12 $= 120$

Now subtract the values of this temporary intermediate step from the new row associated with S_W in the next iteration, to yield

	x_1	x_2	S_A	S_W	S_T	Current Value
S_W	$10 - 10 = 0$	$17 - 6.25$ $= 10.75$	$0 - 1.25$ $= -1.25$	$1 - 0 = 1$	$0 - 0 = 0$	$220 - 120$ $= 100$

Table 12–7 shows these new values for the S_W row.

To generalize this procedure, for each row other than the pivot row, substitute the elements into the following equation:

$$\begin{pmatrix} \text{Desired} \\ \text{element} \end{pmatrix} = \begin{pmatrix} \text{element from} \\ \text{previous} \\ \text{iteration} \end{pmatrix} - \begin{pmatrix} \text{previous iteration} \\ \text{row element} \\ \text{coinciding with} \\ \text{the pivot column} \end{pmatrix} \times \begin{pmatrix} \text{value of incoming} \\ \text{variable's row and} \\ \text{desired element's} \\ \text{column} \end{pmatrix}$$

Performing these steps to the S_T row completes the tableau of Table 12–7 (notice the values correspond to the polygon's upper left corner of the graphical solution in Figure 12–9).

No additional knowledge is required to complete the simplex solution to this example. Continuing the algorithm, calculate the opportunity cost row and the simplex criterion row for this iteration and then apply the three criteria discussed earlier until criterion 1 indicates that an optimal solution has been reached. Table 12–8 depicts the additional iteration required to solve this problem. The arrows in Table 12–6 indicate the pivot columns and rows appropriate for the transformation. The $C_j - Z_j$ row entries are all zero or negative, satisfying criterion 1 and indicating an optimum solution.

The optimal answer is read from the table by looking at the basic variable and current value columns:

$$x_1 = 7$$
$$S_W = 14$$
$$x_2 = 8$$

The optimal solution is to produce 7 ($\times 10^3$) tonnes of food crop x_1 and 8 ($\times 10^3$) tonnes of livestock feed x_2. Since $S_W = 14$, the solution indicates that the maximum available irrigation and water supplies is sufficient and S_W

TABLE 12–8 The Final Iteration, Example 12.4

C_j	Basic Variables	8 x_1	6 x_2	0 S_A	0 S_W	0 S_T	Current Values
8	x_1	1	0	−0.083	0	−1.666	7
0	S_W	0	0	4.83	1	−28.66	14
6	x_2	0	1	0.333	0	2.66	8
	Z_j	8	6	1.334	0	2.668	104
	$C_j - Z_j$	0	0	−1.334	0	−2.668	

is a noncritical constraint. If it is possible to trade some of the surplus water for arable land or for animal and tractor power services, an increase in these resources, which currently bind the solution, will increase the objective function value.

The matrix containing this optimal solution of Table 12–8 provides the analyst with additional important insights concerning the economics of the system under study. The coefficients in the matrix represent substitution rates between the variables. In this EWB scenario, the S_A column can be interpreted to represent information concerning how much of each of the basic solution variables, x_1, S_W, and x_2, would have to be removed if one unit of S_A is brought back into the solution. Since S_A equals the amount of unused arable land, an increase in the variable indicates a decrease in the amount of land available for distribution. The matrix indicates that one unit of S_A will impact upon x_1 and x_2 by requiring 0.083 less units of the food crops and 0.333 less units of livestock feed, respectively.

The Z_j row indicates the opportunity costs of each variable and depicts how much each of these items is currently contributing to the solution. In microeconomics, the Z_j values are referred to as *shadow prices*. These prices indicate the change in the value of the objective function if the resource associated with the column's slack variable is increased by one unit from its current value. Reviewing the final tableau, it is seen that S_A, S_W, and S_T have values of 1.334, 0, and 2.668 in the Z_j row. This indicates that the objective function will increase by $\$1.334 \times 10^3$, nothing (because it is not fully utilized), and $\$2.668 \times 10^3$, respectively for each 1×10^3 unit increase of resource. Therefore, an additional 1000 hectares per season of arable land will yield an increased profit of $1334 and an additional 1000 hours of planting and harvesting per period will yield an increase of $2668 in profit. If these resources can be purchased for a price less than or equal to the shadow price, the project decision makers will be justified in purchasing them. The optimal amount to be purchased is determined when another constraint becomes binding, since the shadow prices are only applicable for small changes in the resources that will not impact the current solution.

When resource levels are held constant, the simplex criterion row $C_j - Z_j$ indicates the impact upon the objective function that the inclusion of additional variables would create. Zero values in this row imply that there will be no change in profit with corresponding variations from the current solution. Similarly, negative values imply that there will be decreases in profit with corresponding variations.

The shadow prices derived through the linear programming simplex model provide a marginal cost evaluation for the contributions of the various inputs to the system. These data are very important for future engineering economic evaluation studies that seek to expand the system under study. For the EWB project, the agricultural sector can be expanded to include additional inputs beyond land, water, and tractor services. It can also incorporate inputs of seeds, fertilizers, and pesticides, as well as various modal choices within each category. If an increase in the overall production capabilities is desired, the shadow prices generated through the model can indicate the relative benefits of project options for augmenting the resources required to expand the inputs. As such, the model will be able to provide valuable evidence toward making decisions directing future investments.

Linear programming is a powerful algorithm that is among the most used quantitative tools for tradeoff analysis in engineering decision making. There are many textbooks dedicated to the subject, such as Hillier and Lieberman's *Introduction to Operations Research*, 8th ed. The optimization principles are expanded in these textbooks along with a variety of engineering applications. In general, problems that exhibit linear objective functions and linear constraints (within the range of relevant operating characteristics being considered) are applicable to an LP analysis.

CHAPTER SUMMARY

Investment capital is always a scarce resource, so it must be rationed among competing projects using specific economic and noneconomic criteria. Capital budgeting involves proposed projects, each with an initial investment and net cash flows estimated over the life of the project. The lives may be the same or different. The fundamental capital budgeting problem has some specific characteristics (Figure 12–1).

- Selection is made from among independent projects.
- Each project must be accepted or rejected as a whole.
- Maximizing the present worth of the net cash flows is the objective.
- The total initial investment is limited to a specified maximum.

The present worth method is used for evaluation. To start the procedure, formulate all mutually exclusive bundles that do not exceed the investment limit, including the do-nothing bundle. There are a maximum of 2^m bundles for m projects. Calculate the PW at MARR for each bundle, and select the one bundle with the largest PW value. Reinvestment of net positive cash flows at the MARR is assumed for all projects with lives shorter than the longest-lived project.

The capital budgeting problem may be formulated as a linear programming problem to select projects directly in order to maximize the total PW. Mutually exclusive bundles are not developed using this solution approach. Excel and SOLVER can be used to solve this problem by computer.

The simplex algorithm for solving general linear programming problems can be used to address relevant tradeoffs in engineering economic studies. Although linearity is required for the applicable range of values that the variables can operate within, hundreds of variables with hundreds of constraints can be assessed.

PROBLEMS

Understanding the Capital Rationing Problem

12.1 Write a short paragraph that explains the problem of rationing investment capital among several projects that are independent of one another.

12.2 State the reinvestment assumption about project cash flows that is made when one is solving the capital budgeting problem.

12.3 Four independent projects (1, 2, 3, and 4) are to be evaluated for investment by Perfect Manufacturing. Develop all the acceptable mutually exclusive bundles based on the following selection restrictions developed by the department of engineering production:

Project 2 can be selected only if project 3 is selected.

Projects 1 and 4 should not both be selected; they are essentially duplicates.

12.4 Develop all acceptable mutually exclusive bundles for the four independent projects described below if the investment limit is $400 and the following project selection restriction applies: Project 1 can be selected only if both projects 3 and 4 are selected.

Project	Initial Investment, $
1	−250
2	−150
3	−75
4	−235

Selection from Independent Projects

12.5 (*a*) Determine which of the following independent projects should be selected for investment if $325,000 is available and the MARR is 10% per year. Use the PW method to evaluate mutually exclusive bundles to make the selection.

Project	Initial Investment, $	Net Cash Flow, $/Year	Life, Years
A	−100,000	50,000	8
B	−125,000	24,000	8
C	−120,000	75,000	8
D	−220,000	39,000	8
E	−200,000	82,000	8

(*b*) If the five projects are mutually exclusive alternatives, perform the present worth analysis and select the best alternative.

12.6 Work Problem 12.5(*a*), using a spreadsheet.

12.7 Vancouver-based Ayogo Games Inc. is considering 4 independent video game projects to fund this year to tackle health and environmental topics. The project costs and 12% per-year PW values are available. What projects are acceptable if the budget limit is (*a*) no limit and (*b*) $60,000?

Project	Initial Investment, $	Life, Years	PW at 12% per Year, $
1	−15,000	3	−400
2	−25,000	3	8500
3	−20,000	2	500
4	−40,000	5	7600

12.8 The engineering department at General Tire has a total of $900,000 for no more than two projects in capital improvement for the year. Use a spreadsheet-based

PW analysis and a minimum 12% per year return to answer the following.

(a) Which projects are acceptable from the three described below?

(b) What is the minimum required annual net cash flow necessary to select the bundle that expends as much as possible without violating either the budget limit or the two-project maximum restriction?

Project	Initial Investment, $	Estimated NCF, $/Year	Life, Years	Salvage Value, $
A	−400,000	120,000	4	40,000
B	−200,000	90,000	4	30,000
C	−700,000	200,000	4	20,000

12.9 Jesse wants to choose exactly two independent projects from four opportunities. Each project has an initial investment of $300,000 and a life of 5 years. The annual NCF estimates for the first three projects are available, but a detailed estimate for the fourth is not yet prepared and time has run out for the selection. Using MARR = 9% per year, determine the minimum NCF for the fourth project (Z) that will guarantee that it is part of the selected twosome.

Project	Annual NCF, $/year
W	90,000
X	50,000
Y	130,000
Z	At least 50,000

12.10 The engineer at Clean Water Engineering has established a capital investment limit of $800,000 for next year for projects that target improved recovery of highly brackish groundwater. Select any or all of the following projects,

using a MARR of 10% per year. Present your solution by hand calculations, not Excel.

Project	Initial Investment, $	Annual NCF, $/Year	Life, Years	Salvage Value, $
A	−250,000	50,000	4	45,000
B	−300,000	90,000	4	−10,000
C	−550,000	150,000	4	100,000

12.11 Develop an Excel spreadsheet for the three projects in Problem 12.10. Assume that the engineer wants project C to be the only one selected. Considering the viable project options and $b = \$800,000$, determine (a) the largest initial investment for C and (b) the largest MARR allowed to guarantee that C is selected.

12.12 Eight projects are available for selection at HumVee Motors. The listed PW values are determined at the corporate MARR of 10% per year and rounded to the nearest $1000. Project lives vary from 5 to 15 years.

Project	Initial Investment, $	PW Value at 10%, $
1	−1,500,000	−50,000
2	−300,000	+35,000
3	−95,000	−9,000
4	−400,000	+75,000
5	−195,000	+125,000
6	−175,000	−27,000
7	−100,000	+62,000
8	−400,000	+110,000

Project selection guidelines:

1. No more than $400,000 in investment capital is available.

2. No negative PW project may be selected.

3. At least one project, but no more than three, must be selected.

4. The following selection restrictions apply to specific projects:
   - Project 4 can be selected only if project 1 is selected.
   - Projects 1 and 2 are duplicative; don't select both.
   - Projects 8 and 4 are also duplicative.
   - Project 7 requires that project 2 also be selected.

   (a) Identify the viable project bundles and select the best economically justified projects. What is the investment assumption for any remaining capital funds?

   (b) If as much of the $400,000 as possible *must* be invested, use the same restrictions and determine the project(s) to select. Is this a viable second choice for investing the $400,000? Why?

12.13 Use the analysis below of five independent projects to select the best, if the capital limitation is (a) $30,000, (b) $60,000, and (c) unlimited.

Project	Initial Investment, $	Life, Years	PW at 12% per Year, $
S	−15,000	6	8,540
A	−25,000	8	12,325
M	−10,000	6	3,000
E	−25,000	4	10
H	−40,000	12	15,350

12.14 The independent project estimates below have been developed by the engineering and finance managers. The corporate MARR is 15% per year, and the capital investment limit is $4 million.

   (a) Use the PW method and hand solution to select the economically best projects.

   (b) Use the PW method and computer solution to select the economically best projects.

Project	Project Cost, $ Millions	Life, Years	NCF, $/Year
1	−1.5	8	360,000
2	−3.0	10	600,000
3	−1.8	5	520,000
4	−2.0	4	820,000

12.15 The following capital rationing problem is defined. Three projects are to be evaluated at a MARR of 12.5% per year. No more than $3.0 million can be invested.

   (a) Use a spreadsheet to select from the independent projects.

   (b) Use SOLVER to determine the minimum year 1 NCF for project 3 alone to have the same PW as the best bundle in part (a) if project 3 life can be increased to 10 years for the same $1 million investment. All other estimates remain the same. With this increased NCF and life, what are the best projects for investment?

Project	Investment, $ Millions	Life, Years	Estimated NCF, $/Year	
			Year 1	Gradient After Year 1
1	−0.9	6	250,000	−5000
2	−2.1	10	485,000	+5000
3	−1.0	5	200,000	+10%

12.16 Use the PW method to evaluate four independent projects. Select as many as three of the four projects. The MARR is 12% per year, and an available capital investment limit is $16,000.

	Project			
	1	2	3	4
Investment, $	−5000	−8000	−9000	−10,000
Life, Years	5	5	3	4
Year		NCF Estimates, $		
1	1000	500	5000	0
2	1700	500	5000	0
3	2400	500	2000	0
4	3000	500		17,000
5	3800	10,500		

12.17 Work Problem 12.16, using a spreadsheet.

12.18 Using the NCF estimates in Problem 12.16 for projects 3 and 4, demonstrate the reinvestment assumption made when the capital budgeting problem is solved for the four projects by using the PW method. (*Hint:* Refer to Equation [12.2].)

Linear Programming and Capital Budgeting

12.19 Formulate the linear programming model, develop a spreadsheet, and solve the capital rationing problem in Example 12.1 (*a*) as presented and (*b*) using an investment limit of $13 million.

12.20 For Problem 12.5, use Excel and SOLVER to (*a*) answer the question in part (*a*) and (*b*) select the projects if MARR = 12% per year and the investment limit is increased to $500,000.

12.21 Use SOLVER to work Problem 12.11.

12.22 Use SOLVER to find the minimum NCF required for project Z as detailed by Jesse in Problem 12.9.

12.23 Use linear programming and a spreadsheet-based solution technique

to select from the independent unequal-life projects in Problem 12.14.

12.24 Solve the capital budgeting problem in Problem 12.15(*a*), using the linear programming model and Excel.

12.25 Solve the capital budgeting problem in Problem 12.16, using the linear programming model and Excel.

12.26 Using the data in Problem 12.16 and Excel solutions of the capital rationing problem for capital budget limits ranging from $b = \$5000$ to $b = \$25,000$, develop an Excel chart that plots b versus the value of Z.

Linear Programming Graphical Solution

12.27 Use the graphical approach to solving linear programming problems for the following data:

$$\text{Maximize: } 12x_1 + 15x_2$$
$$\text{Subject to: } 4x_1 + 3x_2 \leq 12$$
$$2x_1 + 5x_2 \leq 10$$
$$x_1, x_2 \geq 0$$

12.28 Consider the following information:

$$\text{Maximize: } 3x_1 + 2x_2$$
$$\text{Subject to: } x_1 + x_2 \leq 16$$
$$x_1 \leq 10$$
$$x_2 \leq 8$$
$$x_1, x_2 \geq 0$$

Using the LP graphical approach, find the optimal solution.

12.29 A motorcycle accessories manufacturer wants to optimize the daily production mix of two types of rear-view mirrors. One is oval with engraved flames on its chrome back (x_1) and the other is a mirror inset within a chrome body shaped in the design of flames (x_2). Profit on x_1 is $20 per set while the profit on x_2 is $50 per set. Because the company wants the exposure of offering low-priced models, at least 25% of the sets must be the x_1 design. There are 40 labour-hours available per day for manufacturing the two sets and 16 labour-hours for packaging. Each x_1 set requires 0.2 hours to manufacture while each x_2 set requires 0.4 hours to manufacture. Packaging requires 0.1 hours per set for either model. Graphically determine the optimal mix.

Linear Programming Simplex Algorithm

12.30 Using the LP simplex algorithm, solve the following problem:

$$\text{Maximize: } 3x_1 + x_2$$
$$\text{Subject to: } 2x_1 + x_2 \leq 10$$
$$x_1 + x_2 \leq 8$$
$$x_1, x_2 \geq 0$$

12.31 Use the simplex algorithm to solve the following problem:

$$\text{Maximize: } 2x_1 + 4x_2 - x_3$$
$$\text{Subject to: } x_1 + 2x_2 - 3x_3 \leq 6$$
$$3x_1 + 3x_3 \leq 9$$
$$x_1, x_2, x_3 \geq 0$$

12.32 Dynabike Corporation of Victoria is producing high-end competition bicycles by using dynamite to combine dissimilar materials of titanium and aluminum to optimize the ride and power characteristics of the frame. They produce road-racing bikes (x_1) and time trial bikes (x_2) to the exact specifications of riders. Profits are $8 ($\times 10^3$) for x_1 and 6 ($\times 10^3$) for x_2 bikes. Product x_1 requires 0.25 months of design time, 1.5 months of machine time and 0.75 months of metallurgy. Product x_2 requires 0.5 months of design, 1 month of machining, and 0.75 months of metallurgy. Determine the optimal level of production for each product to maximize economic profit. The maximum design time is 8 months, the maximum machine time is 24 months, and the maximum time for metallurgy is 16 months.

CASE STUDY

LIFELONG ENGINEERING EDUCATION IN A WEB ENVIRONMENT

The Report

The Institute of Microelectronics (IME) is a not-for-profit engineering professional society. A task force was established last year with the charge to recommend ways to improve services to members in the area of lifelong learning. Overall sales to individuals, libraries, and businesses of technical journals, magazines, books, monographs, CDs, and videos have decreased by 35% over the last 3 years. IME, like virtually all for-profit corporations, is being negatively impacted by e-commerce. The just-published report of the task force contains the following conclusion and recommendations:

It is essential that IME take rapid, proactive steps to initiate Web-based learning materials itself and/or in conjunction with other organizations. Topically, these materials should concentrate on areas such as:

Professional engineer certification and licensing
Leading-edge technical topics

Retooling topics for mature engineers

Basic tools for individuals doing engineering analysis with inadequate training or education

Projects should be started immediately and evaluated over the next 3 years to determine future directions of electronic learning materials for IME

The Project Proposals

In the Action Items section of the report, four projects are identified, along with cost and net revenue estimates made on a 6-month basis. The project summaries that follow all require development and marketing of online learning materials.

Project A, niche markets. IME identifies several new technical areas and offers learning materials to members and nonmembers. An initial investment of $500,000 and a follow-up investment of another $500,000 after 18 months are necessary.

Project B, partnering. IME joins with several other professional societies to offer materials on a relatively wide spectrum. This business strategy could bring a larger investment to bear on lifelong learning materials. An initial investment by IME of $2 million is necessary. This project will require that a smaller project for network improvement be undertaken. This is project C, which follows.

Project C, Web search engine. With an investment of only $200,000 six months from now, IME can offer members a Web search engine for access to current publications of IME. An outside contractor can quickly install this capability on current equipment. This entry point to Web-based learning is a stopgap measure, which may increase services and revenue over the short-term only. This project is necessary if project B is pursued, but project C can be pursued separately from any other project.

Project D, service improvement. This project is a complete substitute for project B. This is a longer-term effort to improve the electronic publication and continuing education offerings of IME. Investments of $300,000 now with commitments of $400,000 in 6 months and another $300,000 after 6 more months will be necessary. Project D is slower-moving, but it will develop a firm base for most future Web-based learning services of the IME.

The estimated net cash flows (in $1000) by 6-month period for IME are summarized as shown.

| | Project | | | |
Period	A	B	C	D
1	$ 0	$ 500	$ 0	$ 100
2	100	500	50	200
3	200	600	100	300
4	400	700	150	300
5	400	800	0	300
6	0	1000	0	300

The Finance Committee has responded that no more than $3.5 million can be committed to these projects. It also stated that the total amount per project should be committed up front, regardless of when the initial and follow-on investment cash flows actually occur. The Finance Committee and a Board Committee will review progress each 3 months to determine if the selected projects should be continued, expanded, or discontinued. The IME capital, primarily in equity investments, has returned an average of 10% per 6-months over the last 5 years. There is no debt liability carried by IME at this time.

Case Study Exercises

1. Formulate all the investment opportunities for IME and the cash flow profiles, given the information in the task force report.

2. What projects should the Finance Committee recommend on a purely economic basis?

3. The Executive Director of IME has great interest in pursuing project D because of its perceived positive, longer-lasting effects upon the membership size of the Institute and future services offered to new and current members. Using a spreadsheet that details the project net cash flow estimates, determine some of the changes that the director may make to ensure that project D is accepted. No restrictions should be placed on this analysis; for example, investments and cash flows can be changed, and the restrictions between projects described in the task force report can be removed.

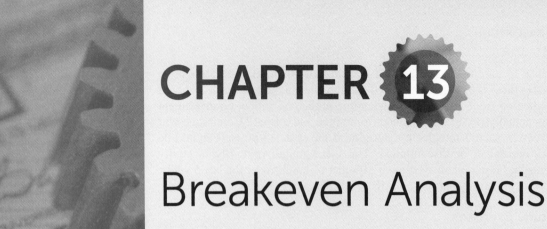

CHAPTER 13

Breakeven Analysis

Breakeven analysis is performed to determine the value of a variable or parameter of a project or alternative that makes two elements equal, for example, the sales volume that will equate revenues and costs. A breakeven study is performed for two alternatives to determine when either alternative is equally acceptable, for example, the replacement value of the defender in a replacement study that makes the challenger an equally good choice (Section 11.3). Breakeven analysis is commonly applied in *make-or-buy decisions* when corporations and businesses must decide upon the source for manufactured components, services of all kinds, etc.

We have utilized the breakeven approach previously in payback analysis (Section 5.6) and for breakeven ROR analysis of two alternatives (Section 8.4). This chapter expands our scope and understanding of performing a breakeven study.

Breakeven studies use estimates that are considered to be certain; that is, if the estimated values are expected to vary enough to possibly change the outcome, another breakeven study is necessary using different estimates. This leads to the observation that breakeven analysis is a part of the larger efforts of *sensitivity analysis*. If the variable of interest in a breakeven study is allowed to vary, the approaches of sensitivity analysis (Chapter 17) should be used. Additionally, if probability and risk assessment are considered, the tools of simulation (Chapter 18) can be used to supplement the static nature of a breakeven study.

This chapter's case study focuses on cost and efficiency measures in a public sector (municipal) setting.

LEARNING OBJECTIVES

Purpose: For one or more alternatives, determine the level of activity necessary or the value of a parameter to break even.

Breakeven point

Two alternatives—breakeven

Spreadsheets

By the end of this chapter you should be able to

1. Determine the breakeven value for a single project.

2. Calculate the breakeven value between two alternatives and use it to select one alternative.

3. Create a spreadsheet that uses the Excel tool SOLVER to perform breakeven analysis.

13.1 BREAKEVEN ANALYSIS FOR A SINGLE PROJECT

When one of the engineering economy variables—P, F, A, i, or n—is not known or not estimated, a breakeven quantity can be determined by setting an equivalence relation for PW or AW equal to zero. This form of breakeven analysis has been used many times so far. For example, we have solved for the rate of return i^*, found the payback period n_p, and determined the P, F, A, or salvage value S at which a series of cash flow estimates return a specific MARR. Methods used to determine the quantity are

> *Direct solution* by hand if only one factor is present (say, P/A) or only single amounts are estimated (e.g., P and F).
>
> *Trial and error* by hand when multiple factors are present.
>
> *Computer spreadsheet* when cash flow and other estimates are entered into spreadsheet cells and used in resident functions, such as PV, FV, RATE, IRR, NPV, PMT, and NPER.

We now concentrate on the determination of the *breakeven quantity for a decision variable*. For example, the variable may be a design element to minimize cost, or the production level needed to realize revenues that exceed costs by 10%. This quantity, called the *breakeven point* Q_{BE}, is determined using relations for revenue and cost at different values of the variable Q. The size of Q may be expressed in units per year, percentage of capacity, hours per month, and many other dimensions.

Figure 13–1a presents different shapes of a revenue relation identified as R. A linear revenue relation is commonly assumed, but a nonlinear relation is often more realistic. It can model an increasing per unit revenue with larger volumes (curve 1 in panel (a)), or a decreasing per unit price that usually prevails at higher quantities (curve 2).

Costs, which may be linear or nonlinear, usually include two components— fixed and variable—as indicated in panel (b).

Fixed costs (FC). Includes costs such as buildings, insurance, fixed overhead, some minimum level of labour, equipment capital recovery, and information systems.

Variable costs (VC). Includes costs such as direct labour, materials, indirect costs, contractors, marketing, advertisement, and warranty.

The fixed-cost component is essentially constant for all values of the variable, so it does not vary for a large range of operating parameters, such as production level or workforce size. Even if no units are produced, fixed costs are incurred at some threshold level. Of course, this situation cannot last long before the plant must shut down to reduce fixed costs. Fixed costs are reduced through improved equipment, information systems and workforce utilization, less costly fringe benefit packages, subcontracting specific functions, and so on.

Variable costs change with production level, workforce size, and other parameters. It is usually possible to decrease variable costs through better product design, manufacturing efficiency, improved quality and safety, and higher sales volume.

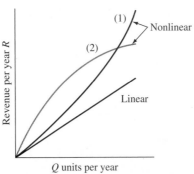

FIGURE 13–1

Linear and nonlinear revenue and cost relations.

(a) Revenue relations—(1) increasing and
(2) decreasing revenue per unit

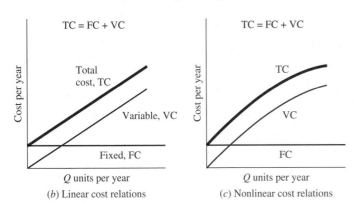

(b) Linear cost relations

(c) Nonlinear cost relations

When FC and VC are added, they form the total cost relation TC. Panel (b) of the figure illustrates the TC relation for linear fixed and variable costs. Panel (c) shows a general TC curve for a nonlinear VC in which unit variable costs decrease as the quantity level rises.

At a specific but unknown value Q of the decision variable, the revenue and total cost relations will intersect to identify the breakeven point Q_{BE} (Figure 13–2). If $Q > Q_{BE}$, there is a predictable profit; but if $Q < Q_{BE}$, there is a loss. For linear models of R and VC, the greater the quantity, the larger the profit. Profit is calculated as

$$\textbf{Profit} = \textbf{revenue} - \textbf{total cost}$$
$$= R - TC \qquad \textbf{[13.1]}$$

A relation for the breakeven point may be derived when revenue and total cost are linear functions of quantity Q by setting the relations for R and TC equal to each other, indicating a profit of zero.

$$R = TC$$
$$rQ = FC + VC = FC + vQ$$

FIGURE 13–2

Effect on the breakeven
point when the variable
cost per unit is reduced.

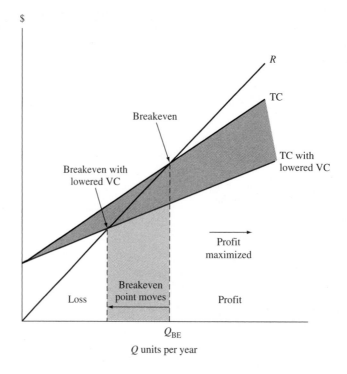

where r = revenue per unit
            v = variable cost per unit

Solve for the breakeven quantity Q_{BE} to obtain

$$Q_{BE} = \frac{FC}{r - v}$$

[13.2]

The breakeven graph is an important management tool, because it is easy to
understand and may be used in decision making and analysis in a variety of
ways. For example, if the variable cost per unit is reduced, the TC line has a
smaller slope (Figure 13–2), and the breakeven point will decrease. This is an
advantage because the smaller the value of Q_{BE}, the greater the profit for a given
amount of revenue.

If nonlinear R or TC models are used, there may be more than one breakeven
point. Figure 13–3 presents this situation for two breakeven points. The maximum profit occurs at Q_P between the two breakeven points where the distance
between the R and TC relations is greatest.

Of course, no static R and TC relations—linear or nonlinear—are able to
estimate exactly the revenue and cost amounts over an extended period of time.
But the breakeven point is an excellent target for planning purposes.

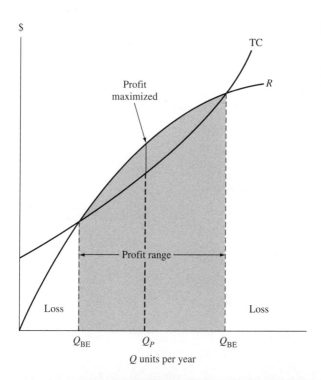

FIGURE 13–3
Breakeven points and maximum profit point for a nonlinear analysis.

EXAMPLE 13.1

Lufkin Trailer Corporation assembles up to 30 trailers per month for 18-wheel trucks in its Ontario facility. Production has dropped to 25 units per month over the last 5 months due to a worldwide economic slowdown in transportation services. The following information is available.

Fixed costs	FC = $750,000 per month
Variable cost per unit	$v = \$35,000$
Revenue per unit	$r = \$75,000$

(a) How does the reduced production level of 25 units per month compare with the current breakeven point?
(b) What is the current profit level per month for the facility?
(c) What is the difference between the revenue and variable cost per trailer that is necessary to break even at a monthly production level of 15 units, if fixed costs remain constant?

Solution

(a) Use Equation [13.2] to determine the breakeven number of units. All dollar amounts are in $1000 units.

$$Q_{BE} = \frac{FC}{r - v}$$

$$= \frac{750}{75 - 35} = 18.75 \text{ units per month}$$

Figure 13–4 is a plot of R and TC lines. The breakeven value is 18.75, or 19 in integer trailer units. The reduced production level of 25 units is above the breakeven value.

(b) To estimate profit in $1000 at $Q = 25$ units per month, use Equation [13.1].

$$\text{Profit} = R - \text{TC} = rQ - (\text{FC} + vQ)$$
$$= (r - v)Q - \text{FC}$$
$$= (75 - 35)25 - 750$$
$$= \$250 \hspace{4cm} [13.3]$$

There is a profit of $250,000 per month currently.

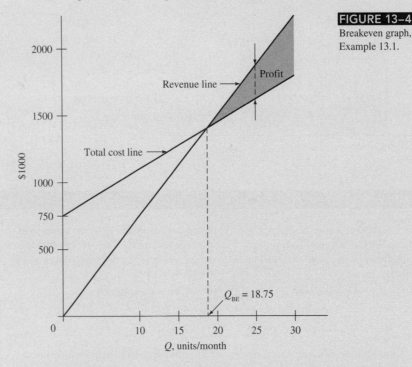

FIGURE 13–4
Breakeven graph,
Example 13.1.

(c) To determine the required difference $r - v$, use Equation [13.3] with profit $= 0$, $Q = 15$, and FC $= \$750,000$. In $1000 units,

$$0 = (r - v)(15) - 750$$
$$r - v = \frac{750}{15} = \$50 \text{ per unit}$$

The spread between r and v must be $50,000. If v stays at $35,000, the revenue per trailer must increase from $75,000 to $85,000 just to break even at a production level of $Q = 15$ per month.

In some circumstances, breakeven analysis performed on a per-unit basis is more meaningful. The value of Q_{BE} is still calculated using Equation [13.2], but the TC relation is divided by Q to obtain an expression for cost per unit, also termed *average cost per unit C_u.*

$$C_u = \frac{TC}{Q} = \frac{FC + vQ}{Q} = \frac{FC}{Q} + v \qquad [13.4]$$

At the breakeven quantity $Q = Q_{BE}$, the revenue per unit is exactly equal to the cost per unit. If graphed, the FC per unit term in Equation [13.4] takes on the shape of a hyperbola.

In Chapter 5, payback period analysis was discussed. Payback is the number of years n_p necessary to recover an initial investment. Payback analysis at a zero interest rate is performed only when there is no requirement to earn a rate of return greater than zero in addition to recovering the initial investment. (As discussed earlier, the technique is best used as a supplement to PW analysis at the MARR.) If payback analysis is coupled with breakeven, the quantity of the decision variable for different payback periods can be determined, as illustrated in the next example.

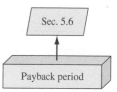

Sec. 5.6

Payback period

EXAMPLE 13.2

The president of a local company, Online Ontime, Inc., expects a product to have a profitable life of between 1 and 5 years. He wants to know the breakeven number of units that must be sold annually to realize payback within each of the time periods of 1 year, 2 years, and so on up to 5 years. Find the answers using hand and computer solutions. The cost and revenue estimates are as follows:

Fixed costs: Initial investment of \$80,000 with \$1000 annual operating cost
Variable cost: \$8 per unit
Revenue: Twice the variable cost for the first 5 years and 50% of the variable cost thereafter

Solution by Hand

Define X as the units sold per year to break even and n_p as the payback period, where $n_p = 1, 2, 3, 4,$ and 5 years. There are two unknowns and one relation, so it is necessary to establish values of one variable and solve for the other. The following approach is used: Establish annual cost and revenue relations with no time value of money considered, then use n_p values to find the breakeven value of X.

$$\text{Fixed costs} \qquad \frac{80{,}000}{n_p} + 1000$$

$$\text{Variable cost} \qquad 8X$$

$$\text{Revenue} \qquad \begin{cases} 16X & \text{years 1 through 5} \\ 4X & \text{year 6 and thereafter} \end{cases}$$

Set revenue equal to total cost, and solve for X.

$$\text{Revenue} = \text{total cost}$$

$$16X = \frac{80{,}000}{n_p} + 1000 + 8X \qquad [13.5]$$

$$X = \frac{10{,}000}{n_p} + 125$$

Insert the values 1 through 5 for n_p and solve for X (Figure 13–5). For example, payback in 2 years requires sales of 5125 units per year in order to break even. There is no consideration of interest in this solution; that is, $i = 0\%$.

Solution by Computer

Solve Equation [13.5] for X, retaining the symbols r and v for use in the spreadsheet.

$$X = \frac{80,000/n_p + 1000}{r - v} \qquad [13.6]$$

The spreadsheet in Figure 13–6 includes the breakeven Equation [13.6] in cells C9 through C13 as detailed in the cell tag. Column C and the xy scatter chart display the results. For example, payback in 1 year requires sales of $X = 10,125$, while a 5-year payback requires only 2125 units per year.

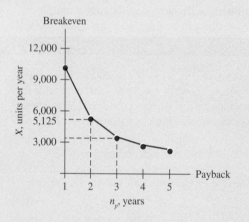

Breakeven

12,000

9,000

6,000
5,125

3,000

X, units per year

Payback

1   2   3   4   5

n_p, years

FIGURE 13–5
Breakeven sales volumes for different payback periods, Example 13.2.

	A	B	C	D	E	F	G
1	Initial investment,$	80,000					
2	AOC, $/year	1,000					
3	Revenues, $/unit	16					
4	Variable costs, $/unit	8					
5							
6							
7		Breakeven analysis					
8		Payback years, n	X, units/year				
9		1	10125				
10		2	5125				
11		3	3458				
12		4	2625				
13		5	2125				
14							
15	= ($B$1/$B11 + $B$2)/($B$3 − $B$4)						
16							
17							
18	Equation for breakeven analysis: (80,000/n + 1000) / (16-8)						
19							

FIGURE 13–6
Spreadsheet solution of breakeven values for different payback years, Example 13.2.

13.2 BREAKEVEN ANALYSIS BETWEEN TWO ALTERNATIVES

Breakeven analysis involves the determination of a common variable or economic parameter between two alternatives. The parameter can be the interest rate i, first cost P, annual operating cost (AOC), or any parameter. We have already performed breakeven analysis between alternatives on several parameters. For example, the incremental ROR value (Δi^*) is the breakeven rate between alternatives. If the MARR is lower than Δi^*, the extra investment of the larger-investment alternative is justified. In Section 11.3, the replacement value (RV) of a defender was determined. If the market value is larger than RV, the decision should favour the challenger.

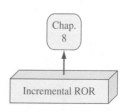

Often breakeven analysis involves revenue or cost variables common to both alternatives, such as price per unit, operating cost, cost of materials, and labour cost. Figure 13–7 illustrates this concept for two alternatives with linear cost relations. The fixed cost of alternative 2 is greater than that of alternative 1. However, alternative 2 has a smaller variable cost, as indicated by its lower slope. The intersection of the total cost lines locates the breakeven point. Thus, if the number of units of the common variable is greater than the breakeven amount, alternative 2 is selected, since the total cost will be lower. Conversely, an anticipated level of operation below the breakeven point favours alternative 1.

Instead of plotting the total costs of each alternative and estimating the breakeven point graphically, it may be easier to calculate the breakeven point numerically using engineering economy expressions for the PW or AW at the MARR. The AW is preferred when the variable units are expressed on a yearly basis, and AW calculations are simpler for alternatives with unequal lives. The following steps may be used to determine the breakeven point of the common variable and to select an alternative:

1. Define the common variable and its dimensional units.
2. Use AW or PW analysis to express the total cost of each alternative as a function of the common variable.
3. Equate the two relations and solve for the breakeven value of the variable.
4. If the anticipated level is below the breakeven value, select the alternative with the higher variable cost (larger slope). If the level is above the breakeven point, select the alternative with the lower variable cost. Refer to Figure 13–7.

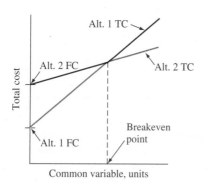

FIGURE 13–7

Breakeven between two alternatives with linear cost relations.

EXAMPLE 13.3

A small manufacturing company is evaluating two alternatives: the purchase of an automatic feed machine and a manual feed machine for a finishing process. The auto-feed machine has an initial cost of $23,000, an estimated salvage value of $4000, and a predicted life of 10 years. One person will operate the machine at a rate of $24 per hour. The expected output is 8 tonnes per hour. Annual maintenance and operating cost is expected to be $3500.

The alternative manual feed machine has a first cost of $8000, no expected salvage value, a 5-year life, and an output of 6 tonnes per hour. However, three workers will be required at $12 per hour each. The machine will have an annual maintenance and operation cost of $1500. All projects are expected to generate a return of 10% per year. How many tonnes per year must be finished in order to justify the higher purchase cost of the auto-feed machine?

Solution
Use the steps above to calculate the breakeven point between the two alternatives.

1. Let x represent the number of tonnes per year.
2. For the auto-feed machine the annual variable cost is

$$\text{Annual VC} = \frac{\$24}{\text{hour}} \frac{1 \text{ hour}}{8 \text{ tonnes}} \frac{x \text{ tonnes}}{\text{year}}$$

$$= 3x$$

The VC is developed in dollars per year. The AW expression for the auto-feed machine is

$$AW_{auto} = -23,000(A/P,10\%,10) + 4000(A/F,10\%,10) - 3500 - 3x$$
$$= \$-6992 - 3x$$

Similarly, the annual variable cost and AW for the manual feed machine are

$$\text{Annual VC} = \frac{\$12}{\text{hour}} (3 \text{ operators}) \frac{1 \text{ hour}}{6 \text{ tonnes}} \frac{x \text{ tonnes}}{\text{year}}$$

$$= 6x$$
$$AW_{manual} = -8000(A/P,10\%,5) - 1500 - 6x$$
$$= \$-3610 - 6x$$

3. Equate the two cost relations and solve for x.

$$AW_{auto} = AW_{manual}$$
$$-6992 - 3x = -3610 - 6x$$
$$x = 1127 \text{ tonnes per year}$$

4. If the output is expected to exceed 1127 tonnes per year, purchase the auto-feed machine, since its VC slope of 3 is smaller than the manual feed VC slope of 6.

The breakeven analysis approach is commonly used for make-or-buy decisions. The alternative to buy usually has no fixed cost and a larger variable cost than the option to make. Where the two cost relations cross is the make-or-buy decision quantity. Amounts above this indicate that the item should be made, not purchased outside.

EXAMPLE 13.4

Guardian is a national manufacturing company of home health care appliances. It is faced with a make-or-buy decision. A newly engineered lift can be installed in a car trunk to raise and lower a wheelchair. The steel arm of the lift can be purchased for $0.60 per unit or made in house. If manufactured on site, two machines will be required. Machine A is estimated to cost $18,000, have a life of 6 years, and have a $2000 salvage value; machine B will cost $12,000, have a life of 4 years, and have a $−500 salvage value (carry-away cost). Machine A will require an overhaul after 3 years costing $3000. The annual operating cost for machine A is expected to be $6000 per year and for machine B $5000 per year. A total of four operators will be required for the two machines at a rate of $12.50 per hour per operator. In a normal 8-hour period, the operators and two machines can produce parts sufficient to manufacture 1000 units. Use a MARR of 15% per year to determine the following.

(a) Number of units to manufacture each year to justify the in-house (make) option.
(b) The maximum capital expense justifiable to purchase machine A, assuming all other estimates for machines A and B are as stated. The company expects to produce 125,000 units per year.

Solution

(a) Use steps 1 to 3 stated previously to determine the breakeven point.

1. Define x as the number of lifts produced per year.
2. There are variable costs for the operators and fixed costs for the two machines for the make option.

$$\text{Annual VC} = (\text{cost per unit})(\text{units per year})$$

$$= \frac{4 \text{ operators}}{1000 \text{ units}} \frac{\$12.50}{\text{hour}} (8 \text{ hours})x$$

$$= 0.4x$$

The annual fixed costs for machines A and B are the AW amounts.

$$AW_A = -18,000(A/P,15\%,6) + 2000(A/F,15\%,6)$$
$$- 6000 - 3000(P/F,15\%,3)(A/P,15\%,6)$$
$$AW_B = -12,000(A/P,15\%,4) - 500(A/F,15\%,4) - 5000$$

Total cost is the sum of AW_A, AW_B, and VC.

3. Equating the annual costs of the buy option ($0.60x$) and the make option yields

$$-0.60x = AW_A + AW_B - VC$$
$$= -18,000(A/P,15\%,6) + 2000(A/F,15\%,6) - 6000$$
$$- 3000(P/F,15\%,3)(A/P,15\%,6) - 12,000(A/P,15\%,4)$$
$$- 500(A/F,15\%,4) - 5000 - 0.4x \qquad \text{[13.7]}$$
$$-0.2x = -20,352.43$$
$$x = 101,762 \text{ units per year}$$

A minimum of 101,762 lifts must be produced each year to justify the make option, which has the lower variable cost of $0.40x$.

(b) Substitute 125,000 for x and P_A for the to-be-determined first cost of machine A (currently $18,000) in Equation [13.7]. Solution yields $P_A = \$35,588$. This is approximately twice the estimated first cost of $18,000, because the production of 125,000 per year is larger than the breakeven amount of 101,762.

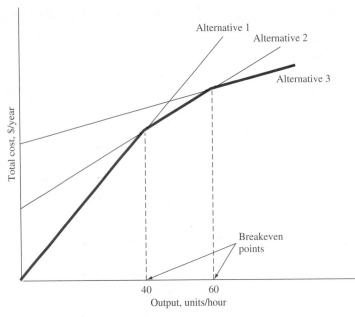

FIGURE 13–8
Breakeven points
for three
alternatives.

Even though the preceding examples treat two alternatives, the same type of analysis can be performed for three or more alternatives. To do so, compare the alternatives in pairs to find their respective breakeven points. The results are the ranges through which each alternative is more economical. For example, in Figure 13–8, if the output is less than 40 units per hour, alternative 1 should be selected. Between 40 and 60, alternative 2 is more economical; and above 60, alternative 3 is favoured.

If the variable cost relations are nonlinear, analysis is more complicated. If the costs increase or decrease uniformly, mathematical expressions that allow direct determination of the breakeven point can be developed.

Excel's optimizing tool, SOLVER, can be used for performing a computer-based breakeven analysis between two alternatives. We have used this tool previously in Section 12.4 on the linear programming model and in Section 11.3 in a replacement study. An illustration of its application for breakeven analysis can be found on the Online Learning Centre.

CHAPTER SUMMARY

The breakeven point for a variable X for one project is expressed in terms such as units per year or hours per month. At the breakeven amount Q_{BE}, there is indifference to accept or reject the project. Use the following decision guideline:

Single Project (refer to Figure 13–2)

Estimated quantity is *larger* than $Q_{BE} \rightarrow$ accept project

Estimated quantity is *smaller* than $Q_{BE} \rightarrow$ reject project

For two or more alternatives, determine the breakeven value of the common variable X. Use the following guideline to select an alternative:

Two Alternatives (refer to Figure 13–7)

Estimated level of X is *below* breakeven → select alternative with the higher variable cost (larger slope)

Estimated level of X is *above* breakeven → select alternative with the lower variable cost (smaller slope)

Breakeven analysis between two alternatives is accomplished by equating the PW or AW relations and solving for the parameter in question.

PROBLEMS

Breakeven Analysis for a Project

13.1 The fixed costs at Harley Motors are $1 million annually. The main product has revenue of $8.50 per unit and $4.25 variable cost. Determine the following.
   (a) Breakeven quantity per year.
   (b) Annual profit if 200,000 units are sold and if 350,000 units are sold. Use both an equation and a plot of the revenue and total cost relations to answer.

13.2 If both linear and nonlinear revenue and total cost relations are considered, state at least one combination of mathematical relations for which there could easily be exactly two breakeven points.

13.3 A metallurgical engineer has estimated that the capital investment for recovering valuable metals (nickel, silver, gold, etc.) from a copper refinery's wastewater stream will be $15 million. The equipment will have a useful life of 10 years, with no salvage value. The amount of metals currently discharged is 12,000 kilograms per month. The monthly operating cost is represented by $(4,100,000)E^{1.8}$, where E is the efficiency of metal recovery in decimal form. Determine the minimum removal efficiency required for the company to break even, if the average selling price of the metals is $250 per kilogram. Use an interest rate of 1% per month.

13.4 For the estimates below, calculate the following.
   (a) Breakeven quantity per month.
   (b) Profit (loss) per unit at sales levels that are 10% above and 10% below breakeven.
   (c) Plot average cost per unit for quantities ranging from 25% below to 30% above breakeven.

$$r = \$39.95 \text{ per unit}$$
$$v = \$24.75 \text{ per unit}$$
$$FC = \$4,000,000 \text{ per year}$$

13.5 Develop a plot of the average cost per unit versus production quantity for the houseware appliance assembly department of Ace-One, Inc., that has a fixed cost of $160,000 per year and a variable cost of $4 per unit; use it to answer the following questions.
   (a) At what quantity is a $5 per unit average cost justified?

(b) If the fixed cost increases to $200,000, plot the new curve on the same graph and estimate the quantity that justifies an average cost of $6 per unit.

13.6 A call centre in India used by Canadian credit card holders has a capacity of 1,400,000 calls annually. The fixed cost of the centre is $775,000 with an average variable cost of $2 and revenue of $3.50 per call.

(a) Find the percentage of the capacity that must be placed each year to break even.

(b) The centre manager expects to dedicate the equivalent of 500,000 of the 1,400,000 capacity to a new product line. This is expected to increase the centre's fixed cost to $900,000, of which 50% will be allocated to the new product line. Determine the average revenue per call necessary to make 500,000 calls the breakeven point for only the new product. How does this required revenue compare with the current center revenue of $3.50 per call?

13.7 For the last 2 years, Laurentien Leather Products has experienced a fixed cost of $850,000 per year and an $(r - v)$ value of $1.25 per unit. International competition has become severe enough that some financial changes must be made to keep market share at the current level. Perform a graphical analysis, using Excel, that estimates the effect on the breakeven point if the difference between revenue and variable cost per unit increases somewhere between 1% and 15% of its current value. If fixed costs and revenue per unit remain at their current values, what must change to make the breakeven point go down?

13.8 (This is an extension of Problem 13.7.) Expand the analysis performed in Problem 13.7, where a change in variable cost per unit is examined. The financial manager estimates that fixed costs will fall to $750,000 when the required production rate to break even is at or below 600,000 units. What happens to the breakeven points over the $(r - v)$ range of 1% to 15% increase as evaluated previously?

13.9 An automobile company is investigating the advisability of converting a plant that manufactures economy cars into one that will make retro sports cars. The initial cost for equipment conversion will be $200 million with a 20% salvage value anytime within a 5-year period. The cost of producing a car will be $21,000, but it is expected to have a selling price of $33,000 (to dealers). The production capacity for the first year will be 4000 units. At an interest rate of 12% per year, by what uniform amount will production have to increase each year in order for the company to recover its investment in 3 years?

13.10 Last year the Okanagan Fruitgrowers Cooperative purchased a juice pasteurizer for $150,000. Revenue for the first year was $50,000. Over the total estimated life of 8 years, what must the remaining annual revenues (years 2 through 8) equal to recover the investment, if costs are constant at $42,000 and a return of 10% per year is expected? A salvage value of $20,000 is anticipated.

13.11 Rod, an industrial engineer manager with Zema Corporation, has determined via the least squares method that the annual total cost per case of producing its top-selling drink can best be described by the quadratic relation $TC = 0.001Q^2 + 3Q + 2$, and that revenue is approximately linear with $r = $25 per case. Rod asks you to do the following.

(a) Tabulate the profit function between the values of $Q = 5000$ and $25,000$

cases. Estimate the maximum profit and the quantity at which it occurs.

(b) Find the answers to part (a) by using an Excel graph.

(c) Determine an equation for Qmax, the quantity at which the maximum profit should occur, and determine the amount of the profit at this point for the TC and r identified by the manager.

13.12 A civil engineer has been promoted to manager of engineered public systems. One of the products is an emergency intercept pump for potable water. If the tested water quality or volume varies by a preset percentage, the pump automatically switches to preselected options of treatments or water sources. The manufacturing process for the pump had the following fixed and variable costs over a 1-year period.

	Fixed Costs, $		Variable Costs, $/Unit
Administrative	30,000	Materials	2500
Salaries and benefits: 20% of	350,000	Labour	200
Equipment	100,000	Indirect labour	2000
Space, utilities, etc.	55,000	Subcontractors	800
Computers: 1/3 of	150,000		

(a) Determine the minimum revenue per unit to break even at the current production volume of 5000 units per year.

(b) If selling internationally and to large corporations is pursued, an increased production of 3000 additional units will be necessary. Determine the revenue per unit required if a profit goal of $500,000 is set for the entire product line. Assume the cost estimates above remain the same.

Breakeven Analysis Between Alternatives

13.13 A Yellow Pages directory company must decide whether it should compose the ads for its clients inhouse or pay a production company to compose them. To develop the ads in house, the company will have to purchase computers, printers, and other peripherals at a cost of $12,000. The equipment will have a useful life of 3 years, after which it will be sold for $2000. The employee who creates the ads will be paid $45,000 per year. In addition, each ad will have an average cost of $8 to prepare for delivery to the printer. A total of 4000 ads are anticipated for the next few years. Alternatively, the company can outsource ad development at a fee of $20 per ad regardless of the quantity. The current interest rate is 8% per year. What is the breakeven amount, and which alternative is economically better?

13.14 An engineering firm can lease a measurement system for $1000 per month or purchase one for $15,000. The leased system will have no monthly maintenance cost, but the purchased one will cost $80 per month. At an interest rate of 0.5% per month, how many months must the system be required to break even?

13.15 Two pumps can be used for pumping a corrosive liquid. A pump with a brass impeller costs $800 and is expected to last 3 years. A pump with a stainless steel impeller costs $1900 and will last 5 years. A rebuild costing $300 will be required after 2000 operating hours for the brass impeller pump while an overhaul costing $700 will be required for the stainless steel pump after 8000 hours. If the operating cost of each pump is $1 per hour, how many hours per year must the pump be required to justify the purchase of the more expensive pump? Use an interest rate of 10% per year.

13.16 Two bids have been received to repave a commercial parking lot. Proposal 1 includes new curbs, grading, and paving at an initial cost of $250,000. The life of the parking lot surface constructed in this manner is expected to be 4 years with annual costs for maintenance and repainting of pavement markings at $3000. Proposal 2 offers pavement of a significantly higher quality with an expected life of 8 years. The annual maintenance cost will be negligible for the pavement, but the markings will have to be repainted every 2 years at a cost of $3000. Markings are not repainted the last year of its expected life under proposal 2. If the company's current MARR is 12% per year, how much can it afford to spend on proposal 2 initially so the two break even?

13.17 Ontario Site Remediation, Inc., is evaluating 2 "pump and treat" schemes for decontamination of the groundwater aquifer near the Richmond Landfill.
  (a) Use an AW relation to determine the minimum number of hours per year of operation to justify system A, if the MARR is 10% per year.
  (b) Which system is economically better, if it operates 7 hours per day, 365 days per year?

	System A	System N
Initial cost, $	−10,300	−4000
Life, years	6	3
Rebuild cost, $	−2,200	−1000
Time before rebuild, annually or minimum hours	8000	2000
Cost to operate, $/hour	0.90	1.00

13.18 Jeremy is evaluating the operational costs of the manufacturing processes for specific components of a wireless home security system. The same components are produced at plants in Hamilton and Winnipeg. The records for the last 3 years from Hamilton report a fixed cost of $400,000 per year and a variable cost of $95 per unit in year 1, decreasing by $3 per unit per year. The Winnipeg reports indicate a fixed cost of $750,000 per year and a variable cost of $50 per unit, increasing by $4 per unit per year. If the trends continue, how many units must be produced in year 4 for the two processes break even? Use an interest rate of 10% per year.

13.19 Alfred Home Construction is considering the purchase of five dumpsters and a transport truck to store and transfer construction debris from building sites. The entire rig is estimated to have an initial cost of $125,000, a life of 8 years, a $5000 salvage value, an operating cost of $40 per day, and an annual maintenance cost of $2000. Alternatively, Alfred can obtain the same services from the city as needed at each construction site for an initial delivery cost of $125 per dumpster per site and a daily charge of $20 per day per dumpster. An estimated 45 construction sites will need debris storage throughout the average year. The minimum attractive rate of return is 12% per year. (a) How many days per year must the equipment be required to just break even? (b) If the expected usage is 75 days per year, which option—buy or lease—should be selected based on this economic analysis? Determine the expected annual cost of this decision.

13.20 Machine A has a fixed cost of $40,000 per year and a variable cost of $60 per unit. Machine B has an unknown fixed cost, but with this process 200 units can be produced each month at a total variable cost of $2000. If the total costs of the two machines break even at a production rate of 2000 units per year, what is the fixed cost of machine B?

13.21   A waste-holding lagoon situated near the main plant receives sludge daily. When the lagoon is full, it is necessary to remove the sludge to a site located 8.2 kilometres from the main plant. Currently, when the lagoon is full, the sludge is removed by pump into a tank truck and hauled away. This process requires the use of a portable pump that initially cost $800 and has an 8-year life. The company pays a contract individual to operate the pump and oversee environmental and safety factors at a rate of $100 per day, but the truck and driver must be rented for $200 per day.

The company has the option to install a pump and pipeline to the remote site. The pump would have an initial cost of $1600 and a life of 10 years and will cost $3 per day to operate. The company's MARR is 10% per year.

(*a*)   If the pipeline will cost $12 per metre to construct and will have a 10-year life, how many days per year must the lagoon require pumping to justify construction of the pipeline?

(*b*)   If the company expects to pump the lagoon once per week every week of the year, how much money can it afford to spend now on the 10-year-life pipeline to just break even?

CASE STUDY

WATER TREATMENT PLANT PROCESS COSTS

Introduction

Aeration and sludge recirculation have been practised for many years at municipal and industrial water treatment plants. Aeration is used primarily for the physical removal of gases or volatile compounds while sludge recirculation can be beneficial for turbidity removal and hardness reduction.

When the advantages of aeration and sludge recirculation in water treatment were first recognized, energy costs were so low that such considerations were seldom of concern in treatment plant design and operation. With the 10-fold increase in electricity cost that occurred in some localities, however, it became necessary to review the cost-effectiveness of all water treatment processes that consume significant amounts of energy. This study was conducted at a municipal water treatment plant for evaluating the cost-effectiveness of the pre-aeration and sludge recirculation practices.

Experimental Procedure

This study was conducted at a 106 cubic metres per minute water treatment plant where, under normal operating circumstances, sludge from the secondary clarifiers is returned to the aerator and subsequently removed in the primary clarifiers. Figure 13–9 is a schematic of the process.

To evaluate the effect of sludge recirculation, the sludge pump was turned off, but aeration was continued. Next, the sludge pump was turned back on, and aeration was discontinued. Finally, both processes were discontinued. Results

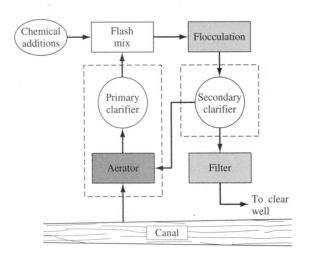

FIGURE 13–9
Schematic of water treatment plant.

obtained during the test periods were averaged and compared to the values obtained when both processes were operational.

Results and Discussion

The results obtained from the four operating modes showed that the hardness decreased by 4.7% when both processes were in operation (i.e., sludge recirculation and aeration). When only sludge was recirculated, the reduction was 3.8%. There was no reduction due to aeration only, or when there was neither aeration nor recirculation. For turbidity, the reduction was 28% when both recirculation and aeration were used. The reduction was 18% when *neither* aeration nor recirculation was used. The reduction was also 18% when aeration alone was used, which means that aeration alone was of no benefit for turbidity reduction. With sludge recirculation alone, the turbidity reduction was only 6%, meaning that sludge recirculation alone actually resulted in an *increase* in turbidity—the difference between 18% and 6%.

Since aeration and sludge recirculation did cause readily identifiable effects on treated water quality (some good and others bad), the cost-effectiveness of each process for turbidity and hardness reduction was investigated. The calculations are based on the following data:

Aerator motor = 40 hp
Aerator motor efficiency = 90%
Sludge recirculation motor = 5 hp
Recirculation pump efficiency = 90%
Electricity cost = 9¢/kWh
Lime cost = 7.9¢/kg
Lime required = 0.62 mg/L per mg/L hardness
Coagulant cost = 16.5¢/kg
Days/month = 30.5

As a first step, the costs associated with aeration and sludge recirculation were calculated. In each case, costs are independent of flow rate.

Aeration cost:

40 hp $\times$ 0.75 kW/hp $\times$ 0.09 $/kWh $\times$ 24 h/day $\div$ 0.90 = $72 per day
or $2196 per month

Sludge recirculation cost:

5 hp $\times$ 0.75 kW/hp $\times$ 0.09 $/kWh $\times$ 24 h/day $\div$ 0.90 = $9 per day
or $275 per month

The estimates appear in columns 1 and 2 of the cost summary in Table 13–1.

Costs associated with turbidity and hardness removal are a function of the chemical dosage required and the water flow rate. The calculations below are based on a design flow of 53 cubic metres per minute.

As stated earlier, there was less turbidity reduction through the primary clarifier without aeration than there was with it (28% versus 6%). The extra turbidity reaching the flocculators could require further additions of the coagulating chemical. If it is assumed that, as a worst case, these chemical additions would be proportional to the extra turbidity, then 22 percent more coagulant would be required. Since the average dosage before discontinuation of aeration was 10 milligrams per litre, the *incremental chemical cost* incurred because of the increased turbidity in the clarifier effluent would be

(10×0.22) mg/L $\times$ 10^{-6} kg/mg $\times$ 53 m^3/min $\times$ 1000 L/m^3 $\times$ 0.165 $/kg
$\times$ 60 min/h $\times$ 24 h/day = $27.70/day or $845/month

Similar calculations for the other operating conditions (i.e., aeration only, and neither aeration nor sludge recirculation) reveal that the additional cost for turbidity removal would be $469 per month in each case, as shown in column 5 of Table 13–1.

Changes in hardness affect chemical costs by virtue of the direct effect on the amount of lime required for water softening. With aeration and sludge recirculation, the average hardness reduction was 12.1 milligrams per litre (i.e., 258 mg/L $\times$ 4.7%). However, with sludge recirculation only, the reduction was 9.8 milligrams per litre, resulting in a difference of 2.3 milligrams per litre attributed to aeration. The *extra cost of lime* incurred because of the discontinuation of aeration, therefore, was

2.3 mg/L $\times$ 0.62 mg/L lime $\times$ 10^{-6} kg/mg
$\times$ 53 m^3/min $\times$ 1000 L/m^3 $\times$ 0.079 $/kg
$\times$ 60 min/h $\times$ 24 h/day = $8.60/day or $262/month

When sludge recirculation was discontinued, there was no hardness reduction through the clarifier, so that the extra lime cost would be $1380 per month.

The total savings and total costs associated with changes in plant operating conditions are tabulated in columns 3 and 6 of Table 13–1, respectively, with the net savings shown in column 7. Obviously, the optimum condition is represented by "sludge recirculation only." This condition would result in a net savings of

TABLE 13–1 Cost Summary in Dollars per Month

Alt. ID	Alternative Description	Savings from Discontinuation Of:		Total Savings (3) = (1) + (2)	Extra Cost for Removal Of:		Total Extra Cost (6) = (4) + (5)	Net Savings (7) = (3) − (6)
		Aeration (1)	Recirculation (2)		Hardness (4)	Turbidity (5)		
1	Sludge recirculation and aeration			Normal operating condition				
2	Aeration only	—	275	275	1380	469	1849	−1574
3	Sludge recirculation only	2196	—	2196	262	845	1107	+1089
4	Neither aeration nor sludge recirculation	2196	275	2471	1380	469	1849	+622

$1089 per month, compared to a net savings of $622 per month when both processes are discontinued and a net *cost* of $1574 per month for aeration only. Since the calculations made here represent worst-case conditions, the actual savings that resulted from modifying the plant operating procedures were greater than those indicated.

In summary, the commonly applied water treatment practices of sludge recirculation and aeration can significantly affect the removal of some compounds in the primary clarifier. However, increasing energy and chemical costs warrant continued investigations on a case-by-case basis of the cost-effectiveness of such practices.

Case Study Exercises

1. What would be the monthly savings in electricity from discontinuation of aeration if the cost of electricity were 6 cents per kilowatt-hour?

2. Does a decrease in the efficiency of the aerator motor make the selected alternative of sludge recirculation only more attractive, less attractive, or the same as before?

3. If the cost of lime were to increase by 50%, would the cost difference between the best alternative and second-best alternative increase, decrease, or remain the same?

4. If the efficiency of the sludge recirculation pump were reduced from 90% to 70%, would the net savings difference between alternatives 3 and 4 increase, decrease, or stay the same?

5. If hardness removal were to be discontinued at the treatment plant, which alternative would be the most cost-effective?

6. If the cost of electricity decreased to 4 cents per kilowatt-hour which alternative would be the most cost-effective?

7. At what electricity cost would the following alternatives just break even: (*a*) alternatives 1 and 2, (*b*) alternatives 1 and 3, (*c*) alternatives 1 and 4?

LEVEL ④

Rounding Out the Study

This Level includes topics to enhance your ability to perform a thorough engineering economic study of one or more alternatives. The effects of inflation, depreciation, income taxes in all types of studies, and indirect costs are incorporated into the methods of previous chapters. The last two chapters include additional material on the use of engineering economics in decision making. An expanded version of sensitivity analysis is developed; it formalizes the approach to examine parameters that vary over a predictable range of values. Finally, the elements of risk and probability are explicitly considered using expected values, probabilistic analysis, computer simulation, senaric analysis, and utility theory.

Several of these topics can be covered earlier in the text, depending on the objectives of the course. Use the chart in the Preface to determine appropriate points at which to introduce the material.

LEVEL ③ Making Decisions on Real-World Projects

CHAPTER 11
Replacement and Retention Decisions

CHAPTER 12
Selection from Independent Projects Under Budget Limitation

CHAPTER 13
Breakeven Analysis

LEVEL ④ Rounding Out the Study

CHAPTER 14
Effects of Inflation

CHAPTER 15
Depreciation Methods

CHAPTER 16
After-Tax Economic Analysis

CHAPTER 17
Formalized Sensitivity Analysis and Expected Value Decisions

CHAPTER 18
More on Variation and Decision Making Under Risk

CHAPTER 14

Effects of Inflation

This chapter concentrates upon understanding and calculating the effects of inflation in time value of money computations. Inflation is a reality that we deal with nearly everyday in professional and personal life.

The annual inflation rate is closely watched and historically analyzed by government units, businesses, and industrial corporations. An engineering economy study can have different outcomes in an environment in which inflation is a serious concern compared to one in which it is of minor consideration. In the last few years of the 20th century, and the beginning of the 21st century, inflation has not been a major concern in Canada or most industrialized nations. But the inflation rate is sensitive to real, as well as perceived, factors of the economy. Factors such as the cost of energy, interest rates, availability and cost of skilled people, scarcity of materials, political stability, and other, less tangible factors have short-term and long-term impacts on the inflation rate. In some industries, it is vital that the effects of inflation be integrated into an economic analysis. The basic techniques to do so are covered here.

LEARNING OBJECTIVES

Purpose: Consider inflation in an engineering economy analysis.

By the end of this chapter you should be able to

Impact of inflation	**1.** Determine the difference inflation makes between money now and money in the future.
PW with inflation	**2.** Calculate present worth with an adjustment for inflation.
FW with inflation	**3.** Determine the real interest rate and calculate a future worth with an adjustment for inflation.
AW with inflation	**4.** Calculate an annual amount in future dollars that is equivalent to a specified present or future sum.

14.1 UNDERSTANDING THE IMPACT OF INFLATION

We are all very well aware that $20 now does not purchase the same amount as $20 did in 2000 and purchases significantly less than in 1990. Why? Primarily because of inflation.

Inflation is an increase in the amount of money necessary to obtain the same amount of product or service before the inflated price was present.

Inflation occurs because the value of the currency has changed—it has gone down in value. The value of money has decreased, and as a result, it takes more dollars for the same amount of goods or services. This is a sign of *inflation*. To make comparisons between monetary amounts which occur in different time periods, the different-valued dollars must first be converted to constant-value dollars in order to represent the same purchasing power over time. This is especially important when future sums of money are considered, as is the case with all alternative evaluations.

Money in one period of time t_1 can be brought to the same value as money in another period of time t_2 by using the equation

$$\text{Dollars in period } t_1 = \frac{\text{dollars in period } t_2}{\text{inflation rate between } t_1 \text{ and } t_2} \qquad [14.1]$$

Dollars in period t_1 are called *constant-value dollars* or *today's dollars*. Dollars in period t_2 are called *future dollars* or *then-current dollars*. If f represents the inflation rate per period (year) and n is the number of time periods (years) between t_1 and t_2, Equation [14.1] is

$$\textbf{Constant-value dollars = today's dollars} = \frac{\textbf{future dollars}}{(1+f)^n} \qquad [14.2]$$

$$\textbf{Future dollars = today's dollars}(1+f)^n \qquad [14.3]$$

It is correct to express future (inflated) dollars in terms of constant-value dollars, and vice versa, by applying the last two equations. This is how the consumer price index (CPI) and cost estimation indices are determined. As an illustration, use the price of a small Tim Hortons iced cappuccino in some parts of Canada.

$2.23   August 2011

If inflation averaged 4% during the last year, in *constant-value 2010 dollars,* this cost is last year's equivalent of

$2.23/(1.04) = $2.14   August 2010

A predicted price in 2012 is

$2.23(1.04) = $2.32   August 2012

If inflation averages 4% per year over the next 10 years, Equation [14.3] is used to predict the ice-cap's price in 2021:

$2.23(1.04)^{10} = $3.30   August 2021

This is a 48% increase over the 2011 price at 4% inflation, which is considered low to average nationally and internationally. If inflation averages 6% per year, the ice-cap's cost in 10 years will be $3.99, an increase of 79%. In some areas of the world, hyperinflation may average 50% per year. In such an unfortunate economy, the ice-cap in 10 years rises from the dollar equivalent of $2.23 to $128.59! This is why countries experiencing hyperinflation must devalue the currency by factors of 100 and 1000 when unacceptable inflation rates persist.

Placed into an industrial or business context, at a reasonably low inflation rate averaging 4% per year, equipment or services with a first cost of $209,000 will increase by 48% to $309,000 over a 10-year span. This is before any consideration of the rate of return requirement is placed upon the equipment's revenue-generating ability. *Make no mistake: inflation is a formidable force in our economy.*

There are actually three different rates that are important: the real interest rate (i), the market interest rate (i_f), and the inflation rate (f). Only the first two are interest rates.

Real or inflation-free interest rate i. This is the rate at which interest is earned when the effects of changes in the value of currency (inflation) have been removed. Thus, the real interest rate presents an actual gain in purchasing power. (The equation used to calculate i, with the influence of inflation removed, is derived later in Section 14.3.) The real rate of return that generally applies for individuals is approximately 3.5% per year. This is the "safe investment" rate. The required real rate for corporations (and many individuals) is set above this safe rate when a MARR is established without an adjustment for inflation.

Inflation-adjusted interest rate i_f. As its name implies, this is the interest rate that has been adjusted to take inflation into account. The *market interest rate,* which is the one we hear every day, is an inflation-adjusted rate. This rate is a combination of the real interest rate i and the inflation rate f, and, therefore, it changes as the inflation rate changes. It is also known as the *inflated interest rate.*

Inflation rate f. As described above, this is a measure of the rate of change in the value of the currency.

A company's MARR adjusted for inflation is referred to as the inflation-adjusted MARR. The determination of this value is discussed in Section 14.3.

Deflation is the opposite of inflation in that when deflation is present, the purchasing power of the monetary unit is greater in the future than at present. That is, it will take fewer dollars in the future to buy the same amount of goods or services as it does today. Inflation occurs much more commonly than deflation, especially at the national economy level. In deflationary economic conditions, the market interest rate is always less than the real interest rate.

Temporary price deflation may occur in specific sectors of the economy due to the introduction of improved products, cheaper technology, or imported materials or products that force current prices down. In normal situations, prices equalize at a competitive level after a short time. However, deflation over a short time in a specific sector of an economy can be orchestrated through *dumping*. An example of dumping may be the importation of materials, such as steel, cement, or cars, into one country from international competitors at very low prices compared to current market prices in the targeted country. The prices will go down for the consumer, thus forcing domestic manufacturers to reduce their prices in order to compete for business. If domestic manufacturers are not in good financial condition, they may fail, and the imported items replace the domestic supply. Prices may then return to normal levels and, in fact, become inflated over time, if competition has been significantly reduced.

On the surface, having a moderate rate of deflation sounds good when inflation has been present in the economy over long periods. However, if deflation occurs at a more general level, say nationally, it is likely to be accompanied by the lack of money for new capital. Another result is that individuals and families have less money to spend due to fewer jobs, less credit, and fewer loans available; an overall "tighter" money situation prevails. As money gets tighter, less is available to be committed to industrial growth and capital investment. In the extreme case, this can evolve over time into a deflationary spiral that disrupts the entire economy. This has happened on occasion, notably in Canada and the United States during the Great Depression of the 1930s. Japan has experienced deflation in real estate and equity prices over the past 20 years, despite inflationary tactics to increase money supply and lower interest rates below 1%. However, the country has managed to maintain positive real growth, because of factors not currently benefiting Western economies such as a high national savings rate and a large export sector. Other developed economies are thought to be increasingly at risk of deflation in the aftermath of the banking and mortgage crisis of 2008, which has resulted in continuing slow economic growth and loss in the traditional industrial base upon which job development and innovation depend.

Engineering economy computations that consider deflation use the same relations as those for inflation. For basic equivalence between today's dollars and future dollars, Equations [14.2] and [14.3] are used, except the deflation rate is a $-f$ value. For example, if deflation is estimated to be 2% per year, an asset that costs $10,000 today would have a first cost 5 years from now determined by Equation [14.3].

$$10,000(1 - f)^n = 10,000(0.98)^5 = 10,000(0.9039) = \$9039$$

The Bank of Canada describes changes in inflation according to a set of indicators that assess capacity and inflation pressures for the nation. Their website (www.bankofcanada.ca) has articles concerning monetary policy addressing the Bank's goal of keeping core inflation at a 2% target and provides fact sheets concerning its targets, policies, and goals. It also includes graphs and tables of historical data.

Canada's national statistical agency, Statistics Canada, provides articles and data on economic indicators such as the CPI, the unemployment rate, the gross domestic product, and estimates of population on their website (www.statcan.ca). It is also a source for specific statistics in subjects concerning agriculture, business services, construction, energy, environment, health, trade, manufacturing, price indices, science and technology, and transportation. Each subcategory has documents concerning recent news releases, summary tables, and publications. The site includes valuable information on the CPI, relating its current level to that of previous months and years for both the nation and each province and territory. It also breaks down the index into its major components: food, shelter, health, transportation, etc.

14.2 PRESENT WORTH CALCULATIONS ADJUSTED FOR INFLATION

When the dollar amounts in different time periods are expressed in *constant-value dollars,* the equivalent present and future amounts are determined using the real interest rate i. The calculations involved in this procedure are illustrated in Table 14–1 where the inflation rate is 4% per year. Column 2 shows the inflation-driven increase for each of the next 4 years for an item that has a cost of $5000 today. Column 3 shows the cost in future dollars, and column 4 verifies the cost in constant-value dollars via Equation [14.2]. When the future dollars of column 3 are converted to constant-value dollars (column 4), the cost is always $5000, the same as the cost at the start. This is predictably true when the costs are increasing by an amount *exactly equal* to the inflation rate. The actual (inflation-adjusted) cost of the item 4 years from now will be $5849, but in constant-value dollars the cost in 4 years will still amount to $5000. Column 5 shows the present worth of future amounts of $5000 at a real interest rate of $i = 10\%$ per year.

TABLE 14–1 Inflation Calculations Using Constant-Value Dollars ($f = 4\%, i = 10\%$)

Year n (1)	Cost Increase Due to 4% Inflation (2)	Cost in Future Dollars (3)	Future Cost in Constant-Value Dollars $(4) = (3)/1.04^n$	Present Worth at Real $i = 10\%$ $(5) = (4)(P/F,10\%,n)$
0		$5000	$5000	$5000
1	$5000(0.04) = $200	5200	$5200/(1.04)^1 = 5000$	4545
2	5200(0.04) = 208	5408	$5408/(1.04)^2 = 5000$	4132
3	5408(0.04) = 216	5624	$5624/(1.04)^3 = 5000$	3757
4	5624(0.04) = 225	5849	$5849/(1.04)^4 = 5000$	3415

Two conclusions can be made. At $f = 4\%$, $5000 today inflates to $5849 in 4 years. And $5000 four years from now has a PW of only $3415 constant-value dollars at a real interest rate of 10% per year.

Figure 14–1 shows the differences over a 4-year period of the constant-value amount of $5000, the future-dollar costs at 4% inflation, and the present worth at

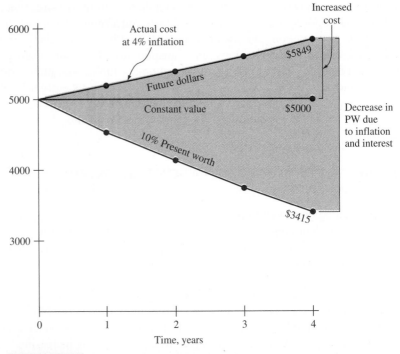

FIGURE 14–1

Comparison of constant-value dollars, future dollars, and their present worth values.

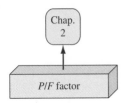

10% real interest with inflation considered. The effect of compounded inflation and interest rates is large, as you can see by the shaded area.

An alternative, and less complicated, method of accounting for inflation in a present worth analysis involves adjusting the interest formulas themselves to account for inflation. Consider the P/F formula, where i is the real interest rate.

$$P = F\frac{1}{(1+i)^n}$$

The F is a future-dollar amount with inflation built in. And F can be converted into today's dollars by using Equation [14.2].

$$P = \frac{F}{(1+f)^n}\frac{1}{(1+i)^n}$$

$$= F\frac{1}{(1+i+f+if)^n} \qquad [14.4]$$

If the term $i + f + if$ is defined as i_f, the equation becomes

$$P = F\frac{1}{(1+i_f)^n} = F(P/F,i_f,n) \qquad [14.5]$$

The symbol i_f is called the *inflation-adjusted interest rate* and is defined as

$$i_f = i + f + if \qquad [14.6]$$

where i = real interest rate
$ f$ = inflation rate
For a real interest rate of 10% per year and an inflation rate of 4% per year, Equation [14.6] yields an inflated interest rate of 14.4%.

$$i_f = 0.10 + 0.04 + 0.10(0.04) = 0.144$$

Table 14–2 illustrates the use of $i_f = 14.4\%$ in PW calculations for $5000 now, which inflates to $5849 in future dollars 4 years hence. As shown in column 4, the present worth for each year is the same as column 5 of Table 14–1.

The present worth of any series of cash flows—equal, arithmetic gradient, or geometric gradient—can be found similarly. That is, either i or i_f is introduced into the P/A, P/G, or P_g factors, depending upon whether the cash flow is expressed in constant-value (today's) dollars or future dollars. If the series is expressed in today's dollars, then its PW is simply the discounted value using the real interest rate i. If the cash flow is expressed in future dollars, the PW value is obtained using i_f. Alternatively, you can first convert all future dollars to today's dollars using Equation [14.2] and then find the PW at i.

TABLE 14–2 Present Worth Calculation Using an Inflated Interest Rate

Year n (1)	Cost in Future Dollars (2)	$(P/F,14.4\%,n)$ (3)	PW (4)
0	$5000	1	$5000
1	5200	0.8741	4545
2	5408	0.7641	4132
3	5624	0.6679	3757
4	5849	0.5838	3415

EXAMPLE 14.1

A former Queens University student wishes to donate to the engineering faculty's scholarship fund. Three options are available:

Plan A. $60,000 now.
Plan B. $15,000 per year for 8 years beginning 1 year from now.
Plan C. $50,000 three years from now and another $80,000, five years from now.

From the faculty's perspective, it wants to select the plan that maximizes the buying power of the dollars received, so the engineering professor evaluating the plans wishes to account for inflation in the calculations. If the donation earns a real 10% per year and the inflation rate is expected to average 3% per year, which plan should be accepted?

Solution

The quickest evaluation method is to calculate the present worth of each plan in today's dollars. For plans B and C, the easiest way to obtain the present worth is through the use of the inflated interest rate. By Equation [14.6],

$$i_f = 0.10 + 0.03 + 0.10(0.03) = 0.133$$

$$PW_A = \$60,000$$

$$PW_B = \$15,000(P/A,13.3\%,8) = \$15,000(4.7508) = \$71,262$$

$$PW_C = \$50,000(P/F,13.3\%,3) + 80,000(P/F,13.3\%,5)$$

$$= \$50,000(0.68756) + 80,000(0.53561) = \$77,227$$

Since PW_C is the largest in today's dollars, select plan C.

For spreadsheet analysis, the PV function is used to find PW_B and PW_C: PV(13.3%,8,−15000) in one cell, and PV(13.3%,3,,−50000) + PV(13.3%,5,,−80000) in another cell.

Comment

The present worths of plans B and C can also be found by first converting the cash flows to today's dollars using $f = 3\%$ in Equation [14.2] and then using the real i of 10% in the P/F factors. This procedure is more time-consuming, but the answers are the same.

EXAMPLE 14.2

A self-employed chemical engineer is on contract with Dow Chemical, currently working in a relatively high-inflation country. She wishes to calculate a project's PW with estimated costs of \$35,000 now and \$7000 per year for 5 years beginning 1 year from now with increases of 12% per year thereafter for the next 8 years. Use a real interest rate of 15% per year to make the calculations (*a*) without an adjustment for inflation and (*b*) considering inflation at a rate of 11% per year.

Solution

(*a*)   Figure 14–2 presents the cash flows. The PW without an adjustment for inflation is found using $i = 15\%$ and $g = 12\%$ in Equations [2.23] and [2.24] for the geometric series.

$$PW = -35,000 - 7000(P/A,15\%,4)$$

$$- \left\{ \frac{7000\left[1 - \left(\dfrac{1.12}{1.15}\right)^9\right]}{0.15 - 0.12} \right\}(P/F,15\%,4)$$

$$= -35,000 - 19,985 - 28,247$$

$$= \$-83,232$$

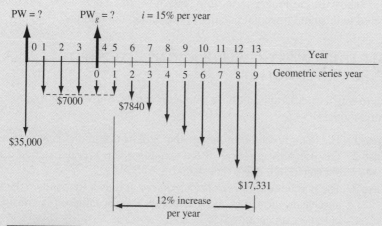

FIGURE 14–2

Cash flow diagram, Example 14.2.

In the P/A factor, $n = 4$ because the $7000 cost in year 5 is the A_1 term in Equation [2.23].

(b)   To adjust for inflation, calculate the inflated interest rate by Equation [14.6].

$$i_f = 0.15 + 0.11 + (0.15)(0.11) = 0.2765$$

$$\text{PW} = -35,000 - 7000(P/A,27.65\%,4)$$

$$-\left\{ \frac{7000\left[1 - \left(\dfrac{1.12}{1.2765}\right)^9\right]}{0.2765 - 0.12} \right\}(P/F,27.65\%,4)$$

$$= -35,000 - 7000(2.2545) - 30,945(0.3766)$$

$$= \$-62,436$$

This result demonstrates that in a high-inflation economy, when negotiating the amount of the payments to repay a loan, it is economically advantageous for the borrower to use future (inflated) dollars whenever possible to make the payments. The present value of future inflated dollars is significantly less when the inflation adjustment is included. And the higher the inflation rate, the larger the discounting because the P/F and P/A factors decrease in size.

The last example seems to add credence to the "buy now, pay later" philosophy of financial management. However, at some point, the debt-ridden company or individual will have to pay off the debts and the accrued interest with the inflated dollars. If cash is not readily available, the debts cannot be repaid. This can happen, for example, when a company unsuccessfully launches a new product, when there is a serious downturn in the economy, or when an individual loses a salary. In the longer term, this "buy now, pay later" approach must be tempered with sound financial practices now, and in the future.

14.3 FUTURE WORTH CALCULATIONS ADJUSTED FOR INFLATION

In future worth calculations, a future amount F can have any one of four different interpretations:

Case 1. The *actual amount* of money that will be accumulated at time n.

Case 2. The *purchasing power* of the actual amount accumulated at time n, but stated in today's (constant-value) dollars.

Case 3. The number of *future dollars required* at time n to maintain the same purchasing power as a dollar today; that is, inflation is considered, but interest is not.

Case 4. The number of dollars required at time n to *maintain purchasing power and earn a stated real interest rate*.

Depending upon which interpretation is intended, the F value is calculated differently, as described below. Each case is illustrated.

Case 1: Actual Amount Accumulated   It should be clear that F, the actual amount of money accumulated, is obtained using the inflation-adjusted (market) interest rate.

$$F = P(1 + i_f)^n = P(F/P,i_f,n) \qquad [14.7]$$

For example, when we are quoted a market rate of 10%, the inflation rate is included. Over a 7-year period, $1000 will accumulate to

$$F = 1000(F/P,10\%,7) = \$1948$$

Case 2: Constant Value with Purchasing Power   The purchasing power of future dollars is determined by first using the market rate i_f to calculate F and then deflating the future amount through division by $(1 + f)^n$.

$$F = \frac{P(1+i_f)^n}{(1+f)^n} = \frac{P(F/P,i_f,n)}{(1+f)^n} \qquad [14.8]$$

This relation, in effect, recognizes the fact that inflated prices mean $1 in the future purchases less than $1 now. The percentage loss in purchasing power is a measure of how much less. As an illustration, consider the same $1000 now, a 10% per year market rate, and an inflation rate of 4% per year. In 7 years, the purchasing power has risen, but only to $1481.

$$F = \frac{1000(F/P,10\%,7)}{(1.04)^7} = \frac{\$1948}{1.3159} = \$1481$$

This is $467 (or 24%) less than the $1948 actually accumulated at 10% (case 1). Therefore, we conclude that 4% inflation over 7 years reduces the purchasing power of money by 24%.

Also for case 2, the future amount of money accumulated with today's buying power could equivalently be determined by calculating the real interest rate and using it in the F/P factor to compensate for the decreased purchasing power of the dollar. This *real interest rate* is the i in Equation [14.6].

$$i_f = i + f + if$$
$$= i(1 + f) + f$$

$$i = \frac{i_f - f}{1 + f} \qquad \textbf{[14.9]}$$

The real interest rate i represents the rate at which today's dollars expand with their *same purchasing power* into equivalent future dollars. An inflation rate larger than the market interest rate leads to a negative real interest rate. The use of this interest rate is appropriate for calculating the future worth of an investment (such as a savings account or money market fund) when the effect of inflation must be removed. For the example of $1000 in today's dollars from Equation [14.9]

$$i = \frac{0.10 - 0.04}{1\,0.04} = 0.0577, \text{ or } 5.77\%$$

$$F = 1000(F/P,5.77\%,7) = \$1481$$

The market interest rate of 10% per year has been reduced to a real rate that is less than 6% per year because of the erosive effects of inflation.

Case 3: Future Amount Required, No Interest   This case recognizes that prices increase when inflation is present. Simply put, future dollars are worth less, so more are needed. No interest rate is considered at all in this case. This is the situation present if someone asks, How much will a car cost in 5 years if its current cost is $20,000 and its price will increase by 6% per year? (The answer is $26,765.) No interest rate, only inflation, is involved. To find the future cost, substitute f for the interest rate in the F/P factor.

$$F = P(1 + f)^n = P(F/P,f,n) \qquad \textbf{[14.10]}$$

Reconsider the $1000 used previously. If it is escalating at exactly the inflation rate of 4% per year, the amount 7 years from now will be

$$F = 1000(F/P,4\%,7) = \$1316$$

Case 4: Inflation and Real Interest   This is the case applied when a MARR is established. Maintaining purchasing power and earning interest must account for both increasing prices (case 3) and the time value of money. If the growth of capital is to keep up, funds must grow at a rate equal to or above the real interest rate i plus a rate equal to the inflation rate f. Thus, to make a *real rate of return of 5.77%* when the inflation rate is 4%, i_f is the market (inflation-adjusted) rate that must be used. For the same $1000 amount,

$$i_f = 0.0577 + 0.04 + 0.0577(0.04) = 0.10$$

$$F = 1000(F/P,10\%,7) = \$1948$$

This calculation shows that $1948 seven years in the future will be equivalent to $1000 now with a real return of $i = 5.77\%$ per year and inflation of $f = 4\%$ per year.

Table 14–3 summarizes which rate is used in the equivalence formulas for the different interpretations of F. The calculations made in this section reveal that $1000 now at a market rate of 10% per year would accumulate to $1948 in 7 years; the $1948 would have the purchasing power of $1481 of today's dollars if $f = 4\%$ per year; an item with a cost of $1000 now would cost $1316 in 7 years at an inflation rate of 4% per year; and it would take $1948 of future dollars to be equivalent to the $1000 now at a real interest rate of 5.77% with inflation considered at 4%.

TABLE 14–3 Calculation Methods for Various Future Worth Interpretations		
Future Worth Desired	**Method of Calculation**	**Example for $P = \$1000$, $n = 7$, $i_f = 10\%$, $f = 4\%$**
Case 1: Actual dollars accumulated	Use stated market rate i_f in equivalence formulas	$F = 1000(F/P,10\%,7)$ $= \$1948$
Case 2: Purchasing power of accumulated dollars in terms of today's dollars	Use market rate i_f in equivalence and divide by $(1 + f)^n$ or Use real i	$F = \dfrac{1000(F/P,10\%.7)}{(1.04)^7}$ or $F = 1000(F/P,5.77\%,7)$ $= \$1481$
Case 3: Dollars required for same purchasing power	Use f in place of i in equivalence formulas	$F = 1000(F/P,4\%,7)$ $= \$1316$
Case 4: Future dollars to maintain purchasing power and to earn a return	Calculate i_f and use in equivalence formulas	$F = 1000(F/P,10\%,7)$ $= \$1948$

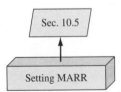

Sec. 10.5

Setting MARR

Most corporations evaluate alternatives at a MARR large enough to cover inflation plus some return greater than their cost of capital, and significantly higher than the safe investment return of approximately 3.5% mentioned earlier. Therefore, for case 4, the resulting MARR will normally be higher than the market rate i_f. Define the symbol $MARR_f$ as the inflation-adjusted MARR, which is calculated in a fashion similar to i_f.

$$MARR_f = i + f + i(f) \qquad [14.11]$$

The real rate of return i used here is the required rate for the corporation relative to its cost of capital. Now the future worth F, or FW, is calculated as

$$F = P(1 + MARR_f)^n = P(F/P,MARR_f,n) \qquad [14.12]$$

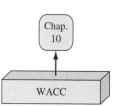

For example, if a company has a WACC (weighted average cost of capital) of 10% per year and requires that a project return 3% per year above its WACC, the real return is $i = 13\%$. The inflation-adjusted MARR is calculated by including the inflation rate of, say, 4% per year. Then, the project PW, AW, or FW will be determined at the rate obtained from Equation [14.11].

$$MARR_f = 0.13 + 0.04 + 0.13(0.04) = 17.52\%$$

A similar computation can be made for an individual using i as the expected real rate that is above the safe investment rate. When an individual is satisfied with a required real return equal to a safe investment rate, approximately $i = 3.5\%$, or a corporation is satisfied with a real return equal to a safe investment rate, Equations [14.11] and [14.6] have the same result; that is, $MARR_f = i_f$, for the corporation or the individual.

EXAMPLE 14.3

Abbott Mining Systems wants to determine whether it should "buy" now or "buy" later for upgrading a piece of equipment used in deep mining operations in one of its international operations. If the company selects plan A, the equipment will be purchased now for $200,000. However, if the company selects plan I, the purchase will be deferred for 3 years when the cost is expected to rise rapidly to $340,000. Abbott is ambitious; it expects a real MARR of 12% per year. The inflation rate in the country has averaged 6.75% per year. From only an economic perspective, determine whether the company should purchase now or later (*a*) when inflation is not considered and (*b*) when inflation is considered.

Solution

(*a*) Inflation not considered: The real rate, or MARR, is $i = 12\%$ per year. The cost of plan I is $340,000 three years hence. Calculate the FW value for plan A three years from now and select the lower cost.

$$FW_A = -200,000(F/P,12\%,3) = \$-280,986$$

$$FW_I = \$-340,000$$

Select plan A (purchase now).

(*b*) Inflation considered: This is case 4; there is a real rate (12%), and inflation of 6.75% must be accounted for. First, compute the inflation-adjusted MARR by Equation [14.11].

$$i_f = 0.12 + 0.0675 + 0.12(0.0675) = 0.1956$$

Use i_f to compute the FW value for plan A in future dollars.

$$FW_A = -200,000(F/P,19.56\%,3) = \$-341,812$$

$$FW_I = \$-340,000$$

Purchase later (plan I) is now selected, because it requires fewer equivalent future dollars. The inflation rate of 6.75% per year has raised the equivalent future worth of costs by 21.6% to $341,812. This is the same as an increase of 6.75% per year, compounded over 3 years, or $(1.0675)^3 - 1 = 21.6\%$.

Most countries have inflation rates in the range of 2% to 8% per year, but *hyperinflation* is a problem in countries where political instability, overspending by the government, weak international trade balances, etc., are present. Hyperinflation rates may be very high—10% to 100% *per month*. In these cases, the government may take drastic action: redefine the currency in terms of the currency of another country, control banks and corporations, and control the flow of capital into and out of the country in order to decrease inflation. In order to stabilize its economy, Zimbabwe adopted the U.S. dollar in 2009 when official inflation reached a yearly rate of 231,000,000%.

In a hyperinflated environment, people usually spend all their money immediately, since the cost will be so much higher the next month, week, or day. To appreciate the disastrous effect of hyperinflation on a company's ability to keep up, we can rework Example 14.3b using an inflation rate of 10% per month, that is, a nominal 120% per year (not considering the compounding of inflation). The FW_A amount skyrockets and plan I is a clear choice. Of course, in such an environment the $340,000 purchase price for plan I three years hence would obviously not be guaranteed, so the entire economic analysis is unreliable. Good economic decisions in a hyperinflated economy are very difficult to make using traditional engineering economy methods, since the estimated future values are totally unreliable and the future availability of capital is uncertain.

14.4 CAPITAL RECOVERY CALCULATIONS ADJUSTED FOR INFLATION

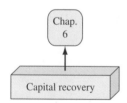

It is particularly important in capital recovery calculations used for AW analysis to include inflation because current capital dollars must be recovered with future inflated dollars. Since future dollars have less buying power than today's dollars, it is obvious that more dollars will be required to recover the present investment. This suggests the use of the inflated interest rate in the A/P formula. For example, if $1000 is invested today at a real interest rate of 10% per year when the inflation rate is 8% per year, the equivalent amount that must be recovered each year for 5 years in future dollars is

$$A = 1000(A/P,18.8\%,5) = \$325.59$$

On the other hand, the decreased value of dollars through time means that investors can spend fewer present (higher-value) dollars to accumulate a specified amount of future (inflated) dollars. This suggests the use of a higher interest rate, that is, the i_f rate, to produce a lower A value in the A/F formula. The annual equivalent (with adjustment for inflation) of $F = \$1000$ five years from now in future dollars is

$$A = 1000(A/F,18.8\%,5) = \$137.59$$

This method is illustrated in the next example.

For comparison, the equivalent annual amount to accumulate $F = \$1000$ at a real $i = 10\%$ (without adjustment for inflation) is $1000(A/F,10\%,5) = \$163.80$. Thus, when F is fixed, uniformly distributed future costs should be spread over as long a time period as possible so that the leveraging effect of inflation will reduce the payment ($\$137.59$ versus $\$163.80$ here).

EXAMPLE 14.4

What annual deposit is required for 5 years to accumulate an amount of money with the same purchasing power as $680.58 today, if the market interest rate is 10% per year and inflation is 8% per year?

Solution

First, find the actual number of future (inflated) dollars required 5 years from now. This is case 3.

$$F = (\text{present buying power})(1 + f)^5 = 680.58(1.08)^5 = \$1000$$

The actual amount of the annual deposit is calculated using the market (inflated) interest rate of 10%. This is case 4 using A instead of P.

$$A = 1000(A/F,10\%,5) = \$163.80$$

Comment

The real interest rate is $i = 1.85\%$ as determined using Equation [14.9]. To put these calculations into perspective, if the inflation rate is zero when the real interest rate is 1.85%, the future amount of money with the same purchasing power as $680.58 today is obviously $680.58. Then the annual amount required to accumulate this future amount in 5 years is $A = 680.58(A/F,1.85\%,5) = \$131.17$. This is $32.63 lower than the $163.80 calculated above for $f = 8\%$. This difference is due to the fact that during inflationary periods, dollars deposited have more buying power than the dollars returned at the end of the period. To make up the buying power difference, more lower-value dollars are required. That is, to maintain equivalent purchasing power at $f = 8\%$ per year, an extra $32.63 per year is required.

The logic discussed here explains why, in times of increasing inflation, lenders of money (credit card companies, mortgage companies, and banks) tend to further increase their market interest rates. People tend to pay off less of their incurred debt at each payment because they use any excess money to purchase additional items before the price is further inflated. Also, the lending institutions must have more dollars in the future to cover the expected higher costs of lending money. All this is due to the spiralling effect of increasing inflation. Breaking this cycle is difficult to do at the individual level and much more difficult to alter at a national level.

CHAPTER SUMMARY

Inflation, treated computationally as an interest rate, makes the cost of the same product or service increase over time due to the decreased value of money. There are several ways to consider inflation in engineering economy computations in terms of today's (constant-value) dollars and in terms of future dollars. Some important relations are:

Inflated interest rate: $i_f = i + f + if$

Real interest rate: $i = (i_f - f)/(1 + f)$

PW of a future amount with inflation considered: $P = F(P/F,i_f,n)$

Future worth of a present amount in constant-value dollars with the same purchasing power: $F = P(F/P,i,n)$

Future amount to cover a current amount with no interest: $F = P(F/P,f,n)$

Future amount to cover a current amount with interest: $F = P(F/P,i_f,n)$

Annual equivalent of a future dollar amount: $A = F(A/F,i_f,n)$

Annual equivalent of a present amount in future dollars: $A = P(A/P,i_f,n)$

Hyperinflation implies very high f values. Available funds are expended immediately, because costs increase so rapidly that larger cash inflows cannot offset the fact that the currency is losing value. This can, and usually does, cause a national financial disaster when it continues over extended periods of time.

PROBLEMS

Adjusting for Inflation

14.1 Describe how to convert inflated dollars into constant-value dollars.

14.2 What is the inflation rate if something costs exactly twice as much as it did 10 years earlier?

14.3 In an effort to reduce pipe breakage, water hammer, and product agitation, a chemical company plans to install several chemically resistant pulsation dampeners. The cost of the dampeners today is $106,000, but the chemical company has to wait until a permit is approved for its bidirectional port-to-plant product pipeline. The permit approval process will take at least 2 years because of the time required for preparation of an environmental impact statement. Because of intense foreign competition, the manufacturer plans to increase the price only by the inflation rate each year. If the inflation rate is 3% per year, estimate the cost of the dampeners in 2 years in terms of (a) then-current dollars and (b) today's dollars.

14.4 Convert $10,000 present dollars into then-current dollars of year 10 if the inflation rate is 7% per year.

14.5 Convert $10,000 future dollars in year 10 into *constant-value dollars* (not equivalent dollars) of today if the inflation-adjusted (market) interest rate is

11% per year and the inflation rate is 7% per year.

14.6 Convert $10,000 future dollars in year 10 into *constant-value dollars* (not equivalent dollars) today if the inflation-adjusted (market) interest rate is 12% per year and the real interest rate is 3% per year.

14.7 The average annual salary of a civil engineer in Canada in 2011 was $74,400. Predict the average salary in 2020, assuming salaries increase only by the inflation rate of a constant 2.5% per year.

14.8 Estimated costs for maintenance and operation of a certain machine are expected to be $13,000 per year (then-current dollars) in years 1 to 3. At an inflation rate of 6% per year, what is the constant-value amount (in terms of today's dollars) of *each year's* future dollar amount?

14.9 If the market interest rate is 12% per year and the inflation rate is 5% per year, determine the number of future dollars in year 5 that have the *same buying power* as $2000 now.

14.10 Ford Motor Company announced that the price of its F-150 pickup trucks is going to increase by only the inflation rate for the next 2 years. If the current price of a truck is $21,000 and the inflation rate is expected to average 2.8% per year, what is the expected *price* of a comparably equipped truck 2 years from now?

14.11 A newspaper article states that tuition at the nearby university has increased by 56% over the past 5 years. (*a*) What was the average annual percentage increase over that time? (*b*) If the inflation rate was 2.5% per year, how many percentage

points over the inflation rate was the annual tuition increase?

14.12 A machine purchased by Holtzman Industries had a cost of $45,000 four years ago. If a similar machine costs $55,000 now and its price increased only by the inflation rate, what was the annual inflation rate over that 4-year period?

Real and Market Interest Rates

14.13 State the conditions under which the market interest is (*a*) higher than, (*b*) lower than, and (*c*) the same as the real interest rate.

14.14 Calculate the inflation-adjusted interest rate when the annualized inflation rate is 27% per year (Venezuela, 2010) and the real interest rate is 4% per year.

14.15 What annual inflation rate is implied from a market interest rate of 15% per year when the real interest rate is 4% per year?

14.16 What market interest rate per quarter would be associated with a quarterly inflation rate of 5% and a real interest rate of 2% per quarter?

14.17 When the market interest rate is 48% per year, compounded monthly (due to hyperinflation), what is the monthly inflation rate if the real interest rate is 6% per year, compounded monthly?

14.18 What real rate of return will an investor make on a rate of return of 25% per year when the inflation rate is 10% per year?

14.19 What is the real interest rate per semiannual period when the market interest rate is 22% per year, compounded semiannually, and the inflation rate is 7% per 6 months?

14.20 A cash-value life insurance policy will pay a sum of $1,000,000 when the insured reaches the age of 65. If the insured will be 65 years old 27 years from today, what will be the value of the $1,000,000 in terms of dollars with today's buying power if the inflation rate is 3% per year over that time period?

Alternative Comparison with Adjustment for Inflation

14.21 A civil engineer is analyzing bids for a water treatment facility for a new housing development. Bid A is $2.1 million, which is $400,000 more than bid B, but the development will not have to pay bidder A for the project for 2 years. The developer's MARR is 12% per year and the inflation rate is 4% per year. Which bid is better?

14.22 A regional infrastructure building and maintenance contractor is trying to decide whether to buy a new compact horizontal directional drilling (HDD) machine now or wait to buy it 2 years from now (when a large pipeline contract will require the new equipment). The HDD machine will include an innovative pipe loader design and a maneuverable undercarriage system. The cost of the system is $68,000 if purchased now or $81,000 if purchased 2 years from now. At a real interest MARR of 10% per year and an inflation rate of 5% per year, determine if the company should buy now or later (a) without any adjustment for inflation and (b) with inflation considered.

14.23 As an innovative way to pay for various software packages, a new high-technology service company has offered to pay your company in one of three ways: (1) pay $400,000 now, (2) pay $1.1 million 5 years from now, or (3) pay an amount of money 5 years from now that has the same *buying power* as $750,000 now. If you want to earn a real interest rate of 10% per year and the inflation rate is 6% per year, which offer should you accept?

14.24 Consider alternatives A and B on the basis of their present worth values, using a real interest rate of 10% per year and an inflation rate of 3% per year, (a) without any adjustment for inflation and (b) with inflation considered.

	Machine A	Machine B
First cost, $	−31,000	−48,000
Annual operating cost, $/year	−28,000	−19,000
Salvage value, $	5,000	7,000
Life, years	5	5

14.25 Compare the alternatives below on the basis of their capitalized costs with adjustments made for inflation. Use $i_r =$ 12% per year and $f = 3\%$ per year.

	Alternative X	Alternative Y
First cost, $	−18,500,000	−9,000,000
Annual operating cost, $/year	−25,000	−10,000
Salvage value, $	105,000	82,000
Life, years	∞	10

14.26 An engineer must recommend one of two machines for integration into an upgraded manufacturing line. She obtains estimates from two salespeople. Salesperson A gives her the estimates in future (then-current) dollars, while salesperson B provides the estimates in today's (constant-value) dollars. The company has a MARR of a real 15% per year, and it expects inflation to be 5% per year. Use PW analysis to determine which machine the engineer should recommend.

	Salesperson A, Future $	Salesperson B, Today's $
First cost, $	−60,000	−95,000
AOC, $/year	−55,000	−35,000
Life, years	10	10

Future Worth and Other Calculations with Inflation

14.27 Hydro-Québec plans to replace pollution control equipment in 5 years. $60,000 per year will be set aside in a replacement fund beginning 1 year from now. What buying power will be accumulated, in terms of today's dollars, if the fund grows by 10% per year, but inflation averages 4% per year?

14.28 An engineer purchased an inflation-linked corporate bond (i.e., bond interest changes with inflation) issued by Household Finance Bank that has a face value of $25,000. At the time the bond was purchased, the yield on the bond was 2.16% per year *plus* inflation, payable monthly. The bond interest rate is adjusted each month based on the change in the consumer price index (CPI) from the same month of the previous year. In one particular month, the CPI was 3.02% higher than it was in the same month of the previous year.
   (*a*) What is the new yield on the bond?
   (*b*) If interest is paid monthly, how much interest did the engineer receive that month (i.e., after the adjustment)?

14.29 An engineer deposits $10,000 into an account when the market interest rate is 10% per year and the inflation rate is 5% per year. The account is left undisturbed for 5 years.
   (*a*) How much money will be in the account?
   (*b*) What will be the buying (purchasing) power in terms of today's dollars?

   (*c*) What is the real rate of return that is made on the account?

14.30 A chemical company wants to set aside money now so that it will be able to purchase new data loggers 3 years from now. The price of the data loggers is expected to increase only by the inflation rate of 3.7% per year for each of the next 3 years. If the total cost of the data loggers now is $45,000, determine (*a*) their expected cost 3 years from now and (*b*) how much the company will have to set aside now, if it earns interest at a rate of 8% per year.

14.31 The cost of constructing a certain highway exit ramp was $625,000 seven years ago. An engineer designing another one that is almost exactly the same estimates the cost today will be $740,000. If the cost had increased only by the inflation rate over that time period, what was the inflation rate per year?

14.32 If you make an investment in commercial real estate that is guaranteed to net you $1.5 million 25 years from now, what will be the *buying power* of that money with respect to today's dollars if the market interest rate is 8% per year and the inflation rate stays at 3.8% per year over that time period?

14.33 Domtar Corp. can purchase a piece of equipment now for $80,000 or buy it 3 years from now for $128,000. The MARR requirement is a real return of 15% per year. If an inflation rate of 4% per year must be accounted for, should the company buy the machine now or later?

14.34 In a period of 3% per year inflation, how much will a machine cost 3 years from now in terms of *constant-value dollars*, if the cost today is $40,000 and the cost of the machine is expected to increase only by the inflation rate?

14.35 In a period of 4% per year inflation, how much will a machine cost 3 years from now in terms of *constant-value dollars,* if the cost today is $40,000 and the manufacturer plans to raise the price so that the manufacturer will make a real rate of return of 5% per year over that time period?

14.36 Convert $100,000 of today's dollars into then-current dollars in year 10 when the *deflation rate* is 1.5% per year.

14.37 A company has been invited to invest $1 million in a partnership and receive a guaranteed total amount of $2.5 million after 4 years. By corporate policy, the MARR is always established at 4% above the real cost of capital. If the real interest rate paid on capital is currently 10% per year and the inflation rate during the 4-year period is expected to average 3% per year, is the investment economically justified?

14.38 The first Nobel Prize was awarded in 1901 in the amount of $150,000. In 1996, the award was raised from $489,000 to $653,000. (*a*) At what inflation rate would an award of $653,000 in 1996 be equivalent (in purchasing power) to the original award in 1901? (*b*) If the foundation expects inflation to average 3.5% per year from 1996 through 2010, how large will the award have to be in 2010 to make it worth the same as in 1996?

14.39 Factors that increase costs and prices—especially for materials and manufacturing costs sensitive to market, technology, and labour availability—can be considered separately using the real interest rate i, the inflation rate f, and additional increases that grow at a geometric rate g. The future amount is calculated based on a current estimate by using the relation

$$F = P(1 + i)^n(1 + f)^n(1 + g)^n$$
$$= P[(1 + i)(1 + f)(1 + g)]^n$$

The product of the first two terms enclosed in parentheses results in the inflated interest rate i_f. The geometric rate is the same one used in the geometric gradient series (Chapter 2). It commonly applies to maintenance and repair cost increases as machinery ages. This is over and above the inflation rate. If the current cost to manufacture an electronic subcomponent is $250,000 per year, what is the equivalent value in 5 years, if average annual rates are estimated to be $i = 5\%, f = 3\%$, and $g = 2\%$ per year?

Capital Recovery with Inflation

14.40 Aquatech Microsystems spent $183,000 for a communications protocol to achieve interoperability among its utility systems. If the company uses a real interest rate of 15% per year on such investments and a recovery period of 5 years, what is the annual worth of the expenditure in then-current dollars at an inflation rate of 6% per year?

14.41 You wisely invest $12,000 per year for 20 years into your RRSP account to plan for your retirement. How much will you be able to withdraw each year for 10 years, starting 1 year after your last deposit, if you earn a real return of 10% per year and the inflation rate averages 2.8% per year?

14.42 A DSL company has made an equipment investment of $40 million with the expectation that it will be recovered in

10 years. The company has a MARR based on a real rate of return of 12% per year. If inflation is 7% per year, how much must the company make each year (*a*) in constant-value dollars and (*b*) in future dollars to meet its expectation?

14.43 What is the annual worth in then-current dollars in years 1 through 5 of a receipt of $750,000 now, if the *market interest rate* is 10% per year and the inflation rate is 5% per year?

14.44 A recently graduated mechanical engineer wants to build a reserve fund as a safety net to pay his expenses in the unlikely event that he is without work for a short time. His aim is to have $15,000 developed over the next 3 years, with the proviso that the amount have the same purchasing power as $15,000 today. If the expected market rate on investments is 8% per year and inflation is averaging 2% per year, find the annual amount necessary to meet his goal.

14.45 A European-based cattle genetics engineering research lab is planning for a major expenditure on research equipment. The lab needs $5 million of today's dollars so it can make the acquisition 4 years from now. The inflation rate is steady at 5% per year. (*a*) How many future dollars will be needed when the equipment is purchased, if purchasing power is maintained? (*b*) What is the required amount of the annual deposit into a fund that earns the market rate of 10% per year to ensure that the amount calculated in part (*a*) is accumulated?

14.46 (*a*) Calculate the perpetual equivalent annual worth in future dollars (for years 1 through ∞) for income of $50,000 now and $5000 per year thereafter. Assume the market interest rate is 8% per year and inflation averages 4% per year. All amounts are quoted as future dollars.

(*b*) If the amounts are quoted in *constant-value dollars,* how do you find the annual worth in *future dollars*?

14.47 The two machines detailed are being considered for a chip manufacturing operation. Assume the company's MARR is a real return of 12% per year and that the inflation rate is 7% per year. Which machine should be selected on the basis of an annual worth analysis, if the estimates are in (*a*) constant-value dollars and (*b*) future dollars?

	Machine A	Machine B
First cost, $	−150,000	−1,025,000
Annual M&O cost, $/year	−70,000	−5,000
Salvage value, $	40,000	200,000
Life, years	5	∞

CHAPTER

Depreciation Methods

The capital investments of a corporation in tangible assets—equipment, computers, vehicles, buildings, and machinery—are commonly recovered on the books of the corporation through *depreciation*. Although the depreciation amount is not an actual cash flow, the process of depreciating an asset accounts for the decrease in an asset's value because of age, wear, and obsolescence. Even though an asset may be in excellent working condition, the fact that it is worth less through time is taken into account in economic evaluation studies. An introduction to the classical depreciation methods is followed by a discussion of Canada Revenue Agency's capital cost allowance (CCA) system, which is the only approved method of depreciation for tax purposes. Other countries commonly use the classical methods for tax computations.

Why is depreciation important to engineering economy? Depreciation is a *tax-allowed deduction* included in tax calculations in virtually all industrialized countries. Depreciation lowers income taxes via the relation

$$\text{Taxes} = (\text{income} - \text{deductions})(\text{tax rate})$$

Income taxes are discussed further in Chapter 16.

This chapter concludes with an introduction to *depletion,* which is used to recover capital investments in deposits of natural resources such as minerals, ores, and timber.

> *Important note:* **To consider depreciation and after-tax analysis early in a course, cover this chapter and the next one (After-Tax Economic Analysis) after Chapter 6 (AW), Chapter 9 (BCA), or Chapter 11 (Replacement Analysis). Consult the Preface for more options on subject ordering.**

LEARNING OBJECTIVES

Purpose: Use classical and government-approved methods to reduce the value of the capital investment in an asset or natural resource.

By the end of this chapter you should be able to

Depreciation terms

1. Use the basic terminology of depreciation.

Straight line

2. Apply the straight line model of depreciation.

Declining balance

3. Apply the declining balance model of depreciation.

CCA

4. Apply the capital cost allowance system of depreciation for Canadian businesses.

Depletion

5. Utilize the cost depletion method for natural resource investments.

15.1 DEPRECIATION TERMINOLOGY

Primary terms used in depreciation are defined here.

Depreciation is the reduction in value of an asset. The method used to depreciate an asset is a way to account for the decreasing value of the asset to the owner *and* to represent the diminishing value (amount) of the capital funds invested in it. The annual depreciation amount D_t does not represent an actual cash flow, nor does it necessarily reflect the actual usage pattern of the asset during ownership.

Book depreciation and **tax depreciation** are terms used to describe the purpose for reducing asset value. Depreciation may be performed for two reasons:

1. Use by a corporation or business for internal financial accounting. This is book depreciation.
2. Use in tax calculations per government regulations. This is tax depreciation.

The methods applied for these two purposes may or may not utilize the same formulas, as is discussed later. *Book depreciation* indicates the reduced investment in an asset based upon the usage pattern and expected useful life of the asset. The classical, internationally accepted depreciation methods used to determine book depreciation are straight line and declining balance. The amount of *tax depreciation* is important in an after-tax engineering economy study because of the following:

> **In Canada and many industrialized countries, the annual tax depreciation is tax-deductible; that is, it is subtracted from income when calculating the amount of taxes due each year. However, the tax depreciation amount must be calculated using a government-approved method.**

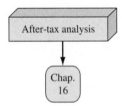

Tax depreciation may be calculated and referred to differently in countries outside Canada. Canadian tax laws permit businesses to claim a depreciation expense, or capital cost allowance (CCA), calculated for the most part using the declining balance method with a rate assigned to each prescribed *class* of assets. The method used in the United States, the modified accelerated cost recovery system (MACRS) allows depreciation of each asset separately using an accelerated rate of depreciation for the first years of an asset's use.

Cost basis or **first cost** is the delivered and installed cost of the asset including purchase price, delivery and installation fees, legal, accounting, and engineering fees, and other depreciable direct costs incurred to prepare the asset for use. The term **capital cost** is used in tax depreciation.

Book value represents the remaining, undepreciated capital investment on the books after the total amount of depreciation charges to date have been subtracted from the cost basis. The book value BV_t is determined at the end of each year. **Undepreciated capital cost (UCC)** is the corresponding term used for tax purposes.

Useful life is the depreciable life n of the asset in years.

Market value, a term also used in replacement analysis, is the estimated amount realizable if the asset were sold on the open market. Because of the structure of depreciation laws, the book value and market value may be substantially different. For example, a commercial building tends to increase in market value, but the book value will decrease as depreciation charges are taken. However, a computer workstation may have a market value much lower than its book value due to rapidly changing technology.

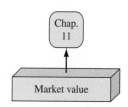

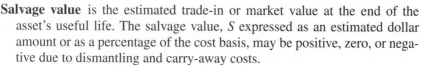

Salvage value is the estimated trade-in or market value at the end of the asset's useful life. The salvage value, S expressed as an estimated dollar amount or as a percentage of the cost basis, may be positive, zero, or negative due to dismantling and carry-away costs.

Depreciation rate is the fraction of the cost basis removed by depreciation each year. This rate, denoted by d_t, may be the same each year, which is called the *straight line rate*, or different for each year of depreciation.

Depreciable property, or capital assets, are the tangible possessions of a business used to produce income. Included is most manufacturing and service industry property—vehicles, manufacturing equipment, materials handling devices, computers and networking equipment, telephone equipment, office furniture, refining process equipment, construction assets, and much more.

Real property includes real estate and all improvements—office buildings, manufacturing structures, test facilities, warehouses, apartments, and other structures. *Land itself is considered real property, but it is not depreciable.*

The 50% rule of Canadian tax law stipulates that, for the year in which an asset is placed in service, only one-half of the maximum depreciation (CCA) can be claimed.

As mentioned before, there are several models for depreciating assets. The straight line (SL) model is used, historically and internationally. Accelerated models, such as the declining balance (DB) model, decrease the book value to zero (or to the salvage value) more rapidly than the straight line method, as shown by the general book value curves in Figure 15–1.

For the classical methods—straight line and declining balance—there are Excel functions available to determine annual depreciation. Each function is introduced and illustrated as the method is explained.

As might be expected, there are many rules and exceptions to the depreciation laws of a country.

Tax depreciation must be calculated using Canada Revenue Agency's capital cost allowance system; book depreciation may be calculated using any classical method or CCA.

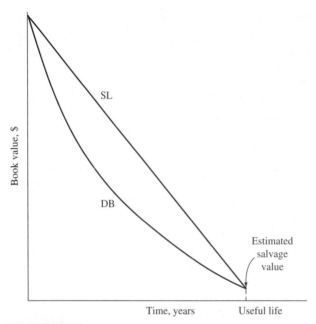

FIGURE 15–1

General shape of book value curves for different depreciation models.

Although the CCA is usually based on the declining balance method, because of the grouping of assets into classes, DB cannot be used directly if the annual depreciation is to be tax-deductible. Many Canadian companies still apply the classical methods for keeping their own books, because these methods are more representative of how the usage patterns of the asset reflect the remaining capital invested in it. Additionally, most other countries still recognize the classical methods of straight line and declining balance for tax or book purposes. Because of the continuing importance of the SL and DB methods, they are explained in the next two sections prior to CCA.

Tax law revisions occur often, and depreciation rules are changed from time to time in Canada and other countries. The 2010 federal budget sought to encourage the purchase of specific assets with expanded CCA classes and accelerated rates of depreciation. Class 43.2 provides an accelerated CCA of 50% on high-efficiency equipment for clean energy generation. Businesses will also be allowed 100% CCA for new computer equipment and software (Class 52) acquired by February 2011, making a full write-off possible in the first tax year. A temporary incentive to acquire new manufacturing and processing equipment by 2011 was created by moving these purchases from Class 43 to Class 29, where they are eligible for a 50% straight line CCA rate. Although the tax rates and depreciation guidelines at the time you read this material may be slightly different, the general principles are applicable to all Canadian businesses.

15.2 STRAIGHT LINE (SL) DEPRECIATION

Straight line depreciation derives its name from the fact that the book value decreases linearly with time. The depreciation rate $d = 1/n$ is the same each year of useful life n.

Straight line is considered the standard against which any depreciation model is compared. For *book depreciation* purposes, it offers an excellent representation of book value for any asset that is used regularly over an estimated number of years. For *tax depreciation,* as mentioned earlier, it is not used directly in Canada, but it is commonly used in other countries for tax purposes.

The annual SL depreciation is determined by multiplying the cost basis minus the salvage value by d. In equation form,

$$D_t = (B - S)d$$
$$= \frac{B - S}{n} \qquad \text{[15.1]}$$

where t = year $(t = 1, 2, \ldots, n)$
  D_t = annual depreciation charge
  B = cost basis of the asset
  S = estimated salvage value
  n = useful life
  d = depreciation rate = $1/n$

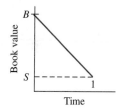

Since the asset is depreciated by the same amount each year, the book value after t years of service, denoted by BV_t, will be equal to the cost basis B minus the annual depreciation times t.

$$BV_t = B - tD_t \qquad \text{[15.2]}$$

Earlier we defined d_t as a depreciation rate for a specific year t. However, the SL model has the same rate for all years, that is,

$$d = d_t = \frac{1}{n} \qquad \text{[15.3]}$$

The format for the Excel function to display the annual depreciation D_t in a single-cell operation is

$$\text{SLN}(B, S, n)$$

EXAMPLE 15.1

If an asset has a cost basis of $50,000 with a $10,000 estimated salvage value after 5 years, (*a*) calculate the annual depreciation and (*b*) compute and plot the book value of the asset after each year, using straight line depreciation.

Solution

(a) The depreciation each year for 5 years can be found by Equation [15.1].

$$D_t = \frac{B - S}{n} = \frac{50{,}000 - 10{,}000}{5} = \$8000$$

Enter the function SLN(50000,10000,5) in any cell to display the D_t of $8000.

(b) The book value after each year t is computed using Equation [15.2]. The BV_t values are plotted in Figure 15–2. For years 1 and 5, for example,

$$BV_1 = 50{,}000 - 1(8000) = \$42{,}000$$

$$BV_5 = 50{,}000 - 5(8000) = \$10{,}000 = S$$

Q-SOLVE

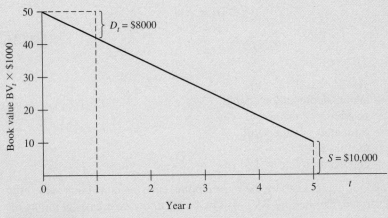

FIGURE 15–2
Book value of an asset depreciated using the straight line model, Example 15.1.

15.3 DECLINING BALANCE (DB) DEPRECIATION

The declining balance method is commonly applied as the book depreciation method. This method is used routinely in most other countries for tax and book depreciation purposes.

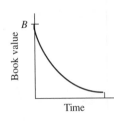

Declining balance is also known as the *fixed percentage* or *uniform percentage* method. DB depreciation accelerates the write-off of asset value because the annual depreciation is determined by multiplying the *book value at the beginning of a year* by a fixed (uniform) percentage d, expressed in decimal form. If $d = 0.1$, then 10% of the book value is removed each year. Therefore, the depreciation amount decreases each year.

The depreciation for year t is the fixed rate d times the book value at the end of the previous year.

$$D_t = (d)BV_{t-1} \qquad\qquad [15.4]$$

The actual depreciation rate for each year t, relative to the cost basis B, is

$$d_t = d(1 - d)^{t-1} \qquad\qquad [15.5]$$

If BV_{t-1} is not known, the depreciation in year t can be calculated using B and d_t from Equation [15.5].

$$D_t = dB(1 - d)^{t-1} \qquad\qquad [15.6]$$

Book value in year t is determined in one of two ways: by using the rate d and cost basis B, or by subtracting the current depreciation charge from the previous book value. The equations are

$$\mathbf{BV}_t = \mathbf{B}(1 - d)^t \qquad\qquad [15.7]$$

$$\mathbf{BV}_t = \mathbf{BV}_{t-1} - \mathbf{D}_t \qquad\qquad [15.8]$$

It is important to understand that the book value for the DB method seldom goes to zero, because the book value is always decreased by a fixed percentage. The implied salvage value after n years is the BV_n amount, that is,

$$\text{Implied salvage value} = \text{implied } S = BV_n = B(1 - d)^n \qquad [15.9]$$

If a salvage value is estimated for the asset, this *estimated S value is not used in the DB method* to calculate the depreciation rate. However, if the implied $S <$ estimated S, it is correct to stop charging further depreciation when the book value is at or below the estimated salvage value. In most cases, the estimated S is in the range of zero to the implied S value. (This guideline is important when the DB method can be used directly for tax depreciation purposes.)

If the fixed percentage d is not stated, it is possible to determine an implied fixed rate using the estimated S value, if $S > 0$.

$$\mathbf{Implied}\ d = 1 - \left(\frac{S}{B}\right)^{1/n} \qquad\qquad [15.10]$$

The Excel function DB is used to display depreciation amounts for specific years (or any other unit of time). The function is repeated in consecutive spreadsheet cells because the depreciation amount D_t changes with t.

 E-SOLVE

The DB function must be used carefully. Its format is DB(B,S,n,t). The fixed rate d is not entered in the DB function; d is an embedded calculation using a spreadsheet equivalent of Equation [15.10]. Also, only three significant digits are maintained for d, so the book value may go below the estimated salvage value due to round-off errors. The next example illustrates DB depreciation and these spreadsheet functions.

EXAMPLE 15.2

Freeport-McMoRan Mining Company has purchased a computer-controlled gold ore grading unit for $80,000. The unit has an anticipated life of 10 years and a salvage value of $10,000. Use the DB method to compare the schedule of depreciation and book values for each year. Solve by hand and by computer.

Solution by Hand
An implied DB depreciation rate is determined by Equation [15.10].

$$d = 1 - \left(\frac{10,000}{80,000}\right)^{1/10} = 0.1877$$

Table 15–1 presents the D_t values using Equation [15.4] and the BV_t values from Equation [15.8] rounded to the nearest dollar. For example, in year $t = 2$, the DB results are

$$D_2 = d(BV_1) = 0.1877(64,984) = \$12,197$$

$$BV_2 = 64,984 - 12,197 = \$52,787$$

Because we round off to even dollars, $2312 is calculated for depreciation in year 10, but $2318 is deducted to make $BV_{10} = S = \$10,000$ exactly.

TABLE 15–1 D_t and BV_t Values for DB Example 15.2

	Declining Balance	
Year t	D_t	BV_t
0	—	$80,000
1	$15,016	64,984
2	12,197	52,787
3	9,908	42,879
4	8,048	34,831
5	6,538	28,293
6	5,311	22,982
7	4,314	18,668
8	3,504	15,164
9	2,846	12,318
10	2,318	10,000

E-SOLVE

Solution by Computer
The spreadsheet in Figure 15–3 displays the results for the DB method. The *xy* scatter chart plots book values for each year.

Comment
As mentioned earlier, the DB function automatically calculates the implied rate by Equation [15.10] and maintains it to only three significant digits. Therefore, if the DB

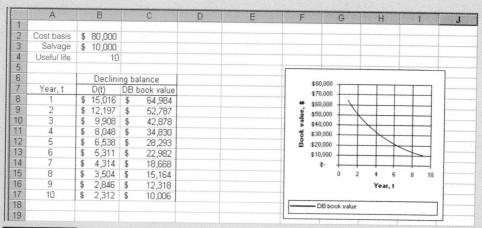

FIGURE 15–3
Spreadsheet solution for annual depreciation and book values for DB depreciation, Example 15.2.

function were used in column B (Figure 15–3), the fixed rate applied would be 0.188. The resulting D_t and BV_t values for years 8, 9, and 10 would be as follows:

t	D_t	BV_t
8	$3,501	$15,120
9	2,842	12,277
10	2,308	9,969

Also noteworthy is the fact that the DB function uses the implied rate without a check to halt the book value at the estimated salvage value. Thus, BV_{10} will go slightly below $S = \$10,000$, as shown above.

15.4 CAPITAL COST ALLOWANCE (CCA)

The capital cost allowance system is required by the Canada Revenue Agency for deducting the cost of a capital asset over time. The length of time specified to write off an asset reflects the time it takes for the asset to become obsolete or wear out. The maximum amount a business is allowed to deduct from income earned each year is called the *capital cost allowance* or *CCA*. Many companies, especially small ones, use CCA for financial as well as tax reporting in order to save the expense of keeping two sets of records. The amount of CCA that can be claimed each year depends on the type of asset and when it was available for use.

Rather than depreciating each asset individually, the *Income Tax Regulations* group assets into a comparatively small number of prescribed classes. Table 15–2 contains a list of the majority of commonly used classes. Similar assets are grouped and treated as one asset or class. For most classes, the CCA is calculated using the declining balance method. A maximum rate of depreciation is specified for each class of property.

TABLE 15–2   List of CCA Rates and Classes

This is a partial list and description of the most common capital cost allowance (CCA) classes from the *T2 Corporation—Income Tax Guide*. You will find a complete list in Schedule II of the *Income Tax Regulations*.

Class Number	Description	CCA Rate
1	Most buildings made of brick, stone, or cement acquired after 1987, including their component parts such as electric wiring, lighting fixtures, plumbing, heating and cooling equipment, elevators, and escalators	4%
3	Most buildings made of brick, stone, or cement acquired before 1988, including their component parts as listed in Class 1 above	5%
6	Buildings made of frame, log, stucco on frame, galvanized iron, or corrugated metal that are used in the business of farming or fishing, or that have no footings below ground; fences and most greenhouses	10%
7	Canoes, boats, and most other vessels, including their furniture, fittings, or equipment	15%
8	Property that is not included in any other class such as furniture, calculators and cash registers (that do not record multiple sales taxes), photocopy and fax machines, printers, display fixtures, refrigeration equipment, machinery, tools costing $200 or more, and outdoor advertising billboards and greenhouses with rigid frames and plastic covers	20%
9	Aircraft, including furniture, fittings, or equipment attached, and their spare parts	25%
10	Automobiles (except taxis and others used for lease or rent), vans, wagons, trucks, buses, tractors, trailers, drive-in theatres, general-purpose electronic data processing equipment (e.g., personal computers) and systems software, and timber-cutting and removing equipment	30%
10.1	Passenger vehicles costing more than $30,000 if acquired after 2000	30%
12	Chinaware, cutlery, linen, uniforms, dies, jigs, molds or lasts, computer software (except systems software), cutting or shaping parts of a machine, certain property used for earning rental income such as apparel or costumes, and videotape cassettes; certain property costing less than $200 such as kitchen utensils, tools, and medical or dental equipment	100%
13	Property that is leasehold interest (the maximum CCA rate depends on the type of leasehold and the terms of the lease)	N/A
14	Patents, franchises, concessions, and licences for a limited period—the CCA is limited to whichever is less: • The capital cost of the property spread out over the life of the property; or • The undepreciated capital cost of the property at the end of the taxation year Class 14 also includes patents, and licences to use patents for a limited period, that you elect not to include in Class 44.	N/A
16	Automobiles for lease or rent, taxicabs, and coin-operated video games or pinball machines; certain tractors and large trucks acquired after December 6, 1991, that are used to haul freight and that weigh more than 11,788 kilograms	40%
17	Roads, sidewalks, parking-lot or storage areas, telephone, telegraph, or non-electronic data communication switching equipment	8%
38	Most power-operated movable equipment acquired after 1987 used for moving, excavating, placing, or compacting earth, rock, concrete, or asphalt	30%
39	Machinery and equipment acquired after 1987 that is used in Canada primarily to manufacture and process goods for sale or lease	25%
43	Manufacturing and processing machinery and equipment acquired after February 25, 1 992, described in Class 39 above	30%
44	Patents and licences to use patents for a limited or unlimited period that the corporation acquired after April 26, 1993—however, you can elect not to include such property in Class 44 by attaching a letter to the return for the year the corporation acquired the property. In the letter, indicate the property you do not want to include in Class 44.	25%
45	Computer equipment that is "general-purpose electronic data processing equipment and system software" included in paragraph f of Class 10 acquired after March 22, 2004. Also see Classes 50 and 52.	45%

TABLE 15-2   (Continued)

Class Number	Description	CCA Rate
46	Data network infrastructure equipment that supports advanced telecommunication applications, acquired after March 22, 2004. It includes assets such as switches, multiplexers, routers, hubs, modems, and domain name servers that are used to control, transfer, modulate and direct data, but does not include office equipment such as telephones, cell phones or fax machines, or property such as wires, cables, or structures.	30%
50	General-purpose computer equipment and systems software acquired after March 18, 2007, and before January 28, 2009, that is not used principally as electronic process control, communications control, or monitor equipment, and the systems software related to such equipment, and data handling equipment that is not ancillary to general-purpose computer equipment	55%
52	General-purpose computer equipment and systems software acquired after January 27, 2009, and before February 2011	100%

For example, office furniture and equipment belong to Class 8 with a CCA rate of 20%. Manufacturing and processing machinery acquired after February 25, 1992, are grouped in Class 43 and have a CCA rate of 30%. This relatively high CCA rate is an example of one way the Government of Canada provides an incentive for a strong manufacturing sector. The higher the CCA rate, the lower the after-tax cost of purchasing manufacturing equipment. Buildings may belong to Class 1, 3, or 6 depending on what the building is made of and the date it was acquired. The internal fixtures of the building such as wiring, lighting, plumbing, air conditioning and heating systems, and elevators are also included in these classes. The straight line method is used to calculate the CCA for patents, franchises, concessions, and licences of Classes 13, 14, 24, and 29.

Capital cost allowance is claimed on the capital cost of the asset minus the CCA deducted in previous years, if any. The remaining balance, the undepreciated capital cost or UCC, declines over the years as CCA is claimed. The maximum CCA a business is allowed in a year is determined by multiplying the UCC at year-end by the CCA rate for the class. CCA can be claimed even if the resulting UCC is less than the estimated salvage value. CCA is an optional tax deduction, but the maximum CCA is normally claimed if a business has taxable income after deducting the allowed CCA.

Land does not depreciate with use, and therefore is not eligible for CCA. However, CCA can be claimed on timber limits, cutting rights, and wood assets. Patents, franchises, concessions, and licences having a limited life are considered depreciable properties of Class 14.

A capital cost allowance can usually be claimed only when a property is available for use. This means that assets under renovation or construction, or ordered but not delivered, may not be depreciated. In the year in which an asset is purchased only one-half of the normal CCA can be claimed. This *50% rule* prevents businesses from buying assets on the last day of the fiscal year and claiming a full year of depreciation. Some assets are not subject to the 50% rule, such a properties in Classes 13, 14, 23, 24, 27, 29, 34, 50, and 52, as well as tools in Class 12 that cost less than $200.

Capital cost allowance calculations assume a full 12-month taxation year. If the tax year is shorter, the CCA claim is prorated. If, for example, a business began on September 1, and December 31 was the chosen fiscal year-end, the CCA claim would be 122 days/365 days × CCA.

The following example illustrates the calculations of CCA and UCC.

EXAMPLE 15.3

Nichols-Cole Laboratories purchased a machine belonging to Class 8 for $100,000 in 2006. The CCA for Class 8 is 20%. Determine the annual tax depreciation schedule for the first three years and the UCC at the end of each year. Assume this is the only property in this asset class.

Class 8—20%	CCA	UCC
January 1, 2006		0
Additions less disposals in 2006:		
Cost of machine acquisition		$100,000
Disposals during 2006		0
CCA 2006: $100,000 × 50% × 20%	$10,000	(10,000)
December 31, 2006		$ 90,000
Additions less disposals, 2007		0
		90,000
CCA 2007: $90,000 × 20%	$18,000	(18,000)
December 31, 2007		$ 72,000
Additions less disposals 2008		0
		72,000
CCA 2008: $72,000 × 20%	$14,400	(14,400)
December 31, 2008		$ 57,600

During the first year the 50% rule has reduced the allowable CCA from $20,000 to $10,000. If any other method of depreciation is used for fiscal reporting, the book values of the asset will differ from the values of UCC, or tax values, shown here.

Recapture and *terminal loss* are adjustments that must be made when assets are either not depreciated enough over time or depreciated too much. When depreciable property is sold in a year, the lesser of the proceeds of disposition minus related expenses and the original cost is subtracted from the UCC. If the UCC balance of the asset class is then negative, more depreciation has been taken over the years than the true value of the assets. The Canada Revenue Agency will want to recapture this amount, and it must be declared as taxable income. If the UCC balance is positive after sale of the remaining assets in a class, this amount is a terminal loss. In this case, not enough depreciation was taken over the years and the full amount can be deducted from income. Neither recapture nor terminal loss can be claimed while some assets remain in a CCA class.

EXAMPLE 15.4

In 2009, Nichols-Cole Laboratories buys a second machine in Class 8 for $150,000. In 2010, the company sells the first machine for $60,000. The second machine is sold in 2011 for $100,000. Now no assets remain in Class 8. The previous example's CCA and UCC calculations are continued as follows:

Class 8—20%	CCA	UCC
December 31, 2008		$ 57,600
Additions less disposals, 2009:		
Cost of machine #2 acquisition		$150,000
		$207,600
CCA 2009: $57,600 × 20% = 11,520 + $150,000 × 50% × 20% = 15,000	$26,520	(26,520)
December 31, 2009		$181,080
Additions less disposals, 2010:		
Machine 1 (lesser of original cost of $100,000 and proceeds of disposal $60,000)		(60,000)
		$121,080
CCA 2010: $121,080 × 20%	$24,216	(24,216)
December 31, 2010		$ 96,864
Additions less disposals, 2011:		
Machine 2 (lesser of original cost of $150,000 and proceeds of disposal $100,000)		(100,000)
		(3,136)
Recaptured CCA	($3,136)	3,136
December 31, 2011		0

When a net addition (purchases less disposals) to a class occurs, such as in 2009 above, the maximum CCA allowed is 50% of the net addition multiplied by the allowed CCA rate. The CCA for the net addition plus the CCA on the remaining UCC in a class is the total CCA for the class. If machine 1 or 2 had been sold for an amount greater than its original cost, a capital gain occurs that is taxed at a different rate and not dealt with in CCA calculations. Because Nichols-Cole has sold machine 2 for more than the UCC in this class, Canada Revenue Agency taxes the difference by requiring the company to add the recaptured CCA of $3136 to their taxable income for the year.

A corporation claims capital cost allowance on Schedule 8 according to the *T2 Corporation—Income Tax Guide*. Tax forms T2032 or T2124 are the corresponding forms used by self-employed professionals, sole proprietors, or business partnerships. Completion of Schedule 8 is illustrated in Example 15.5.

TABLE 15–3 T2 Schedule 8—Capital Cost Allowance

Canada Revenue Agency	Agence du revenu du Canada	**CAPITAL COST ALLOWANCE (CCA) (2006 and later tax years)**		**SCHEDULE 8** Code 0601

		Business Number		Taxation year end
				Year 2 0 1 1 Month 1 1 2 Day 3 1

Name of corporation
Nichols-Cole, Laboratories

For more information, see the section called "Capital Cost Allowance" in the *T2 Corporation Income Tax Guide*.

Is the corporation electing under Regulation 1101(5q)? **101** 1 Yes ☐ 2 No ☐

	1 Class number	2 Undepreciated capital cost at the beginning of the year (undepreciated capital cost at the end of the year from column 13 of last year's CCA schedule)	3 Cost of acquisitions during the year (new property must be available for use) See note 1 below	4 Net adjustments (show negative amounts in brackets) See note 2 below	5 Proceeds of dispositions during the year (amount not to exceed the capital cost)	6 Undepreciated capital cost (column 2 **plus** column 3 **plus** column 4 **minus** column 5)	7 50% rule (1/2 of the amount, if any, by which the net cost of acquisitions exceeds column 5) See note 3 below	8 Reduced undepreciated capital cost (column 6 **minus** column 7)	9 CCA rate %	10 Recapture of capital cost allowance	11 Terminal loss	12 Capital cost allowance (column 8 **multiplied by** column 9; or a lower amount) See note 4 below	13 Undepreciated capital cost at the end of the year (column 6 **minus** column 12)
	200	**201**	**203**	**205**	**207**		**211**		**212**	**213**	**215**	**217**	**220**
1.	8	96,864	0	—	100,000	–3,136	—		20%	3,136			
2.	10	15,200	16,000			31,200	8,000	23,200	30%			6,960	24,240
3.	12	0	6,000			6,000	3,000	3,000	100%			3,000	3,000
4.													
5.													
6.													
7.													
8.													
9.													
10.													

Totals | 3,136 | | | 9,960 |

Enter the total of column 10 on line 107 of Schedule 1.
Enter the total of column 11 on line 404 of Schedule 1.
Enter the total of column 12 on line 403 of Schedule 1.

Note 1. Include any property acquired in previous years that has now become available for use. This property would have been previously excluded from column 3. List separately any acquisitions that are not subject to the 50% rule, see Regulation 1100(2) and (2.2).

Note 2. Include amounts transferred under section 85, or on amalgamation and winding-up of a subsidiary. See the *T2 Corporation Income Tax Guide* for other examples of adjustments to include in column 4.

Note 3. The net cost of acquisitions is the cost of acquisitions (column 3) plus or minus certain adjustments from column 4. For exceptions to the 50% rule, see Interpretation Bulletin IT–285, *Capital Cost Allowance—General Comments*.

Note 4. If the tax year is shorter than 365 days, prorate the CCA claim. Some classes of property do not have to be prorated. See the *T2 Corporation Income Tax Guide* for more information.

T2 SCH 8 (06)

> ### EXAMPLE 15.5
>
> In 2011, Nichols-Cole Laboratories purchased computers for $16,000 (Class 10—CCA rate 30%) and specialized software (Class 12—CCA rate 100%) for $6000. A year-end UCC in Class 10 was recorded on their 2010 Schedule 8 from the past purchase of a company car. Complete a Schedule 8 for their property in Classes 8, 10, and 12.
>
> Because the amount for Class 8 (see Example 15.4) is negative, there is a recapture of CCA. A recapture of CCA occurs when the proceeds from the sale of depreciable property are more than the total of the UCC of the class at the start of the year plus the capital cost of any new additions. Recapture of the CCA from Class 8 is recorded in column 10.
>
> The 50% rule has limited the CCA that can be claimed for the Class 10 and 12 acquisitions in 2011. The assets of Class 10 are pooled and the past year's UCC of $15,200 is added to the cost of new acquisitions for a total of $31,200, to which the 50% rule must be applied for the portion of the computer acquisition before calculating CCA.

The pooling of assets creates difficulties in assessing the tax implications of the purchase of one asset (such as the computer system of the last example). In order to determine the viability of a project, engineering economic analysis usually considers the CCA of new assets separately from other acquisitions and dispositions in a class.

The examples of this chapter are based on the *Federal Tax Act*. Provincial taxes can vary in how depreciation is calculated for determining income. Because tax laws are extremely extensive and change periodically, the use of a tax specialist is recommended for the analysis of the tax repercussions of specific business decisions. Canada Revenue Agency (CRA) provides relevant information in the *T2 Corporation—Income Tax Guide* and in *Business and Professional Income,* which includes forms T2124 and T2032 that partnerships, sole proprietors, and professionals use to claim CCA. Other CRA publications discussing tax depreciation include the interpretation bulletins *IT-285R2 Capital Cost Allowance— General Comments, IT-128R Capital Cost Allowance—Depreciable Property, IT-472 Capital Cost Allowance—Class 8 Property, IT-481 (Consolidated) Timber Resource Property and Timber Limits,* and *IT-492 Capital Cost Allowance— Industrial Mineral Mines.* A complete list of publications and forms can be found at the CRA website (www.cra.gc.ca).

15.5) DEPLETION METHODS

Up to this point, we have discussed depreciation for assets that can be replaced. Depletion, though similar to depreciation, is applicable only to natural resources. When the resources are removed, they cannot be replaced or repurchased in the same manner as can a machine, computer, or structure. Depletion is applicable to natural deposits removed from mines, wells, quarries, geothermal deposits, forests, and the like.

This method of depreciation, *cost depletion,* sometimes referred to as *factor depletion,* is based on the level of activity or usage, not time, as in depreciation. It may be applied to most types of natural resources. The cost depletion factor for year t, denoted by p_t, is the ratio of the cost basis of the resource to the estimated number of units recoverable.

$$p_t = \frac{\textbf{cost basis}}{\textbf{resource capacity}}$$ [15.11]

The annual depletion charge is p_t times the year's usage or volume. *The total cost depletion cannot exceed the cost basis of the resource.* If the capacity of the property is reestimated some year in the future, a new cost depletion factor is determined based upon the undepleted amount and the new capacity estimate.

EXAMPLE 15.6

Temple-Inland Corporation has negotiated the rights to cut timber on privately held forest resource property for $700,000. An estimated 350 million cubic metres of lumber are harvestable.

(a) Determine the depletion amount for the first 2 years if 15 million and 22 million cubic metres are removed.

(b) After 2 years the total recoverable cubic metres was reestimated to be 450 million from the time the rights were purchased. Compute the new cost depletion factor for years 3 and later.

Solution

(a) Use Equation [15.11] for p_t in dollars per million cubic metres.

$$p_t = \frac{\$700,000}{350} = \$2000 \text{ per million cubic metres}$$

Multiply p_t by the annual harvest to obtain depletion of $30,000 in year 1 and $44,000 in year 2. Continue using p_t until a total of $700,000 is written off.

(b) After 2 years, a total of $74,000 has been depleted. A new p_t value must be calculated based on the remaining $700,000 − 74,000 = \$626,000 investment. Additionally, with the new estimate of 450 million cubic metres, a total of $450 − 15 − 22 = 413$ million cubic metres remain. For years $t = 3, 4, \ldots$, the cost depletion factor is

$$p_t = \frac{\$626,000}{413} = \$1516 \text{ per million cubic metres}$$

CHAPTER SUMMARY

Depreciation may be determined for internal company records (book depreciation) or for income tax purposes (tax depreciation). In Canada, the capital cost allowance (CCA) is used for tax depreciation. In many other countries, straight line and declining balance methods are applied for both tax and book depreciation. Depreciation does not result in actual cash flow directly. It is a book method by which the capital investment in tangible property is recovered. The annual depreciation amount is tax-deductible, which can result in actual cash flow changes.

Some important points about the straight line, declining balance, and CCA models are presented below.

Straight Line (SL)

- It writes off capital investment linearly over n years.
- The estimated salvage value is always considered.
- This is the classical, nonaccelerated depreciation model.

Declining Balance (DB)

- The model accelerates depreciation, compared to straight line.
- The book value is reduced each year by a fixed percentage.
- It is frequently used for book depreciation purposes.

Capital Cost Allowance

- It is the only approved tax depreciation system in Canada.
- It is usually based on the DB method.
- Assets are grouped into classes, each with a specified rate of depreciation.
- The maximum CCA allowed is the UCC at year-end multiplied by the CCA rate for each class.
- In the year an asset is acquired, only one-half the amount of the net acquisition is used in calculating CCA.
- Recapture or terminal loss adjustments may be necessary when all assets in a class are disposed of.
- CCA can be claimed even if the resulting UCC is less than the estimated salvage value.

The *cost depletion method* is used to recover investment in natural resources. The annual cost depletion factor is applied to the amount of resource removed. No more than the initial investment can be recovered with cost depletion.

PROBLEMS

Fundamentals of Depreciation

15.1 Write another term that may be used in lieu of each of the following that has the same interpretation in asset depreciation: *book value, fair market value,* and *tangible property.*

15.2 State the difference between book depreciation and tax depreciation.

15.3 Explain why in Canada the explicit consideration of depreciation and income taxes in an engineering economy study may make a difference in the decision to accept or reject an alternative to acquire a depreciable asset.

15.4 Status Corporation purchased for $350,000 a new numerical controller during the last month of 2008. Extra installation costs were $40,000. The recovery period was 7 years with an estimated salvage value of 10% of the original purchase price. Status sold the system at the end of 2011 for $45,000.

   (a) What are the values needed to develop a depreciation schedule at purchase time?

   (b) State the numerical values for the following: remaining life at sale time, market value in 2011, book value at sale time if 65% of the cost basis had been depreciated.

15.5 A $100,000 piece of testing equipment was installed and depreciated for 5 years. Each year the end-of-year book value decreased at a rate of 10% of the book value at the beginning of the year. The system was sold for $24,000 at the end of 5 years.

(a) Compute the amount of the annual depreciation.

(b) What is the actual depreciation rate for each year?

(c) At the time of sale, what is the difference between the book value and the market value?

(d) Plot the book value for each of the 5 years.

Straight Line Depreciation

15.6 LaRue Engineering purchased a laser-based holographic imaging unit for analyzing the structural integrity of existing overpasses and bridges for $300,000 and had it mounted on a truck body for an additional $100,000, including the truck chassis. The unit-truck system will be depreciated as one asset. The functional life is 8 years, and salvage is estimated at 10% of the purchase price of the imaging unit. (a) Use classical straight line depreciation and hand calculations to determine the salvage value, annual depreciation, and book value after 4 years. (b) Develop the cell reference worksheet in Excel to obtain the answers in part (a) for the original data. (c) Use your Excel worksheet to determine the answers, if the holographic unit cost goes up to $350,000 and the expected life is decreased to 5 years.

15.7 Air handling equipment that costs $12,000 has a life of 8 years with a $2000 salvage value. (a) Calculate the straight line depreciation amount for each year. (b) Determine the book value after 3 years. (c) What is the rate of depreciation?

15.8 An asset has a cost basis of $200,000, a salvage value of $10,000, and a useful life of 7 years. Write a single-cell Excel function to display the book value after 5 years of straight line depreciation.

15.9 Simpson and Jones Pharmaceuticals purchased a prescription drug tablet-forming machine in 2008 for $750,000. They had planned to use the machine for 10 years, but due to rapid obsolescence it should be retired after 4 years. Develop the spreadsheet for depreciation and book value amounts necessary to answer the following.

(a) What is the amount of capital investment remaining when the asset is retired due to obsolescence?

(b) If the asset is sold at the end of 4 years for $75,000, what is the amount of capital investment lost based on straight line depreciation?

(c) If the new technology machine has an estimated cost of $300,000, how many more years should the company retain and depreciate the currently owned machine to make its book value and the cost basis of the new machine equal?

15.10 A special-purpose computer workstation has $B = \$50,000$ with a 4-year useful life. Tabulate and plot the values for SL depreciation, accumulated depreciation, and book value for each year if (a) there is no salvage value and (b) $S = \$16,000$. (c) Use a spreadsheet to solve this problem.

Declining Balance Depreciation

15.11 Aecon Group Ltd. is purchasing construction equipment for its contract with Northland Power for a gas-powered peaking plant in Saskatchewan. The equipment costs $500,000 with an estimated salvage value of $50,000 at the end of the expected life of 5 years. Determine the depreciation for year 3 if using (a) the SL method and (b) the DB method.

15.12 Allison and Carl are civil engineers who own a soil and water analysis business for which they have purchased computer equipment for $25,000. They do not expect the computers to have a positive salvage or trade-in value after the anticipated 5-year life. For book depreciation purposes, they want book value schedules for the SL and DB methods. They want to use a fixed depreciation rate of 25% annually for the DB model. Use a spreadsheet or hand computation to develop the schedules.

15.13 Equipment for immersion cooling of electronic components has an installed value of $182,000 with an estimated trade-in value of $50,000 after 18 years. For years 2 and 18, determine the annual depreciation charge using DB depreciation by hand.

15.14 For book depreciation purposes, declining balance depreciation at a rate of 1.5 times the straight line rate is used for automated process control equipment with $B = \$175,000$, $n = 12$, and $S = \$32,000$. (*a*) Compute the depreciation and book value for years 1 and 12. (*b*) Compare the estimated salvage value and the book value after 12 years.

CCA Depreciation

15.15 Claude, a self-employed engineering economist, has just purchased a new car for the sole use of his consulting business. The cost basis of this Class 10 property (CCA rate of 30%) is $30,000. If he keeps the car for 7 years, he expects its trade-in value to be $2000. Compare the book values for CCA and classical SL depreciation over 7 years.

15.16 An automated assembly robot (Class 43, 30%) that cost $450,000 installed has a depreciable life of 5 years and no salvage value. An analyst in the financial management department used classical SL depreciation to determine end-of-year book values for the robot when the original economic evaluation was performed. What is the difference in the book value by the classical SL method and CCA depreciation after the 3 years?

15.17 Develop the ten-year CCA depreciation schedule for a commercial building (Class 1, 4%) purchased by Alpha Enterprises for $1,800,000.

15.18 Explain why a shorter depreciation period coupled with higher depreciation rates in the initial years of an asset's life may be financially advantageous to a corporation.

Depletion

15.19 When WTA Corporation purchased rights to extract silver from a mine for a total price of $1.1 million 3 years ago, an estimated 350,000 ounces of silver was to be removed over the next 10 years. A total of 175,000 ounces has been removed and sold thus far. (*a*) What is the total cost depletion allowed over the 3 years? (*b*) New exploratory tests indicate that only an estimated 100,000 ounces remain in the veins of the mine. What is the cost depletion factor applicable for the next year?

15.20 Caw Ridge Coal in Alberta has used the cost depletion factor of $2500 per 100 tonnes to write off the investment of $35 million in its No. 6 coal mine that produces premium, low-volatile metallurgic coal for the steel industry. Depletion thus far totals $24.8 million. A new study to appraise mine reserves indicates that no more than 800,000 tonnes of saleable coal remains. Determine next year's cost depletion amount if estimated gross income is expected to be between $6.125 and $8.50 million on a production level of 72,000 tonnes.

CHAPTER 16

After-Tax Economic Analysis

This chapter provides an overview of tax terminology, income tax rates, and tax equations pertinent to an after-tax economic analysis. The transfer from estimating cash flow before taxes (CFBT) to cash flow after taxes (CFAT) involves a consideration of significant tax effects that may alter the final decision, as well as estimate the magnitude of the tax effect on cash flow over the life of the alternative.

Mutually exclusive alternative comparisons using after-tax PW, AW, and ROR methods are explained with major tax implications considered. Replacement studies are discussed with tax effects that occur at the time that a defender is replaced, and capital cost tax factors are introduced to simplify the PW calculation of a corporation's tax savings. All these methods use the procedures learned in earlier chapters, except now with tax effects considered.

LEARNING OBJECTIVES

Purpose: Perform an economic evaluation of one or more alternatives considering the effect of income taxes and other pertinent tax regulations.

By the end of this chapter you should be able to

Terminology and rates	**1.** Correctly use the basic terminology and income tax rates for corporate (and individual) taxpayers.
CFBT and CFAT	**2.** Calculate before-tax and after-tax cash flow.
Depreciation recapture, capital gains, and terminal losses	**3.** Compute the tax impact of depreciation recapture, capital gains, and terminal losses.
After-tax analysis	**4.** Evaluate alternatives using after-tax PW, AW, and ROR analysis.
After-tax replacement	**5.** Evaluate a defender and a challenger in an after-tax replacement study.
Capital cost factors	**6.** Calculate the present worth of a CCA-based tax savings.

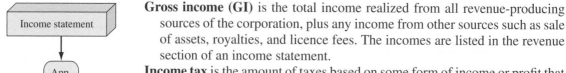

16.1   INCOME TAX TERMINOLOGY AND RELATIONS FOR CORPORATIONS (and individuals)

Some basic corporate tax terms and relationships useful in engineering economy studies are explained here.

Income statement

App. A

Gross income (GI) is the total income realized from all revenue-producing sources of the corporation, plus any income from other sources such as sale of assets, royalties, and licence fees. The incomes are listed in the revenue section of an income statement.

Income tax is the amount of taxes based on some form of income or profit that must be delivered to a federal (or lower-level) government agency. A large percentage of tax revenue is based upon taxation of income. The Canada Revenue Agency collects the taxes. Corporate income tax payments are usually submitted monthly, and the last payment of the year is submitted with the annual tax return. Taxes are actual cash flows.

Sec. 15.4

CCA

Operating expenses E include all corporate costs incurred in the transaction of business. These expenses are tax-deductible for corporations. For engineering economy alternatives, the AOC (annual operating cost) and M&O (maintenance and operations) costs are applicable here.

The amount of GI and E must be estimated for an economy study and expressed as

$$\text{Gross income} - \text{expenses} = \text{GI} - E$$

Capital cost allowance (CCA) is the portion of the **undepreciated capital cost (UCC)**, or **book value**, of a depreciable asset that Canadian businesses can deduct from income earned each year. Most assets are subject to a 50% reduction of the allowance in the first year.

Given

$CCA_n =$ capital cost allowance for year n

$UCC_n =$ undepreciated capital cost at end of year n

$P =$ asset cost basis or first cost

$d =$ CCA class rate

the following formulas are used to determine the CCA and UCC for year n:

$$CCA_1 = P(d/2) \text{ for } n = 1 \qquad\qquad \text{[16.1]}$$

$$CCA_n = Pd(1 - d/2)(1 - d)^{n-2} \text{ for } n \geq 2 \qquad \text{[16.2]}$$

$$UCC_n = P(1 - d/2)(1 - d)^{n-1} \qquad\qquad \text{[16.3]}$$

Taxable income (TI) is the amount upon which taxes are based. For corporations, the capital cost allowance (CCA) and operating expenses are tax-deductible, so

$$\textbf{TI} = \textbf{gross income} - \textbf{expenses} - \textbf{CCA}$$

$$= \textbf{GI} - E - \textbf{CCA} \qquad\qquad \text{[16.4]}$$

Tax rate T is a percentage, or decimal equivalent, of TI owed in taxes. The general formula for tax computation uses the applicable T value.

$$\textbf{Taxes = (taxable income)(applicable tax rate)}$$

$$= \textbf{(TI)}(T) \qquad\qquad\qquad \textbf{[16.5]}$$

Net profit after taxes (NPAT), or **net income** (NI), is the amount remaining each year when income taxes are subtracted from taxable income.

$$\textbf{NPAT = taxable income} - \textbf{taxes = TI} - \textbf{(TI)}(T)$$

$$= \textbf{(TI)}(1-T) \qquad\qquad\qquad \textbf{[16.6]}$$

This is the amount of money returned to the corporation as a result of the capital invested during the year.

A variety of different bases may be used by federal, provincial, and territorial agencies for tax revenue. Some bases (and taxes) other than income are the total sales (sales tax); appraised value of property (property tax); net capital investment (asset tax); winnings from gambling (part of income tax); and retail value of items imported (import tax). Canada's Goods & Services Tax (GST) is a value-added tax (VAT) of 5% charged by the federal government. A VAT is a tax on the value added at each stage of a product's manufacture and distribution. The Harmonized Sales Tax (HST), which combines the GST and provincial sales tax, is collected in British Columbia (12%), New Brunswick (13%), Newfoundland (13%), Nova Scotia (15%), and Ontario (13%). Similar and different bases are utilized by different countries, provinces, and local tax districts. Governments that have no income tax must utilize bases other than income to develop revenue. No government entity survives for long without some form of tax revenue.

The base federal tax rate, T, for Canadian corporations is 38% of taxable income, but the actual rate varies from corporation to corporation depending on factors such as size of corporation, source and type of income, and type of business, such as manufacturing or processing. These factors may qualify the corporation for certain deductions from taxable income and credits from tax owed. For example, Canadian-controlled private corporations with taxable capital of less than $10 million may qualify for the small business deduction (SBD) of 17% on the first $500,000 of taxable income. If this is combined with the federal tax abatement, which reduces tax by 10% on income earned inside Canada, a small corporation may have a federal tax rate as low as 11% (38% – 17% – 10%). The manufacturing and processing profits deduction reduces the federal tax rate by 7% on income not eligible for the SBD. Other credits such as those related to resource development or scientific research and experimental development also affect the tax rate.

In addition to federal tax, a corporation pays a provincial or territorial income tax. Though generally based on the same considerations as the federal rate, income taxes vary from province to province with rates ranging from 1% to 17% of taxable income. All provinces and territories legislate their corporate income tax provisions and, with the exception of Quebec, Ontario, and Alberta, the

Canada Revenue Agency administers them. Corporations with income earned in these three provinces must file separate provincial income tax returns.

Tax credits and deductions change according to legislation, CRA interpretation of tax law, and economic conditions. For the sake of simplicity, the tax rate used in an economy study is often a single-figure effective tax rate T_e, which accounts for all taxes, federal and provincial. Effective tax rates are in the range of 13% to 45%. The effective tax rate and taxes are calculated as

$$T_e = \frac{\text{total taxes paid}}{\text{taxable income}} = \frac{\text{taxes}}{\text{TI}} \qquad \textbf{[16.7]}$$

$$\textbf{Taxes} = \textbf{(TI)}(T_e) \qquad \textbf{[16.8]}$$

The portion of each new dollar of taxable income is taxed at what is called the *marginal tax rate*.

EXAMPLE 16.1

Freshflow is a Canadian-controlled private corporation in Fredericton, N.B., that manufactures biofilters for wastewater treatment plants. The company had a gross income of $1,100,000 and CCA of $30,000 on their production machinery. Expenses were

Cost of production	$250,000
Salaries and benefits	200,000
Other expenses	50,000
Total	$500,000

(a) What amount of tax will the company pay on their federal and provincial taxable income?
(b) What is the company's effective tax rate?

Solution

(a) Taxable income = gross income − expenses − CCA $\qquad$ [16.4]

$$\text{TI} = 1,100,000 - 500,000 - 30,000 = 570,000$$

Federal income tax. Because the company qualifies for the SBD, the first $500,000 is taxable at a rate of 11% (38% − 17% − 10%).

$$\text{Taxes} = (\text{taxable income})(\text{applicable tax rate}) \qquad [16.5]$$

$$= (\$500,000)(0.11) = \$55,000$$

Freshflow qualifies for the manufacturing and processing profits deduction of 7% on the remainder of the income taxable at the rate of 21% (38% − 10% − 7%).

$$\text{Taxes} = (\$70,000)(0.21) = \$14,700$$

$$\text{Total federal tax} = \$55,000 + \$14,700 = \$69,700$$

New Brunswick income tax. In New Brunswick, $500,000 is the business limit used in calculating the income eligible for the small business rate of 5%. Income above $500,000 is taxed at a rate of 11%.

Provincial small business tax payable = ($500,000)(0.05) = $25,000

Provincial general tax payable = ($70,000)(0.11) = $7,700

Total provincial tax payable = $25,000 + $7,700 = $32,700

Total combined federal and provincial income tax payable = $69,700 + $32,700 = $102,400

(b)
$$T_e = \frac{\text{taxes}}{\text{TI}}$$

$$T_e = \frac{102,400}{570,000} = 18\%$$

It is interesting to understand how corporate tax and individual tax computations differ. Gross income for an individual taxpayer is comparable, with business revenue replaced by salaries and wages. However, for an individual's taxable income, most of the expenses for living and working are not tax-deductible to the same degree as business expenses are for corporations. For individual taxpayers,

Gross income = GI = salaries + net self-employment income
+ investment income + other income

Deductions from gross income may include such items as a self-employed person's expenses in carrying on a business, pension plan and RRSP deductions, professional dues, child care expenses, moving expenses, support payments, and interest expenses. Losses from other years and the security options deduction are examples of deductions that can be made from net income to arrive at taxable income.

Taxable income = GI − deductions

For taxable income, corporate operating expenses are replaced by specific deductions and tax credits. The biggest difference between corporate and individual tax is that the individual tax rate is progressive—that is, the rate of tax increases as income increases. The federal tax rates are graduated by four TI levels that range from 15% to 29%, as illustrated in Table 16–1.

TABLE 16–1   Federal Base Income Taxes for Individuals, 2010

Taxable Income	Tax Rate
First $40,971	15%
Between $40,971 and $81,941	22%
Between $81,941 and $127,021	26%
Over $127,021	29%
Base federal tax = (taxable income)(applicable tax rate) = (TI)(T)	

Federal non-refundable tax credits reduce federal tax. If the total of credits is more than the tax owed, a refund will not be made for the difference. These credits include a basic personal amount ($10,320 in 2010), amounts for age, spouse, eligible dependents, pension contribution, disability, tuition and education, medical expenses, and donations and gifts. The federal dividend tax credit and overseas employment and foreign tax credits are added to the non-refundable tax credits and subtracted from tax owed to calculate federal tax.

$$\text{Federal tax} = \text{base federal tax} - \text{tax credits}$$

Provincial and territorial individual income taxes, like corporate taxes, are calculated from deductions and tax credits similarly to the federal system.

$$\text{Total income taxes} = \text{federal income taxes} + \text{provincial or territorial income taxes}$$

16.2 BEFORE-TAX AND AFTER-TAX CASH FLOW

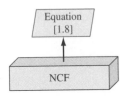

Early in the text, the term *net cash flow* (*NCF*) was identified as the best estimate of actual cash flow each year. The NCF is calculated as cash inflows minus cash outflows. Since then, the annual NCF amounts have been used many times to perform alternative evaluations via the PW, AW, ROR, and benefit-cost methods. Now that the impact on cash flow of depreciation and related taxes will be considered, it is time to expand our terminology. NCF is replaced by the term *cash flow before taxes* (*CFBT*), and we introduce the new term *cash flow after taxes* (*CFAT*).

CFBT and CFAT are *actual cash flows*; that is, they represent the estimated actual flow of money in and out of the corporation that will result from the alternative. The remainder of this section explains how to transition from before-tax to after-tax cash flows using income tax rates and other pertinent tax regulations described in the next few sections.

Once the CFAT estimates are developed, the economic evaluation is performed using the same methods and selection guidelines applied previously. However, the analysis is performed on the CFAT estimates.

The annual CFBT estimate must include the initial capital investment and salvage value for the years in which they occur. Incorporating the definitions of gross income and operating expenses, CFBT for any year is defined as

CFBT = gross income − expenses − initial investment + salvage value

$$= \text{GI} - E - P + S \qquad \text{[16.9]}$$

As in previous chapters, P is the initial investment (usually in year 0) and S is the estimated salvage value in year n. Once all taxes are estimated, the annual after-tax cash flow is simply

CFAT = CFBT − taxes $\qquad$ **[16.10]**

where taxes are estimated using the relation (TI)(T) or (TI)(T_e), as discussed earlier.

We know from Equation [16.4] that the capital cost allowance is subtracted to obtain TI. It is very important to understand the different roles of depreciation for income tax computations and in CFAT estimation.

Depreciation is a *non*cash flow. Depreciation is tax-deductible for determining the amount of income taxes only, but it does not represent a direct, after-tax cash flow to the corporation. Therefore, the after-tax engineering economy study must be based on actual cash flow estimates, that is, annual CFAT estimates that do not include depreciation as a negative cash flow.

Accordingly, if the CFAT expression is determined using the TI relation, depreciation must not be included outside of the TI component. Equations [16.9] and [16.10] are now combined as

$$\text{CFAT} = \text{GI} - E - P + S - (\text{GI} - E - \text{CCA})(T_e) \qquad [16.11]$$

Suggested table column headings for CFBT and CFAT calculations by hand or by computer are shown in Table 16–2. The equations are shown in column numbers, with the effective tax rate T_e used for income taxes. Expenses E and initial investment P will be negative values.

The TI value in some years may be negative due to a depreciation amount that is larger than $(\text{GI} - E)$. It is possible to account for this in a detailed after-tax analysis using carry-forward and carry-back rules for operating losses. It is the exception that the engineering economy study will consider this level of detail. Rather, *the associated negative income tax is considered as a tax savings for the year.* The assumption is that the negative tax will offset taxes for the same year in other income-producing areas of the corporation.

TABLE 16–2   Table Column Headings for Calculation of (*a*) CFBT and (*b*) CFAT

(a) CFBT table headings

Year	Gross Income GI (1)	Operating Expenses E (2)	Investment P and Salvage S (3)	CFBT (4) = (1) + (2) + (3)

(b) CFAT table headings

Year	Gross Income GI	Operating Expenses E	Investment P and Salvage S	Undepreciated Capital Cost UCC	Capital Cost Allowance CCA	Taxable Income TI	Taxes $(TI)(T_e)$	CFAT
						(6) = (1) + (2) − (5)		(8) = (1) + (2) + (3) − (7)
	(1)	(2)	(3)	(4)	(5)	(1) + (2) − (5)	(7)	(3) − (7)

EXAMPLE 16.2

Markham Corporation is considering the purchase of new production machinery at an initial cost of $550,000 and a resale (salvage) value of $150,000 expected after 6 years. Financial personnel estimate annual bottom-line increases to the corporation of $200,000 in revenue and $90,000 in costs. The machinery belongs to CCA Class 43 with a rate of 30%. Using an effective tax rate of 35%, calculate the CFBT and CFAT estimates associated with the purchase.

Solution
CFBT
Table 16–3 presents before-tax cash flows using the format of Table 16–2. The expenses and initial investment are shown as negative cash flows. The $150,000 salvage is a positive cash flow in year 6. CFBT is calculated by

$$CFBT = GI - E - P + S \qquad [16.9]$$

In year 6, for example,

$$CFBT_6 = 200,000 - 90,000 + 150,000 = \$260,000$$

TABLE 16–3 Computation of CFBT Using CCA Depreciation and a 35% Effective Tax Rate, Example 16.2

Year	GI	E	P and S	CFBT
			(550,000)	(550,000)
1	200,000	(90,000)		110,000
2	200,000	(90,000)		110,000
3	200,000	(90,000)		110,000
4	200,000	(90,000)		110,000
5	200,000	(90,000)		110,000
6	200,000	(90,000)	150,000	260,000

CFAT
Cash flow after taxes for Example 16.2, in the format of Table 16–2, is illustrated in Table 16–4. Calculations for the column headings for year 4 are the following:

$$UCC_n = P(1 - d/2)(1 - d)^{n-1} \qquad [16.3]$$

$$UCC_4 = 550,000(1 - 0.30/2)(1 - 0.30)^3$$

$$= 160,353$$

$$CCA_n = Pd(1 - d/2)(1 - d)^{n-2} \qquad [16.2]$$

$$CCA_4 = (550,000)(0.30)(1 - 0.30/2)(1 - 0.30)^2$$

$$= 68,723$$

$$TI = GI - E - CCA \qquad [16.4]$$

$$TI_4 = 200,000 - 90,000 - 68,723$$

$$= 41,277$$

$$Taxes = (TI)(T) \qquad [16.5]$$

$$Taxes_4 = (41,277)(0.35)$$

$$= 14,447$$

$$CFAT = GI - E - P + S - taxes \qquad [16.11]$$

$$CFAT_4 = 200,000 - 90,000 - 14,447$$

$$= 95,553$$

TABLE 16–4   Computation of CFAT Using CCA Depreciation and a 35% Effective Tax Rate, Example 16.2

Year	GI	E	P and S	UCC	CCA	TI	Taxes	CFAT
0			(550,000)	(550,000)				(550,000)
1	200,000	(90,000)		467,500	82,500	27,500	9,625	100,375
2	200,000	(90,000)		327,250	140,250	(30,250)[a]	(10,588)	120,588
3	200,000	(90,000)		229,075	98,175	11,825	4,139	105,861
4	200,000	(90,000)		160,353	68,723	41,277	14,447	95,553
5	200,000	(90,000)		112,247	48,106	61,894	21,663	88,337
6	200,000	(90,000)	150,000	0	(37,753)[b]	147,753	51,714	58,286

[a]In year 2, CCA is large enough to cause TI to be negative ($-30,250$). As mentioned above, the negative tax ($-10,588$) is considered to be a *tax savings* in year 2, increasing CFAT.

[b]In year 6, the machinery has sold for more than the UCC in this class, indicating too much depreciation has been claimed. The CRA requires the recapture of this difference ($37,753$) between salvage value and the UCC, as explained further in the next section.

16.3 DEPRECIATION RECAPTURE, CAPITAL GAINS, AND TERMINAL LOSSES: FOR CORPORATIONS

All the tax implications discussed here are the result of disposing of a depreciable asset before, at, or after its useful life. In an after-tax economic analysis of large investment assets, these tax effects should be considered. The key is the size of the salvage value (or selling price or market value) relative to the book value, or undepreciated capital cost (UCC), at disposal time, and relative to the cost basis. There are three relevant terms.

FIGURE 16–1

Summary of calculations and tax treatment for depreciation recapture, capital gains, and terminal losses.

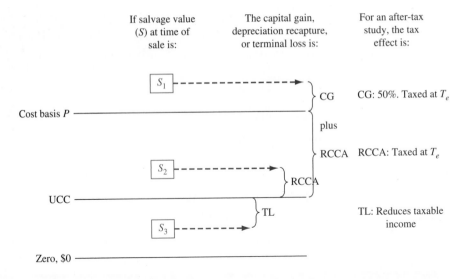

Capital gain (CG) is an amount incurred when the salvage value exceeds its cost basis. See Figure 16–1. At the time of asset disposal,

$$\text{Capital gain} = \text{salvage value} - \text{cost basis}$$

$$CG = S - P \qquad [16.12]$$

Since future capital gains are difficult to predict, they are usually not detailed in an after-tax economy study. An exception is for assets that historically increase in value, such as buildings and land. *Under current tax rules, 50% of the gain is taxed as ordinary taxable income at the effective tax rate T_e.*

Recapture of CCA (RCCA) or *depreciation recapture*, occurs when a depreciable asset is sold for more than the UCC, or book value. As shown in Figure 16–1,

$$\text{Recapture of CCA} = \text{salvage value} - \text{UCC}$$

$$RCCA = S - UCC \qquad [16.13]$$

The amount is treated as taxable income in the year of asset disposal.

When the salvage value exceeds the cost basis, a capital gain is also incurred and the TI due to the sale is 50% of the gain *plus* the depreciation recapture, as shown in Figure 16–1.

Terminal loss (TL) occurs when a depreciable asset is disposed of for less than its undepreciated capital cost.

$$\text{Terminal loss} = \text{UCC} - \text{salvage value}$$

$$TL = UCC - S \qquad [16.14]$$

The full amount of a terminal loss may be deducted from gross income in the year the property was disposed.

An economic analysis does not commonly account for terminal loss, simply because it is not estimable for a specific alternative. However, an

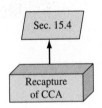

after-tax replacement study may account for a terminal loss if the defender must be traded at a "sacrifice" price. For the purposes of the economic study, this provides a tax savings in the year of replacement. Use the effective tax rate to estimate the tax savings.

After-tax replacement

Sec. 16.5

For most after-tax studies, it is *sufficient to apply the effective tax rate T_e to the* alternative's TI in the year that the RCCA, CG, or TL occurs, with a tax savings generated by the TL.

Equation [16.4] and the expression for TI in Equation [16.11] can now be expanded to include the additional cash flow estimates for asset disposal:

TI = gross income − expenses − CCA + recaptured CCA
+ 0.5 capital gain − terminal loss

$$TI = GI - E - CCA + RCCA + 0.5CG - TL \qquad [16.15]$$

It is important to realize that this description and this tax treatment simplifies and magnifies the tax effects of disposing of a particular depreciable asset. Because assets are pooled in classes, the disposal of a particular property does not usually deplete an entire asset class. With the exception of when an asset is sold for more than its original cost, gains and losses disappear into the pool of undepreciated capital costs, making the calculation of tax effects of disposal difficult. Therefore, engineering economic analysis assumes that the tax ramifications of the disposal of an asset are completely realized in the year of the disposal and that the CCA in the year of disposal is calculated before consideration of the disposal.

EXAMPLE 16.3

Biotech, a medical imaging and modelling company, must purchase a bone cell analysis system (CCA Class 8, 20%) for use by a team of bioengineers and mechanical engineers studying bone density in athletes. This particular part of a 3-year contract with the NHL will provide additional gross income of $100,000 per year. The effective tax rate is 35%. Estimates for two alternatives are summarized below.

	Analyzer 1	Analyzer 2
Cost basis, $	150,000	225,000
Operating expenses, $ per year	30,000	10,000

Answer the following questions.

(*a*) The Biotech president, who is very tax-conscious, wishes to use a criterion of minimizing total taxes incurred over the 3 years of the contract. Which analyzer should be purchased?

(*b*) Assume that 3 years have now passed, and the company is about to sell the analyzer. Using the same total tax criterion, did either analyzer have an advantage? Assume the selling price is $130,000 for analyzer 1, or $225,000 for analyzer 2, the same as its cost basis.

Solution

(*a*) Table 16–5 details the tax computations. First, the yearly UCC and capital cost allowance are determined. Equation [16.4], TI = GI − E − CCA, is used to calculate TI, after which the 35% tax rate is applied each year. Taxes for the 3-year period are summed, with no consideration of the time value of money.

Analyzer 1 tax total: $51,240   Analyzer 2 tax total: $57,400

The two analyzers are close, but analyzer 1 wins with $6160 less in total taxes.

(*b*) When the analyzer is sold after 3 years of service, there is a recapture of CCA that is taxed at the 35% rate. For each analyzer, account for the RCCA by Equation [16.13]; then determine the TI, using Equation [16.15], TI = GI − E − CCA + RCCA. Again, find the total taxes for 3 years, and select the analyzer with the smaller total.

TABLE 16–5 Comparison of Total Taxes for Two Alternatives ($), Example 16.3(*a*)

Analyzer 1

Year	GI	E	P and S	UCC	CCA	TI	Taxes
0			(150,000)	(150,000)			
1	100,000	(30,000)		135,000	15,000	55,000	19,250
2	100,000	(30,000)		108,000	27,000	43,000	15,050
3	100,000	(30,000)		86,400	21,600	48,400	16,940
Total							$51,240

Analyzer 2

Year	GI	E	P and S	UCC	CCA	TI	Taxes
0			(225,000)				
1	100,000	(10,000)		225,000	25,000	65,000	22,750
2	100,000	(10,000)		180,000	45,000	45,000	15,750
3	100,000	(10,000)		144,000	36,000	54,000	18,900
Total							$57,400

Analyzer 1

$$\text{RCCA} = S - \text{UCC} \qquad [16.13]$$
$$= 130,000 - 86,400$$
$$= 43,600$$

$$\text{TI}_3 = \text{GI} - E - \text{CCA} + \text{RCCA} \qquad [16.15]$$
$$= 100,000 - 30,000 - 21,600 + 43,600$$
$$= \$92,000$$

$$\text{Taxes} = (\text{TI})(T) \qquad [16.5]$$
$$\text{Year 3 taxes} = 92,000(0.35)$$
$$= \$32,200$$
$$\text{Total taxes} = 19,250 + 15,050 + 32,200 = \$66,500$$

Analyzer 2

$$RCCA = 225,000 - 144,000$$

$$= \$81,000$$

$$TI_3 = 100,000 - 10,000 - 36,000 + 81,000$$

$$= \$135,000$$

$$\text{Year 3 taxes} = 135,000(0.35)$$

$$= \$47,250$$

$$\text{Total taxes} = 22,750 + 15,750 + 47,250 = \$85,750$$

Now, analyzer 1 has a considerable advantage in total taxes ($66,500 versus $85,750).

Comment

Note that no time value of money is considered in these analyses, as we have used in previous alternative evaluations. In the next Section we will rely upon PW, AW, and ROR analyses at an established MARR to make an after-tax decision based upon CFAT values.

16.4 AFTER-TAX PW, AW, AND ROR EVALUATION

The required after-tax MARR is established using the market interest rate, the corporation's effective tax rate, and its average cost of capital. The CFAT estimates are used to compute the PW or AW at the after-tax MARR. When positive and negative CFAT values are present, the result of PW or AW < 0 indicates the MARR is not met. For a single project or mutually exclusive alternative selection, apply the same logic as in Chapters 5 and 6. The guidelines are as follows:

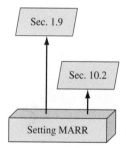

One project. PW or AW ≥ 0, the project is financially viable because the after-tax MARR is met or exceeded.

Two or more alternatives. Select the alternative with the best (numerically largest) PW or AW value.

If only cost CFAT amounts are estimated, calculate the after-tax savings generated by the operating expenses and depreciation. Assign a plus sign to each saving and apply the selection guideline above.

Remember, the equal-service assumption requires that the PW analysis be performed over the least common multiple (LCM) of alternative lives. This requirement must be met for every analysis—before or after taxes.

Since the CFAT estimates usually vary from year to year in an after-tax evaluation, the spreadsheet offers a much speedier analysis than solution by hand. *For AW analysis*, use PMT with an embedded NPV function *over one life cycle* of the alternative. The general format is as follows, with the NPV function all in italics.

$$PMT(MARR, n, NPV(MARR, year\_1\_CFAT: year\_n\_CFAT) + year\_0\_CFAT)$$

For PW analysis, obtain the PMT function results first, followed by the PV function taken over the alternatives' LCM. (There is an LCM function in Excel.) The cell containing the PMT function result is entered as the A value. The general format is

$$PV(MARR, LCM\_years, PMT\_result\_cell)$$

EXAMPLE 16.4

Paul is designing the interior walls of an industrial building. In some places, it is important to reduce noise transmission across the wall. Two construction options—stucco on metal lath (S) and bricks (B)—each have about the same transmission loss, approximately 33 decibels. This will reduce noise attenuation costs in adjacent office areas. Paul has estimated the first costs and after-tax savings each year for both designs. Use the CFAT values and an after-tax MARR of 7% per year to determine which is economically better. Solve both by hand and by computer.

Plan S		Plan B	
Year	CFAT	Year	CFAT
0	$-28,800	0	$-50,000
1–6	5,400	1	14,200
7–10	2,040	2	13,300
10	2,792	3	12,400
		4	11,500
		5	10,600

Solution by Hand
In this example, both AW and PW analyses are shown. Develop the AW relations using the CFAT values over each plan's life. Select the larger value.

$$AW_S = [-28,800 + 5400(P/A,7\%,6) + 2040(P/A,7\%,4)(P/F,7\%,6)$$
$$+ 2792(P/F,7\%,10)](A/P,7\%,10)$$
$$= \$422$$
$$AW_B = [-50,000 + 14,200(P/F,7\%,1) + \cdots + 10,600(P/F,7\%,5)](A/P,7\%,5)$$
$$= \$327$$

Both plans are financially viable; select plan S because AW_S is larger.

For the PW analysis, the LCM is 10 years. Use the AW values and the P/A factor for the LCM of 10 years to select stucco on metal lath, plan S.

$$PW_S = AW_S(P/A,7\%,10) = 422(7.0236) = \$2964$$

$$PW_B = AW_B(P/A,7\%,10) = 327(7.0236) = \$2297$$

Solution by Computer

The AW and PW values are displayed in rows 17 and 18 of Figure 16–2. The functions have been set up differently here than in previous examples because of the unequal lives. Follow along in the cell tags, which are shown in the order of development for each alternative.

	A	B	C	D	E	F	G	H
1								
2	After-tax MARR =		7%					
3								
4		Plan S	Plan B					
5	Year	CFAT	CFAT					
6	0	$(28,800)	$(50,000)					
7	1	$ 5,400	$ 14,200					
8	2	$ 5,400	$ 13,300					
9	3	$ 5,400	$ 12,400					
10	4	$ 5,400	$ 11,500					
11	5	$ 5,400	$ 10,600					
12	6	$ 5,400		= NPV($C$2,B7:B16)+B6				
13	7	$ 2,040						
14	8	$ 2,040	= PMT($C$2,10, –B18)					
15	9	$ 2,040						
16	10	$ 4,832						
17	AW values	$422	$327	= PMT($C$2,5, –(NPV($C$2,C7:C11)+C6))				
18	PW values	$ 2,963	$2,297	= PV($C$2,10, –C17)				
19								

FIGURE 16–2
After-tax PW and AW evaluation, Example 16.4.

For plan S, first the NPV function in B18 is developed for PW, followed by the PMT function in B17 for the AW value. Note the minus sign in PMT to ensure that the function results in the correct sign on the PW value. This is not necessary for the NPV function, because it takes the cash flow sign from the cell entry itself.

The opposite order of function development is used for plan B. The PMT in C17 uses an embedded NPV function over the 5-year life. Again, note the minus sign. Finally, the PV function in C18 displays the PW value over 10 years.

Comment
It is important to remember the minus signs in PMT and PV functions when utilizing them to obtain the corresponding PW and AW values, respectively. If the minus is omitted, the AW and PW values are the opposite of the correct cash flow direction. Then it may appear that the plans are not financially viable in that they do not return at least the after-tax MARR. This is what would happen in this example. However, we know they are financially viable, based on the previous solution by hand. (Refer to Excel online help for more details on sign convention in PMT, PV, and NPV functions.)

To utilize the *ROR method* apply exactly the same procedures as in Chapter 7 (single project) and Chapter 8 (two or more alternatives) to the CFAT series. A PW or AW relation is developed to estimate the rate of return i^* for a project, or Δi^* for the incremental CFAT between two alternatives. Multiple roots may exist in the CFAT series, as they can for any cash flow series. For a single project, set the PW or AW equal to zero and solve for i^*.

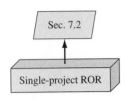

Present worth : $0 = \sum_{t=1}^{t=n} \text{CFAT}_t(P/F, i^*, t)$ [16.16]

Annual worth : $0 = \sum_{t=1}^{t=n} \text{CFAT}_t(P/F, i^*, t)(A/P, i^*, n)$ [16.17]

E-SOLVE

Spreadsheet solution for i^* may be helpful for relatively complex CFAT series. It is performed using the IRR function with the general format

$$\text{IRR(year\_0\_CFAT:year\_n\_CFAT)}$$

If the after-tax ROR is important to the analysis, but the details of an after-tax study are not of interest, the before-tax ROR (or MARR) can be adjusted with the effective tax rate T_e using the *approximating* relation

$$\textbf{Before-tax ROR} = \frac{\textbf{after-tax ROR}}{1 - T_e} \qquad [16.18]$$

For example, assume a company has an effective tax rate of 40% and normally uses an after-tax MARR of 12% per year for economic analyses that consider taxes explicitly. To *approximate* the effect of taxes without performing the details of an after-tax study, the before-tax MARR can be estimated as

$$\text{Before-tax MARR} = \frac{0.12}{1 - 0.40} = 20\% \text{ per year}$$

If the decision concerns the economic viability of a project, and the resulting PW or AW value is close to zero, the details of an after-tax analysis should be developed.

EXAMPLE 16.5

A fibre optics manufacturing company operating in Hong Kong using straight line depreciation has spent $50,000 for a 5-year-life machine that has a projected $20,000 annual CFBT and annual depreciation (D) of $10,000. The company has a T_e of 40%. (*a*) Determine the after-tax rate of return. (*b*) Approximate the before-tax return.

Solution

(*a*) The CFAT in year 0 is $-50,000. For years 1 through 5, combine Equations [16.10] and [16.11] to estimate the CFAT.

$$\text{CFAT} = \text{CFBT} - \text{taxes} = \text{CFBT} - (\text{GI} - E - D)(T_e)$$

$$= 20,000 - (20,000 - 10,000)(0.40)$$

$$= \$16,000$$

Since the CFAT for years 1 through 5 has the same value, use the P/A factor in Equation [16.16]

$$0 = -50,000 + 16,000(P/A,i^*,5)$$

$$(P/A,i^*,5) = 3.125$$

Solution gives $i^* = 18.03\%$ as the after-tax rate of return.

(b) Use Equation [16.18] for the before-tax return estimate.

$$\text{Before-tax ROR} = \frac{0.1803}{1 - 0.40} = 30.05\%$$

The actual before-tax i^* using CFBT = \$20,000 for 5 years is 28.65% from the relation

$$0 = -50,000 + 20,000(P/A,i^*,5)$$

The tax effect will be slightly overestimated if a MARR of 30.05% is used in a before-tax analysis.

A rate of return evaluation performed by hand on two or more alternatives must utilize a PW or AW relation to determine the incremental return Δi^* of the incremental CFAT series between two alternatives. Solution by computer is accomplished using the incremental CFAT values and the IRR function. The equations and procedures applied are the same as in Chapter 8 for selection from mutually exclusive alternatives using the ROR method. You should review and understand the following sections before proceeding further with this section.

Section 8.4   ROR evaluation using PW: incremental and breakeven
Section 8.5   ROR evaluation using AW
Section 8.6   Incremental ROR analysis of multiple, mutually exclusive alternatives

From this review, several important facts should be recalled:

Selection guideline: The fundamental rule of incremental ROR evaluation at a stated MARR is as follows:

Select the one alternative that requires the largest initial investment, provided the extra investment is justified relative to another justified alternative.

Incremental ROR: Incremental analysis must be performed. Overall i^* values cannot be depended upon to select the correct alternative, unlike the PW or AW method at the MARR, which will always indicate the correct alternative.

Equal-service assumption: Incremental ROR analysis requires that the alternatives be evaluated over equal time periods. The LCM of the two alternative lives must be used to find the PW or AW of incremental cash flows. (The only exception, mentioned in Section 8.5, occurs when the AW analysis is performed on *actual cash flows, not the increments*; then one-life-cycle analysis is acceptable over the respective alternative lives.)

Revenue and service alternatives: Revenue alternatives (positive and negative cash flows) may be treated differently from service alternatives (cost-only cash flow estimates). For revenue alternatives, the overall i^* may be used to perform an initial screening. Alternatives that have $i^* <$ MARR can be removed from further evaluation. An i^* for cost-only (service) alternatives cannot be determined, so incremental analysis is required with all alternatives included.

These principles and the same procedures developed in Chapter 8 are applied to the CFAT series. The summary table at the back of this book (which is also Table 10–2) details the requirements of all evaluation techniques. For the ROR method, in the column labelled "Series to Evaluate" change the words *cash flows* to *CFAT values*. Additionally, use the after-tax MARR as the decision guideline (far right column). Now, all entries for the ROR method are correct for an after-tax analysis.

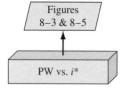

Once the CFAT series are developed, the *breakeven ROR* can be obtained using a plot of PW vs. i^*. Solution of the PW relation for each alternative over the LCM at several interest rates can be accomplished by hand or by using the NPV spreadsheet function. For any after-tax MARR greater than the breakeven ROR, the extra investment is not justified.

Example 16.6 illustrates an after-tax ROR evaluation of two alternatives solved by hand.

EXAMPLE 16.6

Johnson Controls must decide between two alternatives in its Kitchener, Ont., plant: system 1—a single robot assembly system for ICs will require a $100,000 investment now; and system 2—a combination of two robots requires a total of $130,000. Management intends to implement one of the plans. This manufacturer expects a 20% after-tax return on technology investments. Select one of the systems, if the following series of cost CFAT values have been estimated for the next 4 years.

			Year		
	0	1	2	3	4
System 1 CFAT, $	$-100,000$	$-35,000$	$-30,000$	$-20,000$	$-15,000$
System 2 CFAT, $	$-130,000$	$-20,000$	$-20,000$	$-10,000$	$-5,000$

Solution

System 2 is the alternative with the extra investment that must be justified. Since lives are equal, select PW analysis to estimate Δi^* for the incremental CFAT series shown here. All cash flows have been divided by $1000.

Year	0	1	2	3	4
Incremental CFAT, $1000	-30	$+15$	$+10$	$+10$	$+10$

A PW relation is set up to estimate the after-tax incremental return.

$$-30 + 15(P/F,\Delta i^*,1) + 10(P/A,\Delta i^*,3)(P/F,\Delta i^*,1) = 0$$

Solution indicates an incremental after-tax return of 20.10%, which just exceeds the 20% MARR. The extra investment in system 2 is marginally justified.

16.5 AFTER-TAX REPLACEMENT STUDY

When a currently installed asset (the defender) is challenged with possible replacement, the effect of taxes can have an impact upon the decision of the replacement study. The final decision may not be reversed by taxes, but the difference between before-tax AW values may be significantly different from the after-tax difference. There may be tax considerations in the year of the possible replacement due to *depreciation recapture or capital gain*, or there may be tax savings due to a sizable terminal loss, if it is necessary to trade the defender at a sacrifice price. Additionally, the after-tax replacement study considers tax-deductible *depreciation* and *operating expenses* not accounted for in a before-tax analysis. The effective tax rate T_e is used to estimate the amount of annual taxes (or tax savings) from TI. The same procedure as the before-tax replacement study in Chapter 11 is applied here, but for CFAT estimates. The procedure should be thoroughly understood before proceeding. Special attention to Sections 11.3 and 11.5 is recommended.

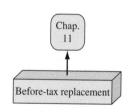

Example 16.7 presents a solution of an after-tax replacement study using a simplifying assumption of classical SL (straight line) depreciation.

EXAMPLE 16.7

Syncrude Corp. purchased bitumen extraction equipment 3 years ago for $600,000. Management has discovered that it is technologically outdated now. New equipment for steam injection in wells to recover bitumen has been identified. If the market value of $400,000 is offered as the trade-in for the current equipment, perform a replacement study using (*a*) a before-tax MARR of 10% per year and (*b*) a 7% per year after-tax MARR. Assume an effective tax rate of 34%. As a simplifying assumption, use classical straight line depreciation with $S = 0$ for both alternatives.

	Defender	Challenger
Market value, $	400,000	
Cost basis, $		1,000,000
Annual cost, $/year	−100,000	−15,000
Useful life, years	8 (originally)	5

Solution

Assume that an ESL (economic service life) analysis has determined the best life values to be 5 more years for the defender and 5 years total for the challenger.

(*a*) For the *before-tax replacement study*, find the AW values. The defender AW uses the market value as the cost basis, $P_D = \$-400,000$.

$$AW_D = -400,000(A/P,10\%,5) - 100,000 = \$-205,520$$

$$AW_C = -1,000,000(A/P,10\%,5) - 15,000 = \$-278,800$$

Applying step 1 of the replacement study procedure (Section 11.3), we select the better AW value. The defender is retained now with a plan to keep it for the 5 remaining years. The defender has a $73,280 lower equivalent annual cost compared to the challenger. This complete solution is included in Table 16–6 (left panel) for comparison with the after-tax study.

(b) For the *after-tax replacement study*, there are no tax effects other than income tax for the defender. The annual SL depreciation is $75,000, determined when the equipment was purchased 3 years ago.

$$D_t = 600,000/8 = \$75,000 \qquad t = 1 \text{ to } 8 \text{ years}$$

Table 16–6 shows the TI and taxes at 34%. The taxes are actually tax savings of $59,500 per year, as indicated by the minus sign. (Remember that for tax savings in an economic analysis it is assumed there is positive taxable income elsewhere in the corporation to offset the saving.) Since only costs are estimated, the annual CFAT is negative, but the $59,500 tax savings has reduced it. The CFAT and AW at 7% per year are

$$\text{CFAT} = \text{CFBT} - \text{taxes} = -100,000 - (-59,500) = \$-40,500$$

$$\text{AW}_D = -400,000(A/P,7\%,5) - 40,500 = \$-138,056$$

For the challenger, depreciation recapture on the defender occurs when it is replaced, because the trade-in amount of $400,000 is larger than the current book value.

TABLE 16–6   Before-Tax and After-Tax Replacement Analyses, Example 16.7

Defender Age	Year	Expenses E	P and S	CFBT	Depreciation D	Taxable Income TI	Taxes* at 0.34TI	CFAT
			Before Taxes			**After Taxes**		
				DEFENDER				
3	0		$-400,000	$-400,000				$-400,000
4	1	$-100,000		-100,000	$75,000	$-175,000	$-59,500	-40,500
5	2	-100,000		-100,000	75,000	-175,000	-59,500	-40,500
6	3	-100,000		-100,000	75,000	-175,000	-59,500	-40,500
7	4	-100,000		-100,000	75,000	-175,000	-59,500	-40,500
8	5	-100,000	0	-100,000	75,000	-175,000	-59,500	-40,500
AW at 10%				$-205,520	AW at 7%			$-138,056
				CHALLENGER				
	0		$-1,000,000	$-1,000,000		$+25,000†	$ 8,500	$-1,008,500
	1	$-15,000		-15,000	$200,000	-215,000	-73,100	+58,100
	2	-15,000		-15,000	200,000	-215,000	-73,100	+58,100
	3	-15,000		-15,000	200,000	-215,000	-73,100	+58,100
	4	-15,000		-15,000	200,000	-215,000	-73,100	+58,100
	5	-15,000	0	-15,000	200,000	-215,000‡	-73,100	+58,100
AW at 10%				$ -278,800	AW at 7%			$ -187,863

*Minus sign indicates a tax savings for the year.
†Depreciation recapture on defender trade-in.
‡Assumes challenger's salvage actually realized is $S = 0$; no tax.

In year 0 for the challenger, Table 16–6 includes the following computations to arrive at a tax of $8500.

Defender book value, year 3: $\quad BV_3 = 600,000 - 3(75,000) = \$375,000$

Depreciation recapture: $\quad DR_3 = TI = 400,000 - 375,000 = \$25,000$

Taxes on the trade-in, year 0: $\quad$ Taxes $= 0.34(25,000) = \$8500$

The SL depreciation is $\$1,000,000/5 = \$200,000$ per year. This results in tax savings and CFAT as follows:

$$\text{Taxes} = (-15,000 - 200,000)(0.34) = \$-73,100$$

$$\text{CFAT} = \text{CFBT} - \text{taxes} = -15,000 - (-73,100) = \$+58,100$$

In year 5, it is assumed the challenger is sold for $0; there is no depreciation recapture. The AW for the challenger at the 7% after-tax MARR is

$$AW_C = -1,000,000(A/P,7\%,5) + 58,100 = \$-187,863$$

The defender is again selected; however, the equivalent annual advantage has decreased from $73,280 before taxes to $49,807 after taxes.

Conclusion: By either analysis, retain the defender now and plan to keep it for 5 more years. Additionally, plan to evaluate the estimates for both alternatives 1 year hence. If and when cash flow estimates change significantly, perform another replacement analysis.

Comment

If the market value (trade-in) had been less than the current defender book value of $375,000, a terminal loss, rather than depreciation recapture, would occur in year 0. The resulting tax savings would decrease the CFAT (which is to reduce costs if CFAT is negative). For example, a trade-in amount of $350,000 would result in a TI of $350,000 - 375,000 = \$-25,000$ and a tax savings of $\$-8500$ in year 0. The CFAT is then $\$-1,000,000 - (-8500) = \$-991,500$.

16.6 CAPITAL COST TAX FACTORS

A coefficient called the *capital cost tax factor (CCTF)* calculates the present worth of a corporation's tax savings when using CCA based on a declining balance basis. Depreciation calculated with the straight-line method creates a uniform series of cash flows and leads to a direct calculation of the present worth. In Canada, the DB method can lead to laborious calculations, because the depreciation value changes every year as it is based on a fixed percentage.

To simplify the PW calculation, capital cost tax factors are employed. Implicit in the calculation is the economic impact of CCA depreciation including the 50% rule, the impact of taxes, and the consequences to taxes from the asset's salvage value. The CCTF for an asset ($CCTF_A$) provides an efficient means of calculating the PW of an asset while considering the benefits of tax savings throughout the life of the asset.

$$CCTF_A = (1 - td)(1 + i/2)/(i + d)(1 + i)$$

$$t = \text{corporate tax rate}$$

$$d = \text{CCA class rate}$$

$$i = \text{after-tax MARR}$$

To calculate the present worth of the after-tax cost basis (P) of an asset with all tax benefits from depreciation accounted for:

$$PW = (CCTF_A)(P)$$

When an asset is sold (assuming there are no new purchases within the same CCA class for that year), the salvage value is subtracted from the undepreciated capital cost (UCC) and therefore reduces future tax savings that this asset would have generated according to the declining balance basis. The CCTF for the salvage value ($CCTF_S$) is calculated as

$$CCTF_S = (1 - td)/(i + d)$$

Therefore, the present worth calculation of an asset's salvage is

$$PW = (CCTF_S)(P)$$

When the asset generates additional expenses or income, the after-tax MARR evaluation will also include these items. Each cash flow is multiplied by $(1 - t)$ to reduce them by the tax rate. They are then converted to their present worth.

EXAMPLE 16.8

Discovery Helicopters of Yellowknife is considering the purchase of a $10 million helicopter for servicing the growing mining and energy sectors in Canada's North. The CCA for the Class 9 asset is 25%. The company estimates a salvage value of $650,000 after a 10-year life. It is estimated that chartering the helicopter will result in an income of $5,000,000 annually. Assume a corporate tax rate of 40% and an after-tax MARR of 10%. What is the present worth of the cost basis of the helicopter if future tax savings resulting from depreciation is considered?

Solution
Purchase cost:

$$CCTF_A = 1 - (0.40)(0.25)(1 + 0.10/2)/(0.10 + 0.25)(1 + 0.10)$$

$$= 0.72$$

The present worth of the cost basis is then

$$PW_{\text{purchase cost}} = (0.72)(-10,000,000)$$

$$= -\$7,200,000$$

Revenue:

The expected revenue stream results in a present worth of

$$PW_{revenue} = 5,000,000(1 - t)(P/A,10\%,10)$$

$$= 5,000,000(1 - 0.40)(6.1446)$$

$$= 18,433,800$$

Salvage:

$$CCTF_S = 1 - (0.40)(0.25)/(0.10 + 0.25)$$

$$= 0.71$$

Converting to PW from $n = 10$ yields

$$PW_{salvage} = 650,000(0.71)(P/F,10\%,10)$$

$$= 650,000(0.71)(0.38554)$$

$$= \$177,927$$

Total:

$$PW_{total} = PW_{purchase\ cost} + PW_{revenue} + PW_{salvage}$$

$$= -7,200,000 + 18,433,800 + 177,927$$

$$= \$11,411,727$$

In terms of the opportunity to purchase the helicopter as an asset, this calculation indicates that the company will realize an $11.412 million positive present worth.

CHAPTER SUMMARY

After-tax analysis does not usually change the decision to select one alternative over another; however, it does offer a much clearer estimate of the monetary impact of taxes. After-tax PW, AW, and ROR evaluations of one or more alternatives are performed on the CFAT series using exactly the same procedures as in previous chapters. The after-tax MARR is used in all PW and AW computations, and in deciding between two or more alternatives using incremental ROR analysis.

In Canada, income tax rates for individual taxpayers are graduated—higher taxable incomes pay higher income taxes. But corporate taxes do not increase with higher earnings; the tax rates depend on characteristics of the corporation. A single-value, effective tax rate T_e is usually applied in an after-tax economic analysis. Taxes are reduced because of tax-deductible items, such as depreciation and operating expenses. Because depreciation is a noncash flow, it is important to consider depreciation only in the TI computations, and not directly in the CFBT and CFAT calculations. Accordingly, key general cash flow after-tax relations for each year are

$$\text{CFBT} = \text{gross income} - \text{expenses} - \text{initial investment} + \text{salvage value}$$

$$\text{CFAT} = \text{CFBT} - \text{taxes} = \text{CFBT} - (\text{taxable income})(T_e)$$

$$\text{TI} = \text{gross income} - \text{expenses} - \text{depreciation} + \text{depreciation recapture}$$

In a replacement study, the tax impact of depreciation recapture or terminal loss, either of which may occur when the defender is traded for the challenger, is accounted for in an after-tax analysis. The replacement study procedure of Chapter 11 is applied. The tax analysis may not reverse the decision to replace or retain the defender, but the effect of taxes will likely reduce (possibly by a significant amount) the economic advantage of one alternative over the other.

Capital cost tax factors are employed in Canada to calculate the economic impact of CCA depreciation. The CCTF for an asset $(\text{CCTF}_A) = (1 - td)(1 + i/2)/(i + d)(1 + i)$ where t is the corporate tax rate, d is the CCA class rate, and i is the after-tax MARR. The CCTF for the salvage value $(\text{CCTF}_S) = (1 - td)/(i + d)$.

PROBLEMS

Basic Tax Computations

16.1 Write the equation to calculate TI and NPAT for a corporation, using only the following terms: *gross income, tax rate, business expenses, and depreciation.*

16.2 Describe the basic difference between an *income tax* and a *property tax* for an individual.

16.3 From the following list, select the tax-related term that is best described by each event below: *depreciation, operating expense, taxable income, income tax, or net profit after taxes.*

(a) A corporation reports that it had a negative $200,000 net profit on its annual income statement.

(b) An asset with a current book value of $80,000 was utilized on a new processing line to increase sales by $200,000 this year.

(c) A machine has an annual, straight line write-off equal to $21,000.

(d) The cost to maintain equipment during the past year was $3,680,200.

(e) A particular supermarket collected $23,550 in lottery ticket sales last year. Based on winnings paid to individuals holding these tickets, a rebate of $250 was sent to the store manager.

16.4 Two companies have the following values on their annual tax returns.

	Company 1	Company 2
Sales revenue, $	1,500,000	820,000
Interest revenue, $	31,000	25,000
Expenses, $	−754,000	−591,000
Depreciation, $	148,000	18,000

Estimate the taxes for each company using an effective rate of 34% of the entire TI.

16.5 Yamachi and Nadler have a gross income of $6.5 million for the year. CCA and expenses total $4.1 million. If the provincial tax rate is 7.6%, use a federal rate of 34% to estimate the income taxes, using the effective tax rate equation.

CFBT and CFAT

16.6 What is the basic difference between cash flow after taxes (CFAT) and net profit after taxes (NPAT)?

16.7 Derive a general relation for calculating CFAT under the situation that there is no annual depreciation to deduct and it is a year in which no investment P or salvage S occurs.

16.8 Where is depreciation considered in the CFBT and CFAT expressions used to analyze an engineering economy alternative's cash flow estimates?

16.9 Four years ago ABB purchased an asset for $300,000 (CCA Class 43, 30%). The following annual gross incomes and expenses were recorded. The asset was sold for $60,000 after 4 years.
  (a) Tabulate the cash flows by hand after an effective 32% tax rate is applied. Use the format of Table 16–2.
  (b) Continue the table above and calculate the net income (NI) estimates.
  (c) Determine the annual CFAT and NI values and plot these values versus year of ownership.

Year of Ownership	1	2	3	4
Gross income, $	80,000	150,000	120,000	100,000
Expenses, $	−20,000	−40,000	−30,000	−50,000

16.10 Four years ago Hartcourt-Banks purchased an asset for $200,000 (CCA Class 10, 30%). The following gross incomes and expenses were recorded, and an effective tax rate of 40% was applied. Tabulate CFAT under the assumption that the asset was (a) discarded for $0 after 4 years and (b) sold for $20,000 after 4 years. For this tabulation only, neglect any taxes that may be incurred on the sale of the asset.

Year of Ownership	1	2	3	4
Gross income, $	80,000	150,000	120,000	100,000
Expenses, $	−20,000	−40,000	−30,000	−50,000

16.11 A petroleum engineer with Halstrom Exploration must estimate the minimum required cash flow before taxes if the CFAT is $2,000,000. The effective federal tax rate is 35%, and the provincial tax rate is 4.5%. A total of $1 million in CCA will be charged this year. Estimate the required CFBT.

16.12 A division of Magna International Inc. has the following data at the end of a year.

$$\text{Total revenue} = \$48 \text{ million}$$
$$\text{CCA} = \$8.2 \text{ million}$$
$$\text{Operating expenses} = \$28 \text{ million}$$

For an effective federal tax rate of 35% and provincial tax rate of 6.5%, determine (a) CFAT, (b) percentage of total revenue expended on taxes, and (c) net income for the year.

16.13 Morgan Solar, a Toronto-based developer of solar power technologies, is preparing to expand production of their Sun Simba Concentrating PhotoVoltaic system. To recover the investment, an annual $2.5 million CFAT is needed. Federal taxes are expected to be 20% and provincial taxes will be 8% of TI. Over a 3-year period, deductible expenses and CCA depreciation are estimated to total $1.3 million for the first year, increasing by $500,000 per year thereafter. Of this, 50% is expenses and 50% CCA depreciation. What is the required gross income for each of the 3 years?

16.14 Couche-Tard Distribution Centres has put into service forklifts and conveyors purchased for $250,000. Tabulate the CFBT, CFAT, and NPAT for 6 years of ownership, using an effective tax rate of 40% and the estimated cash flow and depreciation amounts shown. Salvage is expected to be zero.

Year	Gross Income, $	Operating Expenses, $	CCA Depreciation, $
1	90,000	−20,000	50,000
2	100,000	−20,000	80,000
3	60,000	−22,000	48,000
4	60,000	−24,000	28,800
5	60,000	−26,000	28,800
6	40,000	−28,000	14,400

16.15 A highway construction company purchased pipeline boring equipment for $80,000 (CCA Class 8, 20%). It produced annual $GI − E$ amounts of $50,000, which were taxed at an effective 38%. The company decided to prematurely sell the equipment after 2 full years of use.

(a) Find the price if the company wants to sell it for exactly the amount reflected by the current UCC value.

(b) Determine the CFAT values if the equipment was actually sold after 2 years for the amount determined in part (a) and no replacement was acquired.

Depreciation Recapture, Capital Gains, and Terminal Losses

16.16 Determine any depreciation recapture or capital gain or terminal loss generated by each event described below. Use them to determine the amount of the income tax effect, if the effective tax rate is 30%.

(a) A strip of land zoned as "Commercial" purchased 8 years ago for $2.6 million was just sold at a 15% profit.

(b) Earthmoving equipment (CCA Class 38, 30%) purchased for $155,000 was sold at the end of the fifth year of ownership for $10,000.

16.17 Determine any depreciation recapture or capital gain or terminal loss generated by each event described below. Use them to determine the amount of the income tax effect, if the effective tax rate is 40%.

(a) A 21-year-old asset (CCA Class 38, 30%) was removed from service and sold for $500. When purchased, the asset was entered on the books with a basis of $180,000.

(b) A high-technology machine (CCA Class 8, 20%) was sold for $10,000 more than its purchase price in its second year of service. The asset had $P = \$100,000$.

16.18 Petri-Products purchased sterilization equipment at a cost of $40,000 (CCA Class 8, 20%). The equipment increased gross income by $20,000 and expenses by $3000 per year. In year 3, the equipment was sold for $21,000. The effective tax rate is 35%. Determine the (a) income taxes and (b) cash flow after taxes for the asset in the year of the sale.

16.19 A couple of years ago a company purchased land, a building, and two depreciable assets from another corporation. These have all recently been disposed of. Use the information shown to determine the presence and amount of any capital gain, terminal loss, or depreciation recapture.

Asset	Purchase Price, $	Current UCC, $	Sales Price, $
Land	−200,000		245,000
Building	−800,000	300,000	255,000
Cleaner	−50,500	15,500	18,500
Circulator	−10,000	5,000	10,500

16.20 In Problem 16.10(b), Hartcourt-Banks sold a 4-year-old asset for $20,000. (a) Recalculate the CFAT in the year of sale, taking into account any additional tax effects caused by the $20,000 sale price. (b) What is the change in the CFAT from the amount in the Problem?

After-Tax Economic Analysis

16.21 Compute the required before-tax return if an after-tax return of 9% per year is expected and the provincial tax rate totals 6%. The effective federal tax rate is 35%.

16.22 A division of ConocoPhillips has a federal tax rate of 31% and a provincial rate of 5%. Find the equivalent after-tax ROR required of projects that are justified only if they can demonstrate a before-tax return of 22% per year.

16.23 John made an annual return of 8% after taxes on a stock investment. His sister told him this is equivalent to a 12% per year before-tax return. What percent of taxable income is she assuming will be taken by income taxes?

16.24 An engineer co-owns a real estate rental property business, which just purchased an apartment complex for $3,500,000, using all equity capital. For the next 8 years, an annual gross income before taxes of $480,000 is expected, offset by estimated annual expenses of $100,000. The owners hope to sell the property after 8 years for the currently appraised value of $4,050,000. Assume the applicable tax rate for taxable income is 30%. The property will be straight line depreciated over a 20-year life with a salvage value of zero. Neglect the 50% rule in depreciation computations. (a) Tabulate the after-tax cash flows for the 8 years of ownership and (b) determine the before-tax and after-tax rates of return. Use either hand or computer presentation of the CFAT tabulation template in Table 16–2, altered to accommodate this situation.

16.25 An asset has the following series of CFBT and CFAT estimates that have been entered into the indicated columns and rows of a spreadsheet. The company uses a rate of return of 14% per year before taxes and 9% per year after taxes. Write the spreadsheet functions for each series that will display the three results of PW, AW, and ROR. In solving this problem, use the spreadsheet functions NPV, PV, and IRR at a minimum.

Row 4	Column A	B	C
	Year	CFBT, $	CFAT, $
5	0	−200,000	−200,000
6	1	75,000	62,000
7	2	75,000	60,000
8	3	75,000	52,000
9	4	75,000	53,000
10	5	90,000	65,000

16.26 Two alternatives are to be evaluated by Ned. His boss wants to know the rate of return value compared to the corporate after-tax MARR of 7% per year used to decide upon any new capital investment. Perform the analysis (a) before taxes and (b) after taxes with $T_e = 50\%$ and classical SL depreciation. (Develop the hand or spreadsheet solution per your instructor.)

	X	Y
Cost basis, $	−12,000	−25,000
AOC, $/year	−3,000	−1,500
Salvage, $	3,000	5,000
n, years	10	10

16.27 Two machines have the following estimates.

	Machine A	Machine B
Cost basis, $	−15,000	−22,000
Salvage, $	3,000	5,000
AOC, $/year	−3,000	−1,500
Life, years	10	10

Either machine is to be used for a total of 10 years, then sold for the estimated salvage value. The before-tax MARR is 14% per year, after-tax MARR is 7% per year, and T_e is 50%. Select a machine on the basis of (a) before-tax PW analysis, (b) after-tax PW analysis using classical SL depreciation over the 10-year life.

16.28 A European candy manufacturing plant manager must select a new irradiation system to ensure the safety of specific products, while being economical. The two alternatives available have the following estimates.

	System A	System B
Cost basis, $	−150,000	−85,000
CFBT, $/year	60,000	20,000
Life, years	3	5

The company is in the 35% tax bracket and assumes classical straight line depreciation for alternative comparisons performed at an after-tax MARR of 6% per year. A salvage value of zero is used when depreciation is calculated. System B can be sold after 5 years for an estimated 10% of its first cost. System A has no anticipated salvage value. Determine which is more economical.

16.29 Find the after-tax rate of return for the following desalinization plant equipment over a 5-year time period. The equipment, designed for special jobs, will cost $2500, will have no salvage value, and will last no more than 5 years. Revenue minus expenses is estimated to be $1500 in year 1 and only $300 each additional year of use. The effective tax rate is 30%. Use classical SL depreciation.

16.30 Automatic inspection equipment purchased for $78,000 by Stimson Engineering generated an average of $26,080 annually in before-tax cash flow during its 5-year estimated life. This represents a return of 20%. However, the corporate finance officer determined that the CFAT was $18,000 for the first year only and is decreasing by $1000 per year thereafter. If the president wants to realize an after-tax return of 12% per year, for how many more years must the equipment remain in service?

16.31 In Example 16.5, $P = \$50,000$, $S = 0$, $n = 5$, CFBT $= \$20,000$, and $T_e = 40\%$ for a fibre optics cable manufacturer. Straight line depreciation is used to compute an after-tax $i^* = 18.03\%$. If the owner requires an after-tax return of 20% per year, determine an estimate allowed for (a) the first cost and (b) the annual CFBT. When you determine one of these values, assume that the other parameter retains the value estimated in the Example. Assume the effective tax rate remains at 40%. Solve this problem by hand.

After-Tax Replacement Study

16.32 Scotty Paper Company—Canada employee Stella Needleson was asked to determine if the current process of dying writing paper should be retained or a new, environmentally friendly process should be implemented. Estimates or actual values for the two processes are summarized below. She performed an after-tax replacement analysis at 10% per year and the corporation's effective tax rate of 32% to determine that economically, the new process should be chosen. Was she correct? Why or why not? (Ignore the 50% rule.)

	Current Process	New Process
Cost basis, 7 years ago, $	$-450{,}000$	
Cost basis, $		$-700{,}000$
Remaining life, years	5	10
Current market value, $	50,000	
AOC, $/year	$-160{,}000$	$-150{,}000$
Future salvage, $	0	50,000
Depreciation method	SL	SL

16.33 Nuclear power plant safety devices installed several years ago have been depreciated from a cost basis of $200,000. The devices can be sold on the used equipment market for an estimated $15,000. Or they can be retained in service for 5 more years with a $9000 upgrade now and an AOC of $6000 per year. The upgrade investment will be depreciated over 3 years with no salvage value. The challenger is a replacement with newer technology at a cost basis of $40,000, $n = 5$ years, and $S = 0$. The new units will have operating expenses of $7000 per year.

   (a) Use a 5-year study period, an effective tax rate of 40%, an after-tax MARR of 12% per year, and an assumption of classical straight line depreciation (no 50% rule) to perform an after-tax replacement study.

   (b) If the challenger is known to be salable after 5 years for an amount between $2000 and $4000, will the challenger AW value become more or less costly? Why?

Capital Cost Tax Factors

16.34 Ottawa's Mosaid Technologies Inc. is evaluating the $70 million purchase of a portfolio of 20 patents essential for WiFi and WiMax wireless technology. The patents belong to CCA Class 44, rate 25%. Assume that Mosaid is subject to a corporate tax rate of 35% and the after-tax MARR is 12%. What is the present worth of the cost basis of the patents if the future tax savings resulting from depreciation is considered? Interpret the meaning of the numerical answer.

16.35 Alcan is spending $400,000 upgrading a piece of machinery at their Kitimat aluminum smelter. It will be depreciated at a CCA rate of 30%. The machinery has a 6-year useful life with an expected salvage value of $40,000. Assuming an after-tax 15% MARR and a corporate tax rate of 30%, what is the after-tax present worth of the investment?

16.36 Brandon Tractors Inc. of Manitoba is considering new automated assembly machinery costing $100,000. The equipment is expected to save the company $50,000 per year over its 5-year life with a salvage value of $30,000. If the CCA rate is 30%, with a MARR of 10%, and a corporate tax rate of 28%, what is the present worth of the purchase?

16.37 If Oakhill Electric Ltd. purchases a service van for $65,000 (CCA rate 30%), it is expected to provide a yearly revenue of $15,000. The salvage value of the van is estimated to be $20,000 after its 5-year life. Oakhill pays 35% in taxes and their after-tax MARR is 12%. What is the present worth of this purchase?

CHAPTER  17

Formalized Sensitivity Analysis and Expected Value Decisions

This chapter includes several related topics about alternative evaluation. All these techniques build upon the methods and models used in previous chapters, especially those of the first eight chapters and the basics of breakeven analysis in Chapter 13. This chapter should be considered preparation for the topics of simulation and decision making under risk, presented in the next chapter.

The first two sections expand our capability to perform a *sensitivity analysis* of one or more parameters and of an entire alternative. Then the determination and use of the *expected value* of a cash flow series are treated. The technique of *decision trees* helps an analyst make a series of economic decisions for alternatives that have different, but closely connected, stages. *Scenario analysis* is introduced to address future variables whose values cannot be predicted with mathematical forecasting procedures. Finally, *utility theory* is used to relax the requirement that all variables be assessed in monetary units.

The case study involves a thorough sensitivity analysis of a multiple-alternative, multiple-attribute (factor) project set in the public sector.

LEARNING OBJECTIVES

Purpose: Perform a formal sensitivity analysis of one or more parameters; and perform expected value and decision tree evaluations of alternatives.

Sensitivity to variation	By the end of this chapter you should be able to
	1. Calculate a measure of worth to explain sensitivity to variation in one or more parameters.
Three estimates	**2.** Choose the better alternative using three estimates for selected parameters.
Expected value	**3.** Calculate the expected value of a variable.
Expected value of cash flows	**4.** Evaluate an alternative using the expected value of cash flows.
Decision tree	**5.** Construct a decision tree and use it to evaluate alternatives stage by stage.
Scenario analysis	**6.** Construct and perform a scenario analysis.
Utility theory	**7.** Replace monetary units with a measure of satisfaction from a product or service.

17.1 DETERMINING SENSITIVITY TO PARAMETER VARIATION

The term *parameter* is used in this chapter to represent any variable or factor for which an estimate or stated value is necessary. Example parameters are first cost, salvage value, AOC, estimated life, production rate, materials costs, etc. Estimates such as the loan interest rate and the inflation rate are also parameters of the analysis.

Economic analysis uses estimates of a parameter's future value to assist decision makers. Since future estimates are always incorrect to some degree, inaccuracy is present in the economic projections. The effect of variation may be determined by using sensitivity analysis. In reality, we have applied this approach (informally) throughout previous chapters. Usually, one factor at a time is varied, and independence with other factors is assumed. This assumption is not completely correct in real-world situations, but it is practical since it is difficult to accurately account for these dependencies.

Sensitivity analysis determines how a measure of worth—PW, AW, ROR, or BCR—and the selected alternative will be altered if a particular parameter varies over a stated range of values. For example, variation in a parameter such as MARR would not alter the decision to select an alternative when all compared alternatives return considerably more than the MARR; thus, the decision is relatively insensitive to the MARR. However, variation in the *n* value may indicate that selection from the same alternatives is very sensitive to the estimated life.

Usually the variations in life, annual costs, and revenues result from variations in selling price, operation at different levels of capacity, inflation, etc. For example, if an operating level of 90% of airline seating capacity for a domestic route is compared with 50% for a proposed international route, the operating cost and revenue per passenger mile will increase, but anticipated aircraft life will probably decrease only slightly. Usually several important parameters are studied to learn how the uncertainty of estimates affects the economic analysis.

Sensitivity analysis usually concentrates on the variation expected in estimates of *P*, AOC, *S*, *n*, unit costs, unit revenues, and similar parameters. These parameters are often the result of design questions and their answers. Parameters that are interest rate-based are not treated in the same manner.

Parameters such as MARR, and other interest rates (loan rates, inflation rate) are more stable from project to project. If performed, sensitivity analysis on them is for specific values or over a narrow range of values. Therefore, the sensitivity analysis is more constrained for interest rate parameters.

This point is important to remember if simulation is used for decision making under risk (Chapter 18).

Plotting the sensitivity of PW, AW, or ROR versus the parameter(s) studied is very helpful. Two alternatives can be compared with respect to a given parameter and the breakeven point. This is the value at which the two alternatives are economically equivalent. However, the breakeven chart commonly represents only one parameter per chart. Thus, several charts are constructed, and independence of each parameter is assumed. In previous uses of breakeven analysis, we computed the measure of worth at only two values of a parameter and connected the points with a straight line. However, if the results are sensitive to the parameter value, several intermediate points should be used to better evaluate the sensitivity, especially if the relationships are not linear.

When several parameters are studied, sensitivity analysis can become quite complex. It may be performed one parameter at a time using a spreadsheet or computations by hand. The computer facilitates comparison of multiple parameters and multiple measures of worth, and the software can rapidly plot the results.

There is a general procedure to follow when conducting a thorough sensitivity analysis.

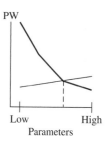

1. Determine which parameter(s) of interest might vary from the most likely estimated value.
2. Select the probable range and an increment of variation for each parameter.
3. Select the measure of worth.
4. Compute the results for each parameter, using the measure of worth as a basis.
5. To better interpret the sensitivity, graphically display the parameter versus the measure of worth.

This sensitivity analysis procedure should indicate the parameters that warrant closer study or require additional information. When there are two or more alternatives, it is better to use the PW or AW measure of worth in step 3. If ROR is used, it requires the extra efforts of incremental analysis between alternatives. Example 17.1 illustrates sensitivity analysis for one project.

EXAMPLE 17.1

Western Growers Inc. expects to purchase a new asset for automated produce sorting. Most likely estimates are a first cost of $80,000, zero salvage value, and a cash flow before taxes (CFBT) per year t that follows the relation $27,000 - 2000t$. The MARR for the company varies from 10% to 25% per year for different types of investments. The economic life of similar machinery varies from 8 to 12 years. Evaluate the sensitivity of PW by varying (*a*) MARR, while assuming a constant n value of 10 years, and (*b*) n, while MARR is constant at 15% per year. Perform the analysis by hand and by computer.

Solution by Hand
(*a*) Follow the procedure above to understand the sensitivity of PW to MARR variation.

   1. MARR is the parameter of interest.
   2. Select 5% increments to evaluate sensitivity to MARR; the range is 10% to 25%.
   3. The measure of worth is PW.
   4. Set up the PW relation for 10 years. When MARR = 10%,

$$PW = -80,000 + 25,000(P/A,10\%,10) - 2000(P/G,10\%,10)$$
$$= \$27,830$$

The PW for all four values at 5% intervals is as follows:

MARR	PW
10%	$ 27,830
15	11,512
20	−962
25	−10,711

5. A plot of MARR versus PW is shown in Figure 17–1. The steep negative slope indicates that the decision to accept the proposal based on PW is quite sensitive to variations in the MARR. If the MARR is established at the upper end of the range, the investment is not attractive.

(b) 1. Asset life n is the parameter.
  2. Select 2-year increments to evaluate PW sensitivity over the range 8 to 12 years.
  3. The measure of worth is PW.
  4. Set up the same PW relation as in part (a) at $i = 15\%$. The PW results are as follows:

n	PW
8	$ 7,221
10	11,511
12	13,145

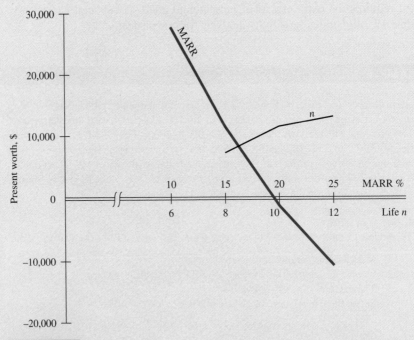

FIGURE 17–1

Plot of PW versus MARR and n for sensitivity analysis, Example 17.1.

5. Figure 17–1 presents the plot of PW vs. *n*. Since the PW measure is positive for all values of *n*, the decision to invest is not materially affected by the estimated life. The PW curve levels out above $n = 10$. This insensitivity to changes in cash flow in the distant future is a predictable observation, because the P/F factor gets smaller as *n* increases.

Solution by Computer

Figure 17–2 presents two spreadsheets and accompanying plots of PW vs. MARR (fixed *n*) and PW vs. *n* (fixed MARR). The general relation for cash flow values is

$$\text{Cash flow}_t = \begin{cases} -80{,}000 & t = 0 \\ +27{,}000 - 2000t & t = 1 \dots \end{cases}$$

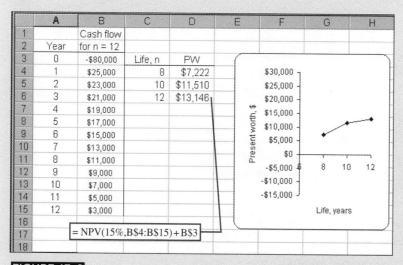

FIGURE 17–2

Sensitivity analysis of PW to variations in the MARR and estimated life, Example 17.1.

> The NPV function calculates PW for *i* values from 10% to 25% and *n* values from 8 to 12 years. As the solution by hand indicated, so does the *xy* scatter chart; PW is sensitive to changes in MARR, but not very sensitive to variations in *n*.

When the sensitivity of *several parameters* is considered for *one alternative* using a *single measure of worth,* it is helpful to graph percentage change for each parameter versus the measure of worth. Figure 17–3 illustrates ROR versus six different parameters for one alternative. The variation in each parameter is indicated as a percentage deviation from the most likely estimate on the horizontal axis. If the ROR response curve is flat and approaches horizontal over the range of total variation graphed for a parameter, there is little sensitivity of ROR to changes in the parameter's value. This is the conclusion for indirect cost in the figure. On the other hand, ROR is very sensitive to sales price. A reduction of 30% from the expected sales price reduces the ROR from approximately 20% to −10%, whereas a 10% increase in price raises the ROR to about 30%.

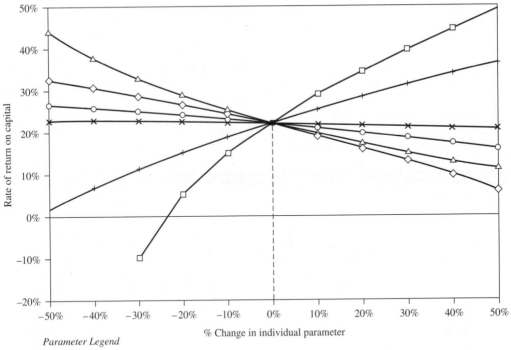

Parameter Legend

□ Sales price   ✕ Indirect cost
◇ Direct material   ○ Direct labour
+ Sales volume   △ Capital

FIGURE 17–3

Sensitivity analysis graph of percent variation from the most likely estimate.

SOURCE: L. T. Blank and A. J. Tarquin, *Engineering Economy*, 6th ed. (New York: McGraw-Hill, 2005), chap. 19.

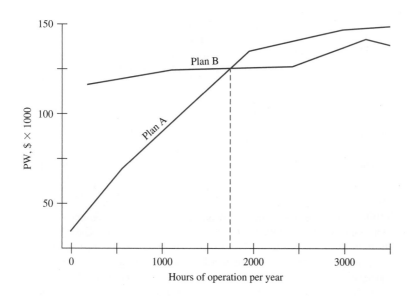

FIGURE 17–4
Sample PW sensitivity to
hours of operation for two
alternatives.

If two *alternatives* are compared and the sensitivity to *one parameter* is sought, the graph may show quite nonlinear results. Observe the general shape of the sample sensitivity graphs in Figure 17–4. The plots are shown as linear segments between specific computation points. The graph indicates that the PW of each plan is a nonlinear function of hours of operation. Plan A is very sensitive in the range of 0 to 2000 hours, but it is comparatively insensitive above 2000 hours. Plan B is more attractive due to its relative insensitivity. The breakeven point is at about 1750 hours per year. It may be necessary to plot the measure of worth at intermediate points to better understand the nature of the sensitivity.

EXAMPLE 17.2

Abbotsford, B.C., needs to resurface a 3-kilometre stretch of highway. Knobel Construction has proposed two methods of resurfacing. The first is a concrete surface for a cost of $1.5 million and an annual maintenance of $10,000.

The second method is an asphalt covering with a first cost of $1 million and a yearly maintenance of $50,000. However, Knobel requests that every third year the asphalt highway be touched up at a cost of $75,000.

The city uses, 6% as the social discount rate.

(*a*) Determine the breakeven number of years of the two methods. If the city expects scheduled federal work on the Trans-Canada Highway to upgrade this stretch of highway in 10 years, which method should be selected?

(*b*) If the touchup cost increases by $5000 per kilometre every 3 years, is the decision sensitive to this increase?

Solution by Computer

(*a*) Use PW analysis to determine the breakeven *n* value.

$$\text{PW of concrete} = \text{PW of asphalt}$$

$$-1,500,000 - 10,000(P/A,6\%,n) = -1,000,000 - 50,000(P/A,6\%,n)$$
$$- 75,000\left[\sum_j (P/F,6\%,j)\right]$$

where $j = 3, 6, 9, \ldots, n$. The relation can be rewritten to reflect the incremental cash flows.

$$- 500,000 + (40,000)(P/A,6\%,n) + 75,000\left[\sum_j (P/F,6\%,j)\right] = 0 \qquad [17.1]$$

The breakeven n value can be determined by hand solution by increasing n until Equation [17.1] switches from negative to positive PW values. Alternatively, a spreadsheet solution using the NPV function can find the breakeven n value (Figure 17–5). The NPV functions in column C are the same each year, except that the cash flows are extended 1 year for each present worth calculation. At approximately $n = 11.4$ years (between cells C15 and C16), concrete and asphalt resurfacing break even economically. Since the road is needed for 10 more years, the extra cost of concrete is not justified; select the asphalt alternative.

(b) The total touchup cost will increase by \$15,000 every 3 years. Equation [17.1] is now

$$- 500,000 + 40,000(P/A,6\%,n) + \left[75,000 + 15,000\left(\frac{j-3}{3}\right)\right]\left[\sum_j (P/F,6\%,j)\right] = 0$$

Now the breakeven n value is between 10 and 11 years—10.8 years using linear interpolation (Figure 17–5, cells E14 and E15). The decision has become marginal for asphalt, since the upgrade is planned for 10 years hence.

	A	B	C	D	E	F	G	H	I	J
1			Part (a)		Part (b)					
2		Incremental	PW for	Incremental	PW for					
3	Year, n	cash flow	n years	cash flow	n years					
4	0	\$ (500,000)		\$ (500,000)						
5	1	\$ 40,000	\$ (462,264)	\$ 40,000	\$ (462,264)					
6	2	\$ 40,000	\$ (426,664)	\$ 40,000	\$ (426,664)					
7	3	\$ 115,000	\$ (330,108)	\$ 115,000	\$ (330,108)					
8	4	\$ 40,000	\$ (298,424)	\$ 40,000	\$ (298,424)					
9	5	\$ 40,000	\$ (268,534)	\$ 40,000	\$ (268,534)					
10	6	\$ 115,000	\$ (187,464)	\$ 130,000	\$ (176,889)					
11	7	\$ 40,000	\$ (160,861)	\$ 40,000	\$ (150,287)					
12	8	\$ 40,000	\$ (135,765)	\$ 40,000	\$ (125,190)					
13	9	\$ 115,000	\$ (67,696)	\$ 145,000	\$ (39,365)			= NPV(6%,\$D\$5:\$D14)+\$D\$4			
14	10	\$ 40,000	\$ (45,361)	\$ 40,000	\$ (17,029)						
15	11	\$ 40,000	\$ (24,289)	\$ 40,000	\$ 4,042			= NPV(6%,\$D\$5:\$D15)+\$D\$4			
16	12	\$ 115,000	\$ 32,862	\$ 160,000	\$ 83,557						
17	13	\$ 40,000	\$ 51,616	\$ 40,000	\$ 102,311						
18	14	\$ 40,000	\$ 69,308	\$ 40,000	\$ 120,003						
19	15	\$ 115,000	\$ 117,293	\$ 175,000	\$ 193,024						
20	16	\$ 40,000	\$ 133,039	\$ 40,000	\$ 208,770						
21				= NPV(6%,\$B\$5:\$B15)+\$B\$4						
22										
23				= NPV(6%,\$B\$5:\$B16)+\$B\$4						
24										

FIGURE 17–5

Sensitivity of the breakeven point between two alternatives using PW analysis, Example 17.2.

Noneconomic considerations may be used to determine if asphalt is still the better alternative. One conclusion is that the asphalt decision becomes more questionable as the asphalt alternative maintenance costs increase; that is, the PW value is sensitive to increasing touchup costs.

17.2 FORMALIZED SENSITIVITY ANALYSIS USING THREE ESTIMATES

We can thoroughly examine the economic advantages and disadvantages among two or more alternatives by borrowing from the field of project scheduling the concept of making three estimates for each parameter: *a pessimistic, a most likely, and an optimistic estimate.* Depending upon the nature of a parameter, the pessimistic estimate may be the lowest value (alternative life is an example) or the largest value (such as asset first cost).

This formal approach allows us to study measure of worth and alternative selection sensitivity within a predicted range of variation for each parameter. Usually the most likely estimate is used for all other parameters when the measure of worth is calculated for one particular parameter or one alternative. This approach, essentially the same as the one-parameter-at-a-time analysis of Section 17.1, is illustrated by Example 17.3.

EXAMPLE 17.3

An engineer is evaluating three alternatives for which she has made three estimates for the salvage value, annual operating cost, and the life. The estimates are presented on an alternative-by-alternative basis in Table 17–1. For example, alternative B has pessimistic

TABLE 17–1 Competing Alternatives with Three Estimates–Made for Salvage Value, AOC, and Life Parameters

Strategy		First Cost, $	Salvage Value, $	AOC, $	Life n, Years
Alternative A					
Estimates	P	−20,000	0	−11,000	3
	ML	−20,000	0	−9,000	5
	O	−20,000	0	−5,000	8
Alternative B					
Estimates	P	−15,000	500	−4,000	2
	ML	−15,000	1,000	−3,500	4
	O	−15,000	2,000	−2,000	7
Alternative C					
Estimates	P	−30,000	3,000	−8,000	3
	ML	−30,000	3,000	−7,000	7
	O	−30,000	3,000	−3,500	9

P = pessimistic; ML = most likely; O = optimistic.

estimates of $S = \$500$, AOC $= \$-4000$, and $n = 2$ years. The first costs are known, so they have the same value. Perform a sensitivity analysis and determine the most economical alternative, using AW analysis at a MARR of 12% per year.

Solution

For each alternative in Table 17–1, calculate the AW value of costs. For example, the AW relation for alternative A, pessimistic estimates, is

$$AW = -20,000(A/P,12\%,3) - 11,000 = \$-19,327$$

Table 17–2 presents all AW values. Figure 17–6 is a plot of AW versus the three estimates of life for each alternative. Since the AW calculated using the ML estimates for alternative B ($\$-8229$) is economically better than even the optimistic AW value for alternatives A and C, alternative B is clearly favoured.

TABLE 17–2   Annual Worth Values, Example 17.3

		Alternative AW Values	
Estimates	A	B	C
P	$\$-19,327$	$\$-12,640$	$\$-19,601$
ML	$-14,548$	$-8,229$	$-13,276$
O	$-9,026$	$-5,089$	$-8,927$

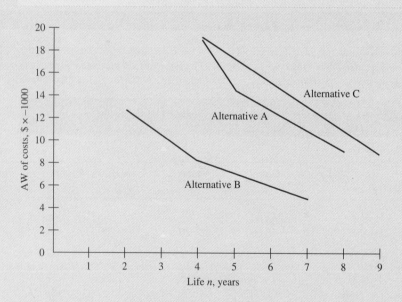

FIGURE 17–6
Plot of AW of costs for different-life estimates, Example 17.3.

Comment

While the alternative that should be selected here is quite obvious, this is not normally the case. For example, in Table 17–2, if the pessimistic alternative B equivalent AW were much higher, say, $-21,000 per year (rather than $-12,640), and the optimistic AW values for alternatives A and C were less than that for B ($-5089), the choice of B is not apparent or correct. In this case, it would be necessary to select one set of estimates (P, ML, or O) upon which to base the decision. Alternatively, the different estimates can be used in an expected value analysis, which is introduced in the next section.

17.3 ECONOMIC VARIABILITY AND THE EXPECTED VALUE

Engineers and economic analysts usually deal with estimates about an uncertain future by placing appropriate reliance on past data. This means that probability and samples are used. Experience and judgment can often be used in conjunction with probabilities and expected values to evaluate the desirability of an alternative.

The *expected value* can be interpreted as a long-run average observable if the project is repeated many times. Since a particular alternative is evaluated or implemented only once, a *point estimate* of the expected value results. However, even for a single occurrence, the expected value is a meaningful number.

To generalize, the expected value $E(X)$ is computed using the relation

$$E(X) = \sum_{i=1}^{i=m} X_i P(X_i) \qquad \text{[17.2]}$$

where X_i = value of the variable X for i from 1 to m different values
$\quad\quad P(X_i)$ = probability that a specific value of X will occur

Probabilities are always correctly stated in decimal form, but they are routinely spoken of in percentages and often referred to as *chance,* such as *the chances are about 10%.* When placing the probability value in Equation [17.2] or any other relation, use the decimal equivalent of 10%, that is, 0.1. In all probability statements the $P(X_i)$ values for a variable X must total to 1.0.

$$\sum_{i=1}^{i=m} P(X_i) = 1.0$$

We will commonly omit the subscript i on X for simplicity.

If X represents the estimated cash flows, some will be positive and others negative. If a cash flow sequence includes revenues and costs, and the present worth at the MARR is calculated, the result is the expected value of the discounted cash flows $E(PW)$. If the expected value is negative, the overall outcome is expected to be a cash outflow. For example, if $E(PW) = -1500, this indicates that the proposal is not expected to return the MARR.

EXAMPLE 17.4

A downtown hotel is offering a new service for weekend travellers through its business and travel centre. The manager estimates that for a typical weekend, there is a 50% chance of having a net cash flow of $5000 and a 35% chance of $10,000. He also estimates there is a small chance—5%—of no cash flow and a 10% chance of a loss of $500, which is the estimated extra personnel and utility costs to offer the service. Determine the expected net cash flow.

Solution

Let X be the net cash flow in dollars, and let $P(X)$ represent the associated probabilities. Using Equation [17.2],

$$E(X) = 5000(0.5) + 10,000(0.35) + 0(0.05) - 500(0.1) = \$5950$$

Although the "no cash flow" possibility does not increase or decrease $E(X)$, it is included because it makes the probability values sum to 1.0 and it makes the computation complete.

17.4 EXPECTED VALUE COMPUTATIONS FOR ALTERNATIVES

The expected value computation $E(X)$ is utilized in a variety of ways. Two ways are: (1) to prepare information for incorporation into a more complete engineering economy analysis and (2) to evaluate the expected viability of a fully formulated alternative. Example 17.5 illustrates the first situation, and Example 17.6 determines the expected PW when the cash flow series and probabilities are estimated.

EXAMPLE 17.5

An electric utility is experiencing a difficult time obtaining natural gas for electric generation. Fuels other than natural gas are purchased at an extra cost, which is transferred to the customer. Total monthly fuel expenses are now averaging $7,750,000. An engineer with this utility has calculated the average revenue for the past 24 months using three fuel-mix situations—gas plentiful, less than 30% other fuels purchased, and 30% or more other fuels. Table 17–3 indicates the number of months that each fuel-mix situation occurred. Can the utility expect to meet future monthly expenses based on the 24 months of data, if a similar fuel-mix pattern continues?

TABLE 17–3 Revenue and Fuel-Mix Data, Example 17.5

Fuel-Mix Situation	Months in Past 24	Average Revenue, $ per Month
Gas plentiful	12	5,270,000
<30% other	6	7,850,000
≥30% other	6	12,130,000

Solution

Using the 24 months of data, estimate a probability for each fuel mix.

Fuel-Mix Situation	Probability of Occurrence
Gas plentiful	$12/24 = 0.50$
<30% other	$6/24 = 0.25$
≥30% other	$6/24 = 0.25$

Let the variable X represent average monthly revenue. Use Equation [17.2] to determine expected revenue per month.

$$E(\text{revenue}) = 5{,}270{,}000(0.50) + 7{,}850{,}000(0.25) + 12{,}130{,}000(0.25)$$
$$= \$7{,}630{,}000$$

With expenses averaging $7,750,000, the average monthly revenue shortfall is $120,000. To break even, other sources of revenue must be generated, or the additional costs must be transferred to the customer.

EXAMPLE 17.6

Lite-Weight Wheelchair Company has a substantial investment in tubular steel bending equipment. A new piece of equipment costs $5000 and has a life of 3 years. Estimated cash flows (Table 17–4) depend on economic conditions classified as receding, stable, or expanding. A probability is estimated that each of the economic conditions will prevail during the 3-year period. Apply expected value and PW analysis to determine if the equipment should be purchased. Use a MARR of 15% per year.

TABLE 17–4   Equipment Cash Flow and Probabilities, Example 17.6

	Economic Condition		
Year	Receding (Prob. = 0.2)	Stable (Prob. = 0.6)	Expanding (Prob. = 0.2)
	Annual Cash Flow Estimates, $		
0	$−5000	$−5000	$−5000
1	+2500	+2000	+2000
2	+2000	+2000	+3000
3	+1000	+2000	+3500

Solution

First determine the PW of the cash flows in the table for each economic condition, and then calculate $E(\text{PW})$, using Equation [17.2]. Define subscripts R for receding economy,

S for stable, and E for expanding. The PW values for the three scenarios are

$$PW_R = -5000 + 2500(P/F,15\%,1) + 2000(P/F,15\%,2) + 1000(P/F,15\%,3)$$

$$= -5000 + 4344 = \$-656$$

$$PW_S = -5000 + 4566 = \$-434$$

$$PW_E = -5000 + 6309 = \$+1309$$

Only in an expanding economy will the cash flows return the 15% and justify the investment. The expected present worth is

$$E(PW) = \sum_{j=R,S,E} PW_j[P(j)]$$

$$= -656(0.2) - 434(0.6) + 1309(0.2)$$

$$= \$-130$$

At 15%, $E(PW) < 0$; the equipment is not justified using an expected value analysis.

Comment

It is also correct to calculate the E(cash flow) for each year and then determine PW of the E(cash flow) series, because the PW computation is a linear function of cash flows. Computing E(cash flow) first may be easier in that it reduces the number of PW computations. In this example, calculate $E(CF_t)$ for each year, then determine $E(PW)$.

$$E(CF_0) = \$-5000$$

$$E(CF_1) = 2500(0.2) + 2000(0.6) + 2000(0.2) = \$2100$$

$$E(CF_2) = \$2200$$

$$E(CF_3) = \$2100$$

$$E(PW) = -5000 + 2100(P/F,15\%,1) + 2200(P/F,15\%,2) + 2100(P/F,15\%,3)$$

$$= \$-130$$

17.5 STAGED EVALUATION OF ALTERNATIVES USING A DECISION TREE

Alternative evaluation may require a series of decisions where the outcome from one stage is important to the next stage of decision making. Decision theory is a technique structured to assist decision making in an environment of uncertainty. Engineering economic analysis involves unknown quantities in future production prices, demand for the product, success in research and development initiatives, state of the global economy, labour productivity, availability of trained engineers, rate of technological evolution, and other scenario-specific and technological-specific variables, all in a relation of interdependence. Changes in one area will impact another, often creating additional uncertainties that can be dealt with by the use of decision analysis. Failure to assess these variables can jeopardize a project's successful implementation.

When each alternative is clearly defined and probability estimates can be made to account for risk, it is helpful to perform the evaluation using a *decision tree*. A decision tree includes

- More than one stage of alternative selection
- Selection of an alternative at one stage that leads to another stage
- Expected results from a decision at each stage
- Probability estimates for each outcome
- Estimates of economic value (cost or revenue) for each outcome
- Measure of worth as the selection criterion, such as $E(PW)$

The decision tree is constructed left to right and includes each possible decision and outcome. A square represents a *decision node* with the possible alternatives indicated on the *branches* from the decision node (Figure 17–7a). A circle represents a *probability node* with the possible outcomes and estimated probabilities on the branches (Figure 17–7b). Since outcomes always follow decisions, the treelike structure in Figure 17–7c results.

Usually each branch of a decision tree has some estimated economic value (often referred to as *payoff*) in cost, revenue, or benefit. These cash flows are expressed in terms of PW, AW, or FW values and are shown to the right of each

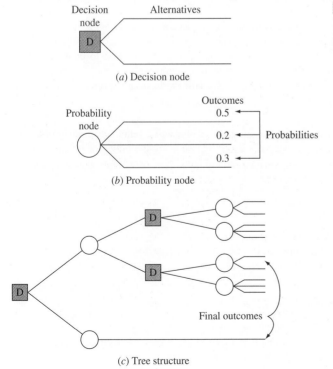

FIGURE 17–7
Decision and probability nodes used to construct a decision tree.

Decision node
Alternatives
D

(*a*) Decision node

Outcomes
Probability node
0.5
0.2   Probabilities
0.3

(*b*) Probability node

D
D
D
Final outcomes

(*c*) Tree structure

final outcome branch. The cash flow and probability estimates on each outcome branch are used in calculating the expected economic value of each decision branch. This process, called *solving the tree* or *foldback,* is explained after Example 17.7, which illustrates the construction of a decision tree.

EXAMPLE 17.7

Jerry Hill is president and CEO of a Canadian-based food processing company, Hill Products and Services. He was recently approached by an international supermarket chain that wants to market in-country its own brand of frozen microwaveable dinners. The offer made to Jerry by the supermarket corporation requires that a series of two decisions be made, now and 2 years hence. The current decision involves two alternatives: (1) *lease* a facility in the United Arab Emirates (UAE) from the supermarket chain, which has agreed to convert a current processing facility for immediate use by Jerry's company; or (2) *build and own* a processing and packaging facility in the UAE. Possible outcomes of this first decision stage are good market or poor market depending upon the public's response.

The decision choices 2 years hence are dependent upon the lease-or-own decision made now. If Hill *decides to lease,* good market response means that the future decision alternatives are to produce at twice, equal to, or one-half of the original volume. This will be a mutual decision between the supermarket chain and Jerry's company. A poor market response will indicate a one-half level of production, or complete removal from the UAE market. Outcomes for the future decisions are, again, good and poor market responses.

As agreed by the supermarket company, the current decision for Jerry *to own* the facility will allow him to set the production level 2 years hence. If market response is good, the decision alternatives are four or two times original levels. The reaction to poor market response will be production at the same level or no production at all.

Construct the tree of decisions and outcomes for Hill Products and Services.

Solution

This is a two-stage decision tree that has alternatives now and 2 years hence. Identify the decision nodes and branches, and then develop the tree using the branches and the outcomes of good and poor market for each decision. Figure 17–8 details the decision stages and outcome branches.

Decision now:
  Label it D1.
  Alternatives: lease (L) and own (O).
  Outcomes: good and poor markets.

Decisions 2 years hence:
  Label them D2 through D5
  Outcomes: good market, poor market, and out-of-business.

Choice of production levels for D2 through D5:
  Quadruple production (4×); double production (2×); level production (1×); one-half production (0.5×); stop production (0×)

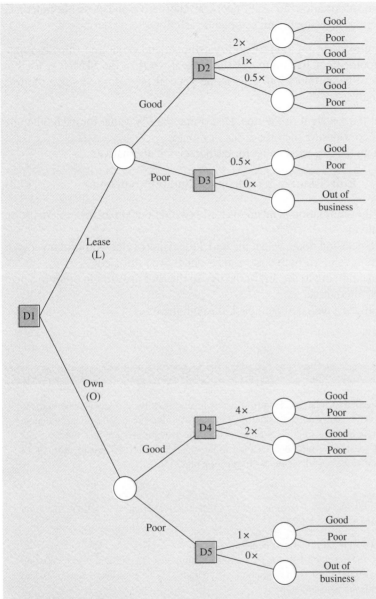

FIGURE 17–8

A two-stage decision tree identifying alternatives and possible outcomes.

The alternatives for future production levels (D2 through D5) are added to the tree and followed by the market responses of good and poor. If the stop-production (0×) decision is made at D3 or D5, the only outcome is out of business.

To utilize the decision tree for alternative evaluation and selection, the following additional information is necessary for each branch:

- The estimated probability that each outcome may occur. These probabilities must sum to 1.0 for each set of outcomes (branches) that result from a decision.

- Economic information for each decision alternative and possible outcome, such as initial investment and estimated cash flows.

Decisions are made using the probability estimate and economic value estimate for each outcome branch. Commonly the present worth at the MARR is used in an expected value computation. This is the general procedure to solve the tree using PW analysis:

1. Start at the top right of the tree. Determine the PW value for each outcome branch considering the time value of money.
2. Calculate the expected value for each decision alternative.

$$E(\text{decision}) = \Sigma \, (\text{outcome estimate})P(\text{outcome}) \qquad [17.3]$$

where the summation is taken over all possible outcomes for each decision alternative.

3. At each decision node, select the best E(decision) value—minimum cost or maximum value (if both costs and revenues are estimated).
4. Continue moving to the left of the tree to the root decision in order to select the best alternative.
5. Trace the best decision path back through the tree.

EXAMPLE 17.8

A decision is needed to either market or sell a new invention. If the product is marketed, the next decision is to take it international or national. Assume the details of the outcome branches result in the decision tree of Figure 17–9. The probabilities for each outcome and PW of CFBT (cash flow before taxes) are indicated. These payoffs are in millions of dollars. Determine the best decision at the decision node D1.

Solution
Use the procedure above to determine that the D1 decision alternative to sell the invention should maximize E(PW of CFBT).

1. Present worth of CFBT is supplied.
2. Calculate the expected PW for alternatives from nodes D2 and D3, using Equation [17.3]. In Figure 17–9, to the right of decision node D2, the expected values of 14 and 0.2 in ovals are determined as

$$E(\text{international decision}) = 12(0.5) + 16(0.5) = 14$$
$$E(\text{national decision}) = 4(0.4) - 3(0.4) - 1(0.2) = 0.2$$

The expected PW values of 4.2 and 2 for D3 are calculated in a similar fashion.
3. Select the larger expected value at each decision node. These are 14 (international) at D2 and 4.2 (international) at D3.
4. Calculate the expected PW for the two D1 branches.

$$E(\text{market decision}) = 14(0.2) + 4.2(0.8) = 6.16$$
$$E(\text{sell decision}) = 9(1.0) = 9$$

The expected value for the sell decision is simple since the one outcome has a payoff of 9. The sell decision yields the larger expected PW of 9.

5. The largest expected PW of CFBT path is to select the sell branch at D1 for a guaranteed $9,000,000.

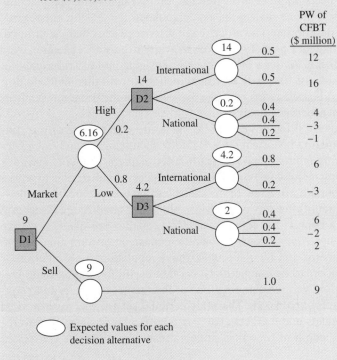

PW of
CFBT
($ million)

FIGURE 17–9

Solution of a decision tree with present worth of estimated CFBT values, Example 17.8.

Expected values for each decision alternative

17.6   SCENARIO ANALYSIS

As discussed in Section 4.1, the Governor of the Bank of Canada, Mark Carney, is hoping to maintain global economic stability by studying possible future scenarios for insights in economic policy analysis. He is concerned that economic distortions caused by various disequilibria (national debt levels, cumulative personal debt levels, fixed international currency rates that seek trade advantages) might cause economic chaos in Canada if the value of the U.S. dollar plunges and then causes a global recession. These concerns are generated and analyzed through the use of scenario analysis. Corporations also use scenario analysis for their strategic planning initiatives when they examine the economic consequences of key variables that can change in value during future quarters. Their use is particularly valuable when a public or private corporation is planning for a future that has no preexisting pattern.

An economic model is built around a scenario. The function of the scenario is to portray the aspects of the environment that have a significant effect on the system. Future scenarios are discussed to establish conditions that are likely to occur within the planning period. Factors that have negligible impacts on the system are not considered in the interests of simplification.

The use of three estimates (Section 17.2) begins the process. Often, an entire scenario is built around "best" and "worst" case outcomes. The "most likely" or expected outcome usually resides somewhere within the range skewed to one side or the other—not in the middle. A dialectical approach to determine situations that the firm needs to prevent is often helpful in establishing and planning for the "worst" case. Phrases such as "be on the lookout for" or "don't disregard" are often used in a description. The process will discover events that the firm will want to create contingency plans for in order to avert or forestall a situation from advancing or occurring. As seen in this chapter, insights into the robustness of economic calculations of PW or ROR can be achieved with this methodology. Efforts to build rigorous scenarios increase the validity of the economic analysis and its concomitant sensitivity analysis.

Economic values are often projected into the future with the use of forecasting models extrapolating historical data. Rapidly fluctuating oil and raw material prices, increasing international competition for markets, changing currency valuations, emerging technologies, and increasing salary requirements to attract highly trained labour are just a few of the variables that prevent precise numerical forecasts. By identifying sets of plausible but not assured futures, scenario analysis provides a context for defining variables, as they are likely to evolve during a planning horizon. A theme (economic expansion or retraction, severe environmental concerns and regulations versus deregulation, high inflation or deflation, and weak or strong competition) is often useful for emphasizing feasible future scenarios. Various combinations of the themes can be used to construct appropriate sets of scenarios. The study period is set as either the historical length of time products and markets evolve in a particular business or government sector or the length of time that strategic planning initiatives are locked into place.

In developing an appropriate scenario, there is a tradeoff in the level of aggregation used. Brainstorming is often used to generate events in the environment that can impact a company's product life cycle. Statements referring to an outlook are appropriate. These often contain words such as "believe," "plan," "estimate," "expect," "anticipate," and "intend." If too few variables are modelled, an unexpected event can destroy the accuracy of the economic analysis. If too many variables are used, the model becomes cumbersome and risks being infeasible due to large demands for data. Attention to the optimal aggregation level is important so that the model will be able to identify and assess the consequences of changes in economic parameters for the decision being made.

When constructing scenarios, it is helpful to subjectively postulate the evolution of various futures and then forecast values for the important variables making up the cash flow analysis. Alternatively, looking at only a few variables that a sensitivity analysis has determined to be critical can shape the scenario. By addressing the overriding themes (competition, inflation) that can affect these variables, variations of their values are derived. Finally, by taking the most likely combinations of the variables, two or three scenarios are created. Basically, construction of the scenario will be configured from the environment to the cash flow factors or from the factors to the environment. It is an iterative process that is refined over time and can be used for various decisions within the unit.

Since the various phenomena captured in a scenario analysis are interdependent, experts are often used to estimate the likelihood of events occurring given the existence of other circumstances. This allows the engineering economic analysis to be done within a methodology that incorporates breakeven and sensitivity analysis along with tradeoff studies. The results will provide more compelling evidence concerning the best-engineered designs and their economic viability.

EXAMPLE 17.9

Tight Gas Inc., operating in Alberta, drills wells targeting natural-gas-charged reservoirs located in the Lower Cretaceous geological layer. They have developed innovative technologies and procedures aimed at exploiting this geological gas development. The company's earnings are highly sensitive to a volatile scenario composed of changing commodity prices that can lead to expanded drilling activity and concomitant shortages of equipment and skilled labour (translation: higher prices for these services) as well as unseasonable weather that can hamper activity when autumns, springs, and summers are too wet and the winter is too mild (prohibiting access to areas only accessible when the ground is frozen). Capital programs associated with drilling, completions, facility construction, and land purchases are dependent on strong production performance coupled with high commodity prices that can have large swings. The company takes responsibility for environmental stewardship and the varying costs associated with mitigating the impact of their activities requiring environmental alteration and reclamation. They are also sensitive to changes in exchange rate fluctuations of \$0.01 (impact: \$4 million) and average interest rate changes of 1% (impact: \$2.5 million).

Tight Gas Inc. has the opportunity to exploit additional undeveloped holdings and further develop some lands that are already producing. They wish to use a 10-year scenario analysis to decide whether to implement the project. They have created three scenarios and cash flow analyses as shown in Table 17–5. The values shown have all been converted to annual worth costs and represent the increments from the expected values (0 = most likely).

These incremental changes can then be evaluated with regard to how they impact the company's overall ROR. With a base profit stream of 30.2 ($\times\ 10^6$), the analysis provides the information that in the worst case, Tight Gas Inc. is still likely to achieve

$$\text{Profit}_{\text{pessimistic scenario}} = \text{base profit} + \text{total incremental changes}$$

$$= 30.2(\times\ 10^6) + [-17.6(\times\ 10^6)]$$

$$= 12.6 \text{ million dollars with the pessimistic scenario}$$

If they are fortunate, the profit might be as high as

$$\text{Profit}_{\text{optimistic scenario}} = 30.2(\times\ 10^6) + 9.4(\times\ 10^6)$$

$$= 39.6 \text{ million dollars with the optimistic scenario}$$

TABLE 17–5 Scenario Analysis, Example 17.7 (all values × 10⁶)

Pessimistic Scenario

Demand decreases due to warmer temperature	−1.2
Cost of environmental compliance increases	−0.5
Unusual geological formations impede drilling	−1.2
Limited access to market from pipeline capacity restriction	−0.8
Negative impact from Canada/U.S. exchange rate fluctuation	−4.0
High demand for equipment and supplies limits expansion	−0.5
High interest rates limit expansion initiatives	−5.0
Change in trust taxation law decreases investment equity	−1.5
Drop in gas prices	−0.2
Delays of required regulatory approvals	−0.1
Failure to successfully market gas to new customers	−0.7
Lower-than-estimated projections of reserves	−1.0
Higher-than-estimated costs in production expenses	−0.2
Higher cost of health and safety equipment and procedures	−0.3
Low success in exploration activities	−0.4
Total incremental changes	**−17.6**

Most Likely Scenario

Projected costs for production accurate	0
Moderate success in exploration activities	0
Small decrease in demand	0
Change in trust taxation laws decrease investment equity	0
Occasional geological impediment to drilling	0
Projected levels of reserves are accurate	0
Medium market growth	0
Reasonable time for regulatory approvals	0
Increasing gas prices	0
Policies on health, safety, and environment exceeding requirements	0
Total incremental changes	**0**

Optimistic Scenario

International political events that cause price of oil to rise significantly	2.3
Flourishing exploration activities	2.0
Favourable exchange rates and interest rates	0
Weather conducive to exploration and production activities	0
Ideal geology of oil and gas deposits	0.2
Underutilized transportation and pipeline infrastructure capacity	0
Availability of resources for booming expansion	0.8
Burgeoning markets	1.0
Higher-than-estimated reserves	1.8
Lower-than-estimated costs in production expenses	1.3
Policies on health, safety, and environment exceeding requirements	0
Total incremental changes	**9.4**

Subjective criteria concerning their potential market share in the light of the above risks can also be included for the final decision concerning the projects' viability in meeting their strategic plans.

17.7 **UTILITY THEORY**

Due to the varied nature of project outcomes, it is not always suitable to reference them in monetary values. The concept of *utility* can improve the analysis. Utility can be defined as the relative satisfaction that one derives from a particular activity or combination of products. In contrast, the antonym of utility is disutility or the relative discontent or inconvenience that a product or service provides. Both terms are measured in the units of *utils* and explain the behaviour of individuals or decision makers when they do not choose an option solely through the economic value calculations. For example, the utility that one receives from a particular outcome is based on individual preferences including the diminishing returns of a product. The satisfaction that one receives from consuming any product or service declines at various personal thresholds of consumption.

Finally, most engineering economic decisions concerning entrepreneurial initiatives involve some risk. The aversion or attraction one has to an investment opportunity enters into one's choice of option. For instance, as companies evolve, their behaviour toward risk will change. Initially, as an entrepreneurial concern, the principal engineers involved behave in a risk-taking fashion. They often invest a lot of their time and personal finances in a labour of love as a catalyst in creating a company. When successful, the company grows and has a responsibility toward the employees and its community, who are dependent on them for jobs and services. They then transition to a less risk-taking, even risk-averse decision behaviour. Later when the success is noted and competitors begin attempts to extract some of their share of the market, they must be more aggressive in expanding their products and services. By this time they will also normally have acquired some extra capital to invest and will become more risk-taking to maintain their position. Eventually, there is often a point in a company's evolution when the original founders are satisfied with the size and scale of the company's operations, do not desire the complications that come with continued expansion, and once again become risk-averse in order to protect what they have achieved.

At each level of the company's evolution, ascertaining the utility or disutility associated with economic risk can increase consistency in decision making. Consistency will optimize the overall economic health and profitability of a company or individual. Asking a series of questions concerning various alternatives can derive utility functions for an individual or group of people. This process captures additional dimensions of decision makers' concerns and thereby improves the engineering economic models used to suggest optimal decisions. Example 17.10 illustrates this process.

EXAMPLE 17.10

Having completed his B.Eng. in mechanical engineering, Liam is considering various universities to pursue a Ph.D. Two universities in the same city have exactly the same academic reputation for excellence, prestige, and specialized programs. One (AU) is downtown in 20-storey concrete buildings that blend into the adjacent financial district architecture. The other (BU) is a campus of ivy-covered collegiate-gothic buildings laid out in beautifully landscaped quadrangles providing a quiet oasis amid the city's chaos. The architects desired an aesthetic ambience to encourage reflection and study as well as provide a sense of belonging to time-honoured scholastic traditions. The campus has become a primary asset in the university's pursuit of the best and brightest students and faculty. Liam is currently accepted to AU, but like 60% of students, perceives environmental quality of the campus as the most important factor in determining the college of his choice. This example addresses how much additional satisfaction he believes he will experience from attending BU.

To establish the utility of the aesthetics of a university campus, the methodology would dictate that preferences for the alternative campuses be derived. The first step in the methodology is to generate a gamble that has a probability of p resulting in a known favourable outcome and a probability of $1 - p$ yielding an unfavourable outcome. Winning a lottery worth $2 million is an example of a prize most students could use to further their intellectual development. The probability of $1 - p$ is then assigned a negative outcome such as the trauma in losing acceptance to the graduate programs of AU and BU as well as the inability to gain admittance to any other graduate program.

Arbitrarily assign two utility numbers for these outcomes. The numbers designated will set the limits to the scale of utils that will be available for the analysis. Since numbers between 1 and 10 would create too small a range, one insufficient to provide detail between various utility demarcations, and numbers between 1 and 1000 might imply more accuracy than will be achieved for the classification of aesthetics, numbers between 1 and 100 will be used for this example.

Let

$$U_{\text{favourable outcome}} = 100 \quad \text{the utility of the \$2 million prize}$$

$$U_{\text{unfavourable outcome}} = 1 \quad \text{the disutility of the loss of opportunity to attend graduate school}$$

Now consider the opportunity to study in the more beautiful campus of BU and the student's utility in going there primarily for the ambiance of the environment. Liam is given the choice of accepting the risky lottery or the offer to attend BU. The value of p for the lottery has not yet been specified. It is left free for the analyst to vary. To summarize, Liam must make a choice between the following two options:

1. Choose to participate in the lottery
2. Choose to be accepted to BU with its sensitively designed and built campus

Liam does not have sufficient information to make this choice until a value of the probability p is provided. To illustrate the process, start with $p = 1.0$, which translates to a certain win of the $2 million. All decision makers will obviously choose alternative 1, since it has a very appealing return and there is no risk associated with it. Next, set $p = 0$. The decision makers will then have no possibility in winning the $2 million and will chose to attend the more aesthetic campus of BU.

If the value of p is varied between these extremes, there will be some in-between value, $p_{\text{aesthetic}}$, at which Liam will hesitate, reflect, and have great difficulty in making a choice. This reflects a point of *indifference* for him. It is here where he could be inconsistent and change his mind often concerning the choice between the two options. The $p_{\text{aesthetic}}$ is the probability point for the lottery where we observe the decision maker to be indifferent between the lottery and the prize. The utility of the prize is then evaluated by calculating the expected value of the lottery. At Liam's indifference point, this value is equal to the utility of the aesthetics of the campus at BU.

When

$p_{\text{aesthetic}}$ = probability value that stimulates indifference between lottery and campus aesthetics

$$U_{\text{lottery}} = p_{\text{aesthetic}} \times U_{\text{favourable outcome}} + (1 - p_{\text{aesthetic}}) \times U_{\text{unfavourable outcome}} = U_{\text{aesthetic}}$$

Next, the methodology stipulates that the values of p be altered between the extremes so that the individual's attitude toward this choice can be simulated until we observe the point of indifference. Suppose

$$p = 50\%$$

Liam states that he will choose option 1 for the lottery so we now vary the p values between 0.5 and 0. When

$$p = 10\%$$

Liam prefers option 2, desiring the improved aesthetics of campus BU.

We now vary the p values between 0.5 and 0.1. Through an interview process requiring several additional iterations, the probability of p is set to 35%. Liam then has difficulty deciding; this is the point of his indifference between the two options.

To complete the methodology, this probability becomes $p_{\text{aesthetic}}$ and is evaluated in the utility equation.

$$U_{\text{lottery}} = 0.35 \times U_{\text{favourable outcome}} + (1 - 0.35) \times U_{\text{unfavourable outcome}} = U_{\text{aesthetic}}$$

$$U_{\text{lottery}} = 0.35 \times 100 + (1 - 0.35) \times 1 = U_{\text{aesthetic}}$$

$$U_{\text{lottery}} = U_{\text{aesthetic}} = 35.65$$

The same process is used to derive utility values for other items (such as a strong theatre program, ice hockey team, or library) that Liam considers important in his decision. Since the process is cardinal, he will be able to sum the utilities generated for items relating to each campus and achieve insight as to the relative satisfaction he will receive.

Once the utilities are derived for various outcomes, they can be substituted into the decision tree in place of the monetary values. From these new numbers, evaluation of the tree occurs yielding computations that reflect the decision makers' perceptions of the outcomes. The final choice is then made to select the branch with the largest calculated utility number. Once the team commits themselves to the utilities generated by the interviews, no additional questioning is required to predict the best set of decisions. The process is able to simulate decision makers' preferences with additional accuracy. The results derived with utility values are intuitively more credible and tenable than those obtained from monetary calculations.

CHAPTER SUMMARY

In this chapter the emphasis is on sensitivity to variation in one or more parameters using a specific measure of worth. When two alternatives are compared, compute and graph the measure of worth for different values of the parameter to determine when each alternative is better.

When several parameters are expected to vary over a predictable range, the measure of worth is plotted and calculated using three estimates for a parameter—most likely, pessimistic, and optimistic. This formalized approach can help determine which alternative is best among several. Independence between parameters is assumed in all these analyses.

The combination of parameter and probability estimates results in the expected value relation

$$E(X) = \Sigma X P(X)$$

This expression is also used to calculate E(revenue), E(cost), E(cash flow), E(PW), and $E(i)$ for the entire cash flow sequence of an alternative.

Decision trees are used to make a series of alternative selections. This is a way to explicitly take risk into account. It is necessary to make several types of estimates for a decision tree: outcomes for each possible decision, cash flows, and probabilities. Expected value computations are coupled with those for the measure of worth to solve the tree and find the best alternatives stage by stage. Much is learned about a project through the construction of relevant decision trees.

Scenario analysis is used to address future variables whose values cannot be predicted with mathematical forecasting procedures. This technique allows decisions to be made by studying various contingencies for the future, taking into consideration the risks associated with outcomes that would otherwise not be considered.

Utility theory is added to the analysis in order to capture the satisfaction derived from a service or product. This provides another dimension for decision makers who use various noneconomic criteria along with the traditional economic value calculation.

PROBLEMS

Sensitivity to Parameter Variation

17.1 The Central Drug Distribution Centre wants to evaluate a new materials handling system for fragile products. The complete device will cost $62,000 and have an 8-year life and a salvage value of $1500. Annual maintenance, fuel, and overhead costs are estimated at $0.50 per tonne moved. Labour cost will be $8 per hour for regular wages and $16 for overtime. A total of 20 tonnes can be moved in an 8-hour period. The centre handles from 10 to 30 tonnes of fragile products per day. The centre uses a MARR of 10%. Determine the sensitivity of present worth of costs to the annual volume moved. Assume the operator is paid regular wages for 200 days of work per year. Use a 10-tonne increment for the analysis.

17.2 An equipment alternative is being economically evaluated separately by three engineers at Research In Motion. The first cost will be $77,000, and the life is estimated at 6 years with a salvage value of $10,000. The engineers disagree, however, on the estimated revenue the equipment will generate. Joe has made an estimate of $10,000 per year. Jane states that this is too low and estimates $14,000, while Carlos estimates $18,000 per year. If the before-tax MARR is 8% per year, use PW to determine if these different estimates will change the decision to purchase the equipment.

17.3 A manufacturing company needs 1000 square metres of storage space. Purchasing land for $80,000 and erecting a temporary metal building at $70 per square metre are one option. The president expects to sell the land for $100,000 and the building for $20,000 after 3 years. Another option is to lease space for $2.50 per square metre per month payable at the beginning of each year. The MARR is 20%. Perform a present worth analysis of the building and leasing alternatives to determine the sensitivity of the decision if construction costs go down 10% and the lease cost goes up to $2.75 per square metre per month.

17.4 Bombardier engineers are analyzing two automated production systems, and wish to determine if system 1 or system 2 is sensitive to the variation in return required by management. Do the analysis for MARR equal to 8%, 10%, 12%, 14%, and 16%.

	System 1	System 2
First cost, $	−50,000	−100,000
AOC, $ per year	−6,000	−1,500
Salvage value, $	30,000	0
Rework at midlife, $	−17,000	−30,000
Life, years	4	12

17.5 A new demonstration system has been designed by Custom Baths & Showers. For the data shown, determine the sensitivity of the rate of return to the amount of the revenue gradient G for values from $1500 to $2500. If the MARR is 18% per year, would this variation in the revenue gradient affect the decision to build the demonstration system? Work this problem (a) by hand and (b) by computer.

$$P = \$74,000 \quad n = 10 \text{ years} \quad S = 0$$

Expense: $30,000 first year, increasing
$3000 per year thereafter
Revenue: $63,000 first year, decreasing
by G per year thereafter

17.6 Consider the two air conditioning systems detailed below.

	System 1	System 2
First cost, $	−10,000	−17,000
Annual operating cost, $/year	−600	−150
Salvage value, $	−100	−300
New compressor and motor cost at midlife, $	−1,750	−3,000
Life, years	8	12

Use AW analysis to determine the sensitivity of the economic decision to MARR values of 4%, 6%, and 8%. Plot the sensitivity curve. Work this problem (a) by hand and (b) by computer.

17.7 (a) Calculate by hand and plot the sensitivity of rate of return versus the bond interest rate of a $50,000 fifteen-year corporate bond that has bond interest paid quarterly and is discounted to $42,000. Consider bond rates of 5%, 7%, and 9%. (b) Use a spreadsheet to solve this problem.

17.8 Leona has been offered an investment opportunity that will require a cash outlay of $30,000 now for a cash inflow of $3500 for each year of investment. However, she must state now the number of years she plans to retain the investment. Additionally, if the investment is retained for 6 years, $25,000 will be returned to investors, but after 10 years the return is anticipated to be only $15,000, and after 12 years it is estimated to be $8000. If money is currently worth 8% per year, is the decision sensitive to the retention period?

17.9 An asset costs $8000 and has a maximum life of 15 years. Its AOC is expected to be $500 the first year and increase by an arithmetic gradient G between $60 and $140 per year thereafter. Determine the sensitivity of the economic service life to the cost gradient in increments of $40, and plot the results on the same graph. Use an interest rate of 5% per year.

17.10 Victoria Shipyards is considering the purchase of a mobile hoist from one of two companies. Use an AW analysis at a MARR of 10% per year and determine if the selection between company A and company B changes when the savings per year varies by ±20% and ±40% from the best estimates made so far.

	Company A	Company B
First cost, $	−50,000	−37,000
AOC, $ per year	−7,500	−8,000
Savings, best estimate, $ per year	15,000	13,000
Salvage value, $	5,000	3,700
Life, years	5	5

17.11 For plans A and B, graph the sensitivity of PW values at 20% per year for the range −50% to +100% of the following single-point estimates for each of the parameters: (a) first cost, (b) AOC, and (c) annual revenue.

	Plan A	Plan B
First cost, $	−500,000	−375,000
AOC, $/year	−75,000	−80,000
Annual revenue, $/year	150,000	130,000
Salvage value, $	50,000	37,000
Expected life, years	5	5

17.12 Use a spreadsheet to determine and graph the sensitivity of the rate of return to a ±25% change in (a) purchase price and (b) selling price for the following investment. An engineer purchased an antique car for $25,000 with the plan to "make it original" and sell it at a profit. Improvements cost $5500 the first year, $1500 the second year, and $1300 the third year. He sold the car after 3 years for $35,000.

17.13 Use a spreadsheet to plot on one graph (similar to Figure 17–3) the sensitivity of AW over the range −30% to +50% of the parameters (a) first cost, (b) AOC, and (c) annual revenue. Use a MARR of 18% per year.

Process	Estimate
First cost, $	−80,000
Salvage value, $	10,000
Life, years	10
AOC, $/year	−15,000
Annual revenue, $/year	39,000

17.14 Graph the sensitivity of what a person should be willing to pay now for a 9% $10,000 bond due in 10 years if there is a ±30% change in (a) face value, (b) dividend rate, or (c) required nominal rate of return, which is expected to be 8% per year, compounded semiannually. The bond dividends are paid semiannually.

Three Estimates

17.15 An engineer must decide between two ways to pump concrete up to the top floors of a seven-storey office building to be constructed. Plan 1 requires the purchase of equipment for $6000 which costs between $0.40 and $0.75 per tonne to operate, with a most likely cost of $0.50 per tonne. The asset is able to pump 100 tonnes per day. If purchased, the asset will last for 5 years, have no salvage value, and be used from 50 to 100 days per year. Plan 2 is an equipment-leasing option and is expected to cost the company $2500 per year for equipment with a low cost estimate of $1800 and a high estimate of $3200 per year. In addition, an extra $5 per hour labour cost will be incurred for operating the leased equipment per 8-hour day. Plot the AW of each plan versus total annual operating cost or lease cost at $i = 12\%$. Which plan should the engineer recommend if the most likely estimate of use is (a) 50 days per year and (b) 100 days per year?

17.16 A meat packing plant must decide between two ways to cool cooked hams. Spraying cools to 30°C using approximately 80 litres of water for each ham.

The immersion method uses 40 litres per ham, but an extra initial cost for equipment of $2000 and extra maintenance costs of $100 per year for the 10-year life are estimated. Ten million hams per year are cooked, and water costs $0.12 per 1000 litres. Another cost is $0.04 per 1000 litres for wastewater treatment, which is required for either method. The MARR is 15% per year.

If the spray method is selected, the amount of water used can vary from an optimistic value of 40 litres to a pessimistic value of 100 litres with 80 litres being the most likely amount. The immersion technique always takes 40 litres per ham. How will this varying use of water for the spray method affect the economic decision?

17.17 When the country's economy is expanding, AB Investment Company is optimistic and expects a MARR of 15% for new investments. However, in a receding economy the expected return is 8%. Normally a 10% return is required. An expanding economy causes the estimates of asset life to go down about 20%, and a receding economy makes the n values increase about 10%. Plot the sensitivity of present worth versus (*a*) the MARR and (*b*) the life values for the two plans detailed below, using the most likely estimates for the other factors. (*c*) Considering all the analyses, under which scenario, if any, should plan M or Q be rejected?

	Plan M	Plan Q
Initial investment, $	−100,000	−110,000
Cash flow, $/year	+15,000	+19,000
Life, years	20	20

Expected Value

17.18 Calculate the expected flow rate for each oil well using the estimated probabilities.

	Expected Flow, Barrels/Day			
	100	200	300	400
North well	0.15	0.75	0.10	—
East well	0.35	0.15	0.45	0.05

17.19 There are four estimates made for the anticipated cycle time to produce a subcomponent. The estimates, in seconds, are 10, 20, 30, and 70. (*a*) If equal weight is placed on each estimate what is the expected time to plan for? (*b*) If the largest time is disregarded, estimate the expected time. Does the large estimate seem to significantly increase the expected value?

17.20 The variable Y is defined as 3^n for $n = 1, 2, 3, 4$ with probabilities of 0.4, 0.3, 0.233, and 0.067, respectively. Determine the expected value of Y.

17.21 The AOC value for an alternative is expected to be one of two values. Your office partner told you that the low value is $2800 per year. If her computations show a probability of 0.75 for the high value and an expected AOC of $4575, what is the high AOC value she used in the computation of the average?

17.22 A total of 40 different proposals were evaluated by the IRAD (Industrial Research and Development) committee during the past year. Twenty were funded. Their rate of return estimates are summarized below with the $i*$ values rounded to the nearest integer. For the accepted proposals, calculate the expected rate of return $E(i)$.

Proposal Rate of Return, %	Number of Proposals
−8	1
−5	1
0	5
5	5
8	2
10	3
15	3
	20

17.23 Starbreak Foods has performed an economic analysis of proposed service in a new region of the country. The three-estimate approach to sensitivity analysis has been applied. The optimistic and pessimistic values each have an estimated 15% chance of occurring. Use the AW values shown to compute the expected AW.

	Optimistic	Most Likely	Pessimistic
AW value, $/year	+300,000	+50,000	−25,000

17.24 (a) Determine the expected present worth of the following cash flow series if each series may be realized with the probability shown at the head of each column. Let $i = 20\%$ per year.

(b) Determine the expected AW value for the same cash flow series.

Annual Cash Flow, $/Year

Year	Prob. = 0.5	Prob. = 0.2	Prob. = 0.3
0	−5000	−6000	−4000
1	1000	500	3000
2	1000	1500	1200
3	1000	2000	−800

17.25 A very successful health and recreation club wants to construct a mock mountain for climbing and exercise outside for its customers' use. Because of its location, there is a 30% chance of a 120-day season of good outdoor weather, a 50% chance of a 150-day season, and a 20% chance of a 165-day season. The mountain will be used by an estimated 350 persons each day of the 4-month (120-day) season, but by only 100 per day for each extra day the season lasts. The feature will cost $375,000 to construct and require a $25,000 rework each 4 years, and the annual maintenance and insurance costs will be $56,000. The climbing fee will be $5 per person. If a life of 10 years is anticipated and a 12% per year return is expected, determine if the addition is economically justified.

17.26 The owner of Ace Roofing may invest $200,000 in new equipment. A life of 6 years and a salvage value of 12% of first cost are anticipated. The annual extra revenue will depend upon the state of the housing and construction industry. The extra revenue is expected to be only $20,000 per year if the current slump in the industry continues. Real estate economists estimate a 50% chance of the slump lasting 3 years and give it a 20% chance of continuing for 3 additional years. However, if the depressed market does improve, during either the first or second 3-year period, the revenue of the investment is expected to increase by a total of $35,000 per year. Can the company expect to make a return of 8% per year on its investment? Use present worth analysis.

17.27 Jeremy has $5000 to invest. If he puts the money in a guaranteed investment certificate (GIC), he is assured of receiving an effective 6.35% per year for 5 years. If he invests the money in stocks, he has a 50-50 chance of one of the following cash flow sequences for the next 5 years.

Annual Cash Flow, $/Year

	Prob. = 0.5	Prob. = 0.5
Year	Stock 1	Stock 2
0	−5000	−5000
1–4	+250	+600
5	+6800	+4000

Finally, Jeremy can invest his $5000 in real estate for the 5 years with the following cash flow and probability estimates.

Annual Cash Flow, $/Year

Year	Prob. = 0.3	Prob. = 0.5	Prob. = 0.2
0	−5000	−5000	−5000
1	−425	0	+500
2	−425	0	+600
3	−425	0	+700
4	−425	0	+800
5	+9500	+7200	+5200

Which of the three investment opportunities offers the best expected rate of return?

17.28 P. Béchard Inc. has $1 million in an investment pool which the board of directors plans to place in projects with different debt-equity mixes varying from 20–80 to 80–20. To assist with the decision, the plot shown below, prepared by the chief financial officer, of currently estimated annual equity rates of return (i on equity capital) versus various D-E mixes will be used. All investments will be for 10 years with no intermediate cash flows in or out of the projects. The motion passed by the board is to invest as follows:

D-E mix	20–80	50–50	80–20
Percent of pool	30%	50%	20%

(a) What is the current estimate of the expected annual rate of return on the company's equity capital for the $1 million investments after 10 years?

(b) What is the actual amount of equity capital invested now, and what is the expected total amount after 10 years for the board-approved investment plan?

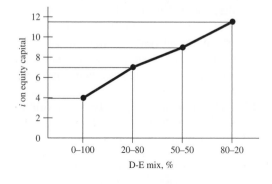

(c) If inflation is expected to average 4.5% per year over the next 10-year period, determine both the real interest rates at which the equity investment funds will grow and the purchasing power in terms of today's (constant-value) dollars of the actual amount accumulated after 10 years.

17.29 A hotel in St. John's must construct a retaining wall next to its parking lot due to the widening of the thoroughfare located in front of the hotel. The amount of rainfall experienced in a short period of time may cause damage in varying amounts, and the wall increases in cost in order to protect against larger and faster rainfalls. The probabilities of a specific amount of rainfall in a 30-minute period and wall cost estimates are as follows:

Rainfall, Inches/30 Minutes	Probability of Greater Rainfall	Estimated First Cost of Wall, $
2.0	0.3	−200,000
2.25	0.1	−225,000
2.5	0.05	−300,000
3.0	0.01	−400,000
3.25	0.005	−450,000

The wall will be financed through a 6% per year loan for the full amount that will be repaid over a 10-year period.

Records indicate an average damage of $50,000 has occurred with heavy rains, due to the relatively poor cohesive properties of the soil along the thoroughfare. A discount rate of 6% per year is applicable. Find the amount of rainfall to protect against by choosing the retaining wall with the smallest AW value over the 10-year period.

Decision Trees

17.30 For the decision tree branch shown, determine the expected values of the two outcomes if decision D3 is already selected and the maximum outcome value is sought. (This decision branch is part of a larger tree.)

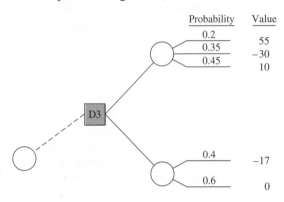

	Probability	Value
	0.2	55
	0.35	-30
	0.45	10

	0.4	-17
	0.6	0

17.31 A large decision tree has an outcome branch that is detailed for this problem. If decisions D1, D2, and D3 are all options in a 1-year time period, find the decision path which maximizes the outcome value. There are specific dollar investments necessary for decision nodes D1, D2, and D3 as indicated on each branch.

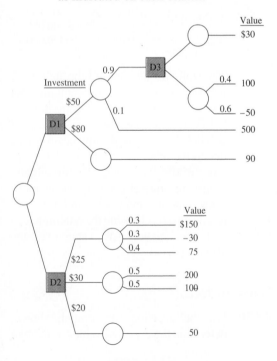

17.32 Decision D4, which has three possible alternatives—*x*, *y*, or *z*—must be made in year 3 of a 6-year study period in order to maximize the expected value of present worth. Using a rate of return of 15% per year, the investment required in year 3, and the estimated cash flows for years 4 through 6, determine which decision should be made in year 3. (This decision node is part of a larger tree.)

	Investment Required, Year 3	Cash Flow (× $1000) Year 4	Year 5	Year 6	Outcome Probability
High	$-200,000	$50	$50	$50	0.7
Low		40	30	20	0.3
High	-75,000	30	40	50	0.45
Low		30	30	30	0.55
High	-350,000	190	170	150	0.7
Low		-30	-30	-30	0.3

17.33 A total of 5000 mechanical subassemblies are needed annually on a final assembly line. The subassemblies can be obtained in one of three ways: (1) *Make them* in one of three plants owned by the company; (2) *buy them off the shelf* from the one and only manufacturer; or (3) *contract to have them made* to specifications by a vendor.

The estimated annual cost for each alternative is dependent upon specific circumstances of the plant, producer, or contractor. The information shown in the table that follows details the circumstance, a probability of occurrence, and the estimated annual cost. Construct and solve a decision tree to determine the least-cost alternative to provide the subassemblies.

17.34 The president of ChemTech is trying to decide whether to start a new product line or purchase a small company. It is

Decision Alternative	Outcomes	Probability	Annual Cost for 5000 Units, $/Year
1. Make	Plant:		
	A	0.3	−250,000
	B	0.5	−400,000
	C	0.2	−350,000
2. Buy off the shelf	Quantity:		
	<5000, pay premium	0.2	−550,000
	5000 available	0.7	−250,000
	>5000, forced to buy	0.1	−290,000
3. Contract	Delivery:		
	Timely delivery	0.5	−175,000
	Late delivery; then buy some off shelf	0.5	−450,000

not financially possible to do both. To make the product for a 3-year period will require an initial investment of $250,000. The expected annual cash flows with probabilities in parentheses are: $75,000 (0.5), $90,000 (0.4), and $150,000 (0.1).

To purchase the small company will cost $450,000 now. Market surveys indicate a 55% chance of increased sales for the company and a 45% chance of severe decreases with an annual cash flow of $25,000. If decreases are experienced in the first year, the company will be sold immediately (during year 1) at a price of $200,000. Increased sales could be $100,000 the first 2 years. If this occurs, a decision to expand after 2 years at an additional investment of $100,000 will be considered. This expansion could generate cash flows with indicated probabilities as follows: $120,000 (0.3), $140,000 (0.3), and $175,000 (0.4). If expansion is not chosen, the current size will be maintained with anticipated sales to continue.

Assume there are no salvage values on any investments. Use the description given and a 15% per year return to do the following:

(a) Construct a decision tree with all values and probabilities shown.
(b) Determine the expected PW values at the "expansion/no expansion"

decision node after 2 years provided sales are up.

(c) Determine what decision should be made now to offer the greatest return possible for ChemTech.

(d) Explain in words what would happen to the expected values at each decision node if the planning horizon were extended beyond 3 years and all cash flow values continued as forecasted in the description.

Scenario Analysis

17.35 The following data is available for company VWX in Newfoundland and Labrador as they make a decision concerning the acquisition of two mutually exclusive production alternatives for the next ten years:

	Alternative 1		
	Pessimistic	Expected	Optimistic
First cost ($)	200,000	175,000	160,000
Annual operating cost ($)	100,000	90,000	75,000
Salvage value ($)	3,000	4,000	7,000
	Alternative 2		
	Pessimistic	Expected	Optimistic
First cost ($)	320,000	255,000	220,000
Annual operating cost ($)	60,000	50,000	35,000
Salvage value ($)	18,000	20,000	27,000

Their MARR is 12%. Management has selected four case situations that they think are the most likely scenarios to represent the future. The following combinations of variables depict them:

	First Cost	Annual Operating Cost	Salvage Value
Case 1:	Expected	Expected	Expected
Case 2:	Optimistic	Optimistic	Expected
Case 3:	Pessimistic	Expected	Pessimistic
Case 4:	Expected	Pessimistic	Optimistic

Using scenario analysis, calculate the expected value of each case's cash flow and determine if one alternative dominates the other. What is the best decision?

17.36 Develop a scenario for the following situation (invent numbers to illustrate the analysis):

The Premier of British Columbia has announced a new program to give $1000 for every newborn baby, to be used for his or her postsecondary education. The government will put the money in an interest-bearing account for 18 years as a tuition subsidy. The program is expected to cost the taxpayers $41 million a year. The government is predicting that this policy will satisfy the needs of current newborns in the year 2025. Those in favour of the policy say it might be viewed as a government-sponsored initiative to start savings accounts for children. Critics point out that the economy is becoming a knowledge-based one, which might inspire free tuition in the future following the lead of many countries. They also point out that this money could be used today for bursaries and education tax breaks, the expansion of college spaces, and apprenticeship programs. Further concerns address distribution not based on need, and the issue of secondary-school graduates who move out of the province or delay their entrance into university.

The policy is looking forward with the goal of providing for the future. What are the key items that can prove this initiative to be a failure or a success?

Utility Theory

17.37 Liam, of Example 17.10, also wants to consider the availability of an intramural sports program as a principal concern in his decision. When the same lottery process is provided for this choice (only considering the sports program) his indifference point occurs at 25%. Calculate Liam's utility for intramural sports.

17.38 Erica is considering two motorcycles for her transportation needs, the Yamaha Roadliner (1854cc cruiser) and the Moto Guzzi Breva (1100cc naked sport bike with touring package). A standard lottery process was used to derive the following utility values of various criteria.

	Moto Guzzi Breva	Yamaha Roadliner
Power	35	40
Ergonomics	40	30
Brand-name cool factor	45	30
Availability of mechanics	30	47
Style	35	40
Function	40	35
Weight	30	25
Handling	40	35

Other items such as reliability and purchase price have such a small difference that for simplicity they are deleted.

(a) Even though the Moto Guzzi is lighter than the Yamaha, why is the value in the weight column higher for the Moto Guzzi?

(b) Given Erica's utility values for individual criteria, what motorcycle will she prefer?

LOOKING AT ALTERNATIVES FROM DIFFERENT ANGLES

Berkshire Controllers usually finances its engineering projects with a combination of debt and equity capital. The resulting MARR ranges from a low of 8% per year, if business is slow, to a high of 15% per year. Normally, a 10% per year return is expected. Also, the life estimates for assets tend to go down about 20% from normal in a vigorous business environment, and up about 10% in a receding economy. The following estimates are the most likely values for two plans currently being evaluated. Use these data and a spreadsheet to answer the questions below.

	Plan A	Plan B Asset 1	Plan B Asset 2
First cost, $	−10,000	−30,000	−5000
AOC, $ per year	−500	−100	−200
Salvage value, $	1000	5000	−200
Estimated life, years	40	40	20

Questions

1. Are the PW values for plans A and B sensitive to changes in the MARR?
2. Are the PW values sensitive to varying life estimates?
3. Plot the results above on separate charts for MARR and life estimates.
4. Is the breakeven point for the first cost of plan A sensitive to the changes in MARR as business goes from vigorous to receding?

SENSITIVITY ANALYSIS OF PUBLIC SECTOR PROJECTS—WATER SUPPLY PLANS

Introduction

One of the most basic services provided by municipal governments is the delivery of a safe, reliable water supply. As cities grow and extend their boundaries to outlying areas, they often inherit water systems that were not constructed according to municipal codes. The upgrading of these systems is sometimes more expensive than installing one correctly in the first place. To avoid these problems, city officials sometimes install water systems beyond the existing city limits in anticipation of future growth. This case study was extracted from such a water and wastewater management plan and is limited to only some of the water supply alternatives.

Procedure

From about a dozen suggested plans, five methods were developed by an executive committee as alternative ways of providing water to the study area. These methods were then subjected to a preliminary evaluation to identify the most promising alternatives. Six attributes or factors used in the initial rating were: ability to serve the area, relative cost, engineering feasibility, institutional issues, environmental considerations, and lead time requirement. Each factor carried the same weighting and had values ranging from 1 to 5, with 5 being best. After the top three alternatives were identified, each was subjected to a detailed economic evaluation for selection of the best alternative. These detailed evaluations included an estimate of the capital investment of each alternative amortized over 20 years at 8% per year interest and the annual maintenance and operation (M&O) costs. The annual cost (an AW value) was then divided by the population served to arrive at a monthly cost per household.

Results of Preliminary Screening

Table 17–6 presents the results of the screening using the six factors rated on a scale of 1 to 5. Alternatives 1A, 3, and 4 were determined to be the three best and were chosen for further evaluation.

Detailed Cost Estimates for Selected Alternatives

All amounts are cost estimates.

Alternative 1A

Capital cost:

Land with water rights: 1720 hectares @ $5000 per hectare	$ 8,600,000
Primary treatment plant	2,560,000
Booster station at plant	221,425
Reservoir at booster station	50,325
Site cost	40,260
Transmission line from river	3,020,000
Transmission line right-of-way	23,350
Percolation beds	2,093,500
Percolation bed piping	60,400
Production wells	510,000
Well field gathering system	77,000
Distribution system	1,450,000
Additional distribution system	3,784,800
Reservoirs	250,000
Reservoir site, land, and development	17,000
Subtotal	22,758,060
Engineering and contingencies	5,641,940
Total capital investment	$28,400,000

TABLE 17–6 Results of Rating Six Factors for Each Alternative, Case Study

Alternative	Description	Ability to Supply Area	Relative Cost	Engineering Feasibility	Institutional Issues	Environmental Considerations	Lead-Time Requirement	Total
					Factor			
1A	Receive city water and recharge wells	5	4	3	4	5	3	24
3	Joint city and regional district plant	5	4	4	3	4	3	23
4	Regional district treatment plant	4	4	3	3	4	3	21
8	Desalt groundwater	1	2	1	1	3	4	12
12	Develop water in provincial park	5	5	4	1	3	1	19

Maintenance and operation costs (annual):
Pumping 9,812,610 kWh/year
 @ \$0.08/kWh   \$ 785,009
 Fixed operating cost   180,520
 Variable operating cost   46,730
 Taxes for water rights   48,160
  Total annual M&O cost   \$1,060,419

Total annual cost = equivalent capital investment + M&O cost
$$= 28{,}400{,}000(A/P,8\%,20) + 1{,}060{,}419$$
$$= 2{,}892{,}540 + 1{,}060{,}419$$
$$= \$3{,}952{,}959$$

Average monthly household cost to serve 95% of 4980 households is

$$\text{Household cost} = (3{,}952{,}959)\frac{1}{12}\frac{1}{4980}\frac{1}{0.95}$$

$$= \$69.63 \text{ per month}$$

Alternative 3

Total capital investment   = \$29,600,000
Total annual M&O cost   = \$867,119
Total annual cost   = 29,600,000(A/P,8%,20) + 867,119
                            = 3,014,760 + 867,119
                            = \$3,881,879
Household cost   = \$68.38 per month

Alternative 4

Total capital investment   = \$29,000,000
Total annual M&O cost   = \$1,063,449
Total annual cost   = 29,000,000(A/P,8%,20) + 1,063,449
                            = 2,953,650 + 1,063,449
                            = \$4,017,099
Household cost   = \$70.76 per month

Conclusion

On the basis of the lowest monthly household cost, alternative 3 (joint city and regional district plant) is the most economically attractive.

Case Study Exercises

1. If the environmental considerations factor is to have a weighting of twice as much as any of the other five factors, what is its percentage weighting?

2. If the ability to supply area and relative cost factors were each weighted 20% and the other four factors 15% each, which alternatives would be ranked in the top three?

3. By how much would the capital investment of alternative 4 have to decrease in order to make it more attractive than alternative 3?

4. If alternative 1A served 100% of the households instead of 95%, by how much would the monthly household cost decrease?

5. (*a*) Perform a sensitivity analysis on the two parameters of M&O costs and number of households to determine if alternative 3 remains the best economic choice. Three estimates are made for each parameter in Table 17–7. M&O costs may vary up (pessimistic) or down (optimistic) from the most likely estimates presented in the case statement. The estimated number of households (4980) is determined to be the pessimistic estimate. Growth of 2% up to 5% (optimistic) will tend to lower the monthly cost per household.

   (*b*) Consider the monthly cost per household for alternative 4, the optimistic estimate. The number of households is 5% above 4980, or 5230. What is the number of households that would have to be available in order for this option only to have exactly the same monthly household cost as that for alternative 3 at the optimistic estimate of 5230 households?

TABLE 17–7 Pessimistic, Most Likely, and Optimistic Estimates for Two Parameters		
	Annual M&O Costs	Number of Households
Alternative 1A		
Pessimistic	+1%	4980
Most likely	$1,060,419	+2%
Optimistic	−1%	+5%
Alternative 3		
Pessimistic	+5%	4980
Most likely	$867,119	+2%
Optimistic	0%	+5%
Alternative 4		
Pessimistic	+2%	4980
Most likely	$1,063,449	+2%
Optimistic	−10%	+5%

CHAPTER 18

More on Variation and Decision Making Under Risk

This chapter further expands our ability to analyze variation in estimates, to consider probability, and to make decisions under risk. Fundamentals discussed include probability distributions, especially their graphs and properties of expected value and dispersion; random sampling; and the use of simulation to account for variation in engineering economy studies.

Through coverage of variation and probability, this chapter complements topics in the first sections of Chapter 1: the role of engineering economy in decision making and economic analysis in the problem-solving process. These techniques are more time-consuming than using estimates made with certainty, so they should be used primarily for critical parameters.

LEARNING OBJECTIVES

Purpose: Learn to incorporate decision making under risk into an engineering economy analysis using the basics of probability distributions, sampling, and simulation.

By the end of this chapter you should be able to

Certainty and risk	**1.** Apply the different approaches to decision making under certainty and under risk.
Variables and distributions	**2.** Construct the probability distribution and cumulative distribution for a variable.
Random sample	**3.** Develop a random sample from the cumulative distribution of a variable.
Average and dispersion	**4.** Estimate the expected value and standard deviation of a population from a random sample.
Monte Carlo sampling	**5.** Use Monte Carlo sampling to select an alternative.
Stochastic and deterministic simulation	**6.** Use stochastic and deterministic simulation to aid decision making.

18.1 INTERPRETATION OF CERTAINTY, RISK, AND UNCERTAINTY

All things in the world vary—one from another, over time, and with different environments. We are guaranteed that variation will occur in engineering economy due to its emphasis on decision making for the future. Except for the use of breakeven analysis, sensitivity analysis, and a brief introduction to expected values and scenario analysis, virtually all our estimates have been *certain*; that is, no variation in the amount has entered into the computations of PW, AW, ROR, or any relations used. For example, the estimate that cash flow next year will be $+4500 is one of certainty. Certainty is, of course, not present in the real world now and surely not in the future. We can observe outcomes with a high degree of certainty, but even this depends upon the accuracy and precision of the scale or measuring instrument.

To allow a parameter of an engineering economy study to vary implies that risk, and possibly uncertainty, is introduced.

Risk. When there may be two or more observable values for a parameter *and* it is possible to estimate the chance that each value may occur, risk is present. As an illustration, decision making under risk is introduced when an annual cash flow estimate has a 50-50 chance of being either $−1000 or $+500. Accordingly, virtually all decision making is performed *under risk*.

Uncertainty. Decision making under uncertainty means there are two or more values observable, but the chances of their occurring cannot be estimated or no one is willing to assign the chances. The observable values in uncertainty analysis are often referred to as *states of nature*. For example, consider the states of nature to be the rate of national inflation in a particular country during the next 2 to 4 years: remain low, increase 5% to 10% annually, or increase 20% to 50% annually. If there is absolutely no indication that the three values are equally likely, or that one is more likely than the others, this is a statement that indicates decision making under uncertainty.

Example 18.1 explains how a parameter can be described and graphed to prepare for decision making under risk.

EXAMPLE 18.1

Sue and Charles are both seniors in college and plan to be married next year. Based upon conversations with friends who have recently married, the couple has decided to make separate estimates of what each expects the ceremony to cost, with the chance that each estimate is actually observed expressed as a percentage. (*a*) Their separate estimates are tabulated at the top of Figure 18–1. Construct two graphs: one of Charles's estimated costs versus his chance estimates, and one for Sue. Comment on the shape of the plots relative to each other. (*b*) After some discussion, they decided the ceremony should cost somewhere between $7500 and $10,000. All values between the two limits are equally likely with a chance of 1 in 25. Plot these values versus chance.

Charles		Sue	
Estimated Cost, $	**Chance, %**	**Estimated Cost, $**	**Chance, %**
3,000	65	8,000	33.3
5,000	25	10,000	33.3
10,000	10	15,000	33.3

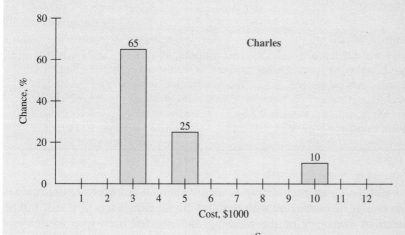

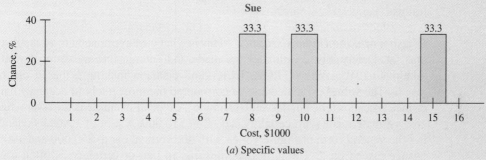

(a) Specific values

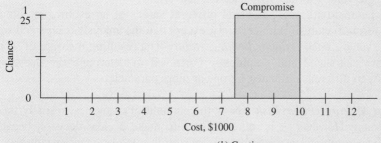

(b) Continuous range

FIGURE 18–1

Plot of cost estimates versus chance, Example 18.1.

Solution

(*a*) Figure 18–1*a* presents the plot for Charles's and Sue's estimates, with the cost scales aligned. Sue expects the cost to be considerably higher than Charles. Additionally, Sue places equal (or uniform) chances on each value. Charles places a much higher chance on lower cost values; 65% of his chances are devoted to $3000, and only 10% to $10,000, which is Sue's middle cost estimate. The plots clearly show the different perceptions about their estimated wedding costs.

(*b*) Figure 18–1*b* is the plot at a chance of 1 in 25 for the continuum of costs from $7500 through $10,000.

Comment

One significant difference between the cost estimates in parts (*a*) and (*b*) is that of discrete and continuous values. Charles and Sue first made specific, discrete estimates with chances associated with each value. The compromise estimate they reached is a continuous range of values from $7500 to $10,000 with some chance associated with every value between these limits. In the next Section, we introduce the term *variable* and define two types of variables—*discrete* and *continuous*—which have been illustrated here.

Before initiating an engineering economy study, it is important to decide if the analysis will be conducted with certainty for all parameters or if risk will be introduced. A summary of the meaning and use for each type of analysis follows.

Decision Making Under Certainty   This is what we have done in most analyses thus far. Deterministic estimates are made and entered into measure of worth relations—PW, AW, FW, ROR, BCR—and decision making is based on the results. The values estimated can be considered the most likely to occur with all chance placed on the single-value estimate. A typical example is an asset's first cost estimate made with certainty, say, $P = \$50,000$. A plot of P versus chance has the general form of Figure 18–1*a* with one vertical bar at $50,000 and 100% chance placed on it. The term *deterministic,* in lieu of certainty, is often used when single-value estimates are used exclusively.

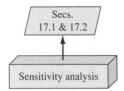

In fact, sensitivity analysis using different values of an estimate is simply another form of analysis with certainty, except that the analysis is repeated with different values, *each estimated with certainty.* The resulting measure of worth values are calculated and graphically portrayed to determine the decision's sensitivity to different estimates for one or more parameters.

Decision Making Under Risk   Now the element of chance is formally taken into account. However, it is more difficult to make a clear decision because the analysis attempts to accommodate *variation.* One or more parameters in an alternative will be allowed to vary. The estimates will be expressed as in

Example 18.1 or in slightly more complex forms. Fundamentally, there are two ways to consider risk in an analysis:

Expected value analysis. Use the chance and parameter estimates to calculate expected values, E(parameter) via formulas such as Equation [17.2]. Analysis results in E(cash flow), E(AOC), and the like; and the final result is the expected value for a measure of worth, such as E(PW), E(AW), E(ROR), E(BCR). To select the alternative, choose the most favourable expected value of the measure of worth. In an elementary form, this is what we learned about expected values in Chapter 17. The computations may become more elaborate, but the principle is fundamentally the same.

Simulation analysis. Use the chance and parameter estimates to generate repeated computations of the measure of worth relation by randomly sampling from a plot for each varying parameter similar to those in Figure 18–1. When a representative and random sample is complete, an alternative is selected utilizing a table or plot of the results. Usually, graphics are an important part of decision making via simulation analysis. Basically, this is the approach discussed in the rest of this chapter.

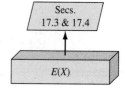

Secs.
17.3 & 17.4

$E(X)$

Decision Making Under Uncertainty   When chances are not known for the identified states of nature (or values) of the uncertain parameters, the use of expected value–based decision making under risk as outlined above is not an option. In fact, it is difficult to determine what criterion to use to even make the decision.

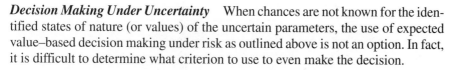

If it is possible to agree that each state is equally likely, then all states have the same chance, and the situation reduces to one of decision making under risk, because expected values can be determined.

In an engineering economy study, as well as all other forms of analysis and decision making, observed parameter values in the future will vary from the value estimated at the time of the study. However, when performing the analysis, not all parameters should be considered as probabilistic (or at risk). Those that are estimable with a relatively high degree of certainty should be fixed for the study. Accordingly, the methods of sampling, simulation, and statistical data analysis are selectively used on parameters deemed important to the decision-making process. As mentioned in Chapter 17, interest rate–based parameters (MARR, other interest rates, and inflation) are usually not treated as random variables in the discussions that follow. Parameters such as P, AOC, n, S, material and unit costs, revenues, etc., are the targets of decision making under risk and simulation. Anticipated and predictable variation in interest rates is more commonly addressed by the approaches of sensitivity analysis covered in the first two sections of Chapter 17.

The remainder of this chapter concentrates upon decision making under risk as applied in an engineering economy study. Sections 18.5, 18.6, and 18.7 provide foundation material necessary to design and correctly conduct a simulation analysis.

18.2 ELEMENTS IMPORTANT TO DECISION MAKING UNDER RISK

Some basics of probability and statistics are essential to correctly perform decision making under risk via expected value or simulation analysis. These basics are explained here. (If you are already familiar with them, this section will provide a review.)

Random Variable (or Variable) This is a characteristic or parameter that can take on any one of several values. Variables are classified as *discrete* or *continuous*. Discrete variables have several specific, isolated values, while continuous variables can assume any value between two stated limits, called the *range* of the variable.

The estimated life of an asset is a discrete variable. For example, n may be expected to have values of $n = 3$, 5, 10, or 15 years, and no others. The rate of return is an example of a continuous variable; i can vary from -100% to ∞, that is, $-100\% \leq i < \infty$. The ranges of possible values for n (discrete) and i (continuous) are shown as the x axes in Figure 18–2a. (In probability texts, capital letters

FIGURE 18–2

(*a*) Discrete and continuous variable scales and (*b*) scales for a variable versus its probability.

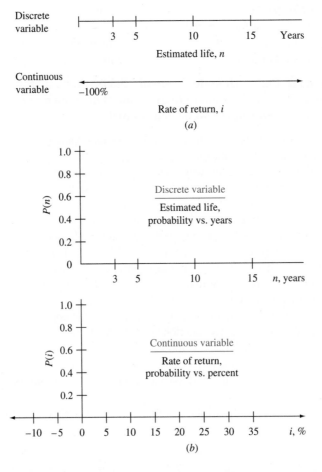

symbolize a variable, say X, and small letters, x, identify a specific value of the variable. Though correct, this level of rigour in terminology is not included in this chapter.)

Probability   This is a number between 0 and 1.0 which expresses the chance in decimal form that a random variable (discrete or continuous) will take on any value from those identified for it. Probability is simply the amount of chance, divided by 100. Probabilities are commonly identified by $P(X_i)$ or $P(X = X_i)$, which is read as the probability that the variable X takes on the value X_i. (Actually, for a continuous variable, the probability at a single value is zero, as shown in a later example.) The sum of all $P(X_i)$ for a variable must be 1.0, a requirement already discussed. The probability scale, like the percentage scale for chance in Figure 18–1, is indicated on the ordinate (y axis) of a graph. Figure 18–2b shows the 0 to 1.0 range of probability for the variables n and i.

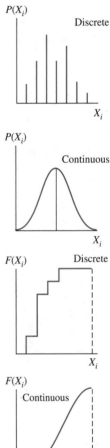

Probability Distribution   This describes how probability is distributed over the different values of a variable. Discrete variable distributions look significantly different from continuous variable distributions, as indicated by the inset at the right. The individual probability values are stated as

$$P(X_i) = \textbf{probability that } X \textbf{ equals } X_i \qquad \textbf{[18.1]}$$

The distribution may be developed in one of two ways: by listing each probability value for each possible variable value (see Example 18.2) or by a mathematical description or expression that states probability in terms of the possible variable values (Example 18.3).

Cumulative Distribution   Also called the cumulative probability distribution, this is the accumulation of probability over all values of a variable up to and including a specified value. Identified by $F(X_i)$, each cumulative value is calculated as

$$F(X_i) = \textbf{sum of all probabilities through the value } X_i$$
$$= P(X \leq X_i) \qquad \textbf{[18.2]}$$

As with a probability distribution, cumulative distributions appear differently for discrete (stair-stepped) and continuous variables (smooth curve). The next two examples illustrate cumulative distributions that correspond to specific probability distributions. These fundamentals about $F(X_i)$ are applied in the next section to develop a random sample.

EXAMPLE 18.2

Alvin is a medical doctor and biomedical engineering graduate who practises at Medical Centre Hospital. He is planning to start prescribing an antibiotic that may reduce infection in patients with flesh wounds. Tests indicate the drug has been applied up to 6 times per day without harmful side effects. If no drug is used, there is always a positive probability that the infection will be reduced by a person's own immune system.

Published drug test results provide good probability estimates of positive reaction (i.e., reduction in the infection count) within 48 hours for different numbers of treatments per day. Use the probabilities listed below to construct a probability distribution and a cumulative distribution for the number of treatments per day.

Number of Treatments per Day	Probability of Infection Reduction
0	0.07
1	0.08
2	0.10
3	0.12
4	0.13
5	0.25
6	0.25

Solution

Define the random variable T as the number of treatments per day. Since T can take on only seven different values, it is a discrete variable. The probability of infection reduction is listed for each value in column 2 of Table 18–1. The cumulative probability $F(T_i)$ is determined using Equation [18.2] by adding all $P(T_i)$ values through T_i, as indicated in column 3.

Figure 18–3a and b shows plots of the probability distribution and cumulative distribution, respectively. The summing of probabilities to obtain $F(T_i)$ gives the cumulative distribution the stair-stepped appearance, and in all cases the final $F(T_i) = 1.0$, since the total of all $P(T_i)$ values must equal 1.0.

TABLE 18–1   Probability Distribution and Cumulative Distribution for Example 18.2

(1) Number per Day T_i	(2) Probability $P(T_i)$	(3) Cumulative Probability $F(T_i)$
0	0.07	0.07
1	0.08	0.15
2	0.10	0.25
3	0.12	0.37
4	0.13	0.50
5	0.25	0.75
6	0.25	1.00

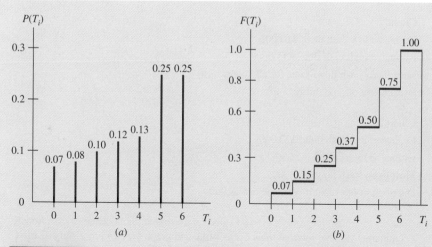

FIGURE 18–3
(a) Probability distribution $P(T_i)$ and (b) cumulative distribution $F(T_i)$ for Example 18.2.

Comment

Rather than use a tabular form as in Table 18–1 to state $P(T_i)$ and $F(T_i)$ values, it is possible to express them for each value of the variable.

$$P(T_i) = \begin{cases} 0.07 & T_1 = 0 \\ 0.08 & T_2 = 1 \\ 0.10 & T_3 = 2 \\ 0.12 & T_4 = 3 \\ 0.13 & T_5 = 4 \\ 0.25 & T_6 = 5 \\ 0.25 & T_7 = 6 \end{cases} \qquad F(T_i) = \begin{cases} 0.07 & T_1 = 0 \\ 0.15 & T_2 = 1 \\ 0.25 & T_3 = 2 \\ 0.37 & T_4 = 3 \\ 0.50 & T_5 = 4 \\ 0.75 & T_6 = 5 \\ 1.00 & T_7 = 6 \end{cases}$$

In basic engineering economy situations, the probability distribution for a continuous variable is commonly expressed as a mathematical function, such as a *uniform distribution,* a *triangular distribution* (both discussed in Example 18.3 in terms of cash flow), or the more complex, but commonly used, *normal distribution.* For continuous variable distributions, the symbol $f(X)$ is routinely used instead of $P(X_i)$, and $F(X)$ is used instead of $F(X_i)$, simply because the point probability for a continuous variable is zero. Thus, $f(X)$ and $F(X)$ are continuous lines and curves.

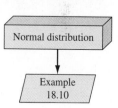

EXAMPLE 18.3

As president of a manufacturing systems consultancy, Sallie has observed the monthly cash flows that have occurred over the last 3 years into company accounts from two longstanding clients. Sallie has concluded the following about the distribution of these monthly cash flows:

Client 1

Estimated low cash flow: $10,000

Estimated high cash flow: $15,000

Most likely cash flow: same for all values

Distribution of probability: uniform

Client 2

Estimated low cash flow: $20,000

Estimated high cash flow: $30,000

Most likely cash flow: $28,000

Distribution of probability: mode at $28,000

The *mode* is the most frequently observed value for a variable. Sallie assumes cash flow to be a continuous variable referred to as C. (*a*) Write and graph the two probability distributions and cumulative distributions for monthly cash flow and (*b*) determine the probability that monthly cash flow is no more than $12,000 for client 1 and no more than $25,000 for client 2.

Solution

All cash flow values are expressed in $1000 units.

Client 1: Monthly cash flow distribution

(*a*) The distribution of cash flows for client 1, identified by the variable C_1, follows the *uniform distribution*. Probability and cumulative probability take the following general forms.

$$f(C_1) = \frac{1}{\text{high} - \text{low}} \qquad \text{low value} \le C_1 \le \text{high value}$$

$$f(C_1) = \frac{1}{H - L} \qquad L \le C_1 \le H \qquad \text{[18.3]}$$

$$F(C_1) = \frac{\text{value} - \text{low}}{\text{high} - \text{low}} \qquad \text{low value} \le C_1 \le \text{high value}$$

$$F(C_1) = \frac{C_1 - L}{H - L} \qquad L \le C_1 \le H \qquad \text{[18.4]}$$

For client 1, monthly cash flow is uniformly distributed with $L = \$10$, $H = \$15$, and $\$10 \le C_1 \le \$15$. Figure 18–4 is a plot of $f(C_1)$ and $F(C_1)$ from Equations [18.3] and [18.4].

$$f(C_1) = \frac{1}{5} = 0.2 \qquad \$10 \le C_1 \le \$15$$

$$F(C_1) = \frac{C_1 - 10}{5} \qquad \$10 \le C_1 \le \$15$$

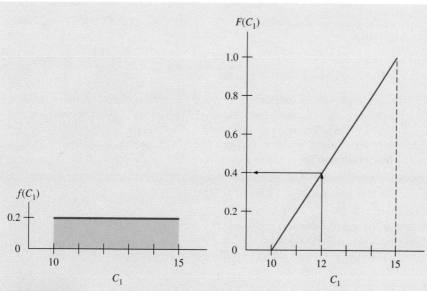

FIGURE 18–4

Uniform distribution for monthly cash flow, Example 18.3.

(b) The probability that client 1 has a monthly cash flow of less than \$12 is easily determined from the $F(C_1)$ plot as 0.4, or a 40% chance. If the $F(C_1)$ relation is used directly, the computation is

$$F(\$12) = P(C_1 \le \$12) = \frac{12 - 10}{5} = 0.4$$

Client 2: Monthly cash flow distribution

(a) The distribution of cash flows for client 2, identified by the variable C_2, follows the *triangular distribution*. This probability distribution has the shape of an upward-pointing triangle with the peak at the mode M, and downward-sloping lines joining the x axis on either side at the low (L) and high (H) values. The mode of the triangular distribution has the maximum probability value.

$$f(\text{mode}) = f(M) = \frac{2}{H - L} \qquad [18.5]$$

The cumulative distribution comprises two curved line segments from 0 to 1 with a break point at the mode, where

$$F(\text{mode}) = F(M) = \frac{M - L}{H - L} \qquad [18.6]$$

For C_2, the low value is $L = \$20$, the high is $H = \$30$, and the most likely cash flow is the mode $M = \$28$. The probability at M from Equation [18.5] is

$$f(28) = \frac{2}{30 - 20} = \frac{2}{10} = 0.2$$

and the break point in the cumulative distribution occurs at $C_2 = 28$. Using Equation [18.6],

$$F(28) = \frac{28 - 20}{30 - 20} = 0.8$$

Figure 18–5 presents the plots for $f(C_2)$ and $F(C_2)$. Note that $f(C_2)$ is skewed, since the mode is not at the midpoint of the range $H - L$, and $F(C_2)$ is a smooth S-shaped curve with an inflection point at the mode.

(b) From the cumulative distribution in Figure 18–5, there is an estimated 31.25% chance that cash flow is $25 or less.

$$F(\$25) = P(C_2 \le \$25) = 0.3125$$

Comment

Note that the general relations $f(C_2)$ and $F(C_2)$ are not developed here. The variable C_2 is *not* a uniform distribution; it is triangular. Therefore, it requires the use of an integral to find cumulative probability values from the probability distribution $f(C_2)$.

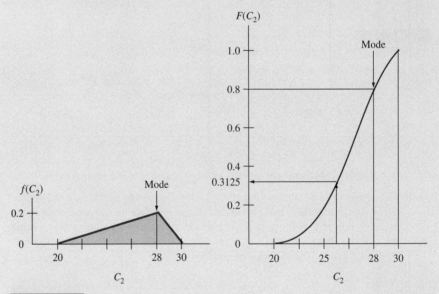

FIGURE 18–5

Triangular distribution for monthly cash flow, Example 18.3.

18.3 RANDOM SAMPLES

Estimating a parameter with a single value in previous chapters is the equivalent of taking a *random sample of size 1 from an entire population* of possible values. If all values in the population were known, the probability distribution and cumulative distribution would be known. Then a sample is not necessary. As an illustration, assume that estimates of first cost, annual operating cost, interest rate, and other parameters are used to compute one PW value in order to accept or reject an alternative. Each estimate is a sample of size 1 from an entire population of possible values for each parameter. Now, if a second estimate is made for each parameter and a second PW value is determined, a sample of size 2 has been taken.

Whenever we perform an engineering economy study and utilize decision making under certainty, we use one estimate for each parameter to calculate a measure of worth (i.e., a sample of size 1 for each parameter). The estimate is the most likely value, that is, one estimate of the expected value. We know that all parameters will vary somewhat; yet some are important enough, or will vary enough, that a probability distribution should be determined or assumed for it and the parameter treated as a random variable. This is using risk, and a sample from the parameter's probability distribution—$P(X)$ for discrete or $f(X)$ for continuous—helps formulate probability statements about the estimates. This approach complicates the analysis somewhat; however, it also provides a sense of confidence (or possibly a lack of confidence in some cases) about the decision made concerning the economic viability of the alternative based on the varying parameter. (We will further discuss this aspect later, after we learn how to correctly take a random sample from any probability distribution.)

A random sample of size n is the selection in a random fashion of n values from a population with an assumed or known probability distribution, such that the values of the variable have the same chance of occurring in the sample as they are expected to occur in the population.

Suppose Yvon is an engineer with 20 years of experience working for the Noncommercial Aircraft Safety Commission. For a two-crew aircraft, there are three parachutes on board. The safety standard states that 99% of the time, all three chutes must be "fully ready for emergency deployment." Yvon is relatively sure that nationwide the probability distribution of N, the number of chutes fully ready, may be described by the probability distribution

$$P(N = N_i) = \begin{cases} 0.005 & N = 0 \text{ chutes ready} \\ 0.015 & N = 1 \text{ chutes ready} \\ 0.060 & N = 2 \text{ chutes ready} \\ 0.920 & N = 3 \text{ chutes ready} \end{cases}$$

This means that the safety standard is clearly not met nationwide. Yvon is in the process of sampling 200 (randomly selected) corporate and private aircraft across Canada to determine how many chutes are classified as fully ready. If the sample is truly random and Yvon's probability distribution is a correct representation of actual parachute readiness, the observed N values in the 200 aircraft will approximate the same proportions as the population probabilities, that is, 1 aircraft with 0 chutes ready, etc. Since this is a sample, it is likely that the results won't track the population exactly. However, if the results are relatively close, the study indicates that the sample results may be useful in predicting parachute safety across the country.

TABLE 18–2   Random Digits Clustered into Two-Digit Numbers

51	82	88	18	19	81	03	88	91	46	39	19	28	94	70	76	33	15	64	20	14	52
73	48	28	59	78	38	54	54	93	32	70	60	78	64	92	40	72	71	77	56	39	27
10	42	18	31	23	80	80	26	74	71	03	90	55	61	61	28	41	49	00	79	96	78
45	44	79	29	81	58	66	70	24	82	91	94	42	10	61	60	79	30	01	26	31	42
68	65	26	71	44	37	93	94	93	72	84	39	77	01	97	74	17	19	46	61	49	67
75	52	14	99	67	74	06	50	97	46	27	88	10	10	70	66	22	56	18	32	06	24

To develop a random sample, use *random numbers* (*RN*) generated from a uniform probability distribution for the discrete numbers 0 through 9, that is,

$$P(X_i) = 0.1 \qquad \text{for } X_i = 0, 1, 2, \ldots, 9$$

In tabular form, the random digits so generated are commonly clustered in groups of two digits, three digits, or more. Table 18–2 is a sample of 264 random digits clustered into two-digit numbers. This format is very useful because the numbers 00 to 99 conveniently relate to the cumulative distribution values 0.01 to 1.00. This makes it easy to select a two-digit RN and enter $F(X)$ to determine a value of the variable with the same proportions as it occurs in the probability distribution. To apply this logic manually and develop a random sample of size n from a known discrete probability distribution $P(X)$ or a continuous variable distribution $f(X)$, the following procedure may be used.

1. Develop the cumulative distribution $F(X)$ from the probability distribution. Plot $F(X)$.
2. Assign the RN values from 00 to 99 to the $F(X)$ scale (the y axis) in the same proportion as the probabilities. For the parachute safety example, the probabilities from 0.0 to 0.15 are represented by the random numbers 00 to 14. Indicate the RNs on the graph.
3. To use a table of random numbers, determine the scheme or sequence of selecting RN values—down, up, across, diagonally. Any direction and pattern is acceptable, but the scheme should be used consistently for one entire sample.
4. Select the first number from the RN table, enter the $F(X)$ scale, and observe and record the corresponding variable value. Repeat this step until there are n values of the variable which constitute the random sample.
5. Use the n sample values for analysis and decision making under risk. These may include

- Plotting the sample probability distribution
- Developing probability statements about the parameter
- Comparing sample results with the assumed population distribution
- Determining sample statistics (Section 18.4)
- Performing a simulation analysis (Section 18.5)

EXAMPLE 18.4

Develop a random sample of size 10 for the variable N, number of months, as described by the probability distribution

$$P(N = N_i) = \begin{cases} 0.20 & N = 24 \\ 0.50 & N = 30 \\ 0.30 & N = 36 \end{cases} \qquad [18.7]$$

Solution

Apply the procedure above, using the $P(N = N_i)$ values in Equation [18.7].

1. The cumulative distribution, Figure 18–6, is for the discrete variable N, which can assume three different values.
2. Assign 20 numbers (00 through 19) to $N_1 = 24$ months, where $P(N = 24) = 0.2$; 50 numbers to $N_2 = 30$; and 30 numbers to $N_3 = 36$.
3. Initially select any position in Table 18–2, and go across the row to the right and onto the row below toward the left. (Any routine can be developed, and a different sequence for each random sample may be used.)
4. Select the initial number 45 (4th row, 1st column), and enter Figure 18–6 in the RN range of 20 to 69 to obtain $N = 30$ months.
5. Select and record the remaining nine values from Table 18–2 as shown below.

RN	45	44	79	29	81	58	66	70	24	82
N	30	30	36	30	36	30	30	36	30	36

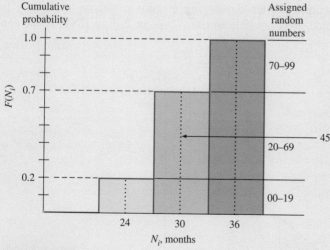

FIGURE 18–6

Cumulative distribution with random number values assigned in proportion to probabilities, Example 18.4.

Now, using the 10 values, develop the sample probabilities.

Months N	Times in Sample	Sample Probability	Equation [18.7] Probability
24	0	0.00	0.2
30	6	0.60	0.5
36	4	0.40	0.3

With only 10 values, we can expect the sample probability estimates to be different from the values in Equation [18.7]. Only the value $N = 24$ months is significantly different, since no RN of 19 or less occurred. A larger sample will definitely make the probabilities closer to the original data.

To take a *random sample of size n for a continuous variable,* the procedure above is applied, except the random number values are assigned to the cumulative distribution on a continuous scale of 00 to 99 corresponding to the $F(X)$ values. As an illustration, consider Figure 18–4, where C_1 is the *uniformly distributed* cash flow variable for client 1 in Example 18.3. Here $L = \$10$, $H = \$15$, and $f(C_1) = 0.2$ for all values between L and H (all values are divided by \$1000). The $F(C_1)$ is repeated as Figure 18–7 with the assigned random number values shown on the right scale. If the two-digit RN of 45 is chosen, the corresponding C_1 is graphically estimated to be \$12.25. It can also be linearly interpolated as $\$12.25 = 10 + (45/100)(15 - 10)$.

For greater accuracy when developing a random sample, especially for a continuous variable, it is possible to use 3-, 4-, or 5-digit RNs. These can be

FIGURE 18–7

Random numbers assigned to the continuous variable of client 1 cash flows in Example 18.3.

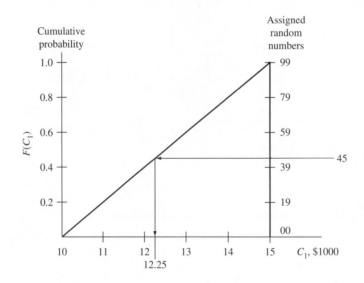

developed from Table 18–2 simply by combining digits in the columns and rows or obtained from tables with RNs printed in larger clusters of digits. In computer-based sampling, most simulation software packages have an RN generator built in which will generate values in the range of 0 to 1 from a continuous variable uniform distribution, usually identified by the symbol $U(0, 1)$. The RN values, usually between 0.00000 and 0.99999, are used to sample directly from the cumulative distribution employing essentially the same procedure explained here. The Excel functions RAND and RANDBETWEEN are described in Appendix A, Section A.3.

An initial question in random sampling usually concerns the *minimum size of n* required to ensure confidence in the results. Without detailing the mathematical logic, sampling theory, which is based upon the law of large numbers and the central-limit theorem (check a basic statistics book to learn about these), indicates that an n of 30 is sufficient. However, since reality does not follow theory exactly, and since engineering economy often deals with sketchy estimates, samples in the *range of 100 to 200* are the common practice. But samples as small as 10 to 25 provide a much better foundation for decision making under risk than the single-point estimate for a parameter that is known to vary widely.

18.4 EXPECTED VALUE AND STANDARD DEVIATION

Two very important measures or properties of a random variable are the expected value and standard deviation. If the entire population for a variable were known, these properties would be calculated directly. Since they are usually not known, random samples are commonly used to estimate them via the sample mean and the sample standard deviation, respectively. The following is a brief introduction to the interpretation and calculation of these properties using a random sample of size n from the population.

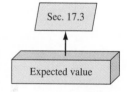

The usual symbols are Greek letters for the true population measures and English letters for the sample estimates.

	True Population Measure		Sample Estimate	
	Symbol	Name	Symbol	Name
Expected value	μ or $E(X)$	Mu or true mean	$\bar{X}$	Sample mean
Standard deviation	σ or $\sqrt{\text{Var}(X)}$ or $\sqrt{\sigma^2}$	Sigma or true standard deviation	s or $\sqrt{s^2}$	Sample standard deviation

The *expected value* is the long-run expected average if the variable is sampled many times.

The population expected value is not known exactly, since the population itself is not known completely, so μ is estimated either by $E(X)$ from a distribution or by $\bar{X}$, the sample mean. Equation [17.2], repeated here as Equation [18.8], is used to compute the $E(X)$ of a probability distribution, and Equation [18.9] is the sample mean, also called the sample average.

Population: $\qquad\qquad\qquad\qquad\qquad\qquad\qquad\qquad \mu$

Probability distribution: $\qquad E(X) = \sum X_i P(X_i)$ $\qquad\qquad$ [18.8]

Sample: $\qquad\qquad\qquad\qquad \overline{X} = \dfrac{\textbf{sum of sample values}}{\textbf{sample size}}$

$$= \frac{\sum X_i}{n} = \frac{\sum f_i X_i}{n} \qquad\qquad [18.9]$$

The f_i in the second form of Equation [18.9] is the frequency of X_i, that is, the number of times each value occurs in the sample. The resulting $\overline{X}$ is not necessarily an observed value of the variable; it is the long-run average value and can take on any value within the range of the variable. (We omit the subscript i on X and f when there is no confusion introduced.)

EXAMPLE 18.5

Kayeu, an engineer with B.C. Hydro, is planning to test several hypotheses about residential electricity bills in North American and Asian countries. The variable of interest is X, the monthly residential bill in Canadian dollars (rounded to the nearest dollar). Two small samples have been collected from different countries of North America and Asia. Estimate the population expected value. Do the samples (from a nonstatistical viewpoint) appear to be drawn from one population of electricity bills or from two different populations?

North American, sample 1, $	40	66	75	92	107	159	275
Asian, sample 2, $	84	90	104	187	190		

Solution
Use Equation [18.9] for the sample mean.

Sample 1: $\qquad n = 7 \qquad \sum X_i = 814 \qquad \overline{X} = \$116.29$

Sample 2: $\qquad n = 5 \qquad \sum X_i = 655 \qquad \overline{X} = \$131.00$

Based solely on the small sample averages, the approximate $15 difference, which is less than 10% of the smaller average bill, does not seem sufficiently large to conclude that the two populations are different. There are several statistical tests available to determine if samples come from the same or different populations. (Check a basic statistics text to learn about them.)

Comment
There are three commonly used measures of central tendency for data. The sample average is the most popular, but the *mode* and the *median* are also good measures. The mode, which is the most frequently observed value, was utilized in Example 18.3 for a triangular distribution. There is no specific mode in Kayeu's two samples, since all values are different.

The median is the middle value of the sample. It is not biased by extreme sample values, as is the mean. The two medians in the samples are $92 and $104. Based solely on the medians, the conclusion is still that the samples do not necessarily come from two different populations of electricity bills.

The *standard deviation* **is the dispersion or spread of values about the expected value** $E(X)$ **or sample average** $\bar{X}$.

The sample standard deviation s estimates the property σ, which is the population measure of dispersion about the expected value of the variable. A probability distribution for data with strong central tendency is more closely clustered about the centre of the data, and has a smaller s than a wider, more dispersed distribution. In Figure 18–8, the samples with larger s values—s_1 and s_4—have a flatter, wider probability distribution.

Actually, the variance s^2 is often quoted as the measure of dispersion. The standard deviation is simply the square root of the variance, so either measure can be used. However, the s value is what we use routinely in making computations about risk and probability. Mathematically, the formulas and symbols for variance and standard deviation of a discrete variable and a random sample of size n are as follows:

Population: $\sigma^2 = \text{Var}(X)$ **and** $\sigma = \sqrt{\sigma^2} = \sqrt{\text{Var}(X)}$

Probability distribution: $\text{Var}(X) = \sum [X_i - E(X)]^2 P(X_i)$ [18.10]

Sample : $s^2 = \dfrac{\textbf{sum of (sample value} - \textbf{sample average)}^2}{\textbf{sample size} - 1}$

$\qquad = \dfrac{\sum (X_i - \bar{X})^2}{n-1}$ [18.11]

$s = \sqrt{s^2}$

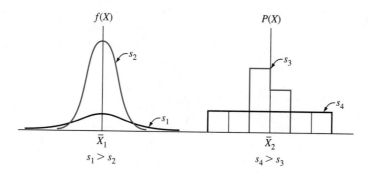

FIGURE 18–8

Sketches of distributions with different average and standard deviation values.

Equation [18.11] for sample variance is usually applied in a more computationally convenient form.

$$s^2 = \frac{\sum X_i^2}{n-1} - \frac{n}{n-1}\overline{X}^2 = \frac{\sum f_i X_i^2}{n-1} - \frac{n}{n-1}\overline{X}^2 \qquad [18.12]$$

The standard deviation uses the sample average as a basis about which to measure the spread or dispersion of data via the calculation $(X - \overline{X})$, which can have a minus or plus sign. To accurately measure the dispersion in both directions from the average, the quantity $(X - \overline{X})$ is squared. To return to the dimension of the variable itself, the square root of Equation [18.11] is extracted. The term $(X - \overline{X})^2$ is called the *mean-squared deviation,* and s has historically also been referred to as the *root-mean-square deviation.* The f_i in the second form of Equation [18.12] uses the frequency of each X_i value to calculate s^2.

One simple way to combine the average and standard deviation is to determine the percentage or fraction of the sample that is within ± 1, ± 2, or ± 3 standard deviations of the average, that is,

$$\overline{X} \pm ts \quad \text{for } t = 1, 2, \text{ or } 3 \qquad [18.13]$$

In probability terms, this is stated as

$$P(\overline{X} - ts \le X \le \overline{X} + ts) \qquad [18.14]$$

Virtually all the sample values will always be within the $\pm 3s$ range of $\overline{X}$, but the percent within $\pm 1s$ will vary depending on how the data points are distributed about $\overline{X}$. The following example illustrates the calculation of s to estimate σ, and incorporates s with the sample average using $\overline{X} \pm ts$.

EXAMPLE 18.6

(a) Use the two samples of Example 18.5 to estimate population variance and standard deviation for electricity bills. (b) Determine the percentages of each sample that are inside the ranges of 1 and 2 standard deviations from the mean.

Solution

(a) For illustration purposes only, apply the two different relations to calculate s for the two samples. For sample 1 (North American) with $n = 7$, use X to identify the values. Table 18–3 presents the computation of $\Sigma(X - \overline{X})^2$ for Equation [18.11], with $X = \$116.29$. The resulting s^2 and s values are

$$s^2 = \frac{37,743.40}{6} = 6290.57$$

$$s = \$79.31$$

For sample 2 (Asian), use Y to identify the values. With $n = 5$ and $\overline{Y} = 131$, Table 18–4 shows ΣY^2 for Equation [18.12]. Then

TABLE 18–3 Computation of Standard Deviation Using Equation [18.11] with $\bar{X} = \$116.29$, Example 18.6

X	$(X - \bar{X})$	$(X - \bar{X})^2$
$ 40	−76.29	$ 5,820.16
66	−50.29	2,529.08
75	−41.29	1,704.86
92	−24.29	590.00
107	−9.29	86.30
159	+42.71	1,824.14
275	+158.71	25,188.86
$ 814		$37,743.40

TABLE 18–4 Computation of Standard Deviation Using Equation [18.12] with $\bar{Y} = \$131$, Example 18.6

Y	Y^2
$ 84	7,056
90	8,100
104	10,816
187	34,969
190	36,100
$655	97,041

$$s^2 = \frac{97,041}{4} - \frac{5}{4}(131)^2 = 42,260.25 - 1.25(17.161) = 2809$$

$$s = \$53$$

The dispersion is smaller for the Asian sample ($53) than for the North American sample ($79.31).

(b) Equation [18.13] determines the ranges of $\bar{X} \pm 1s$ and $\bar{X} \pm 2s$. Count the number of sample data points between the limits, and calculate the corresponding percentage. See Figure 18–9 for a plot of the data and the standard deviation ranges.

North American sample:

$$\bar{X} \pm 1s = 116.29 \pm 79.31 \quad \text{for a range of \$36.98 to \$195.60}$$

Six out of seven values are within this range, so the percentage is 85.7%.

$$\bar{X} \pm 2s = 116.29 \pm 158.62 \quad \text{for a range of \$−42.33 to \$274.91}$$

There are still six of the seven values within the $\bar{X} \pm 2s$ range. The limit $\$-42.33$ is meaningful only from the probabilistic perspective; from the practical viewpoint, use zero, that is, no amount billed.

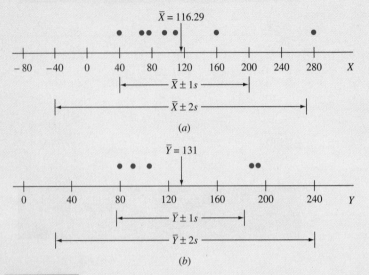

FIGURE 18-9
Values, averages, and standard deviation ranges for (a) North American and (b) Asian samples, Example 18.6.

Asian sample:

$$\bar{Y} \pm 1s = 131 \pm 53 \quad \text{for a range of } \$78 \text{ to } \$184$$

There are three of five values, or 60%, within the range.

$$\bar{Y} \pm 2s = 131 \pm 106 \quad \text{for a range of } \$25 \text{ to } \$237$$

All five of the values are within the $\bar{Y} \pm 2s$ range.

Comment
A second common measure of dispersion is the *range*, which is simply the largest minus the smallest sample values. In the two samples here, the range estimates are $235 and $106.

Before we perform simulation analysis in engineering economy, it may be of use to summarize the expected value and standard deviation relations for a continuous variable, since Equations [18.8] through [18.12] address only discrete variables. The primary differences are that the sum symbol is replaced by the integral over the defined range of the variable, which we identify as R, and that $P(X)$ is replaced by the differential element $f(X)dX$. For a stated continuous probability distribution $f(X)$, the formulas are

Expected value: $E(X) = \int_R X f(X)\, dX$ [18.15]

Variance: $\text{Var}(X) = \int_R X^2 f(X)\, dX - [E(X)]^2$ [18.16]

For a numerical example, again use the uniform distribution in Example 18.3 (Figure 18–4) over the range R from \$10 to \$15. If we identify the variable as X, rather than C_1, the following are correct.

$$f(X) = \frac{1}{5} = 0.2 \quad \$10 \le X \le \$15$$

$$E(X) = \int_R X(0.2)\, dX = 0.1 X^2 \big|_{10}^{15} = 0.1(225 - 100) = \$1.25$$

$$\text{Var}(X) = \int_R X^2(0.2)\, dX - (12.5)^2 = \frac{0.2}{3} X^3 \big|_{10}^{15} - (12.5)^2$$

$$= 0.06667(3375 - 1000) - 156.25 = 2.08$$

$$\sigma = \sqrt{2.08} = \$1.44$$

Therefore, the uniform distribution between $L = \$10$ and $H = \$15$ has an expected value of \$12.5 (the midpoint of the range, as expected) and a standard deviation of \$1.44.

Examples 18.11 and 18.12 can be found at the end of the chapter.

18.5 MONTE CARLO SAMPLING AND SIMULATION ANALYSIS

Up to this point, all alternative selections have been made using estimates with certainty, possibly followed by some testing of the decision via sensitivity analysis or expected values. In this section, we will use a simulation approach that incorporates the material of the previous sections to facilitate the engineering economy decision about one alternative or between two or more alternatives.

The random sampling technique discussed in Section 18.3 is called *Monte Carlo sampling*. The general procedure outlined below uses Monte Carlo sampling to obtain samples of size n for selected parameters of formulated alternatives. These parameters, expected to vary according to a stated probability distribution, warrant decision making under risk. All other parameters in an alternative are considered certain; that is, they are known, or they can be estimated with enough precision to consider them certain. An important assumption is made, usually without realizing it.

All parameters are independent; that is, one variable's distribution does not affect the value of any other variable of the alternative. This is referred to as the *property of independent random variables.*

The simulation approach to engineering economy analysis is summarized in the following basic steps.

Step 1. **Formulate alternative(s).** Set up each alternative in the form to be considered using engineering economic analysis, and select the measure of worth upon which to base the decision. Determine the form of the relation(s) to calculate the measure of worth.

Step 2. **Parameters with variation.** Select the parameters in each alternative to be treated as random variables. Estimate values for all other (certain) parameters for the analysis.

Step 3. **Determine probability distributions.** Determine whether each variable is discrete or continuous, and describe a probability distribution for each variable in each alternative. Use standard distributions where possible to simplify the sampling process and to prepare for computer-based simulation.

Step 4. **Random sampling.** Incorporate the random sampling procedure of Section 18.3 (the first four steps) into this procedure. This results in the cumulative distribution, assignment of RNs, selection of the RNs, and a sample of size n for each variable.

Step 5. **Measure of worth calculation.** Compute n values of the selected measure of worth from the relation(s) determined in step 1. Use the estimates made with certainty and the n sample values for the varying parameters. (This is when the property of independent random variables is actually applied.)

Step 6. **Measure of worth description.** Construct the probability distribution of the measure of worth, using between 10 and 20 cells of data, and calculate measures such as $\overline{X}$, s, $\overline{X} \pm ts$, and relevant probabilities.

Step 7. **Conclusions.** Draw conclusions about each alternative, and decide which is to be selected. If the alternative(s) has (have) been previously evaluated under the assumption of certainty for all parameters, comparison of results may help with the final decision.

Example 18.7 illustrates this procedure using an abbreviated manual simulation analysis, and Example 18.8 utilizes spreadsheet simulation for the same estimates.

EXAMPLE 18.7

Yvonne Hsu is the CEO of a chain of 50 fitness centres in the United States and Canada. An equipment salesperson has offered Yvonne two long-term opportunities on new aerobic exercise systems, for which the usage is charged to customers on a per-use basis on top of the monthly fees paid by customers. As an enticement, the offer includes a guarantee of annual revenue for one of the systems for the first 5 years.

Since this is an entirely new and risky concept of revenue generation, Yvonne wants to do a careful analysis of each alternative. Details for the two systems follow:

System 1. First cost is $P = \$12,000$ for a set period of $n = 7$ years with no salvage value. No guarantee for annual net revenue is offered.

System 2. First cost is $P = \$8000$, there is no salvage value, and there is a guaranteed annual net revenue of \$1000 for each of the first 5 years, but after this period, there is no guarantee. The equipment with updates may be useful up to 15 years, but the exact number is not known. Cancellation anytime after the initial 5 years is allowed, with no penalty.

For either system, new versions of the equipment will be installed with no added costs. If a MARR of 15% per year is required, use PW analysis to determine if neither, one, or both of the systems should be installed.

Solution by Hand

Estimates which Yvonne makes to correctly use the simulation analysis procedure are included in the following steps.

Step 1. **Formulate alternatives.**   Using PW analysis, the relations for system 1 and system 2 are developed including the parameters known with certainty. The symbol NCF identifies the net cash flows (revenues), and NCF_G is the guaranteed NCF of \$1000 for system 2.

$$PW_1 = -P_1 + NCF_1(P/A,15\%,n_1) \qquad [18.17]$$

$$PW_2 = -P_2 + NCF_G(P/A,15\%,5) \qquad [18.18]$$
$$+ NCF_2(P/A,15\%,n_2-5)(P/F,15\%,5)$$

Step 2. **Parameters with variation.**   Yvonne summarizes the parameters estimated with certainty and makes distribution assumptions about three parameters treated as random variables.

> *System 1*
> **Certainty.** $P_1 = \$12,000$; $n_1 = 7$ years.
> **Variable.** NCF_1 is a continuous variable, uniformly distributed between $L = \$-4000$ and $H = \$6000$ per year, because this is considered a high-risk venture.

> *System 2*
> **Certainty.** $P_2 = \$8000$; $NCF_G = \$1000$ for first 5 years.
> **Variable.** NCF_2 is a discrete variable, uniformly distributed over the values $L = \$1000$ to $H = \$6000$ only in \$1000 increments, that is, \$1000, \$2000, etc.
> **Variable.** n_2 is a continuous variable that is uniformly distributed between $L = 6$ and $H = 15$ years.

Now, rewrite Equations [18.17] and [18.18] to reflect the estimates made with certainty.

$$PW_1 = -12,000 + NCF_1(P/A,15\%,7)$$

$$= -12,000 + NCF_1(4.1604) \qquad [18.19]$$
$$PW_2 = -8000 + 1000(P/A,15\%,5)$$

$$+ NCF_2(P/A,15\%,n_2-5)(P/F,15\%,5)$$
$$= -4648 + NCF_2(P/A,15\%,n_2-5)(0.4972) \qquad [18.20]$$

Step 3. **Determine probability distributions.**   Figure 18–10 (left side) shows the assumed probability distributions for NCF_1, NCF_2, and n_2.

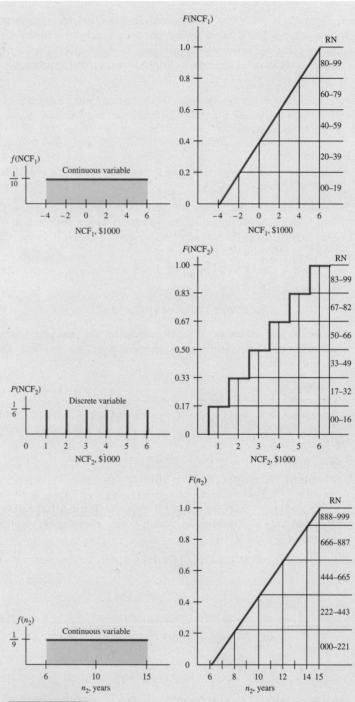

FIGURE 18–10

Distributions used for random samples, Example 18.7.

Step 4. **Random sampling.**   Yvonne decides on a sample of size 30 and applies the first four of the random sample steps in Section 18.3. Figure 18–10 (right side) shows the cumulative distributions (step 1) and assigns RNs to each variable (step 2). The RNs for NCF_2 identify the x axis values so that all net cash flows will be in even \$1000 amounts. For the continuous variable n_2, three-digit RN values are used in order to make the numbers come out evenly, and they are shown in cells only as "indexers" for easy reference when a RN is used to find a variable value. However, we round the number to the next higher value of n_2 because it is likely the contract may be cancelled on an anniversary date. Also, now the tabulated compound interest factors for $(n_2 - 5)$ years can be used directly (see Table 18–5).

Once the first RN is selected randomly from Table 18–2, the sequence (step 3) used will be to proceed down the RN table column and then up the column to the left. Table 18–5 shows only the first five RN values selected for each sample and the corresponding variable values taken from the cumulative distributions in Figure 18–10 (step 4).

Step 5. **Measure of worth calculation.**   With the five sample values in Table 18–5, calculate the PW values using Equations [18.19] and [18.20].

1. $PW_1 = -12,000 + (-2200)(4.1604)$ $= \$-21,153$
2. $PW_1 = -12,000 + 2000(4.1604)$ $= \$-3679$
3. $PW_1 = -12,000 + (-1100)(4.1604)$ $= \$-16,576$
4. $PW_1 = -12,000 + (-900)(4.1604)$ $= \$-15,744$
5. $PW_1 = -12,000 + 3100(4.1604)$ $= \$+897$

1. $PW_2 = -4648 + 1000(P/A,15\%,7)(0.4972)$ $= \$-2579$
2. $PW_2 = -4648 + 1000(P/A,15\%,5)(0.4972)$ $= \$-2981$
3. $PW_2 = -4648 + 5000(P/A,15\%,8)(0.4972)$ $= \$+6507$
4. $PW_2 = -4648 + 3000(P/A,15\%,10)(0.4972)$ $= \$+2838$
5. $PW_2 = -4648 + 4000(P/A,15\%,3)(0.4972)$ $= \$-107$

Now, 25 more RNs are selected for each variable from Table 18–2 and the PW values are calculated.

TABLE 18–5   Random Numbers and Variable Values for NCF_1, NCF_2, and n_2, Example 18.7

	NCF₁		NCF₂		n₂		
RN*	Value	RN†	Value	RN‡	Value	Rounded§	
18	\$-2200	10	\$1000	586	11.3	12	
59	+2000	10	1000	379	9.4	10	
31	-1100	77	5000	740	12.7	13	
29	-900	42	3000	967	14.4	15	
71	+3100	55	4000	144	7.3	8	

*Randomly start with row 1, column 4 in Table 18–2.
†Start with row 6, column 14.
‡Start with row 4, column 6.
§The n_2 value is rounded up.

Step 6. **Measure of worth description.** Figure 18–11a and b presents the PW_1 and PW_2 probability distributions for the 30 samples with 14 and 15 cells, respectively, as well as the range of individual PW values and the $\bar{X}$ and s values.

PW_1. Sample values range from $\$-24,481$ to $\$+12,962$. The calculated measures of the 30 values are

$$\bar{X}_1 = \$-7729$$

$$s_1 = \$10,190$$

PW_2. Sample values range from $\$-3031$ to $\$+10,324$. The sample measures are

$$\bar{X}_2 = \$2724$$

$$s_2 = \$4336$$

Step 7. **Conclusions.** Additional sample values will surely make the central tendency of the PW distributions more evident and may reduce the s values, which are quite

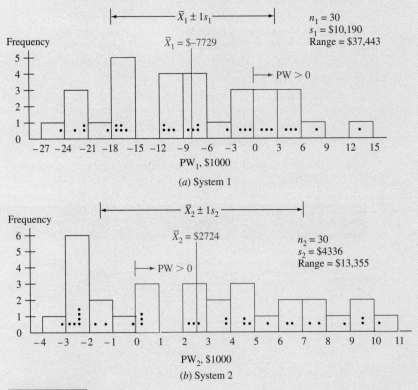

(a) System 1

(b) System 2

FIGURE 18–11

Probability distributions of simulated PW values for a sample of size 30, Example 18.7.

large. Of course, many conclusions are possible once the PW distributions are known, but the following seem clear.

System 1. Based on this small sample of 30 observations, *do not accept* this alternative. The likelihood of making the MARR = 15% is relatively small, since the sample indicates a probability of 0.27 (8 out of 30 values) that the PW will be positive, and $\bar{X}_1$ is a large negative. Though appearing large, the standard deviation may be used to determine that about 20 of the 30 sample PW values (two-thirds) are within the limits $\bar{X} \pm 1s$, which are $-17,919$ and 2461. A larger sample may alter this analysis somewhat.

System 2. If Yvonne is willing to accept the longer-term commitment that may increase the NCF some years out, the sample of 30 observations indicates to *accept* this alternative. At a MARR of 15%, the simulation approximates the chance for a positive PW as 67% (20 of the 30 PW values in Figure 18–11b are positive). However, the probability of observing PW within the $\bar{X} \pm 1s$ limits (-1612 and 7060) is 0.53 (16 of 30 sample values). This indicates that the PW sample distribution is more widely dispersed about its average than the system 1 PW sample.

Conclusion at this point. Reject system 1; accept system 2; and carefully watch net cash flow, especially after the initial 5-year period.

Comment

The estimates in Example 5.8 are very similar to those here, except all estimates were made with certainty (NCF$_1$ = \$3000, NCF$_2$ = \$3000, and n_2 = 14 years). The alternatives were evaluated by the payback period method at MARR = 15%, and the first alternative was selected. However, the subsequent PW analysis in Example 5.8 selected alternative 2 in part on the basis of the anticipated larger cash flow in the later years.

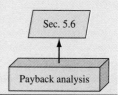

EXAMPLE 18.8

Help Yvonne Hsu set up an Excel spreadsheet simulation for the three random variables and PW analysis in Example 18.7. Does the PW distribution vary appreciably from that developed using manual simulation? Do the decisions to reject the system 1 proposal and accept the system 2 proposal still seem reasonable?

Solution by Computer

Figures 18–12 and 18–13 are spreadsheets that accomplish the simulation portion of the analysis described above in steps 3 (determine probability distribution) through 6 (measure of worth description). Most spreadsheet systems are limited in the variety of distributions they can accept for sampling, but common ones such as uniform and normal are available.

Figure 18–12 shows the results of a small sample of 30 values (only a portion of the spreadsheet is printed here) from the three distributions using the RAND and IF functions. (See Section A.3 in Appendix A.)

B15 = =INT((100*A15-4000)/100)*100

	A	B	C	D	E	F
1		**Sample of size 30 simulated values**				
2	RN1	NCF1, $	RN2	NCF2, $	RN3	N, years
3	12.5625	-$2,800	83.6176	$6,000	556.277	12
4	25.0262	-$1,500	99.5425	$6,000	8.78831	7
5	9.3856	-$3,100	26.4693	$2,000	507.36	11
6	38.0199	-$200	36.8475	$3,000	681.54	13
7	71.5088	$3,100	83.461	$6,000	369.092	10
8	66.782	$2,600	77.8699	$5,000	91.3044	7
9	48.3324	$800	8.43079	$1,000	457.749	11
10	39.3886	-$100	52.863	$4,000	914.543	15
11	21.5429	-$1,900	57.4819	$4,000	698.762	13
12	44.4996	$400	1.93223	$1,000	744.262	13
13	32.9911	-$800	70.6307	$5,000	190.814	8
14	96.0249	$5,600	61.0023	$4,000	714.668	13
15	99.6675	$5,900	55.7741	$4,000	648.227	12
16	13.956	-$2,700	98.9107	$6,000	199.949	8

Random Numbers / PW values / Sheet3 / Sheet4 / Sheet5 / Sheet6 / Sh

$= INT(0.009*E13+1)+6$

$= RAND()*1000$

$= RAND()*100$

$= IF(C13 <= 16,1000,IF(C13 <= 32,2000,IF(C13 <= 49,3000,$
$= IF(C13 <= 66,4000,IF(C13 <= 82,5000,IF(C13 <= 100,6000,6000))))))$

$= INT((100*A13 - 4000)/100)*100$

FIGURE 18–12

Sample values generated using spreadsheet simulation, Example 18.8.

NCF$_1$: Continuous uniform from $–4000 to $6000. The relation in column B translates RN1 values (column A) into NCF1 amounts.

NCF$_2$: Discrete uniform in $1000 increments from $1000 to $6000. Column D cells display NCF2 in the $1000 increments using the logical IF function to translate from the RN2 values.

n_2: Continuous uniform from 6 to 15 years. The results in column F are integer values obtained using the INT function operating on the RN3 values.

Figure 18–13 presents the two alternatives' estimates in the top section. The PW$_1$ and PW$_2$ computations for the 30 repetitions of NCF$_1$, NCF$_2$, and n_2 are the spreadsheet equivalent of Equations [18.19] and [18.20]. The tabular approach used here tallies the number of PW values below zero ($0) and equal to or exceeding zero using the IF operator. For example, cell C17 contains a 1, indicating PW$_1$ > 0 when NCF$_1$ = $3100 (in cell B7 of Figure 18–12) was used to calculate PW$_1$ = $897 by Equation [18.19]. Cells in rows 7 and 8 show the number of times in the 30 samples that system 1 and system 2 may return at least the MARR = 15% because the corresponding PW $\geq$ 0. Sample averages and standard deviations are also indicated.

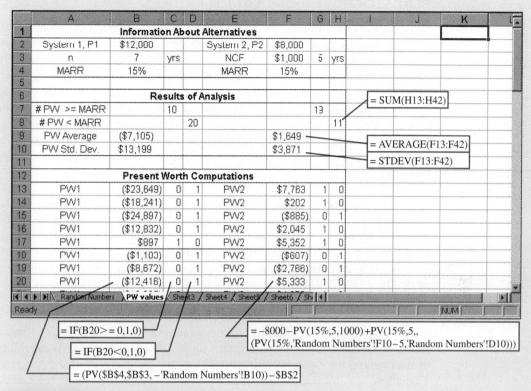

FIGURE 18–13

Spreadsheet simulation results of 30 PW values, Example 18.8.

Comparison between the hand and spreadsheet simulations is presented below.

	System 1 PW			System 2 PW		
	$\bar{X}, \$$	$s, \$$	No. of PW ≥ 0	$\bar{X}, \$$	$s, \$$	No. of PW ≥ 0
Hand	−7,729	10,190	8	2,724	4,336	20
Spreadsheet	−7,105	13,199	10	1,649	3,871	19

For the spreadsheet simulation, 10 (33%) of the PW_1 values exceed zero, while the manual simulation included 8 (27%) positive values. These comparative results will change every time this spreadsheet is activated, since the RAND function is set up (in this case) to produce a new RN each time. It is possible to define RAND to keep the same RN values. See the Excel User's Guide.

The conclusion to reject the system 1 proposal and accept system 2 is still appropriate for the spreadsheet simulation as it was for the hand one, since there are comparable chances that $PW \geq 0$.

18.6 STOCHASTIC SIMULATION MODELS

Simulation models imitate the real-world scenario. Although computers with simulation software are most often used to perform the analysis, they are not required and valuable insight can be gained about a system through a manually computed simulation of its economic performance. The models are developed to parallel the actual activities and economic repercussions of a system using variables that change according to the same cash flow relationships and schedules taking place in the system. The general rule for determining when simulation models should be used is simply to incorporate their use whenever analytical cash flows are either too complex or too costly. Simulation is therefore very beneficial for complex sensitivity analyses and problems that have uncertainty and risk associated with their variables.

The most important advantage in the use of simulation is that it permits the modelling of dynamic and analytically complex behaviour of systems that could otherwise not be analyzed. In fact, even for these sophisticated applications, simulation is frequently relatively straightforward, and therefore very easy to comprehend. It is this attribute that is often the principal incentive for simulation modelling. Since it is easier to understand, less opposition occurs when its results are used as evidence for decision making.

Simulation also allows the analyst to observe the expected behaviour of a system into the future. Several years or decades can be simulated, providing a record of the most important parameters. Other advantages include its capability of maintaining the same operating conditions for various runs of the program. This allows control over the experiments to measure the impacts on the system from specific parameter changes. "What if" questions can be asked by generating and testing alternatives that often could not be implemented as an experiment in the real system.

As with all models, the performance of a sensitivity analysis will insure that the simulated variables act according to reasonable standards as they vary in value separately and in conjunction with other variables. Past data is often included to make certain that the model predicts the correct results through a simulation of the actual scenario. There are also several subjective considerations to entertain. Prior to running the model, some thought should be given to whether the problem is formulated in a manner that accurately captures a balance between simplification and rigorousness. It should be simplified to a degree that is cost-effective while maintaining its descriptive qualities. It also needs to be sufficiently rigorous to reflect the complexities of the behavioural relationships that are inherent to the policy questions being addressed. A sense of elegance and precision in modelling is attained as this balance is achieved.

Models in engineering economics often use random numbers to simulate variables that are projected into the future. Any simulation using random input variables is referred to as a stochastic model. A stochastic simulation addresses a set of interacting random variables patterned after the dynamic behaviour of a socioeconomic technological system.

EXAMPLE 18.9

Software Canada, a company in Toronto, provides technical support for several products that they have recently marketed. They have had one technical support person receiving calls concerning use of this software. Management would like to assess the economic feasibility of adding another tech support person. The purpose of the model is to assess the number of tech support persons that should be available in order to achieve a reasonable service level for the callers.

The structure of the simulation is outlined in Table 18–6, where we assume that there is only one tech support person to take the calls. For this first simulation, columns are organized to record a typical day's work. The second column labelled "Time Since Last Call" represents a distribution of times that would be expected to elapse between arrivals of the calls. Studying the recent past history of the calls and recording the times when the calls arrive can develop a distribution for the model. Random numbers are then generated to simulate the arrivals. In this case it is accepted that there is a uniform distribution between the numbers 0 and 90. There is an equal chance that the next person will call 0 minutes after the previous person as 1 minute or 2 minutes or up to 90 minutes after that person. When we use stochastic simulation software, the program will automatically generate a random number for the analysis. Any distribution can be readily simulated by assigning sets of random numbers to occurrences of specific events weighted according to how they occur in the actual scenario.

The third column records the arrival clock time by cumulatively adding the call times. The first call came 7 minutes after the office opened; the second call arrived 21 minutes later, or 28 minutes into the day. The next column decides when service may begin. It does this by comparing column 3 on the same row for this call's arrival and column 6 in the previous row for the earlier call's conclusion. The model assumes that the tech support

TABLE 18–6 Stochastic Simulation of Tech Service Centre, Example 18.9

Call (1)	Time Since Last Call (2)	Arrival Clock Time (3)	Service Begins (4)	Time Required to Perform Service (5)	Service Ends (6)	Number of Calls in Queue (7)	Time Caller Is on Phone (8)	Time Waiting for Service (9)	Tech Support Idle Time (10)
1	7	0:07	0:07	23	0:30	0	23	0	7
2	21	0:28	0:30	37	1:07	1	39	2	0
3	12	0:40	1:07	16	1:23	1	43	27	0
4	80	2:00	2:00	28	2:28	0	28	0	37
5	8	2:08	2:28	30	2:58	1	50	20	0
6	3	2:11	2:58	18	3:16	2	65	47	0
7	32	2:43	3:16	25	3:41	2	57	32	0
8	65	3:48	3:48	34	4:22	0	34	0	7
9	43	4:31	4:31	19	4:50	0	19	0	9
10	74	5:45	5:45	21	6:06	0	21	0	55
								128	115

Average queue time = 128/10 = 12.8 minutes.
Average tech idle time = 115/366 = 31%.

person can only deal with one call at a time. The larger of the two values is recorded, which represents the latest clock time and does not violate this constraint.

Column 5 is a random number chosen to simulate the time normally required to resolve a problem with the use of the software. Past records are used to generate the distribution. In this case another uniform distribution is assumed varying between the numbers of 15 to 40 minutes. Column 6 adds the service time of column 5 to the beginning of the service listed in column 4. This will record when the service ends. Column 7 compares the clock times of previous caller's arrival and completion times (columns 3 and 6) to ascertain the overlaps and computes the total number of callers in the queue at any given interval.

By subtracting the arrival and completion time along each row, the time that a caller is in the queue is derived and recorded in column 8. This figure is then compared to column 5 that depicts the actual service time. By subtracting column 5 from column 8, the time that the caller had to wait for the service is derived and listed in column 9. The last column records the idle time for the tech support person not when engaged with callers. This information is obtained by subtracting the clock times of column 6 of the previous row from that of column 4 of the present row, which compares when the service ended for the previous caller and began for the current caller.

The table provides a history of the tech service centre's service characteristics as they might occur during a typical day. For clarity, this example is simplified to include only a few variables and was extended to simulate only 10 callers. If a stochastic simulation language is used on a computer, the simulation could easily be performed for any desirable time period.

Summary statistics can also be generated. The average caller queue time is calculated by dividing the summation of the values in column 9 by the total number of callers to obtain the average of 12.8 minutes. The average time that the worker is idle as a percentage of the total time spent at the centre is also calculated. The sum of column 10 of 115 is divided by the total time of the simulation (366 minutes). The results indicate the tech support person is idle for 31% of the simulation.

Table 18–7 depicts a simulation of the tech support centre with a second person added to the staff to complement the first. The same random numbers were used for the simulation, so that a direct comparison could be made by only changing the one variable and keeping all other variables constant. This control during the experiment is very desirable. Two additional columns were added for the simulation. Column 4 assigns the caller to tech support person 1 or 2, depending on which person is free, and columns 11 and 12 disaggregate the single idle time column into two, recording the idle time of each person separately.

The summary statistics calculated in Table 18–7 for the centre with a staff of two can now be compared with those of Table 18–6, where only one worker is employed. The caller queue time decreased from 12.8 to 1.7 minutes. While the time that the first worker was not engaged with callers remained constant at approximately 32%, the second worker in the centre was simulated to be idle 62% of the time. The decision whether to employ one or two workers can now be made with the above evidence to complement other information, including the cost of employing the second worker and how many callers might be expected to leave a queue if it is seen to be too time-consuming. The staff will most likely be able to be used for other productive activities while they are not engaged with callers, so the cost-effectiveness of that information should also be assessed and perhaps simulated.

TABLE 18–7 Simulation of Centre with 2 Tech Staffers, Example 18.9

Call (1)	Time Since Last Call (2)	Arrival Clock Time (min) (3)	Assign to Tech 1 or 2 (4)	Service Begins (5)	Time Required to Serve (min) (6)	Service Ends (7)	Calls in Queue (8)	Time Caller Is on Phone (9)	Time Waiting for Service (10)	1st Tech Idle Time (11)	2nd Tech Idle Time (12)
1	7	0:07	1	0:07	23	0:30	0	23	0	7	—
2	21	0:28	2	0:28	37	1:05	0	37	0	—	28
3	12	0:40	1	0:40	16	0:56	0	16	0	10	—
4	80	2:00	2	2:00	28	2:28	0	28	0	—	55
5	8	2:08	1	2:08	30	2:38	0	30	0	12	—
6	3	2:28	2	2:28	18	2:46	1	35	17	—	0
7	32	2:43	1	2:43	25	3:08	0	25	0	5	—
8	65	3:48	2	3:48	34	4:22	0	34	0	—	62
9	43	4:31	1	4:31	19	4:50	0	19	0	83	—
10	74	5:45	2	5:45	21	6:06	0	21	0	—	83
									17	117	228

Average queue = 17/10 = 1.7 minutes.
Average 1st tech idle time = 117/366 = 32%.
Average 2nd tech idle time = 228/366 = 62%.

Simulation languages such as GPSS, Simscript, and GASP are designed to exploit the stochastic structure of many application areas. The effort required to program a particular model and subsequently run it on the computer is less time-consuming and, therefore, less expensive.

18.7 DETERMINISTIC MODELS AND SYSTEM DYNAMICS SIMULATION

Deterministic models simulate the influence that variables have on each other. The variables change continuously over time according to mathematical relationships (often differential equations) that define the relationships between the variables. Many simulation languages create an animated output so that clients can view the movement of dollars through a financial system, the assembly of products in a manufacturing facility, the movement of vehicles through a transportation infrastructure, and the provision of medical services in a hospital. The results of the study are more readily understood when clients can see themselves or products moving through the animated system at high speed. Statistics are generated at the conclusion for further analysis.

Causal loop diagrams are constructed to capture the system's dynamic relationships between the variables. Arrows are drawn to depict which variables influence others within the system. Positive and negative signs on the arrowheads indicate whether the corresponding relationship is in the same or opposite direction.

If it is positive, a change in the first variable will cause a change in the second variable in the identical direction. In other words, if the first variable increases, the second variable will also increase. If the first variable decreases, the second variable will also decrease (even with the plus sign). If the sign is negative, the change is in the opposite direction (an increasing first variable will cause the second variable to decrease). Many causal loop diagrams contain thousands of variables and much is learned about a system simply by constructing the diagram.

EXAMPLE 18.10

A system dynamics simulation is depicted in Figure 18–14 by a causal loop diagram that summarizes the interaction of variables. This example concerns a metabolomics corporation producing new diagnostic tools analyzing the molecules that are the products of metabolism. The metabolomic information provides accurate early diagnoses for diseases such as diabetes, amyotrophic lateral sclerosis, Huntington's disease, Alzheimer's disease, and autism. New software, analytical hardware, and integrated systems are being rapidly developed to aid medical knowledge in identifying how these diseases begin to develop in this $450 million revenue market. A company on Vancouver Island is experiencing a market-share reduction from international competition, and forecasts a continued threat with only two possible options available to them to recover their market share.

The company requires predictions as to how their market share will change due to their competition's growth, as well as how long a recovery will take after the intervention of these two programs. The first intervention results from an analysis of the elasticity of demand for their diagnostic tools that indicates that the lowering of their prices will recover some market share. This will decrease their profit per unit, but increase their sales, resulting in an overall increase in revenue. The second intervention involves increasing the intensity of their research and development to attain the next-generation diagnostic tools earlier. This requires an investment to accelerate the effort, but it will again provide improvements in their market share.

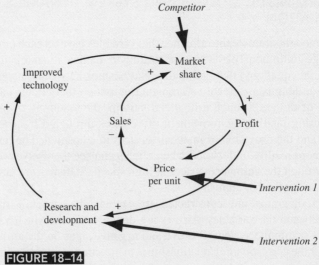

FIGURE 18–14
Causal loop of deterministic simulation model.

Table 18–8 provides a history of the client base fluctuations. The first two columns record the month and total number of clients lost or recovered. Initially, there were 10 clients lost (distracted by the competitor). The rate of column 3 is multiplied by the number of clients in column 2 to determine the amount of patronage switching to the competitor that month

TABLE 18–8 Simulation of Client Base

Month (1)	Total Lost (2)	Rate of Loss (3)	Newly Distracted Clients (4)	Intervention 1: Price Adjustment (5)	Intervention 2: Research and Development (6)
1	10	0.8	8		
2	18	0.8	14		
3	32	0.8	26		
4	58	0.8	46		
5	104	0.8	83	10	
6	177	0.8	142	8	
7	311	0.8	249	14	
8	546	0.7	382	26	0.1
9	902	0.61	550	46	0.9
10	1406	0.53	745	83	0.8
11	2068	0.46	951	142	0.7
12	2877	0.40	1151	249	0.06
13	3779	0.35	1323	382	0.05
14	4720	0.30	1416	550	0.05
15	5586	0.26	1452	745	0.04
16	6293	0.23	1447	951	0.03
17	6789	0.20	1358	1151	0.03
18	6996	0.17	1189	1323	0.03
19	6862	0.15	1029	1416	0.02
20	6475	0.13	842	1452	0.02
21	5865	0.11	645	1447	0.02
22	5063	0.10	506	1358	0.01
23	4211	0.09	379	1189	0.01
24	3401	0.08	272	1029	0.01
25	2644	0.07	185	842	0.01
26	1987	0.06	119	645	0.01
27	1461	0.05	73	506	0.01
28	1028	0.04	41	379	0.01
29	690	0.03	21	272	0.01
30	439	0.03	13	185	0
31	267	0.03	8	119	0
32	156	0.03	5	73	0
33	88	0.03	5	41	0
34	50	0.03	2	21	0
35	31	0.03	1	13	0
36	19	0.03	1	8	0
37	12	0.03	0	5	0
38	7	0.03	0	3	0
39	4	0.03	0	2	0
40	2	0.03	0	1	0
41	1	0.03	0	1	0
42	0	0.03	0	0	0

(column 4). The impact of the first intervention (price reduction) is recorded in column 5. Since there is a 5-month recovery period, the column has a 5-period delay from the onset. The first value in month 5 represents the recovery of the initial 10 customers. Subsequent values indicate the recovery date of the newly lost clients, so simply takes the number of column 4 and places it in column 5 with a 5-month delay (5 rows lower in the column).

The second intervention concerns the improved technology resulting from an intensified research and development effort. This has the effect of decreasing the rate of column 3. It is assumed that the intervention begins during month 8 and it is able to decrease the rate by 13% each month. The 13% is then multiplied by the preceding month's rate of column 3 to determine the current month's rate as the difference between the two. For example, consider the rate for month 8:

$$\text{Rate}_{\text{month 8}} = \text{rate}_{\text{month 7}} - \text{decrease in rate}$$
$$= \text{rate}_{\text{month 7}} - (0.13)(\text{rate}_{\text{month 7}})$$
$$= 0.8 - 0.1$$
$$= 0.7$$

Subtracting the newly adrift (column 4) from the current month's total (column 2) and adding the recoveries listed in columns 5 and 6 yields the total number of clients lost for any subsequent month. By running the model for 42 months, a history of the client base is simulated. Engineers involved in strategic planning efforts for the company can expand these results with simulations involving other interventions to assess the cost-effectiveness of each alternative, thereby gaining insight into a best policy.

A graph of the numerical results of the client simulation is depicted in Figure 18–15. This graph provides a visual summary of the decline and growth of the system's variables.

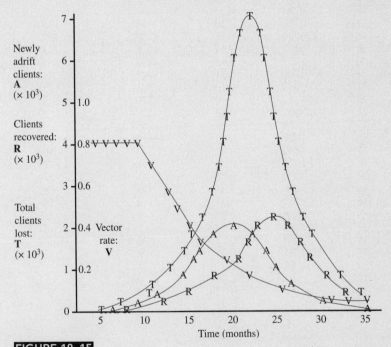

FIGURE 18–15
History of client base.

The horizontal scale always represents time, while the vertical scale represents a variety of items, often on the same graph. For this example, the total number of clients lost and recovered is plotted with symbols "T" and "R," respectively. The rate that the clients are lost is plotted with the symbol "V" on the inside vertical scale of the graph, which varies from 0.2 to 0.8 describing the vector. This output provides the relative shapes of the variables at a glance. Many computer simulation languages (iThink, CSMP, and Dynamo) are structured to provide the graphs automatically as output.

In Section 4.1, macroeconomics was introduced with a discussion of how the Bank of Canada influences the domestic economy with their monetary policies. National economies are often modelled by deterministic simulation software addressing elements of concern such as trade balances of imports and exports, national debt, inflation, wage subsidies, international interest rates, foreign aid, trade barriers, oil prices, domestic consumption, and capital investments by the government. The purpose of the simulations is to achieve effective policies to stabilize economic development.

Simulation languages generate activities and events automatically, and structure the model in a framework that allows the user to request major data manipulations with a single statement. This includes the automatic management of data with its appropriate storage and use during each run being manipulated by the language. Output statistics and graphs are automatically performed.

ADDITIONAL EXAMPLES

EXAMPLE 18.11

PROBABILITY STATEMENTS, SECTION 18.2   Use the cumulative distribution for the variable C_1 in Figure 18–4 (Example 18.3, monthly cash flow for client 1) to determine the following probabilities:

(a) More than $14
(b) Between $12 and $13
(c) No more than $11 or more than $14
(d) Exactly $12

Solution

The shaded areas in Figure 18–16a through d indicate the points on the cumulative distribution $F(C_1)$ used to determine the probabilities.

(a) The probability of more than $14 per month is easily determined by subtracting the value of $F(C_1)$ at 14 from the value at 15. (Since the probability at a point is zero for a continuous variable, the equals sign does not change the value of the resulting probability.)

$$P(C_1 > 14) = P(C_1 \leq 15) - P(C_1 \leq 14)$$

$$= F(15) - F(14) = 1.0 - 0.8$$

$$= 0.2$$

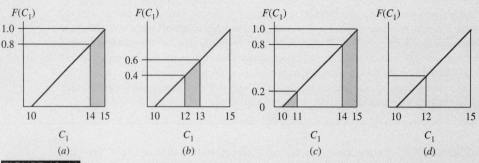

FIGURE 18–16

Calculation of probabilities from the cumulative distribution for a continuous variable that is distributed uniformly, Example 18.11.

(b) $\quad P(12 \leq C_1 \leq 13) = P(C_1 \leq 13) - P(C_1 \leq 12) = 0.6 - 0.4$

$\qquad\qquad\qquad = 0.2$

(c) $\quad P(C_1 \leq 11) + P(C_1 > 14) = [F(11) - F(10)] + [F(15) - F(14)]$

$\qquad\qquad\qquad = (0.2 - 0) + (1.0 - 0.8)$

$\qquad\qquad\qquad = 0.2 + 0.2$

$\qquad\qquad\qquad = 0.4$

(d) $\qquad\qquad P(C_1 = 12) = F(12) - F(12) = 0.0$

There is no area under the cumulative distribution curve at a point for a continuous variable, as mentioned earlier. If two very closely placed points are used, it is possible to obtain a probability, for example, between 12.0 and 12.1 or between 12 and 13, as in part (b).

EXAMPLE 18.12

THE NORMAL DISTRIBUTION, SECTION 18.4 Camilla is the regional safety engineer for a chain of franchise-based gasoline and food stores. The home office has had many complaints and several legal actions from employees and customers about slips and falls due to liquids (water, oil, gas, soda, etc.) on concrete surfaces. Corporate management has authorized each regional engineer to contract locally to apply to all exterior concrete surfaces a newly marketed product that absorbs up to 100 times its own weight in liquid and to charge a home office account for the installation. The authorizing letter to Camilla states that, based upon their simulation and random samples that assume a normal population, the cost of the locally arranged installation should be about $10,000 and almost always is within the range of $8000 to $12,000.

Camilla asks you, TJ, an engineering technology graduate, to write a brief but thorough summary about the normal distribution, explain the $8000 to $12,000 range statement, and explain the phrase "random samples that assume a normal population."

Solution

You kept this book and a basic engineering statistics text when you graduated, and you have developed the following response to Camilla, using them and the letter from the home office.

Camilla,

Here is a brief summary of how the home office appears to be using the normal distribution. As a refresher, I've included a summary of what the normal distribution is all about.

Normal distribution, probabilities, and random samples

The normal distribution is also referred to as the bell-shaped curve, the Gaussian distribution, or the error distribution. It is, by far, the most commonly used probability distribution in all applications. It places exactly one-half of the probability on either side of the mean or expected value. It is used for continuous variables over the entire range of numbers. The normal is found to accurately predict many types of outcomes, such as IQ values; manufacturing errors about a specified size, volume, weight, etc.; and the distribution of sales revenues, costs, and many other business parameters around a specified mean, which is why it may apply in this situation.

The normal distribution, identified by the symbol $N(\mu, \sigma^2)$, where μ is the expected value or mean and σ^2 is the variance, or measure of spread, can be described as follows:

- The mean μ locates the probability distribution (Figure 18–17*a*), and the spread of the distribution varies with variance (Figure 18–17*b*), growing wider and flatter for larger variance values.
- When a sample is taken, the estimates are identified as sample mean $\bar{X}$ for μ and sample standard deviation s for σ.
- The normal probability distribution $f(X)$ for a variable X is quite complicated, because its formula is

$$f(X) = \frac{1}{\sigma\sqrt{2\pi}} \exp\left\{-\left[\frac{(X-\sigma)^2}{2\sigma^2}\right]\right\}$$

where exp represents the number $e = 2.71828+$ and it is raised to the power of the $-[\ ]$ term. In short, if X is given different values, for a given mean μ and standard deviation σ, a curve looking like those in Figure 18–17*a* and *b* is developed.

Since $f(X)$ is so unwieldy, random samples and probability statements are developed using a transformation, called the *standard normal distribution (SND)*, which uses the μ and σ (population) or $\bar{X}$ and s (sample) to compute values of the variable Z.

Population: $Z = \dfrac{\text{deviation from mean}}{\text{standard deviation}} = \dfrac{X - \mu}{\sigma}$ [18.21]

Sample: $Z = \dfrac{X - \bar{X}}{s}$ [18.22]

The SND for Z (Figure 18–17*c*) is the same as for X, except that it always has a mean of 0 and a standard deviation of 1, and it is identified by the symbol $N(0,1)$. Therefore, the probability values under the SND curve can be stated exactly. It is always possible to transfer back to the original values from sample data by solving Equation [18.21] for X:

$$X = Z\sigma + \mu \qquad [18.23]$$

Several probability statements for Z and X are summarized in the following table and are shown on the distribution curve for Z in Figure 18–17c.

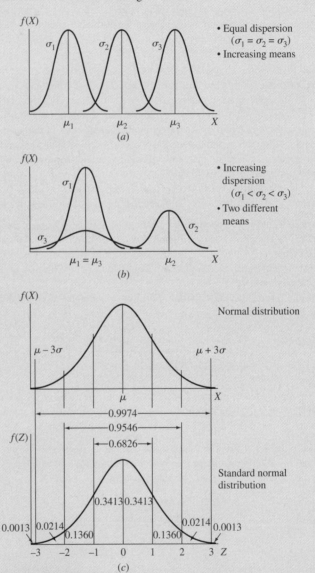

FIGURE 18–17

Normal distribution showing (a) different mean values μ; (b) different standard deviation values σ; and (c) relation of normal X to standard normal Z.

Variable X Range	Probability	Variable Z Range
$\mu + 1\sigma$	0.3413	0 to +1
$\mu \pm 1\sigma$	0.6826	−1 to +1
$\mu + 2\sigma$	0.4773	0 to +2
$\mu \pm 2\sigma$	0.9546	−2 to +2
$\mu + 3\sigma$	0.4987	0 to +3
$\mu \pm 3\sigma$	0.9974	−3 to +3

As an illustration, probability statements from this tabulation and Figure 18–17c for X and Z are as follows:

The probability that X is within 2σ of its mean is 0.9546.

The probability that Z is within 2σ of its mean, which is the same as between the values −2 and +2, is also 0.9546.

In order to take a random sample from a normal $N(\mu,\sigma^2)$ population, a specially prepared table of SND random numbers is used. (Tables of SND values are available in many statistics books.) The numbers are actually values from the Z or $N(0,1)$ distribution and have values such as −2.10, +1.24, etc. Translation from the Z value back to the sample values for X is via Equation [18.23].

Interpretation of the home office memo

The statement that virtually all the local contract amounts should be between $8000 and $12,000 may be interpreted as follows: A normal distribution is assumed with a mean of $\mu = \$10,000$ and a standard deviation for $\sigma = \$667$, or a variance of $\sigma^2 = (\$667)^2$; that is, an $N[\$10,000, (\$667)^2]$ distribution is assumed. The value $\sigma = \$667$ is calculated using the fact that virtually all the probability (99.74%) is within 3σ of the mean, as stated above. Therefore,

$$3\sigma = \$2000 \quad \text{and} \quad \sigma = \$667 \quad \text{(rounded off)}$$

As an illustration, if six SND random numbers are selected and used to take a sample of size 6 from the normal distribution $N[\$10,000, (\$667)^2]$, the results are as follows:

SND Random Number Z	X Using Equation [18.23] $X = Z\sigma + \mu$
−2.10	$X = (−2.10)(667) + 10,000 = \$8599$
+3.12	$X = (+3.12)(667) + 10,000 = \$12,081$
−0.23	$X = (−0.23)(667) + 10,000 = \$9847$
+1.24	$X = (+1.24)(667) + 10,000 = \$10,827$
−2.61	$X = (−2.61)(667) + 10,000 = \$8259$
−0.99	$X = (−0.99)(667) + 10,000 = \$9340$

If we consider this a sample of six typical concrete surfacing contract amounts for sites in our region, the average is $9825 and five of six values are within the range of $8000 and $12,000, with the sixth being only $81 above the upper limit. So we should have no real problems, but it is important that we keep a close watch on the contract amounts, because the assumption of the normal distribution with a mean of about $10,000 and virtually all contract amounts within ±$2000 of it may not prove to be correct for our region.

CHAPTER SUMMARY

To perform decision making under risk implies that some parameters of an engineering alternative are treated as random variables. Assumptions about the shape of the variable's probability distribution are used to explain how the estimates of parameter values may vary. Additionally, measures such as the expected value and standard deviation describe the characteristic shape of the distribution. In this chapter, we learned several of the simple, but useful, discrete and continuous population distributions used in engineering economy—uniform and triangular—as well as specifying our own distribution or assuming the normal distribution.

Since the population's probability distribution for a parameter is not fully known, a random sample of size n is usually taken, and its sample average and standard deviation are determined. The results are used to make probability statements about the parameter, which help make the final decision with risk considered.

The Monte Carlo sampling method is combined with engineering economy relations for a measure of worth such as PW to implement a simulation approach to risk analysis. The results of such an analysis can then be compared with decisions when parameter estimates are made with certainty.

Stochastic and deterministic simulation models are used to mirror large socioeconomic technological systems and provide valuable output for engineering economy studies. Models encompassing thousands of variables are constructed to assist decision makers in better allocating scarce resources to competing needs.

PROBLEMS

Certainty, Risk, and Uncertainty

18.1 For each situation below, determine (1) if the variable(s) is (are) discrete or continuous and (2) if the information involves certainty, risk, and/or uncertainty. Where risk is involved, graph the information in the general form of Figure 18–1.

(a)   A friend in real estate tells you the price per square metre for new houses will go up slowly or rapidly during the next 6 months.

(b)   Your manager informs the staff there is an equal chance that sales will be between 50 and 55 units next month.

(c)   Jane got paid yesterday, and $400 was taken out in income taxes. The amount withheld next month will be larger because of a pay raise between 3% and 5%.

(d)   There is a 20% chance of rain and a 30% chance of snow today.

18.2 An engineer learned that production output is between 1000 and 2000 units per week 90% of the time, and it may fall below 1000 or go above 2000. He wants to use E(output) in the decision making process. Identify at least two additional pieces of information that must be obtained or assumed to finalize the output information for this use.

Probability and Distributions

18.3 A survey of households included a question about the number of operating automobiles N currently owned by people living at the residence and the interest rate i on the lowest-rate loan for the cars. The results for 100 households are shown:

Number of Cars N	Households
0	12
1	56
2	26
3	3
≥ 4	3

Loan Rate i	Households
0.0–2	22
2.01–4	10
4.01–6	12
6.01–8	42
8.01–10	8
10.01–12	6

(a) State whether each variable is discrete or continuous.

(b) Plot the probability distributions and cumulative distributions for N and i.

(c) From the data collected, what is the probability that a household has 1 or 2 cars? Three or more cars?

(d) Use the data for i to estimate the chances that the interest rate is between 7% and 11% per year.

18.4 An officer of the provincial lottery commission has sampled lottery ticket purchasers over a 1-week period at one location. The amounts distributed back to the purchasers and the associated probabilities for 5000 tickets are as follows:

Distribution, $	0	2	5	10	100
Probability	0.91	0.045	0.025	0.013	0.007

(a) Plot the cumulative distribution of winnings.

(b) Calculate the expected value of the distribution of dollars per ticket.

(c) If tickets cost $2, what is the expected long-term income to the province per ticket, based upon this sample?

18.5 Bob is working on two separate probability-related projects. The first involves a variable N, which is the number of consecutively manufactured parts that weigh in above the weight specification limit. The variable N is described by the formula $(0.5)^N$ because each unit has a 50-50 chance of being below or above the limit. The second involves a battery life L which varies between 2 and 5 months. The probability distribution is triangular with the mode at 5 months, which is the design life. Some batteries fail early, but 2 months is the smallest life experienced thus far. (a) Write out and plot the probability distributions and cumulative distributions for Bob. (b) Determine the probability of N being 1, 2, or 3 consecutive units above the weight limit.

18.6 An alternative to buy and an alternative to lease hydraulic lifting equipment have been formulated. Use the parameter estimates and assumed distribution data shown to plot the probability distributions on one graph for corresponding parameters. Label the parameters carefully.

	Purchase Alternative		
	Estimated Value		Assumed
Parameter	High	Low	Distribution
First cost, $	25,000	20,000	Uniform; continuous
Salvage value, $	3,000	2,000	Triangular; mode at $2500
Life, years	8	4	Triangular; mode at 6
AOC, $/year	9,000	5,000	Uniform; continuous

	Lease Alternative		
	Estimated Value		Assumed
Parameter	High	Low	Distribution
Lease first cost, $	2000	1800	Uniform; continuous
AOC, $/year	9000	5000	Triangular; mode at $7000
Lease term, years	2	2	Certainty

18.7 Dominique is a statistician with a bank. She has collected debt-to-equity mix data on mature (M) and young (Y) companies. The debt percentages vary from 20% to 80% in her sample. Dominique has defined D_M as a variable for the mature companies from 0 to 1, with $D_M = 0$ interpreted as the low of 20% debt and $D_M = 1.0$ as the high of 80% debt. The variable for young corporation debt percentages D_Y is similarly defined. The probability distributions used to describe D_M an D_Y are

$$f(D_M) = 3(1-D_M)^2 \qquad 0 \leq D_M \leq 1$$
$$f(D_Y) = 2D_Y \qquad 0 \leq D_Y \leq 1$$

(a) Use different values of the debt percentage between 20% and 80% to calculate values for the probability distributions and then plot them. (b) What can you comment about the probability that a mature company or a young company will have a low debt percentage? A high debt percentage?

18.8 A discrete variable X can take on integer values of 1 to 10. A sample of size 50 results in the following probability estimates:

X_i	1	2	3	6	9	10
$P(X_i)$	0.2	0.2	0.2	0.1	0.2	0.1

(a) Write out and graph the cumulative distribution.

(b) Calculate the following probabilities using the cumulative distribution: X is between 6 and 10, and X has the values 4, 5, or 6.

(c) Use the cumulative distribution to show that $P(X = 7 \text{ or } 8) = 0.0$. Even though this probability is zero, the statement about X is that it can take on integer values of 1 to 10. How do you explain the apparent contradiction in these two statements?

Random Samples

18.9 The Toronto-based specialty metal producer Timminco Ltd. has purchased a new plant in Iceland that will boost its capacity for producing solar-grade silicon. Assume the estimated annual new revenue R for the plant to be $3.1 million per year for the next 5 years. This expected amount is based on the estimate that R could be, with equal probability, $2.6, $2.8, $3.0, $3.2, $3.4, or $3.6 million per year.
(a) Write the probability statements for the estimates identified.
(b) Plot the probability distribution of R.
(c) A sample size of 4 is developed from the distribution for R. The values in $ million are: 2.6; 3.0; 3.2; 3.0. If the interest rate is 12% per year, use the sample to calculate the PW values of R that could be included in an economic evaluation with risk considered.

18.10 Use the discrete variable probability distribution in Problem 18.8 to develop a sample of size 25. Estimate the probabilities for each value of X from your sample, and compare them with those of the originating $P(X_i)$ values.

18.11 The percent price increase p on a variety of retail food prices over a 1-year period varied from 5% to 10% in all cases.

Because of the distribution of p values, the assumed probability distribution for the next year is

$$f(X) = 2X \qquad 0 \leq X \leq 1$$

where

$$X = \begin{cases} 0 & \text{when } p = 5\% \\ 1 & \text{when } p = 10\% \end{cases}$$

For a continuous variable the cumulative distribution $F(X)$ is the integral of $f(X)$ over the same range of the variable. In this case

$$F(X) = X^2 \qquad 0 \leq X \leq 1$$

(a) Graphically assign RNs to the cumulative distribution, and take a sample of size 30 for the variable. Transform the X values into interest rates.

(b) Calculate the average p value for the sample.

18.12 Develop a discrete probability distribution of your own for the variable G, the expected grade in this course, where $G = $ A, B, C, D, F, or I (incomplete). Assign random numbers to $F(G)$, and take a sample from it. Now plot the probability values from the sample for each G value.

18.13 Use the RAND or RANDBETWEEN function in Excel (or corresponding random number generator on another spreadsheet) to generate 100 values from a $U(0,1)$ distribution.

(a) Calculate the average and compare it to 0.5, the expected value for a random sample between 0 and 1.

(b) For the RAND function sample, cluster the results into cells of 0.1 width, that is 0.0–0.1, 0.1–0.2, etc., where the upper-limit value is excluded from each cell. Determine

the probability for each grouping from the results. Does your sample come close to having approximately 10% in each cell?

Sample Estimates

18.14 Sylvie sampled the monthly maintenance costs for automated soldering machines a total of 100 times during 1 year. She clustered the costs into $200 cells, for example, $500 to $700, with cell midpoints of $600, $800, $1000, etc. She indicated the number of times (frequency) each cell value was observed. The costs and frequency data are as follows:

Cell Midpoint	Frequency
600	6
800	10
1000	9
1200	15
1400	28
1600	15
1800	7
2000	10

(a) Estimate the expected value and standard deviation of the maintenance costs the company should anticipate based on Sylvie's sample.

(b) What is the best estimate of the percentage of costs that will fall within 2 standard deviations of the mean?

(c) Develop a probability distribution of the monthly maintenance costs from Sylvie's sample, and indicate the answers to the previous two questions on it.

18.15 (a) Determine the values of sample average and standard deviation of the data in Problem 18.8. (b) Determine the values 1 and 2 standard deviations from the mean. Of the 50 sample points, how many fall within these two ranges?

18.16 (*a*) Use the relations in Section 18.4 for continuous variables to determine the expected value and standard deviation for the distribution of $f(D_Y)$ in Problem 18.7. (*b*) It is possible to calculate the probability of a continuous variable X between two points (a, b) using the following integral:

$$P(a \le X \le b) = \int_a^b f(X)\,dx$$

Determine the probability that D_Y is within 2 standard deviations of the expected value.

18.17 (*a*) Use the relations in Section 18.4 for continuous variables to determine the expected value and variance for the distribution of D_M in Problem 18.7.

$$f(D_M) = 3(1 - D_M)^2 \qquad 0 \le D_M \le 1$$

(*b*) Determine the probability that D_M is within two standard deviations of the expected value. Use the relation in Problem 18.16.

18.18 Calculate the expected value for the variable N in Problem 18.5.

18.19 A newsstand manager is tracking Y, the number of weekly magazines left on the shelf when the new edition is delivered. Data collected over a 30-week period are summarized by the following probability distribution. Plot the distribution and the estimates for expected value and one standard deviation on either side of $E(Y)$ on the plot.

Y copies	3	7	10	12
P(Y)	1/3	1/4	1/3	1/12

Simulation

18.20 Carl, an engineering colleague, estimated net cash flow after taxes (CFAT) for the project he is working on. The additional CFAT of $2800 in year 10 is the salvage value of capital assets.

Year	CFAT, $
0	−28,800
1–6	5,400
7–10	2,040
10	2,800

The PW value at the current MARR of 7% per year is

$$\text{PW} = -28{,}800 + 5400(P/A,7\%,6)$$
$$+ 2040(P/A,7\%,4)(P/F,7\%,6)$$
$$+ 2800(P/F,7\%,10)$$
$$= \$2966$$

Carl believes the MARR will vary over a relatively narrow range, as will the CFAT, especially during the out years of 7 through 10. He is willing to accept the other estimates as certain. Use the following probability distribution assumptions for MARR and CFAT to perform a simulation—hand- or computer-based.

  MARR. Uniform distribution over the range 6% to 10%.

  CFAT, years 7 through 10. Uniform distribution over the range $1600 to $2400 for each year.

Plot the resulting PW distribution. Should the plan be accepted using decision making under certainty? Under risk?

18.21 Repeat Problem 18.20, except use the normal distribution for the CFAT in years 7 through 10 with an expected value of $2040 and a standard deviation of $500.

18.22 Create one causal loop diagram and deterministic simulation for your course load this term. Variables will include your study effort, learning, and expected grades in each course.

18.23 A manufacturer is considering the implementation of an automated guided vehicle system for materials handling. This will eliminate some jobs and change the duties of others, but it will accelerate the delivery of parts through the use of optimal routing and scheduling algorithms. The VP Engineering would like to use simulation to predict the impact on employee morale, productivity, and product quality as well as operational costs and profit. Draw a causal loop diagram and describe the dynamics of the system for a model. Do not generate or use data unless it will help you to illustrate the process.

18.24 The bottleneck of a production line is in the welding sequence. As jobs arrive for welding they are performed on a first-come, first-served basis, independently of the job category. There are two cate-

gories. The first includes jobs that will require 5 ± 2 minutes of welding time; the second, jobs that will require 2 ± 0.5 minutes of welding time. Category 1 and 2 inter-arrival times are 8 ± 6 and 7 ± 5 minutes, respectively. When greater-than-average welding times occur, a queue forms that reduces throughput of the production lines.

Management wishes to test the hypothesis that throughput can be increased if category 2 jobs are serviced first. With this prioritization, category 1 jobs will only be serviced when there are no category 2 jobs in the queue. Design a model for the current and proposed service priority systems and run them for 5 manual iterations of a simulation.

EXTENDED EXERCISE

USING SIMULATION AND THE EXCEL RNG FOR SENSITIVITY ANALYSIS

Note: This exercise requires you to learn about and use the Random Number Generation (RNG) Data Analysis Tool package of Microsoft Excel. The online help function explains how to initiate and use the RNG to generate random numbers from a variety of probability distributions: normal, uniform (continuous variable), binomial, Poisson, and discrete. The discrete option is used to generate random numbers from a discrete variable distribution that you specify on the worksheet. This option is the one to use below for the discrete uniform distribution.

Reread the situation in Example 17.3 in which three mutually exclusive alternatives are compared. The parameters of salvage value S, annual operating cost (AOC), and life n are varied using the three-estimate approach to sensitivity analysis. Set up a simulation by answering the following questions using the data provided.

Questions

1. Become familiar with the RNG Data Analysis Tool in Excel by clicking on the Help button and reading about it, how to install it (if necessary), and how to apply it.

2. Develop a sample of 10 random numbers from each of the following distributions:
   - Normal with a mean of 100 and a standard deviation of 20
   - Uniform (continuous) between 5 and 10

- Uniform (discrete) between 5 and 10 with a probability of 0.2 for 5 through 7, 0.05 for 8 and 9, and 0.3 for 10

3. Develop a simulation of 50 sample points of AW values at a MARR of 12% per year for the three alternatives described in Example 17.3. Use the specified probability distributions below. Do the results of your simulation indicate that alternative B is still the clear choice? If not, what is the better choice?

	Alternative		
Parameter	A	B	C
AOC	Normal Mean: $8000 Std. dev.: $1000	Normal Mean: $3000 Std. dev.: $500	Normal Mean: $6000 Std. dev.: $700
S	Uniform 0 to $1000	Uniform $500 to $2000	Fixed at $3000
n	Discrete uniform 3 to 8 years with equal probability	Discrete uniform 3 to 7 years with equal probability	Discrete uniform 5 to 8 years with equal probability

APPENDIX A

Using Spreadsheets and Microsoft Excel©

This appendix explains the layout of a spreadsheet and the use of Microsoft Excel (hereafter called Excel) functions in engineering economy. Refer to the User's Guide and Excel help system for your particular computer and version of Excel.

A.1 INTRODUCTION TO USING EXCEL

Run Excel on Windows

After booting up the computer, click on the Microsoft Excel icon to start it. If the icon does not show, left-click the Start button located in the lower left corner of the screen. Move the mouse pointer to Programs, and a submenu will appear on the right. Move to the Microsoft Excel icon, and left-click to run.

If the Microsoft Excel icon is not on the Programs submenu, move to the Microsoft Office icon and highlight the Microsoft Excel icon. Left-click to run.

Enter a Formula

Some example computations are detailed below. The = sign is necessary to perform any formula or function computation in a cell.

1. Move the mouse pointer to cell B4 and left-click.
2. Type = 4+3, touch <Enter>, and 7 appears in B4.
3. To edit, use the mouse or <arrow keys> to return to B4, touch <F2>, or use the mouse to move to the Formula Bar in the upper section of the spreadsheet.
4. In either location, touch <Backspace> twice to delete +3.
5. Type −3 and touch <Enter>.
6. The answer 1 appears in cell B4.
7. To delete the cell entirely, move to cell B4 and touch the <Delete> key once.
8. To exit, move the mouse pointer to the top left corner and left-click on File in the top bar menu.
9. Move the mouse down the File submenu, highlight Exit, and left-click.
10. When the Save Changes box appears, left-click "No" to exit without saving.
11. If you wish to save your work, left-click "Yes."
12. Type in a file name (e.g., calcs 1) and click on "Save."

The formulas and functions on the worksheet can be displayed by pressing Ctrl and `. The ` (backtick) symbol is usually in the upper left of the keyboard with the ~ (tilde) symbol. Pressing Ctrl+` a second time hides the formulas and functions.

Use Excel Functions

1. Run Excel.
2. Move to cell C3. (Move the mouse pointer to C3 and left-click.)
3. Type =PV(5%,12,10) and <Enter>. This function will calculate the present value of 12 payments of $10 at a 5% per year interest rate.

Another use: To calculate the future value of 12 payments of $10 at 6% per year interest, do the following:

1. Move to cell B3, and type INTEREST.
2. Move to cell C3, and type 6% or =6/100.
3. Move to cell B4, and type PAYMENT.
4. Move to cell C4, and type 10 (to represent the size of each payment).
5. Move to cell B5, and type NUMBER OF PAYMENTS.
6. Move to cell C5, and type 12 (to represent the number of payments).
7. Move to cell B7, and type FUTURE VALUE.
8. Move to cell C7, and type =FV(C3,C5,C4) and hit <Enter>. The answer will appear in cell C7.

To edit the values in cells (this feature is used repeatedly in sensitivity analysis and breakeven analysis),

1. Move to cell C3 and type =5/100 (the previous value will be replaced).
2. The value in cell C7 will change its answer automatically.

Cell References in Formulas and Functions

If a cell reference is used in lieu of a specific number, it is possible to change the number once and perform sensitivity analysis on any variable (entry) that is referenced by the cell number, such as C5. This approach defines the referenced cell as a *global variable* for the worksheet. There are two types of cell references—relative and absolute.

Relative References   If a cell reference is entered, for example, A1, into a formula or function that is copied or dragged into another cell, the reference is changed relative to the movement of the original cell. If the formula in C5 is =A1, and it is copied into cell C6, the formula is changed to =A2. This feature is used when dragging a function through several cells, and the source entries must change with the column or row.

Absolute References   If adjusting cell references is not desired, place a $ sign in front of the part of the cell reference that is not to be adjusted—the column, row, or both. For example, $=\$A\$1$ will retain the formula when it is moved anywhere on the worksheet. Similarly, $=\$A1$ will retain the column A, but the relative reference on 1 will adjust the row number upon movement around the worksheet.

Absolute references are used in engineering economy for sensitivity analysis of parameters such as MARR, first cost, and annual cash flows. In these cases, a change in the absolute-reference cell entry can help determine the sensitivity of a result, such as PW or AW.

Print the Spreadsheet

First define the portion (or all) of the spreadsheet to be printed.

1. Move the mouse pointer to the top left corner of your spreadsheet.
2. Hold down the left click button. (Do not release the left click button.)
3. Drag the mouse to the lower right corner of your spreadsheet or to wherever you want to stop printing.
4. Release the left click button. (It is ready to print.)
5. Left-click the File top bar menu.
6. Move the mouse down to select Print and left-click.
7. In the Print dialogue box, left-click the option Selection in the Print What box (or similar command).
8. Left-click the OK button to start printing.

Depending on your computer environment, you may have to select a network printer and queue your printout through a server.

Save the Spreadsheet

You can save your spreadsheet at any time during or after completing your work. It is recommended that you save your work regularly.

1. Left-click the File top bar menu.
2. To save the spreadsheet the first time, left-click the Save As . . . option.
3. Type the file name, for example, calcs2, and left-click the Save button.

To save the spreadsheet after it has been saved the first time, that is, a file name has been assigned to it, left-click the File top bar menu, move the mouse pointer down, and left-click on Save.

Create a Column Chart

1. Run Excel.
2. Move to cell A1 and type 1. Move down to cell A2 and type 2. Type 3 in cell A3, 4 in cell A4, and 5 in cell A5.
3. Move to cell B1 and type 4. Type 3.5 in cell B2; 5 in cell B3; 7 in cell B4; and 12 in cell B5.

4. Move the mouse pointer to cell A1, left-click and hold, while dragging the mouse to cell B5. (All the cells with numbers will then be highlighted.)
5. Left-click on the Chart Wizard button on the toolbar.
6. Select the Column option in step 1 of 4 and choose the first subtype of column chart.
7. Left-click and hold the Press and Hold to View Sample button to determine you have selected the type and style of chart desired. Click Next.
8. Since the data were highlighted previously, step 2 can be passed. Left-click Next.
9. For step 3 of 4, click the Titles tab and the Chart Title box. Type Sample 1.
10. Left-click Category (X) axis box and type Year, then left-click Value (Y) axis box and type Rate of return. There are other options (gridlines, legend, etc.) on additional tabs. When finished, left-click Next.
11. For step 4 of 4, left-click As Object In; Sheet1 is highlighted.
12. Left-click Finish, and the chart appears on the spreadsheet.
13. To adjust the size of the chart window, left-click anywhere inside the chart to display small dots on the sides and corners. The words Chart Area will appear immediately below the arrow. Move the mouse to a dot, left-click and hold, then drag the dot to change the size of the chart.
14. To move the chart, left-click and hold within the chart frame, but outside of the graphic itself. A small crosshairs indicator will appear as soon as any movement in the mouse takes place. Changing the position of the mouse moves the entire chart to any location on the worksheet.
15. To adjust the size of the plot area (the graphic itself) within the chart frame, left-click within the graphic. The words Plot Area will appear. Left-click and hold any corner or side dot, and move the mouse to change the size of the graphic up to the size of the chart frame.

Other features are available to change the specific characteristics of the chart. Left-click within the chart frame and click the Chart button on the toolbar at the top of the screen. Options are to alter Chart Type, Source Data, and Chart Options. To obtain detailed help on these, see the help function, or experiment with the sample Column Chart.

Create an xy (Scatter) Chart

This chart is one of the most commonly used in scientific analysis, including engineering economy. It plots pairs of data and can place multiple series of entries on the Y axis. The xy scatter chart is especially useful for results such as the PW vs. i graph, where i is the X axis and the Y axis displays the results of the NPV function for several alternatives.

1. Run Excel.
2. Enter the following numbers in columns A, B, and C, respectively.
   Column A, cell A1 through A6: Rate i%, 4, 6, 8, 9, 10
   Column B, cell B1 through B6: $ for A, 40, 55, 60, 45, 10
   Column C, cell C1 through C6: $ for B, 100, 70, 65, 50, 30.

3. Move the mouse to A1, left-click, and hold while dragging to cell C6. All cells will be highlighted, including the title cell for each column.

4. If all the columns for the chart are not adjacent to one another, first press and hold the Control key on the keyboard during the entirety of step 3. After dragging over one column of data, momentarily release the left click, then move to the top of the next (nonadjacent) column for the chart. Do not release the Control key until all columns to be plotted have been highlighted.

5. Left-click on the Chart Wizard button on the toolbar.

6. Select the *xy* (scatter) option in step 1 of 4, and choose a subtype of scatter chart.

The rest of the steps (7 and higher) are the same as detailed earlier for the Column chart. The Legend tab in step 3 of 4 of the Chart Wizard process displays the series labels from the highlighted columns. (Only the bottom row of the title can be highlighted.) If titles are not highlighted, the data sets are generically identified as Series 1, Series 2, etc. on the legend.

Obtain Help While Using Excel

1. To get general help information, left-click on the Help top bar menu.

2. Left-click on Microsoft Excel Help Topics.

3. For example, if you want to know more about how to save a file, type the word Save in box 1.

4. Select the appropriate matching words in box 2. You can browse through the selected words in box 2 by left-clicking on suggested words.

5. Observe the listed topics in box 3.

6. If you find a topic listed in box 3 that matches what you are looking for, double-left-click the selected topic in box 3.

A.2 ORGANIZATION (LAYOUT) OF THE SPREADSHEET

A spreadsheet can be used in several ways to obtain answers to numerical questions. The first is as a rapid solution tool, often with the entry of only a few numbers or one predefined function. In the text, this application is identified using the Q-Solve icon in the margin.

1. Run Excel.

2. Move the mouse to cell A1 and type $=$SUM(45,15,$-$20). The answer of 40 is displayed in the cell.

3. Move the mouse to cell B4 and type $=$FV(8%,5,$-$2500). The number $14,666.50 is displayed as the 8% per year future worth at the end of the fifth year of five payments of $2500 each.

The second application is more formal. The spreadsheet with the results may serve as documentation of what the entries mean; the sheet may be presented to

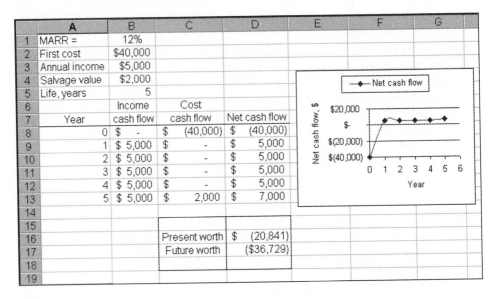

	A	B	C	D	E	F	G
1	MARR =	12%					
2	First cost	$40,000					
3	Annual income	$5,000					
4	Salvage value	$2,000					
5	Life, years	5					
6		Income	Cost				
7	Year	cash flow	cash flow	Net cash flow			
8	0	$ -	$ (40,000)	$ (40,000)			
9	1	$ 5,000	$ -	$ 5,000			
10	2	$ 5,000	$ -	$ 5,000			
11	3	$ 5,000	$ -	$ 5,000			
12	4	$ 5,000	$ -	$ 5,000			
13	5	$ 5,000	$ 2,000	$ 7,000			
14							
15							
16			Present worth	$ (20,841)			
17			Future worth	($36,729)			
18							
19							

Figure A–1
Sample spreadsheet layout with estimates, results of formulas and functions, and an *xy* scatter chart.

a coworker, a boss, or a professor; or the final sheet may be placed into a report to management. This type of spreadsheet is identified by the E-Solve icon in the text. Some fundamental guidelines useful in setting up the spreadsheet follow. A very simple layout is presented in Figure A–1. As the solutions become more complex, an orderly arrangement of information makes the spreadsheet easier to read and use.

Cluster the data and the answers. It is advisable to organize the given or estimated data in the top left of the spreadsheet. A very brief label should be used to identify the data, for example, MARR = in cell A1 and the value, 12%, in cell B1. Then B1 can be the referenced cell for all entries requiring the MARR. Additionally, it may be worthwhile to cluster the answers into one area and frame it using the Outside Border button on the toolbar. Often, the answers are best placed at the bottom or top of the column of entries used in the formula or pre-defined function.

Enter titles for columns and rows. Each column or row should be labeled so its entries are clear to the reader. It is very easy to select from the wrong column or row when no brief title is present at the head of the data.

Enter income and cost cash flows separately. When there are both income and cost cash flows involved, it is strongly recommended that the cash flow estimates for revenue (usually positive) and first cost, salvage value, and annual costs (usually negative, with salvage a positive number) be entered into two adjacent columns. Then a formula combining them in a third column displays the net cash flow. There are two immediate advantages to this practice: fewer errors are made when performing the summation and subtraction mentally, changes for sensitivity analysis are more easily made.

Use cell references. The use of absolute and relative cell references is a must when any changes in entries are expected. For example, suppose the MARR is entered in cell B1, and three separate references are made to the MARR in functions on the spreadsheet. The absolute cell reference entry $B$1 in the three functions allows the MARR to be changed one time, not three.

Obtain a final answer through summing and embedding. When the formulas and functions are kept relatively simple, the final answer can be obtained using the SUM function. For example, if the present worth values (PW) of two columns of cash flows are determined separately, then the total PW is the SUM of the subtotals. This practice is especially useful when the cash flow series are complex.

Although the embedding of functions is allowed in Excel, this means more opportunities for entry errors. Separating the computations makes it easier for the reader to understand the entries. A common application in engineering economy of this practice is in the PMT function that finds the annual worth of a cash flow series. The NPV function can be embedded as the present worth (P) value into PMT. Alternatively, the NPV function can be applied first, after which the cell with the PW answer can be referenced in the PMT function. (See Section 3.1 for further comments.)

Prepare for a chart. If a chart (graph) will be developed, plan ahead by leaving sufficient room on the right of the data and answers. Charts can be placed on the same worksheet or on a separate worksheet when the Chart Wizard is used, as discussed in Section A.1 on creating charts. Placement on the same worksheet is recommended, especially when the results of sensitivity analysis are plotted.

A.3) EXCEL FUNCTIONS IMPORTANT TO ENGINEERING ECONOMY (alphabetical order)

DB (declining balance)

Calculates the depreciation amount for an asset for a specified period n using the declining balance method. The depreciation rate, d, used in the computation is determined from asset values S (salvage value) and B (basis or first cost) as $d = 1 - (S/B)^{1/n}$. This is Equation [16.11]. Three-decimal-place accuracy is used for d.

$$=DB(cost, salvage, life, period, month)$$

cost	First cost or basis of the asset.
salvage	Salvage value.
life	Depreciation life (recovery period).
period	The period, year, for which the depreciation is to be calculated.
month	(Optional entry) If this entry is omitted, a full year is assumed for the first year.

Example A new machine costs $100,000 and is expected to last 10 years. At the end of 10 years, the salvage value of the machine is $50,000. What is the depreciation of the machine in the first year and the fifth year?

Depreciation for the first year: =DB(100000,50000,10,1)
Depreciation for the fifth year: =DB(100000,50000,10,5)

FV (future value)

Calculates the future value (worth) based on periodic payments at a specific interest rate.

$$=FV(rate, nper, pmt, pv, type)$$

rate	Interest rate per compounding period.
nper	Number of compounding periods.
pmt	Constant payment amount.
pv	The present value amount. If pv is not specified, the function will assume it to be 0.
type	(Optional entry) Either 0 or 1. A 0 represents payments made at the end of the period, and 1 represents payments at the beginning of the period. If omitted, 0 is assumed.

Example Jack wants to start a savings account that can be increased as desired. He will deposit $12,000 to start the account and plans to add $500 to the account at the beginning of each month for the next 24 months. The bank pays 0.25% per month. How much will be in Jack's account at the end of 24 months?

Future value in 24 months: =FV(0.25%,24,500,12000,1)

IF (IF logical function)

Determines which of two entries is entered into a cell based on the outcome of a logical check on the outcome of another cell. The logical test can be a function or a simple value check, but it must use an equality or inequality sense. If the response is a text string, place it between quote marks (" "). The responses can themselves be IF functions. Up to seven IF functions can be nested for very complex logical tests.

$$=IF(logical\_test,value\_if\_true,value\_if\_false)$$

logical_test	Any worksheet function can be used here, including a mathematical operation.
value_if_true	Result if the logical_test argument is true.
value_if_false	Result if the logical_test argument is false.

Example The entry in cell B4 should be "selected" if the PW value in cell B3 is greater than or equal to zero and "rejected" if PW < 0.

Entry in cell B4: =IF(B3>=0,"selected","rejected")

Example   The entry in cell C5 should be "selected" if the PW value in cell C4 is greater than or equal to zero, "rejected" if PW < 0, and "fantastic" if PW ≥ 200.

Entry in cell C5:   =IF(C4<0,"rejected",IF(C4>=200,"fantastic", "selected"))

IPMT (interest payment)

Calculates the interest accrued for a given period *n* based on constant periodic payments and interest rate.

=**IPMT(rate, per, nper, pv, fv, type)**

rate	Interest rate per compounding period.
per	Period for which interest is to be calculated.
nper	Number of compounding periods.
pv	Present value. If pv is not specified, the function will assume it to be 0.
fv	Future value. If fv is omitted, the function will assume it to be 0. The fv can also be considered a cash balance after the last payment is made.
type	(Optional entry) Either 0 or 1. A 0 represents payments made at the end of the period, and 1 represents payments made at the beginning of the period. If omitted, 0 is assumed.

Example   Calculate the interest due in the tenth month for a 48-month, $20,000 loan. The interest rate is 0.25% per month.

Interest due: =IPMT(0.25%,10,48,20000)

IRR (internal rate of return)

Calculates the internal rate of return between −100% and infinity for a series of cash flows at regular periods.

=**IRR(values, guess)**

values	A set of numbers in a spreadsheet column (or row) for which the rate of return will be calculated. The set of numbers must consist of at least *one* positive and *one* negative number. Negative numbers denote a payment made or cash outflow, and positive numbers denote income or cash inflow.
guess	(Optional entry) To reduce the number of iterations, a *guessed rate of return* can be entered. In most cases, a guess is not required, and a 10% rate of return is initially assumed. If the #NUM! error appears, try using different values for guess. Inputting different guess values makes it possible to determine the multiple roots for the rate of return equation of a nonconventional cash flow series.

Example   John wants to start a printing business. He will need $25,000 in capital and anticipates that the business will generate the following incomes during the first 5 years. Calculate his rate of return after 3 years and after 5 years.

Year 1	$5,000
Year 2	$7,500

Year 3	$8,000
Year 4	$10,000
Year 5	$15,000

Set up an array in the spreadsheet.

In cell A1, type −25000 (negative for payment).
In cell A2, type 5000 (positive for income).
In cell A3, type 7500.
In cell A4, type 8000.
In cell A5, type 10000.
In cell A6, type 15000.

Therefore, cells A1 through A6 contain the array of cash flows for the first 5 years, including the capital outlay. *Note that any years with a zero cash flow must have a zero entered* to ensure that the year value is correctly maintained for computation purposes.

To calculate the internal rate of return after 3 years, move to cell A7, and type =IRR(A1:A4).

To calculate the internal rate of return after 5 years and specify a guess value of 5%, move to cell A8, and type =IRR(A1:A6,5%).

MIRR (modified internal rate of return)

Calculates the modified internal rate of return for a series of cash flows and reinvestment of income and interest at a stated rate.

=MIRR(values, finance_rate, reinvest_rate)

values	Refers to an array of cells in the spreadsheet. Negative numbers represent payments, and positive numbers represent income. The series of payments and income must occur at regular periods and must contain at least *one* positive number and *one* negative number.
finance_rate	Interest rate of money used in the cash flows.
reinvest_rate	Interest rate for reinvestment on positive cash flows. (This is not the same reinvestment rate on the net investments when the cash flow series is nonconventional. See Section 7.5 for comments.)

Example Jane opened a hobby store 4 years ago. When she started the business, Jane borrowed $50,000 from a bank at 12% per year. Since then, the business has yielded $10,000 the first year, $15,000 the second year, $18,000 the third year, and $21,000 the fourth year. Jane reinvests her profits, earning 8% per year. What is the modified rate of return after 3 years and after 4 years?

In cell A1, type −50000.
In cell A2, type 10000.
In cell A3, type 15000.
In cell A4, type 18000.
In cell A5, type 21000.

To calculate the modified rate of return after 3 years, move to cell A6, and type =MIRR(A1:A4,12%,8%).

To calculate the modified rate of return after 4 years, move to cell A7, and type =MIRR(A1:A5,12%,8%).

NPER (number of periods)

Calculates the number of periods for the present worth of an investment to equal the future value specified, based on uniform regular payments and a stated interest rate.

$$=\textbf{NPER(rate, pmt, pv, fv, type)}$$

rate   Interest rate per compounding period.

pmt   Amount paid during each compounding period.

pv   Present value (lump-sum amount).

fv   (Optional entry) Future value or cash balance after the last payment. If fv is omitted, the function will assume a value of 0.

type   (Optional entry) Enter 0 if payments are due at the end of the compounding period, and 1 if payments are due at the beginning of the period. If omitted, 0 is assumed.

Example Sally plans to open a savings account which pays 0.25% per month. Her initial deposit is $3000, and she plans to deposit $250 at the beginning of every month. How many payments does she have to make to accumulate $15,000 to buy a new car?

Number of payments: =NPER(0.25%,−250,−3000,15000,1)

NPV (net present value)

Calculates the net present value of a series of future cash flows at a stated interest rate.

$$=\textbf{NPV(rate, series)}$$

rate   Interest rate per compounding period.

series   Series of costs and incomes set up in a range of cells in the spreadsheet.

Example Mark is considering buying a sports store for $100,000 and expects to receive the following income during the next 6 years of business: $25,000, $40,000, $42,000, $44,000, $48,000, $50,000. The interest rate is 8% per year.

In cell A1, type −100000.

In cell A2, type 25000.

In cell A3, type 40000.

In cell A4, type 42000.

In cell A5, type 44000.

In cell A6, type 48000.

In cell A7, type 50000.

In cell A8, type =NPV(8%,A2:A7)+A1.

The cell A1 value is already a present value. *Any year with a zero cash flow must have a 0 entered* to ensure a correct result.

PMT (payments)

Calculates equivalent periodic amounts based on present value and/or future value at a constant interest rate.

$$=\textbf{PMT(rate, nper, pv, fv, type)}$$

rate	Interest rate per compounding period.
nper	Total number of periods.
pv	Present value.
fv	Future value.
type	(Optional entry) Enter 0 for payments due at the end of the compounding period, and 1 if payment is due at the start of the compounding period. If omitted, 0 is assumed.

Example   Jim plans to take a $15,000 loan to buy a new car. The interest rate is 7%. He wants to pay the loan off in 5 years (60 months). What are his monthly payments?

Monthly payments: =PMT(7%/12,60,15000)

PPMT (principal payment)

Calculates the payment on the principal based on uniform payments at a specified interest rate.

$$=\textbf{PPMT(rate, per, nper, pv, fv, type)}$$

rate	Interest rate per compounding period.
per	Period for which the payment on the principal is required.
nper	Total number of periods.
pv	Present value.
fv	Future value.
type	(Optional entry) Enter 0 for payments that are due at the end of the compounding period, and 1 if payments are due at the start of the compounding period. If omitted, 0 is assumed.

Example   Jovita is planning to invest $10,000 in equipment which is expected to last 10 years with no salvage value. The interest rate is 5%. What is the principal payment at the end of year 4 and year 8?

At the end of year 4: =PPMT(5%,4,10,−10000)

At the end of year 8: =PPMT(5%,8,10,−10000)

PV (present value)

Calculates the present value of a future series of equal cash flows and a single lump sum in the last period at a constant interest rate.

$$=\textbf{PV(rate, nper, pmt, fv, type)}$$

rate Interest rate per compounding period.
nper Total number of periods.
pmt Cash flow at regular intervals. Negative numbers represent payments (cash outflows), and positive numbers represent income.
fv Future value or cash balance at the end of the last period.
type (Optional entry) Enter 0 if payments are due at the end of the compounding period, and 1 if payments are due at the start of each compounding period. If omitted, 0 is assumed.

There are two primary differences between the PV function and the NPV function: PV allows for end or beginning of period cash flows, and PV requires that all amounts have the same value, whereas they may vary for the NPV function.

Example Jose is considering leasing a car for $300 a month for 3 years (36 months). After the 36-month lease, he can purchase the car for $12,000. Using an interest rate of 8% per year, find the present value of this option.

Present value: $=\text{PV}(8\%/12, 36, -300, -12000)$

Note the minus signs on the pmt and fv amounts.

RAND (random number)

Returns an evenly distributed number that is $(1) \geq 0$ and < 1; $(2) \geq 0$ and < 100; or (3) between two specified numbers.

   $=\textbf{RAND()}$ **for range 0 to 1**
   $=\textbf{RAND()*100}$ **for range 0 to 100**
   $=\textbf{RAND()*(}b-a\textbf{)}+a$ **for range a to b**

a = minimum integer to be generated
b = maximum integer to be generated

The Excel function RANDBETWEEN(a,b) may also be used to obtain a random number between two values.

Example Grace needs random numbers between 5 and 10 with 3 digits after the decimal. What is the Excel function? Here $a = 5$ and $b = 10$.

Random number: $=\text{RAND()}*5 + 5$

Example Randi wants to generate random numbers between the limits of -10 and 25. What is the Excel function? The minimum and maximum values are $a = -10$ and $b = 25$, so $b - a = 25 - (-10) = 35$.

Random number: $=\text{RAND()}*35 - 10$

RATE (interest rate)

Calculates the interest rate per compounding period for a series of payments or incomes.

$$=\textbf{RATE(nper, pmt, pv, fv, type, guess)}$$

nper   Total number of periods.

pmt   Payment amount made each compounding period.

pv   Present value.

fv   Future value (not including the pmt amount).

type   (Optional entry) Enter 0 for payments due at the end of the compounding period, and 1 if payments are due at the start of each compounding period. If omitted, 0 is assumed.

guess   (Optional entry) To minimize computing time, include a guessed interest rate. If a value of guess is not specified, the function will assume a rate of 10%. This function usually converges to a solution, if the rate is between 0% and 100%.

Example Mary wants to start a savings account at a bank. She will make an initial deposit of $1000 to open the account and plans to deposit $100 at the beginning of each month. She plans to do this for the next 3 years (36 months). At the end of 3 years, she wants to have at least $5000. What is the minimum interest required to achieve this result?

Interest rate: $=$RATE$(36,-100,-1000,5000,1)$

A.4 SOLVER—AN EXCEL TOOL FOR BREAKEVEN AND "WHAT IF?" ANALYSIS

SOLVER is a powerful tool used to change the value in one or more cells based upon a specified (target) cell value. It is especially helpful in performing breakeven and sensitivity analysis to answer "what if" questions. The SOLVER template is shown in Figure A–2.

Set Target Cell box. Enter a cell reference or name. The target cell itself must contain a formula or function. The value in the cell can be maximized (Max), minimized (Min), or restricted to a specified value (Value of).

By Changing Cells box. Enter the cell reference for each cell to be adjusted, using commas between nonadjacent cells. Each cell must be directly or indirectly related to the target cell. SOLVER proposes a value for the changing cell based on input provided about the target cell. The Guess button will list all possible changing cells related to the target cell.

Subject to the Constraints box. Enter any constraints that may apply, for example, $C$1 < $50,000. Integer and binary variables are determined in this box.

Options box. Choices here allow the user to specify various parameters of the solution: maximum time and number of iterations allowed, the precision and tolerance of the values determined, and the convergence requirements as the final solution is determined. Also, linear and nonlinear model assumptions can be set here. *If integer or binary variables are involved, the tolerance option must be*

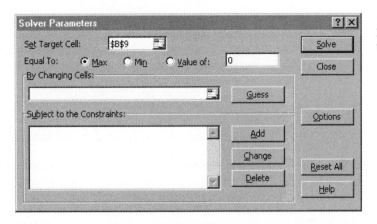

Figure A–2
Excel's SOLVER template.

set to a small number, say, 0.0001. This is especially important for the binary variables when selecting from independent projects (Chapter 12). If tolerance remains at the default value of 5%, a project may be incorrectly included in the solution set at a very low level.

SOLVER Results box. This appears after Solve is clicked and a solution appears. It is possible, of course, that no solution can be found for the scenario described. It is possible to update the spreadsheet by clicking Keep Solver Solution, or return to the original entries using Restore Original Values.

A.5 LIST OF EXCEL FINANCIAL FUNCTIONS

Here is a listing and brief description of the output of all Excel financial functions. Not all these functions are available on all versions of Microsoft Excel. The Add-ins command can help you determine if the function is available on the system you are using.

ACCRINT	Returns the accrued interest for a security that pays periodic interest.
ACCRINTM	Returns the accrued interest for a security that pays interest at maturity.
AMORDEGRC	Returns the depreciation for each accounting period.
AMORLINC	Returns the depreciation for each accounting period.
COUPDAYBS	Returns the number of days from the beginning of the coupon period to the settlement date.
COUPDAYS	Returns the number of days in the coupon period that contains the settlement date.
COUPDAYSNC	Returns the number of days from the settlement date to the next coupon date.
COUPNCD	Returns the next coupon date after the settlement date.
COUPNUM	Returns the number of coupons payable between the settlement date and maturity date.
COUPPCD	Returns the previous coupon date before the settlement date.
CUMIPMT	Returns the cumulative interest paid between two periods.
CUMPRINC	Returns the cumulative principal paid on a loan between two periods.

DB	Returns the depreciation of an asset for a specified period using the fixed declining balance method.
DDB	Returns the depreciation of an asset for a specified period using the double declining balance method or some other method you specify.
DISC	Returns the discount rate for a security.
DOLLARDE	Converts a dollar price expressed as a fraction to a dollar price expressed as a decimal number.
DOLLARFR	Converts a dollar price expressed as a decimal number to a dollar price expressed as a fraction.
DURATION	Returns the annual duration of a security with periodic interest payments.
EFFECT	Returns the effective annual interest rate.
FV	Returns the future value of an investment.
FVSCHEDULE	Returns the future value of an initial principal after applying a series of compound interest rates.
INTRATE	Returns the interest rate for a fully invested security.
IPMT	Returns the interest payment for an investment for a given period.
IRR	Returns the internal rate of return for a series of cash flows.
ISPMT	Returns the interest paid during a specific period of an investment. (Provides compatibility with Lotus 1-2-3.)
MDURATION	Returns the Macauley modified duration for a security with an assumed par value of $100.
MIRR	Returns the internal rate of return where positive and negative cash flows are financed at different rates.
NOMINAL	Returns the annual nominal interest rate.
NPER	Returns the number of periods for an investment.
NPV	Returns the net present value of an investment based on a series of periodic cash flows and a discount rate.
ODDFPRICE	Returns the price per $100 face value of a security with an odd first period.
ODDFYIELD	Returns the yield of a security with an odd first period.
ODDLPRICE	Returns the price per $100 face value of a security with an odd last period.
ODDLYIELD	Returns the yield of a security with an odd last period.
PMT	Returns the periodic payment for an annuity.
PPMT	Returns the payment on the principal for an investment for a given period.
PRICE	Returns the price per $100 face value of a security that pays periodic interest.
PRICEDISC	Returns the price per $100 face value of a discounted security.
PRICEMAT	Returns the price per $100 face value of a security that pays interest at maturity.
PV	Returns the present value of an investment.
RATE	Returns the interest rate per period of an annuity.
RECEIVED	Returns the amount received at maturity for a fully invested security
SLN	Returns the straight line depreciation of an asset for one period.
SYD	Returns the sum-of-year-digits depreciation of an asset for a specified period.

TBILLEQ	Returns the bond-equivalent yield for a Treasury bill.
TBILLPRICE	Returns the price per $100 face value for a Treasury bill.
TBILLYIELD	Returns the yield for a Treasury bill.
VDB	Returns the depreciation of an asset for a specified or partial period using a declining-balance method with a switch to straight line when it is better.
XIRR	Returns the internal rate of return for a schedule of cash flows that is not necessarily periodic.
XNPV	Returns the net present value for a schedule of cash flows that is not necessarily periodic.
YIELD	Returns the yield on a security that pays periodic interest.
YIELDDISC	Returns the annual yield for a discounted security. For example, a Treasury bill.
YIELDMAT	Returns the annual yield of a security that pays interest at maturity.

Many more functions are available on Excel in other areas: mathematics and trigonometry, statistical, date and time, database, logical, and information.

A.6 ERROR MESSAGES

If Excel is unable to complete a formula or function computation, an error message is displayed. Some of the common messages are as follows:

#DIV/0!	Requires division by zero.
#N/A	Refers to a value that is not available.
#NAME?	Uses a name that Excel doesn't recognize.
#NULL!	Specifies an invalid intersection of two areas.
#NUM!	Uses a number incorrectly.
#REF!	Refers to a cell that is not valid.
#VALUE!	Uses an invalid argument or operand.
#####	Produces a result, or includes a constant numeric value, that is too long to fit in the cell. (To fix, widen the column.)

REFERENCE MATERIALS

USING EXCEL IN ENGINEERING ECONOMY

Gottfried, B. S.: *Spreadsheet Tools for Engineers Using Excel® 2007*, McGraw-Hill, New York, 2003.

WEBSITES

Canada Revenue Agency: www.cra.gc.ca

For this textbook: www.mcgrawhill.ca/olc/blank

Plant cost estimation index: www.che.com/pci

Construction cost estimation index: www.construction.com

SELECTED JOURNALS AND PUBLICATIONS

Business and Professional Income, T4002(E), Canada Revenue Agency.
Engineering News-Record, McGraw-Hill, New York, monthly.
Guide for Canadian Small Businesses, RC4070(E), Canada Revenue Agency.
Harvard Business Review, Harvard University Press, Boston, 6 issues per year.
IT-285R2 Capital Cost Allowance—General Comments, Canada Revenue Agency.
Journal of Finance, American Finance Association, New York, 5 issues per year.
The Engineering Economist, joint publication of the Engineering Economy Divisions of ASEE and IIE, published by Taylor and Francis, Philadelphia, PA, quarterly.
T2 Corporation—Income Tax Guide, T4012(E), Canada Revenue Agency.

0.25%			TABLE 1	Discrete Cash Flow: Compound Interest Factors				0.25%
	Single Payments		Uniform Series Payments				Arithmetic Gradients	
n	Compound Amount F/P	Present Worth P/F	Sinking Fund A/F	Compound Amount F/A	Capital Recovery A/P	Present Worth P/A	Gradient Present Worth P/G	Gradient Uniform Series A/G
1	1.0025	0.9975	1.00000	1.0000	1.00250	0.9975		
2	1.0050	0.9950	0.49938	2.0025	0.50188	1.9925	0.9950	0.4994
3	1.0075	0.9925	0.33250	3.0075	0.33500	2.9851	2.9801	0.9983
4	1.0100	0.9901	0.24906	4.0150	0.25156	3.9751	5.9503	1.4969
5	1.0126	0.9876	0.19900	5.0251	0.20150	4.9627	9.9007	1.9950
6	1.0151	0.9851	0.16563	6.0376	0.16813	5.9478	14.8263	2.4927
7	1.0176	0.9827	0.14179	7.0527	0.14429	6.9305	20.7223	2.9900
8	1.0202	0.9802	0.12391	8.0704	0.12641	7.9107	27.5839	3.4869
9	1.0227	0.9778	0.11000	9.0905	0.11250	8.8885	35.4061	3.9834
10	1.0253	0.9753	0.09888	10.1133	0.10138	9.8639	44.1842	4.4794
11	1.0278	0.9729	0.08978	11.1385	0.09228	10.8368	53.9133	4.9750
12	1.0304	0.9705	0.08219	12.1664	0.08469	11.8073	64.5886	5.4702
13	1.0330	0.9681	0.07578	13.1968	0.07828	12.7753	76.2053	5.9650
14	1.0356	0.9656	0.07028	14.2298	0.07278	13.7410	88.7587	6.4594
15	1.0382	0.9632	0.06551	15.2654	0.06801	14.7042	102.2441	6.9534
16	1.0408	0.9608	0.06134	16.3035	0.06384	15.6650	116.6567	7.4469
17	1.0434	0.9584	0.05766	17.3443	0.06016	16.6235	131.9917	7.9401
18	1.0460	0.9561	0.05438	18.3876	0.05688	17.5795	148.2446	8.4328
19	1.0486	0.9537	0.05146	19.4336	0.05396	18.5332	165.4106	8.9251
20	1.0512	0.9513	0.04882	20.4822	0.05132	19.4845	183.4851	9.4170
21	1.0538	0.9489	0.04644	21.5334	0.04894	20.4334	202.4634	9.9085
22	1.0565	0.9466	0.04427	22.5872	0.04677	21.3800	222.3410	10.3995
23	1.0591	0.9442	0.04229	23.6437	0.04479	22.3241	243.1131	10.8901
24	1.0618	0.9418	0.04048	24.7028	0.04298	23.2660	264.7753	11.3804
25	1.0644	0.9395	0.03881	25.7646	0.04131	24.2055	287.3230	11.8702
26	1.0671	0.9371	0.03727	26.8290	0.03977	25.1426	310.7516	12.3596
27	1.0697	0.9348	0.03585	27.8961	0.03835	26.0774	335.0566	12.8485
28	1.0724	0.9325	0.03452	28.9658	0.03702	27.0099	360.2334	13.3371
29	1.0751	0.9301	0.03329	30.0382	0.03579	27.9400	386.2776	13.8252
30	1.0778	0.9278	0.03214	31.1133	0.03464	28.8679	413.1847	14.3130
36	1.0941	0.9140	0.02658	37.6206	0.02908	34.3865	592.4988	17.2306
40	1.1050	0.9050	0.02380	42.0132	0.02630	38.0199	728.7399	19.1673
48	1.1273	0.8871	0.01963	50.9312	0.02213	45.1787	1040.06	23.0209
50	1.1330	0.8826	0.01880	53.1887	0.02130	46.9462	1125.78	23.9802
52	1.1386	0.8782	0.01803	55.4575	0.02053	48.7048	1214.59	24.9377
55	1.1472	0.8717	0.01698	58.8819	0.01948	51.3264	1353.53	26.3710
60	1.1616	0.8609	0.01547	64.6467	0.01797	55.6524	1600.08	28.7514
72	1.1969	0.8355	0.01269	78.7794	0.01519	65.8169	2265.56	34.4221
75	1.2059	0.8292	0.01214	82.3792	0.01464	68.3108	2447.61	35.8305
84	1.2334	0.8108	0.01071	93.3419	0.01321	75.6813	3029.76	40.0331
90	1.2520	0.7987	0.00992	100.7885	0.01242	80.5038	3446.87	42.8162
96	1.2709	0.7869	0.00923	108.3474	0.01173	85.2546	3886.28	45.5844
100	1.2836	0.7790	0.00881	113.4500	0.01131	88.3825	4191.24	47.4216
108	1.3095	0.7636	0.00808	123.8093	0.01058	94.5453	4829.01	51.0762
120	1.3494	0.7411	0.00716	139.7414	0.00966	103.5618	5852.11	56.5084
132	1.3904	0.7192	0.00640	156.1582	0.00890	112.3121	6950.01	61.8813
144	1.4327	0.6980	0.00578	173.0743	0.00828	120.8041	8117.41	67.1949
240	1.8208	0.5492	0.00305	328.3020	0.00555	180.3109	19399	107.5863
360	2.4568	0.4070	0.00172	582.7369	0.00422	237.1894	36264	152.8902
480	3.3151	0.3016	0.00108	926.0595	0.00358	279.3418	53821	192.6699

0.5%		TABLE 2	Discrete Cash Flow: Compound Interest Factors					0.5%
	Single Payments		Uniform Series Payments				Arithmetic Gradients	
	Compound Amount	Present Worth	Sinking Fund	Compound Amount	Capital Recovery	Present Worth	Gradient Present Worth	Gradient Uniform Series
n	F/P	P/F	A/F	F/A	A/P	P/A	P/G	A/G
1	1.0050	0.9950	1.00000	1.0000	1.00500	0.9950		
2	1.0100	0.9901	0.49875	2.0050	0.50375	1.9851	0.9901	0.4988
3	1.0151	0.9851	0.33167	3.0150	0.33667	2.9702	2.9604	0.9967
4	1.0202	0.9802	0.24813	4.0301	0.25313	3.9505	5.9011	1.4938
5	1.0253	0.9754	0.19801	5.0503	0.20301	4.9259	9.8026	1.9900
6	1.0304	0.9705	0.16460	6.0755	0.16960	5.8964	14.6552	2.4855
7	1.0355	0.9657	0.14073	7.1059	0.14573	6.8621	20.4493	2.9801
8	1.0407	0.9609	0.12283	8.1414	0.12783	7.8230	27.1755	3.4738
9	1.0459	0.9561	0.10891	9.1821	0.11391	8.7791	34.8244	3.9668
10	1.0511	0.9513	0.09777	10.2280	0.10277	9.7304	43.3865	4.4589
11	1.0564	0.9466	0.08866	11.2792	0.09366	10.6770	52.8526	4.9501
12	1.0617	0.9419	0.08107	12.3356	0.08607	11.6189	63.2136	5.4406
13	1.0670	0.9372	0.07464	13.3972	0.07964	12.5562	74.4602	5.9302
14	1.0723	0.9326	0.06914	14.4642	0.07414	13.4887	86.5835	6.4190
15	1.0777	0.9279	0.06436	15.5365	0.06936	14.4166	99.5743	6.9069
16	1.0831	0.9233	0.06019	16.6142	0.06519	15.3399	113.4238	7.3940
17	1.0885	0.9187	0.05651	17.6973	0.06151	16.2586	128.1231	7.8803
18	1.0939	0.9141	0.05323	18.7858	0.05823	17.1728	143.6634	8.3658
19	1.0994	0.9096	0.05030	19.8797	0.05530	18.0824	160.0360	8.8504
20	1.1049	0.9051	0.04767	20.9791	0.05267	18.9874	177.2322	9.3342
21	1.1104	0.9006	0.04528	22.0840	0.05028	19.8880	195.2434	9.8172
22	1.1160	0.8961	0.04311	23.1944	0.04811	20.7841	214.0611	10.2993
23	1.1216	0.8916	0.04113	24.3104	0.04613	21.6757	233.6768	10.7806
24	1.1272	0.8872	0.03932	25.4320	0.04432	22.5629	254.0820	11.2611
25	1.1328	0.8828	0.03765	26.5591	0.04265	23.4456	275.2686	11.7407
26	1.1385	0.8784	0.03611	27.6919	0.04111	24.3240	297.2281	12.2195
27	1.1442	0.8740	0.03469	28.8304	0.03969	25.1980	319.9523	12.6975
28	1.1499	0.8697	0.03336	29.9745	0.03836	26.0677	343.4332	13.1747
29	1.1556	0.8653	0.03213	31.1244	0.03713	26.9330	367.6625	13.6510
30	1.1614	0.8610	0.03098	32.2800	0.03598	27.7941	392.6324	14.1265
36	1.1967	0.8356	0.02542	39.3361	0.03042	32.8710	557.5598	16.9621
40	1.2208	0.8191	0.02265	44.1588	0.02765	36.1722	681.3347	18.8359
48	1.2705	0.7871	0.01849	54.0978	0.02349	42.5803	959.9188	22.5437
50	1.2832	0.7793	0.01765	56.6452	0.02265	44.1428	1035.70	23.4624
52	1.2961	0.7716	0.01689	59.2180	0.02189	45.6897	1113.82	24.3778
55	1.3156	0.7601	0.01584	63.1258	0.02084	47.9814	1235.27	25.7447
60	1.3489	0.7414	0.01433	69.7700	0.01933	51.7256	1448.65	28.0064
72	1.4320	0.6983	0.01157	86.4089	0.01657	60.3395	2012.35	33.3504
75	1.4536	0.6879	0.01102	90.7265	0.01602	62.4136	2163.75	34.6679
84	1.5204	0.6577	0.00961	104.0739	0.01461	68.4530	2640.66	38.5763
90	1.5666	0.6383	0.00883	113.3109	0.01383	72.3313	2976.08	41.1451
96	1.6141	0.6195	0.00814	122.8285	0.01314	76.0952	3324.18	43.6845
100	1.6467	0.6073	0.00773	129.3337	0.01273	78.5426	3562.79	45.3613
108	1.7137	0.5835	0.00701	142.7399	0.01201	83.2934	4054.37	48.6758
120	1.8194	0.5496	0.00610	163.8793	0.01110	90.0735	4823.51	53.5508
132	1.9316	0.5177	0.00537	186.3226	0.01037	96.4596	5624.59	58.3103
144	2.0508	0.4876	0.00476	210.1502	0.00976	102.4747	6451.31	62.9551
240	3.3102	0.3021	0.00216	462.0409	0.00716	139.5808	13416	96.1131
360	6.0226	0.1660	0.00100	1004.52	0.00600	166.7916	21403	128.3236
480	10.9575	0.0913	0.00050	1991.49	0.00550	181.7476	27588	151.7949

0.75%		TABLE 3	Discrete Cash Flow: Compound Interest Factors					0.75%
	Single Payments		**Uniform Series Payments**				**Arithmetic Gradients**	
n	Compound Amount F/P	Present Worth P/F	Sinking Fund A/F	Compound Amount F/A	Capital Recovery A/P	Present Worth P/A	Gradient Present Worth P/G	Gradient Uniform Series A/G
1	1.0075	0.9926	1.00000	1.0000	1.00750	0.9926		
2	1.0151	0.9852	0.49813	2.0075	0.50563	1.9777	0.9852	0.4981
3	1.0227	0.9778	0.33085	3.0226	0.33835	2.9556	2.9408	0.9950
4	1.0303	0.9706	0.24721	4.0452	0.25471	3.9261	5.8525	1.4907
5	1.0381	0.9633	0.19702	5.0756	0.20452	4.8894	9.7058	1.9851
6	1.0459	0.9562	0.16357	6.1136	0.17107	5.8456	14.4866	2.4782
7	1.0537	0.9490	0.13967	7.1595	0.14717	6.7946	20.1808	2.9701
8	1.0616	0.9420	0.12176	8.2132	0.12926	7.7366	26.7747	3.4608
9	1.0696	0.9350	0.10782	9.2748	0.11532	8.6716	34.2544	3.9502
10	1.0776	0.9280	0.09667	10.3443	0.10417	9.5996	42.6064	4.4384
11	1.0857	0.9211	0.08755	11.4219	0.09505	10.5207	51.8174	4.9253
12	1.0938	0.9142	0.07995	12.5076	0.08745	11.4349	61.8740	5.4110
13	1.1020	0.9074	0.07352	13.6014	0.08102	12.3423	72.7632	5.8954
14	1.1103	0.9007	0.06801	14.7034	0.07551	13.2430	84.4720	6.3786
15	1.1186	0.8940	0.06324	15.8137	0.07074	14.1370	96.9876	6.8606
16	1.1270	0.8873	0.05906	16.9323	0.06656	15.0243	110.2973	7.3413
17	1.1354	0.8807	0.05537	18.0593	0.06287	15.9050	124.3887	7.8207
18	1.1440	0.8742	0.05210	19.1947	0.05960	16.7792	139.2494	8.2989
19	1.1525	0.8676	0.04917	20.3387	0.05667	17.6468	154.8671	8.7759
20	1.1612	0.8612	0.04653	21.4912	0.05403	18.5080	171.2297	9.2516
21	1.1699	0.8548	0.04415	22.6524	0.05165	19.3628	188.3253	9.7261
22	1.1787	0.8484	0.04198	23.8223	0.04948	20.2112	206.1420	10.1994
23	1.1875	0.8421	0.04000	25.0010	0.04750	21.0533	224.6682	10.6714
24	1.1964	0.8358	0.03818	26.1885	0.04568	21.8891	243.8923	11.1422
25	1.2054	0.8296	0.03652	27.3849	0.04402	22.7188	263.8029	11.6117
26	1.2144	0.8234	0.03498	28.5903	0.04248	23.5422	284.3888	12.0800
27	1.2235	0.8173	0.03355	29.8047	0.04105	24.3595	305.6387	12.5470
28	1.2327	0.8112	0.03223	31.0282	0.03973	25.1707	327.5416	13.0128
29	1.2420	0.8052	0.03100	32.2609	0.03850	25.9759	350.0867	13.4774
30	1.2513	0.7992	0.02985	33.5029	0.03735	26.7751	373.2631	13.9407
36	1.3086	0.7641	0.02430	41.1527	0.03180	31.4468	524.9924	16.6946
40	1.3483	0.7416	0.02153	46.4465	0.02903	34.4469	637.4693	18.5058
48	1.4314	0.6986	0.01739	57.5207	0.02489	40.1848	886.8404	22.0691
50	1.4530	0.6883	0.01656	60.3943	0.02406	41.5664	953.8486	22.9476
52	1.4748	0.6780	0.01580	63.3111	0.02330	42.9276	1022.59	23.8211
55	1.5083	0.6630	0.01476	67.7688	0.02226	44.9316	1128.79	25.1223
60	1.5657	0.6387	0.01326	75.4241	0.02076	48.1734	1313.52	27.2665
72	1.7126	0.5839	0.01053	95.0070	0.01803	55.4768	1791.25	32.2882
75	1.7514	0.5710	0.00998	100.1833	0.01748	57.2027	1917.22	33.5163
84	1.8732	0.5338	0.00859	116.4269	0.01609	62.1540	2308.13	37.1357
90	1.9591	0.5104	0.00782	127.8790	0.01532	65.2746	2578.00	39.4946
96	2.0489	0.4881	0.00715	139.8562	0.01465	68.2584	2853.94	41.8107
100	2.1111	0.4737	0.00675	148.1445	0.01425	70.1746	3040.75	43.3311
108	2.2411	0.4462	0.00604	165.4832	0.01354	73.8394	3419.90	46.3154
120	2.4514	0.4079	0.00517	193.5143	0.01267	78.9417	3998.56	50.6521
132	2.6813	0.3730	0.00446	224.1748	0.01196	83.6064	4583.57	54.8232
144	2.9328	0.3410	0.00388	257.7116	0.01138	87.8711	5169.58	58.8314
240	6.0092	0.1664	0.00150	667.8869	0.00900	111.1450	9494.12	85.4210
360	14.7306	0.0679	0.00055	1830.74	0.00805	124.2819	13312	107.1145
480	36.1099	0.0277	0.00021	4681.32	0.00771	129.6409	15513	119.6620

1%				TABLE 4	Discrete Cash Flow: Compound Interest Factors			1%
	Single Payments		Uniform Series Payments				Arithmetic Gradients	
	Compound Amount	Present Worth	Sinking Fund	Compound Amount	Capital Recovery	Present Worth	Gradient Present Worth	Gradient Uniform Series
n	F/P	P/F	A/F	F/A	A/P	P/A	P/G	A/G
1	1.0100	0.9901	1.00000	1.0000	1.01000	0.9901		
2	1.0201	0.9803	0.49751	2.0100	0.50751	1.9704	0.9803	0.4975
3	1.0303	0.9706	0.33002	3.0301	0.34002	2.9410	2.9215	0.9934
4	1.0406	0.9610	0.24628	4.0604	0.25628	3.9020	5.8044	1.4876
5	1.0510	0.9515	0.19604	5.1010	0.20604	4.8534	9.6103	1.9801
6	1.0615	0.9420	0.16255	6.1520	0.17255	5.7955	14.3205	2.4710
7	1.0721	0.9327	0.13863	7.2135	0.14863	6.7282	19.9168	2.9602
8	1.0829	0.9235	0.12069	8.2857	0.13069	7.6517	26.3812	3.4478
9	1.0937	0.9143	0.10674	9.3685	0.11674	8.5660	33.6959	3.9337
10	1.1046	0.9053	0.09558	10.4622	0.10558	9.4713	41.8435	4.4179
11	1.1157	0.8963	0.08645	11.5668	0.09645	10.3676	50.8067	4.9005
12	1.1268	0.8874	0.07885	12.6825	0.08885	11.2551	60.5687	5.3815
13	1.1381	0.8787	0.07241	13.8093	0.08241	12.1337	71.1126	5.8607
14	1.1495	0.8700	0.06690	14.9474	0.07690	13.0037	82.4221	6.3384
15	1.1610	0.8613	0.06212	16.0969	0.07212	13.8651	94.4810	6.8143
16	1.1726	0.8528	0.05794	17.2579	0.06794	14.7179	107.2734	7.2886
17	1.1843	0.8444	0.05426	18.4304	0.06426	15.5623	120.7834	7.7613
18	1.1961	0.8360	0.05098	19.6147	0.06098	16.3983	134.9957	8.2323
19	1.2081	0.8277	0.04805	20.8109	0.05805	17.2260	149.8950	8.7017
20	1.2202	0.8195	0.04542	22.0190	0.05542	18.0456	165.4664	9.1694
21	1.2324	0.8114	0.04303	23.2392	0.05303	18.8570	181.6950	9.6354
22	1.2447	0.8034	0.04086	24.4716	0.05086	19.6604	198.5663	10.0998
23	1.2572	0.7954	0.03889	25.7163	0.04889	20.4558	216.0660	10.5626
24	1.2697	0.7876	0.03707	26.9735	0.04707	21.2434	234.1800	11.0237
25	1.2824	0.7798	0.03541	28.2432	0.04541	22.0232	252.8945	11.4831
26	1.2953	0.7720	0.03387	29.5256	0.04387	22.7952	272.1957	11.9409
27	1.3082	0.7644	0.03245	30.8209	0.04245	23.5596	292.0702	12.3971
28	1.3213	0.7568	0.03112	32.1291	0.04112	24.3164	312.5047	12.8516
29	1.3345	0.7493	0.02990	33.4504	0.03990	25.0658	333.4863	13.3044
30	1.3478	0.7419	0.02875	34.7849	0.03875	25.8077	355.0021	13.7557
36	1.4308	0.6989	0.02321	43.0769	0.03321	30.1075	494.6207	16.4285
40	1.4889	0.6717	0.02046	48.8864	0.03046	32.8347	596.8561	18.1776
48	1.6122	0.6203	0.01633	61.2226	0.02633	37.9740	820.1460	21.5976
50	1.6446	0.6080	0.01551	64.4632	0.02551	39.1961	879.4176	22.4363
52	1.6777	0.5961	0.01476	67.7689	0.02476	40.3942	939.9175	23.2686
55	1.7285	0.5785	0.01373	72.8525	0.02373	42.1472	1032.81	24.5049
60	1.8167	0.5504	0.01224	81.6697	0.02224	44.9550	1192.81	26.5333
72	2.0471	0.4885	0.00955	104.7099	0.01955	51.1504	1597.87	31.2386
75	2.1091	0.4741	0.00902	110.9128	0.01902	52.5871	1702.73	32.3793
84	2.3067	0.4335	0.00765	130.6723	0.01765	56.6485	2023.32	35.7170
90	2.4486	0.4084	0.00690	144.8633	0.01690	59.1609	2240.57	37.8724
96	2.5993	0.3847	0.00625	159.9273	0.01625	61.5277	2459.43	39.9727
100	2.7048	0.3697	0.00587	170.4814	0.01587	63.0289	2605.78	41.3426
108	2.9289	0.3414	0.00518	192.8926	0.01518	65.8578	2898.42	44.0103
120	3.3004	0.3030	0.00435	230.0387	0.01435	69.7005	3334.11	47.8349
132	3.7190	0.2689	0.00368	271.8959	0.01368	73.1108	3761.69	51.4520
144	4.1906	0.2386	0.00313	319.0616	0.01313	76.1372	4177.47	54.8676
240	10.8926	0.0918	0.00101	989.2554	0.01101	90.8194	6878.60	75.7393
360	35.9496	0.0278	0.00029	3494.96	0.01029	97.2183	8720.43	89.6995
480	118.6477	0.0084	0.00008	11765	0.01008	99.1572	9511.16	95.9200

1.25%			TABLE 5	Discrete Cash Flow: Compound Interest Factors				1.25%
	Single Payments		Uniform Series Payments				Arithmetic Gradients	
	Compound Amount F/P	Present Worth P/F	Sinking Fund A/F	Compound Amount F/A	Capital Recovery A/P	Present Worth P/A	Gradient Present Worth P/G	Gradient Uniform Series A/G
n								
1	1.0125	0.9877	1.00000	1.0000	1.01250	0.9877		
2	1.0252	0.9755	0.49680	2.0125	0.50939	1.9631	0.9755	0.4969
3	1.0380	0.9634	0.32920	3.0377	0.34170	2.9265	2.9023	0.9917
4	1.0509	0.9515	0.24536	4.0756	0.25786	3.8781	5.7569	1.4845
5	1.0641	0.9398	0.19506	5.1266	0.20756	4.8178	9.5160	1.9752
6	1.0774	0.9282	0.16153	6.1907	0.17403	5.7460	14.1569	2.4638
7	1.0909	0.9167	0.13759	7.2680	0.15009	6.6627	19.6571	2.9503
8	1.1045	0.9054	0.11963	8.3589	0.13213	7.5681	25.9949	3.4348
9	1.1183	0.8942	0.10567	9.4634	0.11817	8.4623	33.1487	3.9172
10	1.1323	0.8832	0.09450	10.5817	0.10700	9.3455	41.0973	4.3975
11	1.1464	0.8723	0.08537	11.7139	0.09787	10.2178	49.8201	4.8758
12	1.1608	0.8615	0.07776	12.8604	0.09026	11.0793	59.2967	5.3520
13	1.1753	0.8509	0.07132	14.0211	0.08382	11.9302	69.5072	5.8262
14	1.1900	0.8404	0.06581	15.1964	0.07831	12.7706	80.4320	6.2982
15	1.2048	0.8300	0.06103	16.3863	0.07353	13.6005	92.0519	6.7682
16	1.2199	0.8197	0.05685	17.5912	0.06935	14.4203	104.3481	7.2362
17	1.2351	0.8096	0.05316	18.8111	0.06566	15.2299	117.3021	7.7021
18	1.2506	0.7996	0.04988	20.0462	0.06238	16.0295	130.8958	8.1659
19	1.2662	0.7898	0.04696	21.2968	0.05946	16.8193	145.1115	8.6277
20	1.2820	0.7800	0.04432	22.5630	0.05682	17.5993	159.9316	9.0874
21	1.2981	0.7704	0.04194	23.8450	0.05444	18.3697	175.3392	9.5450
22	1.3143	0.7609	0.03977	25.1431	0.05227	19.1306	191.3174	10.0006
23	1.3307	0.7515	0.03780	26.4574	0.05030	19.8820	207.8499	10.4542
24	1.3474	0.7422	0.03599	27.7881	0.04849	20.6242	224.9204	10.9056
25	1.3642	0.7330	0.03432	29.1354	0.04682	21.3573	242.5132	11.3551
26	1.3812	0.7240	0.03279	30.4996	0.04529	22.0813	260.6128	11.8024
27	1.3985	0.7150	0.03137	31.8809	0.04387	22.7963	279.2040	12.2478
28	1.4160	0.7062	0.03005	33.2794	0.04255	23.5025	298.2719	12.6911
29	1.4337	0.6975	0.02882	34.6954	0.04132	24.2000	317.8019	13.1323
30	1.4516	0.6889	0.02768	36.1291	0.04018	24.8889	337.7797	13.5715
36	1.5639	0.6394	0.02217	45.1155	0.03467	28.8473	466.2830	16.1639
40	1.6436	0.6084	0.01942	51.4896	0.03192	31.3269	559.2320	17.8515
48	1.8154	0.5509	0.01533	65.2284	0.02783	35.9315	759.2296	21.1299
50	1.8610	0.5373	0.01452	68.8818	0.02702	37.0129	811.6738	21.9295
52	1.9078	0.5242	0.01377	72.6271	0.02627	38.0677	864.9409	22.7211
55	1.9803	0.5050	0.01275	78.4225	0.02525	39.6017	946.2277	23.8936
60	2.1072	0.4746	0.01129	88.5745	0.02379	42.0346	1084.84	25.8083
72	2.4459	0.4088	0.00865	115.6736	0.02115	47.2925	1428.46	30.2047
75	2.5388	0.3939	0.00812	123.1035	0.02062	48.4890	1515.79	31.2605
84	2.8391	0.3522	0.00680	147.1290	0.01930	51.8222	1778.84	34.3258
90	3.0588	0.3269	0.00607	164.7050	0.01857	53.8461	1953.83	36.2855
96	3.2955	0.3034	0.00545	183.6411	0.01795	55.7246	2127.52	38.1793
100	3.4634	0.2887	0.00507	197.0723	0.01757	56.9013	2242.24	39.4058
108	3.8253	0.2614	0.00442	226.0226	0.01692	59.0865	2468.26	41.7737
120	4.4402	0.2252	0.00363	275.2171	0.01613	61.9828	2796.57	45.1184
132	5.1540	0.1940	0.00301	332.3198	0.01551	64.4781	3109.35	48.2234
144	5.9825	0.1672	0.00251	398.6021	0.01501	66.6277	3404.61	51.0990
240	19.7155	0.0507	0.00067	1497.24	0.01317	75.9423	5101.53	67.1764
360	87.5410	0.0114	0.00014	6923.28	0.01264	79.0861	5997.90	75.8401
480	388.7007	0.0026	0.00003	31016	0.01253	79.7942	6284.74	78.7619

1.5%				TABLE 6	Discrete Cash Flow: Compound Interest Factors				1.5%
	Single Payments			Uniform Series Payments				Arithmetic Gradients	
	Compound Amount F/P	Present Worth P/F	Sinking Fund A/F	Compound Amount F/A	Capital Recovery A/P	Present Worth P/A		Gradient Present Worth P/G	Gradient Uniform Series A/G
n									
1	1.0150	0.9852	1.00000	1.0000	1.01500	0.9852			
2	1.0302	0.9707	0.49628	2.0150	0.51128	1.9559		0.9707	0.4963
3	1.0457	0.9563	0.32838	3.0452	0.34338	2.9122		2.8833	0.9901
4	1.0614	0.9422	0.24444	4.0909	0.25944	3.8544		5.7098	1.4814
5	1.0773	0.9283	0.19409	5.1523	0.20909	4.7826		9.4229	1.9702
6	1.0934	0.9145	0.16053	6.2296	0.17553	5.6972		13.9956	2.4566
7	1.1098	0.9010	0.13656	7.3230	0.15156	6.5982		19.4018	2.9405
8	1.1265	0.8877	0.11858	8.4328	0.13358	7.4859		25.6157	3.4219
9	1.1434	0.8746	0.10461	9.5593	0.11961	8.3605		32.6125	3.9008
10	1.1605	0.8617	0.09343	10.7027	0.10843	9.2222		40.3675	4.3772
11	1.1779	0.8489	0.08429	11.8633	0.09929	10.0711		48.8568	4.8512
12	1.1956	0.8364	0.07668	13.0412	0.09168	10.9075		58.0571	5.3227
13	1.2136	0.8240	0.07024	14.2368	0.08524	11.7315		67.9454	5.7917
14	1.2318	0.8118	0.06472	15.4504	0.07972	12.5434		78.4994	6.2582
15	1.2502	0.7999	0.05994	16.6821	0.07494	13.3432		89.6974	6.7223
16	1.2690	0.7880	0.05577	17.9324	0.07077	14.1313		101.5178	7.1839
17	1.2880	0.7764	0.05208	19.2014	0.06708	14.9076		113.9400	7.6431
18	1.3073	0.7649	0.04881	20.4894	0.06381	15.6726		126.9435	8.0997
19	1.3270	0.7536	0.04588	21.7967	0.06088	16.4262		140.5084	8.5539
20	1.3469	0.7425	0.04325	23.1237	0.05825	17.1686		154.6154	9.0057
21	1.3671	0.7315	0.04087	24.4705	0.05587	17.9001		169.2453	9.4550
22	1.3876	0.7207	0.03870	25.8376	0.05370	18.6208		184.3798	9.9018
23	1.4084	0.7100	0.03673	27.2251	0.05173	19.3309		200.0006	10.3462
24	1.4295	0.6995	0.03492	28.6335	0.04992	20.0304		216.0901	10.7881
25	1.4509	0.6892	0.03326	30.0630	0.04826	20.7196		232.6310	11.2276
26	1.4727	0.6790	0.03173	31.5140	0.04673	21.3986		249.6065	11.6646
27	1.4948	0.6690	0.03032	32.9867	0.04532	22.0676		267.0002	12.0992
28	1.5172	0.6591	0.02900	34.4815	0.04400	22.7267		284.7958	12.5313
29	1.5400	0.6494	0.02778	35.9987	0.04278	23.3761		302.9779	12.9610
30	1.5631	0.6398	0.02664	37.5387	0.04164	24.0158		321.5310	13.3883
36	1.7091	0.5851	0.02115	47.2760	0.03615	27.6607		439.8303	15.9009
40	1.8140	0.5513	0.01843	54.2679	0.03343	29.9158		524.3568	17.5277
48	2.0435	0.4894	0.01437	69.5652	0.02937	34.0426		703.5462	20.6667
50	2.1052	0.4750	0.01357	73.6828	0.02857	34.9997		749.9636	21.4277
52	2.1689	0.4611	0.01283	77.9249	0.02783	35.9287		796.8774	22.1794
55	2.2679	0.4409	0.01183	84.5296	0.02683	37.2715		868.0285	23.2894
60	2.4432	0.4093	0.01039	96.2147	0.02539	39.3803		988.1674	25.0930
72	2.9212	0.3423	0.00781	128.0772	0.02281	43.8447		1279.79	29.1893
75	3.0546	0.3274	0.00730	136.9728	0.02230	44.8416		1352.56	30.1631
84	3.4926	0.2863	0.00602	166.1726	0.02102	47.5786		1568.51	32.9668
90	3.8189	0.2619	0.00532	187.9299	0.02032	49.2099		1709.54	34.7399
96	4.1758	0.2395	0.00472	211.7202	0.01972	50.7017		1847.47	36.4381
100	4.4320	0.2256	0.00437	228.8030	0.01937	51.6247		1937.45	37.5295
108	4.9927	0.2003	0.00376	266.1778	0.01876	53.3137		2112.13	39.6171
120	5.9693	0.1675	0.00302	331.2882	0.01802	55.4985		2359.71	42.5185
132	7.1370	0.1401	0.00244	409.1354	0.01744	57.3257		2588.71	45.1579
144	8.5332	0.1172	0.00199	502.2109	0.01699	58.8540		2798.58	47.5512
240	35.6328	0.0281	0.00043	2308.85	0.01543	64.7957		3870.69	59.7368
360	212.7038	0.0047	0.00007	14114	0.01507	66.3532		4310.72	64.9662
480	1269.70	0.0008	0.00001	84580	0.01501	66.6142		4415.74	66.2883

	Single Payments		Uniform Series Payments				Arithmetic Gradients	

	Single Payments		Uniform Series Payments				Arithmetic Gradients	
	Compound Amount F/P	Present Worth P/F	Sinking Fund A/F	Compound Amount F/A	Capital Recovery A/P	Present Worth P/A	Gradient Present Worth P/G	Gradient Uniform Series A/G
n								
1	1.0200	0.9804	1.00000	1.0000	1.02000	0.9804		
2	1.0404	0.9612	0.49505	2.0200	0.51505	1.9416	0.9612	0.4950
3	1.0612	0.9423	0.32675	3.0604	0.34675	2.8839	2.8458	0.9868
4	1.0824	0.9238	0.24262	4.1216	0.26262	3.8077	5.6173	1.4752
5	1.1041	0.9057	0.19216	5.2040	0.21216	4.7135	9.2403	1.9604
6	1.1262	0.8880	0.15853	6.3081	0.17853	5.6014	13.6801	2.4423
7	1.1487	0.8706	0.13451	7.4343	0.15451	6.4720	18.9035	2.9208
8	1.1717	0.8535	0.11651	8.5830	0.13651	7.3255	24.8779	3.3961
9	1.1951	0.8368	0.10252	9.7546	0.12252	8.1622	31.5720	3.8681
10	1.2190	0.8203	0.09133	10.9497	0.11133	8.9826	38.9551	4.3367
11	1.2434	0.8043	0.08218	12.1687	0.10218	9.7868	46.9977	4.8021
12	1.2682	0.7885	0.07456	13.4121	0.09456	10.5753	55.6712	5.2642
13	1.2936	0.7730	0.06812	14.6803	0.08812	11.3484	64.9475	5.7231
14	1.3195	0.7579	0.06260	15.9739	0.08260	12.1062	74.7999	6.1786
15	1.3459	0.7430	0.05783	17.2934	0.07783	12.8493	85.2021	6.6309
16	1.3728	0.7284	0.05365	18.6393	0.07365	13.5777	96.1288	7.0799
17	1.4002	0.7142	0.04997	20.0121	0.06997	14.2919	107.5554	7.5256
18	1.4282	0.7002	0.04670	21.4123	0.06670	14.9920	119.4581	7.9681
19	1.4568	0.6864	0.04378	22.8406	0.06378	15.6785	131.8139	8.4073
20	1.4859	0.6730	0.04116	24.2974	0.06116	16.3514	144.6003	8.8433
21	1.5157	0.6598	0.03878	25.7833	0.05878	17.0112	157.7959	9.2760
22	1.5460	0.6468	0.03663	27.2990	0.05663	17.6580	171.3795	9.7055
23	1.5769	0.6342	0.03467	28.8450	0.05467	18.2922	185.3309	10.1317
24	1.6084	0.6217	0.03287	30.4219	0.05287	18.9139	199.6305	10.5547
25	1.6406	0.6095	0.03122	32.0303	0.05122	19.5235	214.2592	10.9745
26	1.6734	0.5976	0.02970	33.6709	0.04970	20.1210	229.1987	11.3910
27	1.7069	0.5859	0.02829	35.3443	0.04829	20.7069	244.4311	11.8043
28	1.7410	0.5744	0.02699	37.0512	0.04699	21.2813	259.9392	12.2145
29	1.7758	0.5631	0.02578	38.7922	0.04578	21.8444	275.7064	12.6214
30	1.8114	0.5521	0.02465	40.5681	0.04465	22.3965	291.7164	13.0251
36	2.0399	0.4902	0.01923	51.9944	0.03923	25.4888	392.0405	15.3809
40	2.2080	0.4529	0.01656	60.4020	0.03656	27.3555	461.9931	16.8885
48	2.5871	0.3865	0.01260	79.3535	0.03260	30.6731	605.9657	19.7556
50	2.6916	0.3715	0.01182	84.5794	0.03182	31.4236	642.3606	20.4420
52	2.8003	0.3571	0.01111	90.0164	0.03111	32.1449	678.7849	21.1164
55	2.9717	0.3365	0.01014	98.5865	0.03014	33.1748	733.3527	22.1057
60	3.2810	0.3048	0.00877	114.0515	0.02877	34.7609	823.6975	23.6961
72	4.1611	0.2403	0.00633	158.0570	0.02633	37.9841	1034.06	27.2234
75	4.4158	0.2265	0.00586	170.7918	0.02586	38.6771	1084.64	28.0434
84	5.2773	0.1895	0.00468	213.8666	0.02468	40.5255	1230.42	30.3616
90	5.9431	0.1683	0.00405	247.1567	0.02405	41.5869	1322.17	31.7929
96	6.6929	0.1494	0.00351	284.6467	0.02351	42.5294	1409.30	33.1370
100	7.2446	0.1380	0.00320	312.2323	0.02320	43.0984	1464.75	33.9863
108	8.4883	0.1178	0.00267	374.4129	0.02267	44.1095	1569.30	35.5774
120	10.7652	0.0929	0.00205	488.2582	0.02205	45.3554	1710.42	37.7114
132	13.6528	0.0732	0.00158	632.6415	0.02158	46.3378	1833.47	39.5676
144	17.3151	0.0578	0.00123	815.7545	0.02123	47.1123	1939.79	41.1738
240	115.8887	0.0086	0.00017	5744.44	0.02017	49.5686	2374.88	47.9110
360	1247.56	0.0008	0.00002	62328	0.02002	49.9599	2482.57	49.7112
480	13430	0.0001			0.02000	49.9963	2498.03	49.9643

TABLE 8 Discrete Cash Flow: Compound Interest Factors

	Single Payments		Uniform Series Payments				Arithmetic Gradients	
	Compound Amount	Present Worth	Sinking Fund	Compound Amount	Capital Recovery	Present Worth	Gradient Present Worth	Gradient Uniform Series
n	F/P	P/F	A/F	F/A	A/P	P/A	P/G	A/G
1	1.0300	0.9709	1.00000	1.0000	1.03000	0.9709		
2	1.0609	0.9426	0.49261	2.0300	0.52261	1.9135	0.9426	0.4926
3	1.0927	0.9151	0.32353	3.0909	0.35353	2.8286	2.7729	0.9803
4	1.1255	0.8885	0.23903	4.1836	0.26903	3.7171	5.4383	1.4631
5	1.1593	0.8626	0.18835	5.3091	0.21835	4.5797	8.8888	1.9409
6	1.1941	0.8375	0.15460	6.4684	0.18460	5.4172	13.0762	2.4138
7	1.2299	0.8131	0.13051	7.6625	0.16051	6.2303	17.9547	2.8819
8	1.2668	0.7894	0.11246	8.8923	0.14246	7.0197	23.4806	3.3450
9	1.3048	0.7664	0.09843	10.1591	0.12843	7.7861	29.6119	3.8032
10	1.3439	0.7441	0.08723	11.4639	0.11723	8.5302	36.3088	4.2565
11	1.3842	0.7224	0.07808	12.8078	0.10808	9.2526	43.5330	4.7049
12	1.4258	0.7014	0.07046	14.1920	0.10046	9.9540	51.2482	5.1485
13	1.4685	0.6810	0.06403	15.6178	0.09403	10.6350	59.4196	5.5872
14	1.5126	0.6611	0.05853	17.0863	0.08853	11.2961	68.0141	6.0210
15	1.5580	0.6419	0.05377	18.5989	0.08377	11.9379	77.0002	6.4500
16	1.6047	0.6232	0.04961	20.1569	0.07961	12.5611	86.3477	6.8742
17	1.6528	0.6050	0.04595	21.7616	0.07595	13.1661	96.0280	7.2936
18	1.7024	0.5874	0.04271	23.4144	0.07271	13.7535	106.0137	7.7081
19	1.7535	0.5703	0.03981	25.1169	0.06981	14.3238	116.2788	8.1179
20	1.8061	0.5537	0.03722	26.8704	0.06722	14.8775	126.7987	8.5229
21	1.8603	0.5375	0.03487	28.6765	0.06487	15.4150	137.5496	8.9231
22	1.9161	0.5219	0.03275	30.5368	0.06275	15.9369	148.5094	9.3186
23	1.9736	0.5067	0.03081	32.4529	0.06081	16.4436	159.6566	9.7093
24	2.0328	0.4919	0.02905	34.4265	0.05905	16.9355	170.9711	10.0954
25	2.0938	0.4776	0.02743	36.4593	0.05743	17.4131	182.4336	10.4768
26	2.1566	0.4637	0.02594	38.5530	0.05594	17.8768	194.0260	10.8535
27	2.2213	0.4502	0.02456	40.7096	0.05456	18.3270	205.7309	11.2255
28	2.2879	0.4371	0.02329	42.9309	0.05329	18.7641	217.5320	11.5930
29	2.3566	0.4243	0.02211	45.2189	0.05211	19.1885	229.4137	11.9558
30	2.4273	0.4120	0.02102	47.5754	0.05102	19.6004	241.3613	12.3141
31	2.5001	0.4000	0.02000	50.0027	0.05000	20.0004	253.3609	12.6678
32	2.5751	0.3883	0.01905	52.5028	0.04905	20.3888	265.3993	13.0169
33	2.6523	0.3770	0.01816	55.0778	0.04816	20.7658	277.4642	13.3616
34	2.7319	0.3660	0.01732	57.7302	0.04732	21.1318	289.5437	13.7018
35	2.8139	0.3554	0.01654	60.4621	0.04654	21.4872	301.6267	14.0375
40	3.2620	0.3066	0.01326	75.4013	0.04326	23.1148	361.7499	15.6502
45	3.7816	0.2644	0.01079	92.7199	0.04079	24.5187	420.6325	17.1556
50	4.3839	0.2281	0.00887	112.7969	0.03887	25.7298	477.4803	18.5575
55	5.0821	0.1968	0.00735	136.0716	0.03735	26.7744	531.7411	19.8600
60	5.8916	0.1697	0.00613	163.0534	0.03613	27.6756	583.0526	21.0674
65	6.8300	0.1464	0.00515	194.3328	0.03515	28.4529	631.2010	22.1841
70	7.9178	0.1263	0.00434	230.5941	0.03434	29.1234	676.0869	23.2145
75	9.1789	0.1089	0.00367	272.6309	0.03367	29.7018	717.6978	24.1634
80	10.6409	0.0940	0.00311	321.3630	0.03311	30.2008	756.0865	25.0353
84	11.9764	0.0835	0.00273	365.8805	0.03273	30.5501	784.5434	25.6806
85	12.3357	0.0811	0.00265	377.8570	0.03265	30.6312	791.3529	25.8349
90	14.3005	0.0699	0.00226	443.3489	0.03226	31.0024	823.6302	26.5667
96	17.0755	0.0586	0.00187	535.8502	0.03187	31.3812	858.6377	27.3615
108	24.3456	0.0411	0.00129	778.1863	0.03129	31.9642	917.6013	28.7072
120	34.7110	0.0288	0.00089	1123.70	0.03089	32.3730	963.8635	29.7737

4%				TABLE 9	Discrete Cash Flow: Compound Interest Factors			4%
	Single Payments		Uniform Series Payments				Arithmetic Gradients	
n	Compound Amount F/P	Present Worth P/F	Sinking Fund A/F	Compound Amount F/A	Capital Recovery A/P	Present Worth P/A	Gradient Present Worth P/G	Gradient Uniform Series A/G
1	1.0400	0.9615	1.00000	1.0000	1.04000	0.9615		
2	1.0816	0.9246	0.49020	2.0400	0.53020	1.8861	0.9246	0.4902
3	1.1249	0.8890	0.32035	3.1216	0.36035	2.7751	2.7025	0.9739
4	1.1699	0.8548	0.23549	4.2465	0.27549	3.6299	5.2670	1.4510
5	1.2167	0.8219	0.18463	5.4163	0.22463	4.4518	8.5547	1.9216
6	1.2653	0.7903	0.15076	6.6330	0.19076	5.2421	12.5062	2.3857
7	1.3159	0.7599	0.12661	7.8983	0.16661	6.0021	17.0657	2.8433
8	1.3686	0.7307	0.10853	9.2142	0.14853	6.7327	22.1806	3.2944
9	1.4233	0.7026	0.09449	10.5828	0.13449	7.4353	27.8013	3.7391
10	1.4802	0.6756	0.08329	12.0061	0.12329	8.1109	33.8814	4.1773
11	1.5395	0.6496	0.07415	13.4864	0.11415	8.7605	40.3772	4.6090
12	1.6010	0.6246	0.06655	15.0258	0.10655	9.3851	47.2477	5.0343
13	1.6651	0.6006	0.06014	16.6268	0.10014	9.9856	54.4546	5.4533
14	1.7317	0.5775	0.05467	18.2919	0.09467	10.5631	61.9618	5.8659
15	1.8009	0.5553	0.04994	20.0236	0.08994	11.1184	69.7355	6.2721
16	1.8730	0.5339	0.04582	21.8245	0.08582	11.6523	77.7441	6.6720
17	1.9479	0.5134	0.04220	23.6975	0.08220	12.1657	85.9581	7.0656
18	2.0258	0.4936	0.03899	25.6454	0.07899	12.6593	94.3498	7.4530
19	2.1068	0.4746	0.03614	27.6712	0.07614	13.1339	102.8933	7.8342
20	2.1911	0.4564	0.03358	29.7781	0.07358	13.5903	111.5647	8.2091
21	2.2788	0.4388	0.03128	31.9692	0.07128	14.0292	120.3414	8.5779
22	2.3699	0.4220	0.02920	34.2480	0.06920	14.4511	129.2024	8.9407
23	2.4647	0.4057	0.02731	36.6179	0.06731	14.8568	138.1284	9.2973
24	2.5633	0.3901	0.02559	39.0826	0.06559	15.2470	147.1012	9.6479
25	2.6658	0.3751	0.02401	41.6459	0.06401	15.6221	156.1040	9.9925
26	2.7725	0.3607	0.02257	44.3117	0.06257	15.9828	165.1212	10.3312
27	2.8834	0.3468	0.02124	47.0842	0.06124	16.3296	174.1385	10.6640
28	2.9987	0.3335	0.02001	49.9676	0.06001	16.6631	183.1424	10.9909
29	3.1187	0.3207	0.01888	52.9663	0.05888	16.9837	192.1206	11.3120
30	3.2434	0.3083	0.01783	56.0849	0.05783	17.2920	201.0618	11.6274
31	3.3731	0.2965	0.01686	59.3283	0.05686	17.5885	209.9556	11.9371
32	3.5081	0.2851	0.01595	62.7015	0.05595	17.8736	218.7924	12.2411
33	3.6484	0.2741	0.01510	66.2095	0.05510	18.1476	227.5634	12.5396
34	3.7943	0.2636	0.01431	69.8579	0.05431	18.4112	236.2607	12.8324
35	3.9461	0.2534	0.01358	73.6522	0.05358	18.6646	244.8768	13.1198
40	4.8010	0.2083	0.01052	95.0255	0.05052	19.7928	286.5303	14.4765
45	5.8412	0.1712	0.00826	121.0294	0.04826	20.7200	325.4028	15.7047
50	7.1067	0.1407	0.00655	152.6671	0.04655	21.4822	361.1638	16.8122
55	8.6464	0.1157	0.00523	191.1592	0.04523	22.1086	393.6890	17.8070
60	10.5196	0.0951	0.00420	237.9907	0.04420	22.6235	422.9966	18.6972
65	12.7987	0.0781	0.00339	294.9684	0.04339	23.0467	449.2014	19.4909
70	15.5716	0.0642	0.00275	364.2905	0.04275	23.3945	472.4789	20.1961
75	18.9453	0.0528	0.00223	448.6314	0.04223	23.6804	493.0408	20.8206
80	23.0498	0.0434	0.00181	551.2450	0.04181	23.9154	511.1161	21.3718
85	28.0436	0.0357	0.00148	676.0901	0.04148	24.1085	526.9384	21.8569
90	34.1193	0.0293	0.00121	827.9833	0.04121	24.2673	540.7369	22.2826
96	43.1718	0.0232	0.00095	1054.30	0.04095	24.4209	554.9312	22.7236
108	69.1195	0.0145	0.00059	1702.99	0.04059	24.6383	576.8949	23.4146
120	110.6626	0.0090	0.00036	2741.56	0.04036	24.7741	592.2428	23.9057
144	283.6618	0.0035	0.00014	7066.55	0.04014	24.9119	610.1055	24.4906

	Single Payments		Uniform Series Payments				Arithmetic Gradients	
	Compound Amount F/P	Present Worth P/F	Sinking Fund A/F	Compound Amount F/A	Capital Recovery A/P	Present Worth P/A	Gradient Present Worth P/G	Gradient Uniform Series A/G
n								
1	1.0500	0.9524	1.00000	1.0000	1.05000	0.9524		
2	1.1025	0.9070	0.48780	2.0500	0.53780	1.8594	0.9070	0.4878
3	1.1576	0.8638	0.31721	3.1525	0.36721	2.7232	2.6347	0.9675
4	1.2155	0.8227	0.23201	4.3101	0.28201	3.5460	5.1028	1.4391
5	1.2763	0.7835	0.18097	5.5256	0.23097	4.3295	8.2369	1.9025
6	1.3401	0.7462	0.14702	6.8019	0.19702	5.0757	11.9680	2.3579
7	1.4071	0.7107	0.12282	8.1420	0.17282	5.7864	16.2321	2.8052
8	1.4775	0.6768	0.10472	9.5491	0.15472	6.4632	20.9700	3.2445
9	1.5513	0.6446	0.09069	11.0266	0.14069	7.1078	26.1268	3.6758
10	1.6289	0.6139	0.07950	12.5779	0.12950	7.7217	31.6520	4.0991
11	1.7103	0.5847	0.07039	14.2068	0.12039	8.3064	37.4988	4.5144
12	1.7959	0.5568	0.06283	15.9171	0.11283	8.8633	43.6241	4.9219
13	1.8856	0.5303	0.05646	17.7130	0.10646	9.3936	49.9879	5.3215
14	1.9799	0.5051	0.05102	19.5986	0.10102	9.8986	56.5538	5.7133
15	2.0789	0.4810	0.04634	21.5786	0.09634	10.3797	63.2880	6.0973
16	2.1829	0.4581	0.04227	23.6575	0.09227	10.8378	70.1597	6.4736
17	2.2920	0.4363	0.03870	25.8404	0.08870	11.2741	77.1405	6.8423
18	2.4066	0.4155	0.03555	28.1324	0.08555	11.6896	84.2043	7.2034
19	2.5270	0.3957	0.03275	30.5390	0.08275	12.0853	91.3275	7.5569
20	2.6533	0.3769	0.03024	33.0660	0.08024	12.4622	98.4884	7.9030
21	2.7860	0.3589	0.02800	35.7193	0.07800	12.8212	105.6673	8.2416
22	2.9253	0.3418	0.02597	38.5052	0.07597	13.1630	112.8461	8.5730
23	3.0715	0.3256	0.02414	41.4305	0.07414	13.4886	120.0087	8.8971
24	3.2251	0.3101	0.02247	44.5020	0.07247	13.7986	127.1402	9.2140
25	3.3864	0.2953	0.02095	47.7271	0.07095	14.0939	134.2275	9.5238
26	3.5557	0.2812	0.01956	51.1135	0.06956	14.3752	141.2585	9.8266
27	3.7335	0.2678	0.01829	54.6691	0.06829	14.6430	148.2226	10.1224
28	3.9201	0.2551	0.01712	58.4026	0.06712	14.8981	155.1101	10.4114
29	4.1161	0.2429	0.01605	62.3227	0.06605	15.1411	161.9126	10.6936
30	4.3219	0.2314	0.01505	66.4388	0.06505	15.3725	168.6226	10.9691
31	4.5380	0.2204	0.01413	70.7608	0.06413	15.5928	175.2333	11.2381
32	4.7649	0.2099	0.01328	75.2988	0.06328	15.8027	181.7392	11.5005
33	5.0032	0.1999	0.01249	80.0638	0.06249	16.0025	188.1351	11.7566
34	5.2533	0.1904	0.01176	85.0670	0.06176	16.1929	194.4168	12.0063
35	5.5160	0.1813	0.01107	90.3203	0.06107	16.3742	200.5807	12.2498
40	7.0400	0.1420	0.00828	120.7998	0.05828	17.1591	229.5452	13.3775
45	8.9850	0.1113	0.00626	159.7002	0.05626	17.7741	255.3145	14.3644
50	11.4674	0.0872	0.00478	209.3480	0.05478	18.2559	277.9148	15.2233
55	14.6356	0.0683	0.00367	272.7126	0.05367	18.6335	297.5104	15.9664
60	18.6792	0.0535	0.00283	353.5837	0.05283	18.9293	314.3432	16.6062
65	23.8399	0.0419	0.00219	456.7980	0.05219	19.1611	328.6910	17.1541
70	30.4264	0.0329	0.00170	588.5285	0.05170	19.3427	340.8409	17.6212
75	38.8327	0.0258	0.00132	756.6537	0.05132	19.4850	351.0721	18.0176
80	49.5614	0.0202	0.00103	971.2288	0.05103	19.5965	359.6460	18.3526
85	63.2544	0.0158	0.00080	1245.09	0.05080	19.6838	366.8007	18.6346
90	80.7304	0.0124	0.00063	1594.61	0.05063	19.7523	372.7488	18.8712
95	103.0347	0.0097	0.00049	2040.69	0.05049	19.8059	377.6774	19.0689
96	108.1864	0.0092	0.00047	2143.73	0.05047	19.8151	378.5555	19.1044
98	119.2755	0.0084	0.00042	2365.51	0.05042	19.8323	380.2139	19.1714
100	131.5013	0.0076	0.00038	2610.03	0.05038	19.8479	381.7492	19.2337

6%			TABLE 11	Discrete Cash Flow: Compound Interest Factors				6%
	Single Payments		Uniform Series Payments				Arithmetic Gradients	
	Compound Amount F/P	Present Worth P/F	Sinking Fund A/F	Compound Amount F/A	Capital Recovery A/P	Present Worth P/A	Gradient Present Worth P/G	Gradient Uniform Series A/G
n								
1	1.0600	0.9434	1.00000	1.0000	1.06000	0.9434		
2	1.1236	0.8900	0.48544	2.0600	0.54544	1.8334	0.8900	0.4854
3	1.1910	0.8396	0.31411	3.1836	0.37411	2.6730	2.5692	0.9612
4	1.2625	0.7921	0.22859	4.3746	0.28859	3.4651	4.9455	1.4272
5	1.3382	0.7473	0.17740	5.6371	0.23740	4.2124	7.9345	1.8836
6	1.4185	0.7050	0.14336	6.9753	0.20336	4.9173	11.4594	2.3304
7	1.5036	0.6651	0.11914	8.3938	0.17914	5.5824	15.4497	2.7676
8	1.5938	0.6274	0.10104	9.8975	0.16104	6.2098	19.8416	3.1952
9	1.6895	0.5919	0.08702	11.4913	0.14702	6.8017	24.5768	3.6133
10	1.7908	0.5584	0.07587	13.1808	0.13587	7.3601	29.6023	4.0220
11	1.8983	0.5268	0.06679	14.9716	0.12679	7.8869	34.8702	4.4213
12	2.0122	0.4970	0.05928	16.8699	0.11928	8.3838	40.3369	4.8113
13	2.1329	0.4688	0.05296	18.8821	0.11296	8.8527	45.9629	5.1920
14	2.2609	0.4423	0.04758	21.0151	0.10758	9.2950	51.7128	5.5635
15	2.3966	0.4173	0.04296	23.2760	0.10296	9.7122	57.5546	5.9260
16	2.5404	0.3936	0.03895	25.6725	0.09895	10.1059	63.4592	6.2794
17	2.6928	0.3714	0.03544	28.2129	0.09544	10.4773	69.4011	6.6240
18	2.8543	0.3503	0.03236	30.9057	0.09236	10.8276	75.3569	6.9597
19	3.0256	0.3305	0.02962	33.7600	0.08962	11.1581	81.3062	7.2867
20	3.2071	0.3118	0.02718	36.7856	0.08718	11.4699	87.2304	7.6051
21	3.3996	0.2942	0.02500	39.9927	0.08500	11.7641	93.1136	7.9151
22	3.6035	0.2775	0.02305	43.3923	0.08305	12.0416	98.9412	8.2166
23	3.8197	0.2618	0.02128	46.9958	0.08128	12.3034	104.7007	8.5099
24	4.0489	0.2470	0.01968	50.8156	0.07968	12.5504	110.3812	8.7951
25	4.2919	0.2330	0.01823	54.8645	0.07823	12.7834	115.9732	9.0722
26	4.5494	0.2198	0.01690	59.1564	0.07690	13.0032	121.4684	9.3414
27	4.8223	0.2074	0.01570	63.7058	0.07570	13.2105	126.8600	9.6029
28	5.1117	0.1956	0.01459	68.5281	0.07459	13.4062	132.1420	9.8568
29	5.4184	0.1846	0.01358	73.6398	0.07358	13.5907	137.3096	10.1032
30	5.7435	0.1741	0.01265	79.0582	0.07265	13.7648	142.3588	10.3422
31	6.0881	0.1643	0.01179	84.8017	0.07179	13.9291	147.2864	10.5740
32	6.4534	0.1550	0.01100	90.8898	0.07100	14.0840	152.0901	10.7988
33	6.8406	0.1462	0.01027	97.3432	0.07027	14.2302	156.7681	11.0166
34	7.2510	0.1379	0.00960	104.1838	0.06960	14.3681	161.3192	11.2276
35	7.6861	0.1301	0.00897	111.4348	0.06897	14.4982	165.7427	11.4319
40	10.2857	0.0972	0.00646	154.7620	0.06646	15.0463	185.9568	12.3590
45	13.7646	0.0727	0.00470	212.7435	0.06470	15.4558	203.1096	13.1413
50	18.4202	0.0543	0.00344	290.3359	0.06344	15.7619	217.4574	13.7964
55	24.6503	0.0406	0.00254	394.1720	0.06254	15.9905	229.3222	14.3411
60	32.9877	0.0303	0.00188	533.1282	0.06188	16.1614	239.0428	14.7909
65	44.1450	0.0227	0.00139	719.0829	0.06139	16.2891	246.9450	15.1601
70	59.0759	0.0169	0.00103	967.9322	0.06103	16.3845	253.3271	15.4613
75	79.0569	0.0126	0.00077	1300.95	0.06077	16.4558	258.4527	15.7058
80	105.7960	0.0095	0.00057	1746.60	0.06057	16.5091	262.5493	15.9033
85	141.5789	0.0071	0.00043	2342.98	0.06043	16.5489	265.8096	16.0620
90	189.4645	0.0053	0.00032	3141.08	0.06032	16.5787	268.3946	16.1891
95	253.5463	0.0039	0.00024	4209.10	0.06024	16.6009	270.4375	16.2905
96	268.7590	0.0037	0.00022	4462.65	0.06022	16.6047	270.7909	16.3081
98	301.9776	0.0033	0.00020	5016.29	0.06020	16.6115	271.4491	16.3411
100	339.3021	0.0029	0.00018	5638.37	0.06018	16.6175	272.0471	16.3711

	Single Payments		Uniform Series Payments				Arithmetic Gradients	
	Compound Amount F/P	Present Worth P/F	Sinking Fund A/F	Compound Amount F/A	Capital Recovery A/P	Present Worth P/A	Gradient Present Worth P/G	Gradient Uniform Series A/G
n								
1	1.0700	0.9346	1.00000	1.0000	1.07000	0.9346		
2	1.1449	0.8734	0.48309	2.0700	0.55309	1.8080	0.8734	0.4831
3	1.2250	0.8163	0.31105	3.2149	0.38105	2.6243	2.5060	0.9549
4	1.3108	0.7629	0.22523	4.4399	0.29523	3.3872	4.7947	1.4155
5	1.4026	0.7130	0.17389	5.7507	0.24389	4.1002	7.6467	1.8650
6	1.5007	0.6663	0.13980	7.1533	0.20980	4.7665	10.9784	2.3032
7	1.6058	0.6227	0.11555	8.6540	0.18555	5.3893	14.7149	2.7304
8	1.7182	0.5820	0.09747	10.2598	0.16747	5.9713	18.7889	3.1465
9	1.8385	0.5439	0.08349	11.9780	0.15349	6.5152	23.1404	3.5517
10	1.9672	0.5083	0.07238	13.8164	0.14238	7.0236	27.7156	3.9461
11	2.1049	0.4751	0.06336	15.7836	0.13336	7.4987	32.4665	4.3296
12	2.2522	0.4440	0.05590	17.8885	0.12590	7.9427	37.3506	4.7025
13	2.4098	0.4150	0.04965	20.1406	0.11965	8.3577	42.3302	5.0648
14	2.5785	0.3878	0.04434	22.5505	0.11434	8.7455	47.3718	5.4167
15	2.7590	0.3624	0.03979	25.1290	0.10979	9.1079	52.4461	5.7583
16	2.9522	0.3387	0.03586	27.8881	0.10586	9.4466	57.5271	6.0897
17	3.1588	0.3166	0.03243	30.8402	0.10243	9.7632	62.5923	6.4110
18	3.3799	0.2959	0.02941	33.9990	0.09941	10.0591	67.6219	6.7225
19	3.6165	0.2765	0.02675	37.3790	0.09675	10.3356	72.5991	7.0242
20	3.8697	0.2584	0.02439	40.9955	0.09439	10.5940	77.5091	7.3163
21	4.1406	0.2415	0.02229	44.8652	0.09229	10.8355	82.3393	7.5990
22	4.4304	0.2257	0.02041	49.0057	0.09041	11.0612	87.0793	7.8725
23	4.7405	0.2109	0.01871	53.4361	0.08871	11.2722	91.7201	8.1369
24	5.0724	0.1971	0.01719	58.1767	0.08719	11.4693	96.2545	8.3923
25	5.4274	0.1842	0.01581	63.2490	0.08581	11.6536	100.6765	8.6391
26	5.8074	0.1722	0.01456	68.6765	0.08456	11.8258	104.9814	8.8773
27	6.2139	0.1609	0.01343	74.4838	0.08343	11.9867	109.1656	9.1072
28	6.6488	0.1504	0.01239	80.6977	0.08239	12.1371	113.2264	9.3289
29	7.1143	0.1406	0.01145	87.3465	0.08145	12.2777	117.1622	9.5427
30	7.6123	0.1314	0.01059	94.4608	0.08059	12.4090	120.9718	9.7487
31	8.1451	0.1228	0.00980	102.0730	0.07980	12.5318	124.6550	9.9471
32	8.7153	0.1147	0.00907	110.2182	0.07907	12.6466	128.2120	10.1381
33	9.3253	0.1072	0.00841	118.9334	0.07841	12.7538	131.6435	10.3219
34	9.9781	0.1002	0.00780	128.2588	0.07780	12.8540	134.9507	10.4987
35	10.6766	0.0937	0.00723	138.2369	0.07723	12.9477	138.1353	10.6687
40	14.9745	0.0668	0.00501	199.6351	0.07501	13.3317	152.2928	11.4233
45	21.0025	0.0476	0.00350	285.7493	0.07350	13.6055	163.7559	12.0360
50	29.4570	0.0339	0.00246	406.5289	0.07246	13.8007	172.9051	12.5287
55	41.3150	0.0242	0.00174	575.9286	0.07174	13.9399	180.1243	12.9215
60	57.9464	0.0173	0.00123	813.5204	0.07123	14.0392	185.7677	13.2321
65	81.2729	0.0123	0.00087	1146.76	0.07087	14.1099	190.1452	13.4760
70	113.9894	0.0088	0.00062	1614.13	0.07062	14.1604	193.5185	13.6662
75	159.8760	0.0063	0.00044	2269.66	0.07044	14.1964	196.1035	13.8136
80	224.2344	0.0045	0.00031	3189.06	0.07031	14.2220	198.0748	13.9273
85	314.5003	0.0032	0.00022	4478.58	0.07022	14.2403	199.5717	14.0146
90	441.1030	0.0023	0.00016	6287.19	0.07016	14.2533	200.7042	14.0812
95	618.6697	0.0016	0.00011	8823.85	0.07011	14.2626	201.5581	14.1319
96	661.9766	0.0015	0.00011	9442.52	0.07011	14.2641	201.7016	14.1405
98	757.8970	0.0013	0.00009	10813	0.07009	14.2669	201.9651	14.1562
100	867.7163	0.0012	0.00008	12382	0.07008	14.2693	202.2001	14.1703

7% **TABLE 12** Discrete Cash Flow: Compound Interest Factors **7%**

8%			TABLE 13	Discrete Cash Flow: Compound Interest Factors				8%
	Single Payments		Uniform Series Payments				Arithmetic Gradients	
	Compound Amount F/P	Present Worth P/F	Sinking Fund A/F	Compound Amount F/A	Capital Recovery A/P	Present Worth P/A	Gradient Present Worth P/G	Gradient Uniform Series A/G
n								
1	1.0800	0.9259	1.00000	1.0000	1.08000	0.9259		
2	1.1664	0.8573	0.48077	2.0800	0.56077	1.7833	0.8573	0.4808
3	1.2597	0.7938	0.30803	3.2464	0.38803	2.5771	2.4450	0.9487
4	1.3605	0.7350	0.22192	4.5061	0.30192	3.3121	4.6501	1.4040
5	1.4693	0.6806	0.17046	5.8666	0.25046	3.9927	7.3724	1.8465
6	1.5869	0.6302	0.13632	7.3359	0.21632	4.6229	10.5233	2.2763
7	1.7138	0.5835	0.11207	8.9228	0.19207	5.2064	14.0242	2.6937
8	1.8509	0.5403	0.09401	10.6366	0.17401	5.7466	17.8061	3.0985
9	1.9990	0.5002	0.08008	12.4876	0.16008	6.2469	21.8081	3.4910
10	2.1589	0.4632	0.06903	14.4866	0.14903	6.7101	25.9768	3.8713
11	2.3316	0.4289	0.06008	1 6.6455	0.14008	7.1390	30.2657	4.2395
12	2.5182	0.3971	0.05270	18.9771	0.13270	7.5361	34.6339	4.5957
13	2.7196	0.3677	0.04652	21.4953	0.12652	7.9038	39.0463	4.9402
14	2.9372	0.3405	0.04130	24.2149	0.12130	8.2442	43.4723	5.2731
15	3.1722	0.3152	0.03683	27.1521	0.11683	8.5595	47.8857	5.5945
16	3.4259	0.2919	0.03298	30.3243	0.11298	8.8514	52.2640	5.9046
17	3.7000	0.2703	0.02963	33.7502	0.10963	9.1216	56.5883	6.2037
18	3.9960	0.2502	0.02670	37.4502	0.10670	9.3719	60.8426	6.4920
19	4.3157	0.2317	0.02413	41.4463	0.10413	9.6036	65.0134	6.7697
20	4.6610	0.2145	0.02185	45.7620	0.10185	9.8181	69.0898	7.0369
21	5.0338	0.1987	0.01983	50.4229	0.09983	10.0168	73.0629	7.2940
22	5.4365	0.1839	0.01803	55.4568	0.09803	10.2007	76.9257	7.5412
23	5.8715	0.1703	0.01642	60.8933	0.09642	10.3711	80.6726	7.7786
24	6.3412	0.1577	0.01498	66.7648	0.09498	10.5288	84.2997	8.0066
25	6.8485	0.1460	0.01368	73.1059	0.09368	10.6748	87.8041	8.2254
26	7.3964	0.1352	0.01251	79.9544	0.09251	10.8100	91.1842	8.4352
27	7.9881	0.1252	0.01145	87.3508	0.09145	10.9352	94.4390	8.6363
28	8.6271	0.1159	0.01049	95.3388	0.09049	11.0511	97.5687	8.8289
29	9.3173	0.1073	0.00962	103.9659	0.08962	11.1584	100.5738	9.0133
30	10.0627	0.0994	0.00883	113.2832	0.08883	11.2578	103.4558	9.1897
31	10.8677	0.0920	0.00811	123.3459	0.08811	11.3498	106.2163	9.3584
32	11.7371	0.0852	0.00745	134.2135	0.08745	11.4350	108.8575	9.5197
33	12.6760	0.0789	0.00685	145.9506	0.08685	11.5139	111.3819	9.6737
34	13.6901	0.0730	0.00630	158.6267	0.08630	11.5869	113.7924	9.8208
35	14.7853	0.0676	0.00580	172.3168	0.08580	11.6546	116.0920	9.9611
40	21.7245	0.0460	0.00386	259.0565	0.08386	11.9246	126.0422	10.5699
45	31.9204	0.0313	0.00259	386.5056	0.08259	12.1084	133.7331	11.0447
50	46.9016	0.0213	0.00174	573.7702	0.08174	12.2335	139.5928	11.4107
55	68.9139	0.0145	0.00118	848.9232	0.08118	12.3186	144.0065	11.6902
60	101.2571	0.0099	0.00080	1253.21	0.08080	12.3766	147.3000	11.9015
65	148.7798	0.0067	0.00054	1847.25	0.08054	12.4160	149.7387	12.0602
70	218.6064	0.0046	0.00037	2720.08	0.08037	12.4428	151.5326	12.1783
75	321.2045	0.0031	0.00025	4002.56	0.08025	12.4611	152.8448	12.2658
80	471.9548	0.0021	0.00017	5886.94	0.08017	12.4735	153.8001	12.3301
85	693.4565	0.0014	0.00012	8655.71	0.08012	12.4820	154.4925	12.3772
90	1018.92	0.0010	0.00008	12724	0.08008	12.4877	154.9925	12.4116
95	1497.12	0.0007	0.00005	18702	0.08005	12.4917	155.3524	12.4365
96	1616.89	0.0006	0.00005	20199	0.08005	12.4923	155.4112	12.4406
98	1885.94	0.0005	0.00004	23562	0.08004	12.4934	155.5176	12.4480
100	2199.76	0.0005	0.00004	27485	0.08004	12.4943	155.6107	12.4545

TABLE 14 Discrete Cash Flow: Compound Interest Factors

	Single Payments		Uniform Series Payments				Arithmetic Gradients	
	Compound Amount F/P	Present Worth P/F	Sinking Fund A/F	Compound Amount F/A	Capital Recovery A/P	Present Worth P/A	Gradient Present Worth P/G	Gradient Uniform Series A/G
n								
1	1.0900	0.9174	1.00000	1.0000	1.09000	0.9174		
2	1.1881	0.8417	0.47847	2.0900	0.56847	1.7591	0.8417	0.4785
3	1.2950	0.7722	0.30505	3.2781	0.39505	2.5313	2.3860	0.9426
4	1.4116	0.7084	0.21867	4.5731	0.30867	3.2397	4.5113	1.3925
5	1.5386	0.6499	0.16709	5.9847	0.25709	3.8897	7.1110	1.8282
6	1.6771	0.5963	0.13292	7.5233	0.22292	4.4859	10.0924	2.2498
7	1.8280	0.5470	0.10869	9.2004	0.19869	5.0330	13.3746	2.6574
8	1.9926	0.5019	0.09067	11.0285	0.18067	5.5348	16.8877	3.0512
9	2.1719	0.4604	0.07680	13.0210	0.16680	5.9952	20.5711	3.4312
10	2.3674	0.4224	0.06582	15.1929	0.15582	6.4177	24.3728	3.7978
11	2.5804	0.3875	0.05695	17.5603	0.14695	6.8052	28.2481	4.1510
12	2.8127	0.3555	0.04965	20.1407	0.13965	7.1607	32.1590	4.4910
13	3.0658	0.3262	0.04357	22.9534	0.13357	7.4869	36.0731	4.8182
14	3.3417	0.2992	0.03843	26.0192	0.12843	7.7862	39.9633	5.1326
15	3.6425	0.2745	0.03406	29.3609	0.12406	8.0607	43.8069	5.4346
16	3.9703	0.2519	0.03030	33.0034	0.12030	8.3126	47.5849	5.7245
17	4.3276	0.2311	0.02705	36.9737	0.11705	8.5436	51.2821	6.0024
18	4.7171	0.2120	0.02421	41.3013	0.11421	8.7556	54.8860	6.2687
19	5.1417	0.1945	0.02173	46.0185	0.11173	8.9501	58.3868	6.5236
20	5.6044	0.1784	0.01955	51.1601	0.10955	9.1285	61.7770	6.7674
21	6.1088	0.1637	0.01762	56.7645	0.10762	9.2922	65.0509	7.0006
22	6.6586	0.1502	0.01590	62.8733	0.10590	9.4424	68.2048	7.2232
23	7.2579	0.1378	0.01438	69.5319	0.10438	9.5802	71.2359	7.4357
24	7.9111	0.1264	0.01302	76.7898	0.10302	9.7066	74.1433	7.6384
25	8.6231	0.1160	0.01181	84.7009	0.10181	9.8226	76.9265	7.8316
26	9.3992	0.1064	0.01072	93.3240	0.10072	9.9290	79.5863	8.0156
27	10.2451	0.0976	0.00973	102.7231	0.09973	10.0266	82.1241	8.1906
28	11.1671	0.0895	0.00885	112.9682	0.09885	10.1161	84.5419	8.3571
29	12.1722	0.0822	0.00806	124.1354	0.09806	10.1983	86.8422	8.5154
30	13.2677	0.0754	0.00734	136.3075	0.09734	10.2737	89.0280	8.6657
31	14.4618	0.0691	0.00669	149.5752	0.09669	10.3428	91.1024	8.8083
32	15.7633	0.0634	0.00610	164.0370	0.09610	10.4062	93.0690	8.9436
33	17.1820	0.0582	0.00556	179.8003	0.09556	10.4644	94.9314	9.0718
34	18.7284	0.0534	0.00508	196.9823	0.09508	10.5178	96.6935	9.1933
35	20.4140	0.0490	0.00464	215.7108	0.09464	10.5668	98.3590	9.3083
40	31.4094	0.0318	0.00296	337.8824	0.09296	10.7574	105.3762	9.7957
45	48.3273	0.0207	0.00190	525.8587	0.09190	10.8812	110.5561	10.1603
50	74.3575	0.0134	0.00123	815.0836	0.09123	10.9617	114.3251	10.4295
55	114.4083	0.0087	0.00079	1260.09	0.09079	11.0140	117.0362	10.6261
60	176.0313	0.0057	0.00051	1944.79	0.09051	11.0480	118.9683	10.7683
65	270.8460	0.0037	0.00033	2998.29	0.09033	11.0701	120.3344	10.8702
70	416.7301	0.0024	0.00022	4619.22	0.09022	11.0844	121.2942	10.9427
75	641.1909	0.0016	0.00014	7113.23	0.09014	11.0938	121.9646	10.9940
80	986.5517	0.0010	0.00009	10951	0.09009	11.0998	122.4306	11.0299
85	1517.93	0.0007	0.00006	16855	0.09006	11.1038	122.7533	11.0551
90	2335.53	0.0004	0.00004	25939	0.09004	11.1064	122.9758	11.0726
95	3593.50	0.0003	0.00003	39917	0.09003	11.1080	123.1287	11.0847
96	3916.91	0.0003	0.00002	43510	0.09002	11.1083	123.1529	11.0866
98	4653.68	0.0002	0.00002	51696	0.09002	11.1087	123.1963	11.0900
100	5529.04	0.0002	0.00002	61423	0.09002	11.1091	123.2335	11.0930

	Single Payments		Uniform Series Payments				Arithmetic Gradients	
	Compound Amount F/P	Present Worth P/F	Sinking Fund A/F	Compound Amount F/A	Capital Recovery A/P	Present Worth P/A	Gradient Present Worth P/G	Gradient Uniform Series A/G
n								
1	1.1000	0.9091	1.00000	1.0000	1.10000	0.9091		
2	1.2100	0.8264	0.47619	2.1000	0.57619	1.7355	0.8264	0.4762
3	1.3310	0.7513	0.30211	3.3100	0.40211	2.4869	2.3291	0.9366
4	1.4641	0.6830	0.21547	4.6410	0.31547	3.1699	4.3781	1.3812
5	1.6105	0.6209	0.16380	6.1051	0.26380	3.7908	6.8618	1.8101
6	1.7716	0.5645	0.12961	7.7156	0.22961	4.3553	9.6842	2.2236
7	1.9487	0.5132	0.10541	9.4872	0.20541	4.8684	12.7631	2.6216
8	2.1436	0.4665	0.08744	11.4359	0.18744	5.3349	16.0287	3.0045
9	2.3579	0.4241	0.07364	13.5795	0.17364	5.7590	19.4215	3.3724
10	2.5937	0.3855	0.06275	15.9374	0.16275	6.1446	22.8913	3.7255
11	2.8531	0.3505	0.05396	18.5312	0.15396	6.4951	26.3963	4.0641
12	3.1384	0.3186	0.04676	21.3843	0.14676	6.8137	29.9012	4.3884
13	3.4523	0.2897	0.04078	24.5227	0.14078	7.1034	33.3772	4.6988
14	3.7975	0.2633	0.03575	27.9750	0.13575	7.3667	36.8005	4.9955
15	4.1772	0.2394	0.03147	31.7725	0.13147	7.6061	40.1520	5.2789
16	4.5950	0.2176	0.02782	35.9497	0.12782	7.8237	43.4164	5.5493
17	5.0545	0.1978	0.02466	40.5447	0.12466	8.0216	46.5819	5.8071
18	5.5599	0.1799	0.02193	45.5992	0.12193	8.2014	49.6395	6.0526
19	6.1159	0.1635	0.01955	51.1591	0.11955	8.3649	52.5827	6.2861
20	6.7275	0.1486	0.01746	57.2750	0.11746	8.5136	55.4069	6.5081
21	7.4002	0.1351	0.01562	64.0025	0.11562	8.6487	58.1095	6.7189
22	8.1403	0.1228	0.01401	71.4027	0.11401	8.7715	60.6893	6.9189
23	8.9543	0.1117	0.01257	79.5430	0.11257	8.8832	63.1462	7.1085
24	9.8497	0.1015	0.01130	88.4973	0.11130	8.9847	65.4813	7.2881
25	10.8347	0.0923	0.01017	98.3471	0.11017	9.0770	67.6964	7.4580
26	11.9182	0.0839	0.00916	109.1818	0.10916	9.1609	69.7940	7.6186
27	13.1100	0.0763	0.00826	121.0999	0.10826	9.2372	71.7773	7.7704
28	14.4210	0.0693	0.00745	134.2099	0.10745	9.3066	73.6495	7.9137
29	15.8631	0.0630	0.00673	148.6309	0.10673	9.3696	75.4146	8.0489
30	17.4494	0.0573	0.00608	164.4940	0.10608	9.4269	77.0766	8.1762
31	19.1943	0.0521	0.00550	181.9434	0.10550	9.4790	78.6395	8.2962
32	21.1138	0.0474	0.00497	201.1378	0.10497	9.5264	80.1078	8.4091
33	23.2252	0.0431	0.00450	222.2515	0.10450	9.5694	81.4856	8.5152
34	25.5477	0.0391	0.00407	245.4767	0.10407	9.6086	82.7773	8.6149
35	28.1024	0.0356	0.00369	271.0244	0.10369	9.6442	83.9872	8.7086
40	45.2593	0.0221	0.00226	442.5926	0.10226	9.7791	88.9525	9.0962
45	72.8905	0.0137	0.00139	718.9048	0.10139	9.8628	92.4544	9.3740
50	117.3909	0.0085	0.00086	1163.91	0.10086	9.9148	94.8889	9.5704
55	189.0591	0.0053	0.00053	1880.59	0.10053	9.9471	96.5619	9.7075
60	304.4816	0.0033	0.00033	3034.82	0.10033	9.9672	97.7010	9.8023
65	490.3707	0.0020	0.00020	4893.71	0.10020	9.9796	98.4705	9.8672
70	789.7470	0.0013	0.00013	7887.47	0.10013	9.9873	98.9870	9.9113
75	1271.90	0.0008	0.00008	12709	0.10008	9.9921	99.3317	9.9410
80	2048.40	0.0005	0.00005	20474	0.10005	9.9951	99.5606	9.9609
85	3298.97	0.0003	0.00003	32980	0.10003	9.9970	99.7120	9.9742
90	5313.02	0.0002	0.00002	53120	0.10002	9.9981	99.8118	9.9831
95	8556.68	0.0001	0.00001	85557	0.10001	9.9988	99.8773	9.9889
96	9412.34	0.0001	0.00001	94113	0.10001	9.9989	99.8874	9.9898
98	11389	0.0001	0.00001		0.10001	9.9991	99.9052	9.9914
100	13781	0.0001	0.00001		0.10001	9.9993	99.9202	9.9927

10%   **TABLE 15**   Discrete Cash Flow: Compound Interest Factors   **10%**

11%				TABLE 16	Discrete Cash Flow: Compound Interest Factors				11%
	Single Payments		Uniform Series Payments					Arithmetic Gradients	
	Compound Amount F/P	Present Worth P/F	Sinking Fund A/F	Compound Amount F/A	Capital Recovery A/P	Present Worth P/A		Gradient Present Worth P/G	Gradient Uniform Series A/G
n									
1	1.1100	0.9009	1.00000	1.0000	1.11000	0.9009			
2	1.2321	0.8116	0.47393	2.1100	0.58393	1.7125		0.8116	0.4739
3	1.3676	0.7312	0.29921	3.3421	0.40921	2.4437		2.2740	0.9306
4	1.5181	0.6587	0.21233	4.7097	0.32233	3.1024		4.2502	1.3700
5	1.6851	0.5935	0.16057	6.2278	0.27057	3.6959		6.6240	1.7923
6	1.8704	0.5346	0.12638	7.9129	0.23638	4.2305		9.2972	2.1976
7	2.0762	0.4817	0.10222	9.7833	0.21222	4.7122		12.1872	2.5863
8	2.3045	0.4339	0.08432	11.8594	0.19432	5.1461		15.2246	2.9585
9	2.5580	0.3909	0.07060	14.1640	0.18060	5.5370		18.3520	3.3144
10	2.8394	0.3522	0.05980	16.7220	0.16980	5.8892		21.5217	3.6544
11	3.1518	0.3173	0.05112	19.5614	0.16112	6.2065		24.6945	3.9788
12	3.4985	0.2858	0.04403	22.7132	0.15403	6.4924		27.8388	4.2879
13	3.8833	0.2575	0.03815	26.2116	0.14815	6.7499		30.9290	4.5822
14	4.3104	0.2320	0.03323	30.0949	0.14323	6.9819		33.9449	4.8619
15	4.7846	0.2090	0.02907	34.4054	0.13907	7.1909		36.8709	5.1275
16	5.3109	0.1883	0.02552	39.1899	0.13552	7.3792		39.6953	5.3794
17	5.8951	0.1696	0.02247	44.5008	0.13247	7.5488		42.4095	5.6180
18	6.5436	0.1528	0.01984	50.3959	0.12984	7.7016		45.0074	5.8439
19	7.2633	0.1377	0.01756	56.9395	0.12756	7.8393		47.4856	6.0574
20	8.0623	0.1240	0.01558	64.2028	0.12558	7.9633		49.8423	6.2590
21	8.9492	0.1117	0.01384	72.2651	0.12384	8.0751		52.0771	6.4491
22	9.9336	0.1007	0.01231	81.2143	0.12231	8.1757		54.1912	6.6283
23	11.0263	0.0907	0.01097	91.1479	0.12097	8.2664		56.1864	6.7969
24	12.2392	0.0817	0.00979	102.1742	0.11979	8.3481		58.0656	6.9555
25	13.5855	0.0736	0.00874	114.4133	0.11874	8.4217		59.8322	7.1045
26	15.0799	0.0663	0.00781	127.9988	0.11781	8.4881		61.4900	7.2443
27	16.7386	0.0597	0.00699	143.0786	0.11699	8.5478		63.0433	7.3754
28	18.5799	0.0538	0.00626	159.8173	0.11626	8.6016		64.4965	7.4982
29	20.6237	0.0485	0.00561	178.3972	0.11561	8.6501		65.8542	7.6131
30	22.8923	0.0437	0.00502	199.0209	0.11502	8.6938		67.1210	7.7206
31	25.4104	0.0394	0.00451	221.9132	0.11451	8.7331		68.3016	7.8210
32	28.2056	0.0355	0.00404	247.3236	0.11404	8.7686		69.4007	7.9147
33	31.3082	0.0319	0.00363	275.5292	0.11363	8.8005		70.4228	8.0021
34	34.7521	0.0288	0.00326	306.8374	0.11326	8.8293		71.3724	8.0836
35	38.5749	0.0259	0.00293	341.5896	0.11293	8.8552		72.2538	8.1594
40	65.0009	0.0154	0.00172	581.8261	0.11172	8.9511		75.7789	8.4659
45	109.5302	0.0091	0.00101	986.6386	0.11101	9.0079		78.1551	8.6763
50	184.5648	0.0054	0.00060	1668.77	0.11060	9.0417		79.7341	8.8185
55	311.0025	0.0032	0.00035	2818.20	0.11035	9.0617		80.7712	8.9135
60	524.0572	0.0019	0.00021	4755.07	0.11021	9.0736		81.4461	8.9762
65	883.0669	0.0011	0.00012	8018.79	0.11012	9.0806		81.8819	9.0172
70	1488.02	0.0007	0.00007	13518	0.11007	9.0848		82.1614	9.0438
75	2507.40	0.0004	0.00004	22785	0.11004	9.0873		82.3397	9.0610
80	4225.11	0.0002	0.00003	38401	0.11003	9.0888		82.4529	9.0720
85	7119.56	0.0001	0.00002	64714	0.11002	9.0896		82.5245	9.0790

	Single Payments		Uniform Series Payments				Arithmetic Gradients	

n	Compound Amount F/P	Present Worth P/F	Sinking Fund A/F	Compound Amount F/A	Capital Recovery A/P	Present Worth P/A	Gradient Present Worth P/G	Gradient Uniform Series A/G
1	1.1200	0.8929	1.00000	1.0000	1.12000	0.8929		
2	1.2544	0.7972	0.47170	2.1200	0.59170	1.6901	0.7972	0.4717
3	1.4049	0.7118	0.29635	3.3744	0.41635	2.4018	2.2208	0.9246
4	1.5735	0.6355	0.20923	4.7793	0.32923	3.0373	4.1273	1.3589
5	1.7623	0.5674	0.15741	6.3528	0.27741	3.6048	6.3970	1.7746
6	1.9738	0.5066	0.12323	8.1152	0.24323	4.1114	8.9302	2.1720
7	2.2107	0.4523	0.09912	10.0890	0.21912	4.5638	11.6443	2.5512
8	2.4760	0.4039	0.08130	12.2997	0.20130	4.9676	14.4714	2.9131
9	2.7731	0.3606	0.06768	14.7757	0.18768	5.3282	17.3563	3.2574
10	3.1058	0.3220	0.05698	17.5487	0.17698	5.6502	20.2541	3.5847
11	3.4785	0.2875	0.04842	20.6546	0.16842	5.9377	23.1288	3.8953
12	3.8960	0.2567	0.04144	24.1331	0.16144	6.1944	25.9523	4.1897
13	4.3635	0.2292	0.03568	28.0291	0.15568	6.4235	28.7024	4.4683
14	4.8871	0.2046	0.03087	32.3926	0.15087	6.6282	31.3624	4.7317
15	5.4736	0.1827	0.02682	37.2797	0.14682	6.8109	33.9202	4.9803
16	6.1304	0.1631	0.02339	42.7533	0.14339	6.9740	36.3670	5.2147
17	6.8660	0.1456	0.02046	48.8837	0.14046	7.1196	38.6973	5.4353
18	7.6900	0.1300	0.01794	55.7497	0.13794	7.2497	40.9080	5.6427
19	8.6128	0.1161	0.01576	63.4397	0.13576	7.3658	42.9979	5.8375
20	9.6463	0.1037	0.01388	72.0524	0.13388	7.4694	44.9676	6.0202
21	10.8038	0.0926	0.01224	81.6987	0.13224	7.5620	46.8188	6.1913
22	12.1003	0.0826	0.01081	92.5026	0.13081	7.6446	48.5543	6.3514
23	13.5523	0.0738	0.00956	104.6029	0.12956	7.7184	50.1776	6.5010
24	15.1786	0.0659	0.00846	118.1552	0.12846	7.7843	51.6929	6.6406
25	17.0001	0.0588	0.00750	133.3339	0.12750	7.8431	53.1046	6.7708
26	19.0401	0.0525	0.00665	150.3339	0.12665	7.8957	54.4177	6.8921
27	21.3249	0.0469	0.00590	169.3740	0.12590	7.9426	55.6369	7.0049
28	23.8839	0.0419	0.00524	190.6989	0.12524	7.9844	56.7674	7.1098
29	26.7499	0.0374	0.00466	214.5828	0.12466	8.0218	57.8141	7.2071
30	29.9599	0.0334	0.00414	241.3327	0.12414	8.0552	58.7821	7.2974
31	33.5551	0.0298	0.00369	271.2926	0.12369	8.0850	59.6761	7.3811
32	37.5817	0.0266	0.00328	304.8477	0.12328	8.1116	60.5010	7.4586
33	42.0915	0.0238	0.00292	342.4294	0.12292	8.1354	61.2612	7.5302
34	47.1425	0.0212	0.00260	384.5210	0.12260	8.1566	61.9612	7.5965
35	52.7996	0.0189	0.00232	431.6635	0.12232	8.1755	62.6052	7.6577
40	93.0510	0.0107	0.00130	767.0914	0.12130	8.2438	65.1159	7.8988
45	163.9876	0.0061	0.0074	1358.23	0.12074	8.2825	66.7342	8.0572
50	289.0022	0.0035	0.00042	2400.02	0.12042	8.3045	67.7624	8.1597
55	509.3206	0.0020	0.00024	4236.01	0.12024	8.3170	68.4082	8.2251
60	897.5969	0.0011	0.00013	7471.64	0.12013	8.3240	68.8100	8.2664
65	1581.87	0.0006	0.00008	13174	0.12008	8.3281	69.0581	8.2922
70	2787.80	0.0004	0.00004	23223	0.12004	8.3303	69.2103	8.3082
75	4913.06	0.0002	0.00002	40934	0.12002	8.3316	69.3031	8.3181
80	8658.48	0.0001	0.00001	72146	0.12001	8.3324	69.3594	8.3241
85	15259	0.0001	0.00001		0.12001	8.3328	69.3935	8.3278

TABLE 18 Discrete Cash Flow: Compound Interest Factors

	Single Payments		Uniform Series Payments				Arithmetic Gradients	
	Compound Amount F/P	Present Worth P/F	Sinking Fund A/F	Compound Amount F/A	Capital Recovery A/P	Present Worth P/A	Gradient Present Worth P/G	Gradient Uniform Series A/G
n								
1	1.1400	0.8772	1.00000	1.0000	1.14000	0.8772		
2	1.2996	0.7695	0.46729	2.1400	0.60729	1.6467	0.7695	0.4673
3	1.4815	0.6750	0.29073	3.4396	0.43073	2.3216	2.1194	0.9129
4	1.6890	0.5921	0.20320	4.9211	0.34320	2.9137	3.8957	1.3370
5	1.9254	0.5194	0.15128	6.6101	0.29128	3.4331	5.9731	1.7399
6	2.1950	0.4556	0.11716	8.5355	0.25716	3.8887	8.2511	2.1218
7	2.5023	0.3996	0.09319	10.7305	0.23319	4.2883	10.6489	2.4832
8	2.8526	0.3506	0.07557	13.2328	0.21557	4.6389	13.1028	2.8246
9	3.2519	0.3075	0.06217	16.0853	0.20217	4.9464	15.5629	3.1463
10	3.7072	0.2697	0.05171	19.3373	0.19171	5.2161	17.9906	3.4490
11	4.2262	0.2366	0.04339	23.0445	0.18339	5.4527	20.3567	3.7333
12	4.8179	0.2076	0.03667	27.2707	0.17667	5.6603	22.6399	3.9998
13	5.4924	0.1821	0.03116	32.0887	0.17116	5.8424	24.8247	4.2491
14	6.2613	0.1597	0.02661	37.5811	0.16661	6.0021	26.9009	4.4819
15	7.1379	0.1401	0.02281	43.8424	0.16281	6.1422	28.8623	4.6990
16	8.1372	0.1229	0.01962	50.9804	0.15962	6.2651	30.7057	4.9011
17	9.2765	0.1078	0.01692	59.1176	0.15692	6.3729	32.4305	5.0888
18	10.5752	0.0946	0.01462	68.3941	0.15462	6.4674	34.0380	5.2630
19	12.0557	0.0829	0.01266	78.9692	0.15266	6.5504	35.5311	5.4243
20	13.7435	0.0728	0.01099	91.0249	0.15099	6.6231	36.9135	5.5734
21	15.6676	0.0638	0.00954	104.7684	0.14954	6.6870	38.1901	5.7111
22	17.8610	0.0560	0.00830	120.4360	0.14830	6.7429	39.3658	5.8381
23	20.3616	0.0491	0.00723	138.2970	0.14723	6.7921	40.4463	5.9549
24	23.2122	0.0431	0.00630	158.6586	0.14630	6.8351	41.4371	6.0624
25	26.4619	0.0378	0.00550	181.8708	0.14550	6.8729	42.3441	6.1610
26	30.1666	0.0331	0.00480	208.3327	0.14480	6.9061	43.1728	6.2514
27	34.3899	0.0291	0.00419	238.4993	0.14419	6.9352	43.9289	6.3342
28	39.2045	0.0255	0.00366	272.8892	0.14366	6.9607	44.6176	6.4100
29	44.6931	0.0224	0.00320	312.0937	0.14320	6.9830	45.2441	6.4791
30	50.9502	0.0196	0.00280	356.7868	0.14280	7.0027	45.8132	6.5423
31	58.0832	0.0172	0.00245	407.7370	0.14245	7.0199	46.3297	6.5998
32	66.2148	0.0151	0.00215	465.8202	0.14215	7.0350	46.7979	6.6522
33	75.4849	0.0132	0.00188	532.0350	0.14188	7.0482	47.2218	6.6998
34	86.0528	0.0116	0.00165	607.5199	0.14165	7.0599	47.6053	6.7431
35	98.1002	0.0102	0.00144	693.5727	0.14144	7.0700	47.9519	6.7824
40	188.8835	0.0053	0.00075	1342.03	0.14075	7.1050	49.2376	6.9300
45	363.6791	0.0027	0.00039	2590.56	0.14039	7.1232	49.9963	7.0188
50	700.2330	0.0014	0.00020	4994.52	0.14020	7.1327	50.4375	7.0714
55	1348.24	0.0007	0.00010	9623.13	0.14010	7.1376	50.6912	7.1020
60	2595.92	0.0004	0.00005	18535	0.14005	7.1401	50.8357	7.1197
65	4998.22	0.0002	0.00003	35694	0.14003	7.1414	50.9173	7.1298
70	9623.64	0.0001	0.00001	68733	0.14001	7.1421	50.9632	7.1356
75	18530	0.0001	0.00001		0.14001	7.1425	50.9887	7.1388
80	35677				0.14000	7.1427	51.0030	7.1406
85	68693				0.14000	7.1428	51.0108	7.1416

15%			TABLE 19	Discrete Cash Flow: Compound Interest Factors				*15%*
	Single Payments		Uniform Series Payments				Arithmetic Gradients	
	Compound Amount F/P	Present Worth P/F	Sinking Fund A/F	Compound Amount F/A	Capital Recovery A/P	Present Worth P/A	Gradient Present Worth P/G	Gradient Uniform Series A/G
n								
1	1.1500	0.8696	1.00000	1.0000	1.15000	0.8696		
2	1.3225	0.7561	0.46512	2.1500	0.61512	1.6257	0.7561	0.4651
3	1.5209	0.6575	0.28798	3.4725	0.43798	2.2832	2.0712	0.9071
4	1.7490	0.5718	0.20027	4.9934	0.35027	2.8550	3.7864	1.3263
5	2.0114	0.4972	0.14832	6.7424	0.29832	3.3522	5.7751	1.7228
6	2.3131	0.4323	0.11424	8.7537	0.26424	3.7845	7.9368	2.0972
7	2.6600	0.3759	0.09036	11.0668	0.24036	4.1604	10.1924	2.4498
8	3.0590	0.3269	0.07285	13.7268	0.22285	4.4873	12.4807	2.7813
9	3.5179	0.2843	0.05957	16.7858	0.20957	4.7716	14.7548	3.0922
10	4.0456	0.2472	0.04925	20.3037	0.19925	5.0188	16.9795	3.3832
11	4.6524	0.2149	0.04107	24.3493	0.19107	5.2337	19.1289	3.6549
12	5.3503	0.1869	0.03448	29.0017	0.18448	5.4206	21.1849	3.9082
13	6.1528	0.1625	0.02911	34.3519	0.17911	5.5831	23.1352	4.1438
14	7.0757	0.1413	0.02469	40.5047	0.17469	5.7245	24.9725	4.3624
15	8.1371	0.1229	0.02102	47.5804	0.17102	5.8474	26.6930	4.5650
16	9.3576	0.1069	0.01795	55.7175	0.16795	5.9542	28.2960	4.7522
17	10.7613	0.0929	0.01537	65.0751	0.16537	6.0472	29.7828	4.9251
18	12.3755	0.0808	0.01319	75.8364	0.16319	6.1280	31.1565	5.0843
19	14.2318	0.0703	0.01134	88.2118	0.16134	6.1982	32.4213	5.2307
20	16.3665	0.0611	0.00976	102.4436	0.15976	6.2593	33.5822	5.3651
21	18.8215	0.0531	0.00842	118.8101	0.15842	6.3125	34.6448	5.4883
22	21.6447	0.0462	0.00727	137.6316	0.15727	6.3587	35.6150	5.6010
23	24.8915	0.0402	0.00628	159.2764	0.15628	6.3988	36.4988	5.7040
24	28.6252	0.0349	0.00543	184.1678	0.15543	6.4338	37.3023	5.7979
25	32.9190	0.0304	0.00470	212.7930	0.15470	6.4641	38.0314	5.8834
26	37.8568	0.0264	0.00407	245.7120	0.15407	6.4906	38.6918	5.9612
27	43.5353	0.0230	0.00353	283.5688	0.15353	6.5135	39.2890	6.0319
28	50.0656	0.0200	0.00306	327.1041	0.15306	6.5335	39.8283	6.0960
29	57.5755	0.0174	0.00265	377.1697	0.15265	6.5509	40.3146	6.1541
30	66.2118	0.0151	0.00230	434.7451	0.15230	6.5660	40.7526	6.2066
31	76.1435	0.0131	0.00200	500.9569	0.15200	6.5791	41.1466	6.2541
32	87.5651	0.0114	0.00173	577.1005	0.15173	6.5905	41.5006	6.2970
33	100.6998	0.0099	0.00150	664.6655	0.15150	6.6005	41.8184	6.3357
34	115.8048	0.0086	0.00131	765.3654	0.15131	6.6091	42.1033	6.3705
35	133.1755	0.0075	0.00113	881.1702	0.15113	6.6166	42.3586	6.4019
40	267.8635	0.0037	0.00056	1779.09	0.15056	6.6418	43.2830	6.5168
45	538.7693	0.0019	0.00028	3585.13	0.15028	6.6543	43.8051	6.5830
50	1083.66	0.0009	0.00014	7217.72	0.15014	6.6605	44.0958	6.6205
55	2179.62	0.0005	0.00007	14524	0.15007	6.6636	44.2558	6.6414
60	4384.00	0.0002	0.00003	29220	0.15003	6.6651	44.3431	6.6530
65	8817.79	0.0001	0.00002	58779	0.15002	6.6659	44.3903	6.6593
70	17736	0.0001	0.00001		0.15001	6.6663	44.4156	6.6627
75	35673				0.15000	6.6665	44.4292	6.6646
80	71751				0.15000	6.6666	44.4364	6.6656
85					0.15000	6.6666	44.4402	6.6661

16%				TABLE 20 Discrete Cash Flow: Compound Interest Factors					16%
	Single Payments		**Uniform Series Payments**				**Arithmetic Gradients**		
n	Compound Amount F/P	Present Worth P/F	Sinking Fund A/F	Compound Amount F/A	Capital Recovery A/P	Present Worth P/A	Gradient Present Worth P/G	Gradient Uniform Series A/G	
1	1.1600	0.8621	1.00000	1.0000	1.16000	0.8621			
2	1.3456	0.7432	0.46296	2.1600	0.62296	1.6052	0.7432	0.4630	
3	1.5609	0.6407	0.28526	3.5056	0.44526	2.2459	2.0245	0.9014	
4	1.8106	0.5523	0.19738	5.0665	0.35738	2.7982	3.6814	1.3156	
5	2.1003	0.4761	0.14541	6.8771	0.30541	3.2743	5.5858	1.7060	
6	2.4364	0.4104	0.11139	8.9775	0.27139	3.6847	7.6380	2.0729	
7	2.8262	0.3538	0.08761	11.4139	0.24761	4.0386	9.7610	2.4169	
8	3.2784	0.3050	0.07022	14.2401	0.23022	4.3436	11.8962	2.7388	
9	3.8030	0.2630	0.05708	17.5185	0.21708	4.6065	13.9998	3.0391	
10	4.4114	0.2267	0.04690	21.3215	0.20690	4.8332	16.0399	3.3187	
11	5.1173	0.1954	0.03886	25.7329	0.19886	5.0286	17.9941	3.5783	
12	5.9360	0.1685	0.03241	30.8502	0.19241	5.1971	19.8472	3.8189	
13	6.8858	0.1452	0.02718	36.7862	0.18718	5.3423	21.5899	4.0413	
14	7.9875	0.1252	0.02290	43.6720	0.18290	5.4675	23.2175	4.2464	
15	9.2655	0.1079	0.01936	51.6595	0.17936	5.5755	24.7284	4.4352	
16	10.7480	0.0930	0.01641	60.9250	0.17641	5.6685	26.1241	4.6086	
17	12.4677	0.0802	0.01395	71.6730	0.17395	5.7487	27.4074	4.7676	
18	14.4625	0.0691	0.01188	84.1407	0.17188	5.8178	28.5828	4.9130	
19	16.7765	0.0596	0.01014	98.6032	0.17014	5.8775	29.6557	5.0457	
20	19.4608	0.0514	0.00867	115.3797	0.16867	5.9288	30.6321	5.1666	
22	26.1864	0.0382	0.00635	157.4150	0.16635	6.0113	32.3200	5.3765	
24	35.2364	0.0284	0.00467	213.9776	0.16467	6.0726	33.6970	5.5490	
26	47.4141	0.0211	0.00345	290.0883	0.16345	6.1182	34.8114	5.6898	
28	63.8004	0.0157	0.00255	392.5028	0.16255	6.1520	35.7073	5.8041	
30	85.8499	0.0116	0.00189	530.3117	0.16189	6.1772	36.4234	5.8964	
32	115.5196	0.0087	0.00140	715.7475	0.16140	6.1959	36.9930	5.9706	
34	155.4432	0.0064	0.00104	965.2698	0.16104	6.2098	37.4441	6.0299	
35	180.3141	0.0055	0.00089	1120.71	0.16089	6.2153	37.6327	6.0548	
36	209.1643	0.0048	0.00077	1301.03	0.16077	6.2201	37.8000	6.0771	
38	281.4515	0.0036	0.00057	1752.82	0.16057	6.2278	38.0799	6.1145	
40	378.7212	0.0026	0.00042	2360.76	0.16042	6.2335	38.2992	6.1441	
45	795.4438	0.0013	0.00020	4965.27	0.16020	6.2421	38.6598	6.1934	
50	1670.70	0.0006	0.00010	10436	0.16010	6.2463	38.8521	6.2201	
55	3509.05	0.0003	0.00005	21925	0.16005	6.2482	38.9534	6.2343	
60	7370.20	0.0001	0.00002	46058	0.16002	6.2492	39.0063	6.2419	

18%			TABLE 21	Discrete Cash Flow: Compound Interest Factors				18%
	Single Payments			Uniform Series Payments			Arithmetic Gradients	
	Compound Amount F/P	Present Worth P/F	Sinking Fund A/F	Compound Amount F/A	Capital Recovery A/P	Present Worth P/A	Gradient Present Worth P/G	Gradient Uniform Series A/G
1	1.1800	0.8475	1.00000	1.0000	1.18000	0.8475		
2	1.3924	0.7182	0.45872	2.1800	0.63872	1.5656	0.7182	0.4587
3	1.6430	0.6086	0.27992	3.5724	0.45992	2.1743	1.9354	0.8902
4	1.9388	0.5158	0.19174	5.2154	0.37174	2.6901	3.4828	1.2947
5	2.2878	0.4371	0.13978	7.1542	0.31978	3.1272	5.2312	1.6728
6	2.6996	0.3704	0.10591	9.4420	0.28591	3.4976	7.0834	2.0252
7	3.1855	0.3139	0.08236	12.1415	0.26236	3.8115	8.9670	2.3526
8	3.7589	0.2660	0.06524	15.3270	0.24524	4.0776	10.8292	2.6558
9	4.4355	0.2255	0.05239	19.0859	0.23239	4.3030	12.6329	2.9358
10	5.2338	0.1911	0.04251	23.5213	0.22251	4.4941	14.3525	3.1936
11	6.1759	0.1619	0.03478	28.7551	0.21478	4.6560	15.9716	3.4303
12	7.2876	0.1372	0.02863	34.9311	0.20863	4.7932	17.4811	3.6470
13	8.5994	0.1163	0.02369	42.2187	0.20369	4.9095	18.8765	3.8449
14	10.1472	0.0985	0.01968	50.8180	0.19968	5.0081	20.1576	4.0250
15	11.9737	0.0835	0.01640	60.9653	0.19640	5.0916	21.3269	4.1887
16	14.1290	0.0708	0.01371	72.9390	0.19371	5.1624	22.3885	4.3369
17	16.6722	0.0600	0.01149	87.0680	0.19149	5.2223	23.3482	4.4708
18	19.6733	0.0508	0.00964	103.7403	0.18964	5.2732	24.2123	4.5916
19	23.2144	0.0431	0.00810	123.4135	0.18810	5.3162	24.9877	4.7003
20	27.3930	0.0365	0.00682	146.6280	0.18682	5.3527	25.6813	4.7978
22	38.1421	0.0262	0.00485	206.3448	0.18485	5.4099	26.8506	4.9632
24	53.1090	0.0188	0.00345	289.4945	0.18345	5.4509	27.7725	5.0950
26	73.9490	0.0135	0.00247	405.2721	0.18247	5.4804	28.4935	5.1991
28	102.9666	0.0097	0.00177	566.4809	0.18177	5.5016	29.0537	5.2810
30	143.3706	0.0070	0.00126	790.9480	0.18126	5.5168	29.4864	5.3448
32	199.6293	0.0050	0.00091	1103.50	0.18091	5.5277	29.8191	5.3945
34	277.9638	0.0036	0.00065	1538.69	0.18065	5.5356	30.0736	5.4328
35	327.9973	0.0030	0.00055	1816.65	0.18055	5.5386	30.1773	5.4485
36	387.0368	0.0026	0.00047	2144.65	0.18047	5.5412	30.2677	5.4623
38	538.9100	0.0019	0.00033	2988.39	0.18033	5.5452	30.4152	5.4849
40	750.3783	0.0013	0.00024	4163.21	0.18024	5.5482	30.5269	5.5022
45	1716.68	0.0006	0.00010	9531.58	0.18010	5.5523	30.7006	5.5293
50	3927.36	0.0003	0.00005	21813	0.18005	5.5541	30.7856	5.5428
55	8984.84	0.0001	0.00002	49910	0.18002	5.5549	30.8268	5.5494
60	20555			114190	0.18001	5.5553	30.8465	5.5526

20%				TABLE 22	Discrete Cash Flow: Compound Interest Factors				20%
	Single Payments		Uniform Series Payments					Arithmetic Gradients	
	Compound Amount F/P	Present Worth P/F	Sinking Fund A/F	Compound Amount F/A	Capital Recovery A/P	Present Worth P/A	Gradient Present Worth P/G	Gradient Uniform Series A/G
n								
1	1.2000	0.8333	1.00000	1.0000	1.20000	0.8333		
2	1.4400	0.6944	0.45455	2.2000	0.65455	1.5278	0.6944	0.4545
3	1.7280	0.5787	0.27473	3.6400	0.47473	2.1065	1.8519	0.8791
4	2.0736	0.4823	0.18629	5.3680	0.38629	2.5887	3.2986	1.2742
5	2.4883	0.4019	0.13438	7.4416	0.33438	2.9906	4.9061	1.6405
6	2.9860	0.3349	0.10071	9.9299	0.30071	3.3255	6.5806	1.9788
7	3.5832	0.2791	0.07742	12.9159	0.27742	3.6046	8.2551	2.2902
8	4.2998	0.2326	0.06061	16.4991	0.26061	3.8372	9.8831	2.5756
9	5.1598	0.1938	0.04808	20.7989	0.24808	4.0310	11.4335	2.8364
10	6.1917	0.1615	0.03852	25.9587	0.23852	4.1925	12.8871	3.0739
11	7.4301	0.1346	0.03110	32.1504	0.23110	4.3271	14.2330	3.2893
12	8.9161	0.1122	0.02526	39.5805	0.22526	4.4392	15.4667	3.4841
13	10.6993	0.0935	0.02062	48.4966	0.22062	4.5327	16.5883	3.6597
14	12.8392	0.0779	0.01689	59.1959	0.21689	4.6106	17.6008	3.8175
15	15.4070	0.0649	0.01388	72.0351	0.21388	4.6755	18.5095	3.9588
16	18.4884	0.0541	0.01144	87.4421	0.21144	4.7296	19.3208	4.0851
17	22.1861	0.0451	0.00944	105.9306	0.20944	4.7746	20.0419	4.1976
18	26.6233	0.0376	0.00781	128.1167	0.20781	4.8122	20.6805	4.2975
19	31.9480	0.0313	0.00646	154.7400	0.20646	4.8435	21.2439	4.3861
20	38.3376	0.0261	0.00536	186.6880	0.20536	4.8696	21.7395	4.4643
22	55.2061	0.0181	0.00369	271.0307	0.20369	4.9094	22.5546	4.5941
24	79.4968	0.0126	0.00255	392.4842	0.20255	4.9371	23.1760	4.6943
26	114.4755	0.0087	0.00176	567.3773	0.20176	4.9563	23.6460	4.7709
28	164.8447	0.0061	0.00122	819.2233	0.20122	4.9697	23.9991	4.8291
30	237.3763	0.0042	0.00085	1181.88	0.20085	4.9789	24.2628	4.8731
32	341.8219	0.0029	0.00059	1704.11	0.20059	4.9854	24.4588	4.9061
34	492.2235	0.0020	0.00041	2456.12	0.20041	4.9898	24.6038	4.9308
35	590.6682	0.0017	0.00034	2948.34	0.20034	4.9915	24.6614	4.9406
36	708.8019	0.0014	0.00028	3539.01	0.20028	4.9929	24.7108	4.9491
38	1020.67	0.0010	0.00020	5098.37	0.20020	4.9951	24.7894	4.9627
40	1469.77	0.0007	0.00014	7343.86	0.20014	4.9966	24.8469	4.9728
45	3657.26	0.0003	0.00005	18281	0.20005	4.9986	24.9316	4.9877
50	9100.44	0.0001	0.00002	45497	0.20002	4.9995	24.9698	4.9945
55	22645		0.00001		0.20001	4.9998	24.9868	4.9976

22%			TABLE 23	Discrete Cash Flow: Compound Interest Factors				22%
	Single Payments		Uniform Series Payments				Arithmetic Gradients	
n	Compound Amount F/P	Present Worth P/F	Sinking Fund A/F	Compound Amount F/A	Capital Recovery A/P	Present Worth P/A	Gradient Present Worth P/G	Gradient Uniform Series A/G
1	1.2200	0.8197	1.00000	1.0000	1.22000	0.8197		
2	1.4884	0.6719	0.45045	2.2200	0.67045	1.4915	0.6719	0.4505
3	1.8158	0.5507	0.26966	3.7084	0.48966	2.0422	1.7733	0.8683
4	2.2153	0.4514	0.18102	5.5242	0.40102	2.4936	3.1275	1.2542
5	2.7027	0.3700	0.12921	7.7396	0.34921	2.8636	4.6075	1.6090
6	3.2973	0.3033	0.09576	10.4423	0.31576	3.1669	6.1239	1.9337
7	4.0227	0.2486	0.07278	13.7396	0.29278	3.4155	7.6154	2.2297
8	4.9077	0.2038	0.05630	17.7623	0.27630	3.6193	9.0417	2.4982
9	5.9874	0.1670	0.04411	22.6700	0.26411	3.7863	10.3779	2.7409
10	7.3046	0.1369	0.03489	28.6574	0.25489	3.9232	11.6100	2.9593
11	8.9117	0.1122	0.02781	35.9620	0.24781	4.0354	12.7321	3.1551
12	10.8722	0.0920	0.02228	44.8737	0.24228	4.1274	13.7438	3.3299
13	13.2641	0.0754	0.01794	55.7459	0.23794	4.2028	14.6485	3.4855
14	16.1822	0.0618	0.01449	69.0100	0.23449	4.2646	15.4519	3.6233
15	19.7423	0.0507	0.01174	85.1922	0.23174	4.3152	16.1610	3.7451
16	24.0856	0.0415	0.00953	104.9345	0.22953	4.3567	16.7838	3.8524
17	29.3844	0.0340	0.00775	129.0201	0.22775	4.3908	17.3283	3.9465
18	35.8490	0.0279	0.00631	158.4045	0.22631	4.4187	17.8025	4.0289
19	43.7358	0.0229	0.00515	194.2535	0.22515	4.4415	18.2141	4.1009
20	53.3576	0.0187	0.00420	237.9893	0.22420	4.4603	18.5702	4.1635
22	79.4175	0.0126	0.00281	356.4432	0.22281	4.4882	19.1418	4.2649
24	118.2050	0.0085	0.00188	532.7501	0.22188	4.5070	19.5635	4.3407
26	175.9364	0.0057	0.00126	795.1653	0.22126	4.5196	19.8720	4.3968
28	261.8637	0.0038	0.00084	1185.74	0.22084	4.5281	20.0962	4.4381
30	389.7579	0.0026	0.00057	1767.08	0.22057	4.5338	20.2583	4.4683
32	580.1156	0.0017	0.00038	2632.34	0.22038	4.5376	20.3748	4.4902
34	863.4441	0.0012	0.00026	3920.20	0.22026	4.5402	20.4582	4.5060
35	1053.40	0.0009	0.00021	4783.64	0.22021	4.5411	20.4905	4.5122
36	1285.15	0.0008	0.00017	5837.05	0.22017	4.5419	20.5178	4.5174
38	1912.82	0.0005	0.00012	8690.08	0.22012	4.5431	20.5601	4.5256
40	2847.04	0.0004	0.00008	12937	0.22008	4.5439	20.5900	4.5314
45	7694.71	0.0001	0.00003	34971	0.22003	4.5449	20.6319	4.5396
50	20797		0.00001	94525	0.22001	4.5452	20.6492	4.5431
55	56207				0.22000	4.5454	20.6563	4.5445

24%				TABLE 24	Discrete Cash Flow: Compound Interest Factors				24%
	Single Payments		Uniform Series Payments				Arithmetic Gradients		
	Compound Amount	Present Worth	Sinking Fund	Compound Amount	Capital Recovery	Present Worth	Gradient Present Worth	Gradient Uniform Series	
n	F/P	P/F	A/F	F/A	A/P	P/A	P/G	A/G	
1	1.2400	0.8065	1.00000	1.0000	1.24000	0.8065			
2	1.5376	0.6504	0.44643	2.2400	0.68643	1.4568	0.6504	0.4464	
3	1.9066	0.5245	0.26472	3.7776	0.50472	1.9813	1.6993	0.8577	
4	2.3642	0.4230	0.17593	5.6842	0.41593	2.4043	2.9683	1.2346	
5	2.9316	0.3411	0.12425	8.0484	0.36425	2.7454	4.3327	1.5782	
6	3.6352	0.2751	0.09107	10.9801	0.33107	3.0205	5.7081	1.8898	
7	4.5077	0.2218	0.06842	14.6153	0.30842	3.2423	7.0392	2.1710	
8	5.5895	0.1789	0.05229	19.1229	0.29229	3.4212	8.2915	2.4236	
9	6.9310	0.1443	0.04047	24.7125	0.28047	3.5655	9.4458	2.6492	
10	8.5944	0.1164	0.03160	31.6434	0.27160	3.6819	10.4930	2.8499	
11	10.6571	0.0938	0.02485	40.2379	0.26485	3.7757	11.4313	3.0276	
12	13.2148	0.0757	0.01965	50.8950	0.25965	3.8514	12.2637	3.1843	
13	16.3863	0.0610	0.01560	64.1097	0.25560	3.9124	12.9960	3.3218	
14	20.3191	0.0492	0.01242	80.4961	0.25242	3.9616	13.6358	3.4420	
15	25.1956	0.0397	0.00992	100.8151	0.24992	4.0013	14.1915	3.5467	
16	31.2426	0.0320	0.00794	126.0108	0.24794	4.0333	14.6716	3.6376	
17	38.7408	0.0258	0.00636	157.2534	0.24636	4.0591	15.0846	3.7162	
18	48.0386	0.0208	0.00510	195.9942	0.24510	4.0799	15.4385	3.7840	
19	59.5679	0.0168	0.00410	244.0328	0.24410	4.0967	15.7406	3.8423	
20	73.8641	0.0135	0.00329	303.6006	0.24329	4.1103	15.9979	3.8922	
22	113.5735	0.0088	0.00213	469.0563	0.24213	4.1300	16.4011	3.9712	
24	174.6306	0.0057	0.00138	723.4610	0.24138	4.1428	16.6891	4.0284	
26	268.5121	0.0037	0.00090	1114.63	0.24090	4.1511	16.8930	4.0695	
28	412.8642	0.0024	0.00058	1716.10	0.24058	4.1566	17.0365	4.0987	
30	634.8199	0.0016	0.00038	2640.92	0.24038	4.1601	17.1369	4.1193	
32	976.0991	0.0010	0.00025	4062.91	0.24025	4.1624	17.2067	4.1338	
34	1500.85	0.0007	0.00016	6249.38	0.24016	4.1639	17.2552	4.1440	
35	1861.05	0.0005	0.00013	7750.23	0.24013	4.1664	17.2734	4.1479	
36	2307.71	0.0004	0.00010	9611.28	0.24010	4.1649	17.2886	4.1511	
38	3548.33	0.0003	0.00007	14781	0.24007	4.1655	17.3116	4.1560	
40	5455.91	0.0002	0.00004	22729	0.24004	4.1659	17.3274	4.1593	
45	15995	0.0001	0.00002	66640	0.24002	4.1664	17.3483	4.1639	
50	46890		0.00001		0.24001	4.1666	17.3563	4.1653	
55					0.24000	4.1666	17.3593	4.1663	

	Single Payments		Uniform Series Payments				Arithmetic Gradients	
	Compound Amount F/P	Present Worth P/F	Sinking Fund A/F	Compound Amount F/A	Capital Recovery A/P	Present Worth P/A	Gradient Present Worth P/G	Gradient Uniform Series A/G
n								
1	1.2500	0.8000	1.00000	1.0000	1.25000	0.8000		
2	1.5625	0.6400	0.44444	2.2500	0.69444	1.4400	0.6400	0.4444
3	1.9531	0.5120	0.26230	3.8125	0.51230	1.9520	1.6640	0.8525
4	2.4414	0.4096	0.17344	5.7656	0.42344	2.3616	2.8928	1.2249
5	3.0518	0.3277	0.12185	8.2070	0.37185	2.6893	4.2035	1.5631
6	3.8147	0.2621	0.08882	11.2588	0.33882	2.9514	5.5142	1.8683
7	4.7684	0.2097	0.06634	15.0735	0.31634	3.1611	6.7725	2.1424
8	5.9605	0.1678	0.05040	19.8419	0.30040	3.3289	7.9469	2.3872
9	7.4506	0.1342	0.03876	25.8023	0.28876	3.4631	9.0207	2.6048
10	9.3132	0.1074	0.03007	33.2529	0.28007	3.5705	9.9870	2.7971
11	11.6415	0.0859	0.02349	42.5661	0.27349	3.6564	10.8460	2.9663
12	14.5519	0.0687	0.01845	54.2077	0.26845	3.7251	11.6020	3.1145
13	18.1899	0.0550	0.01454	68.7596	0.26454	3.7801	12.2617	3.2437
14	22.7374	0.0440	0.01150	86.9495	0.26150	3.8241	12.8334	3.3559
15	28.4217	0.0352	0.00912	109.6868	0.25912	3.8593	13.3260	3.4530
16	35.5271	0.0281	0.00724	138.1085	0.25724	3.8874	13.7482	3.5366
17	44.4089	0.0225	0.00576	173.6357	0.25576	3.9099	14.1085	3.6084
18	55.5112	0.0180	0.00459	218.0446	0.25459	3.9279	14.4147	3.6698
19	69.3889	0.0144	0.00366	273.5558	0.25366	3.9424	14.6741	3.7222
20	86.7362	0.0115	0.00292	342.9447	0.25292	3.9539	14.8932	3.7667
22	135.5253	0.0074	0.00186	538.1011	0.25186	3.9705	15.2326	3.8365
24	211.7582	0.0047	0.00119	843.0329	0.25119	3.9811	15.4711	3.8861
26	330.8722	0.0030	0.00076	1319.49	0.25076	3.9879	15.6373	3.9212
28	516.9879	0.0019	0.00048	2063.95	0.25048	3.9923	15.7524	3.9457
30	807.7936	0.0012	0.00031	3227.17	0.25031	3.9950	15.8316	3.9628
32	1262.18	0.0008	0.00020	5044.71	0.25020	3.9968	15.8859	3.9746
34	1972.15	0.0005	0.00013	7884.61	0.25013	3.9980	15.9229	3.9828
35	2465.19	0.0004	0.00010	9856.76	.025010	3.9984	15.9367	3.9858
36	3081.49	0.0003	0.00008	12322	0.25008	3.9987	15.9481	3.9883
38	4814.82	0.0002	0.00005	19255	0.25005	3.9992	15.9651	3.9921
40	7523.16	0.0001	0.00003	30089	0.25003	3.9995	15.9766	3.9947
45	22959		0.00001	91831	0.25001	3.9998	15.9915	3.9980
50	70065				0.25000	3.9999	15.9969	3.9993
55					0.25000	4.0000	15.9989	3.9997

25% **TABLE 25** Discrete Cash Flow: Compound Interest Factors **25%**

30%		TABLE 26		Discrete Cash Flow: Compound Interest Factors				30%
	Single Payments		Uniform Series Payments				Arithmetic Gradients	
	Compound Amount F/P	Present Worth P/F	Sinking Fund A/F	Compound Amount F/A	Capital Recovery A/P	Present Worth P/A	Gradient Present Worth P/G	Gradient Uniform Series A/G
n								
1	1.3000	0.7692	1.00000	1.0000	1.30000	0.7692		
2	1.6900	0.5917	0.43478	2.3000	0.73478	1.3609	0.5917	0.4348
3	2.1970	0.4552	0.25063	3.9900	0.55063	1.8161	1.5020	0.8271
4	2.8561	0.3501	0.16163	6.1870	0.46163	2.1662	2.5524	1.1783
5	3.7129	0.2693	0.11058	9.0431	0.41058	2.4356	3.6297	1.4903
6	4.8268	0.2072	0.07839	12.7560	0.37839	2.6427	4.6656	1.7654
7	6.2749	0.1594	0.05687	17.5828	0.35687	2.8021	5.6218	2.0063
8	8.1573	0.1226	0.04192	23.8577	0.34192	2.9247	6.4800	2.2156
9	10.6045	0.0943	0.03124	32.0150	0.33124	3.0190	7.2343	2.3963
10	13.7858	0.0725	0.02346	42.6195	0.32346	3.0915	7.8872	2.5512
11	17.9216	0.0558	0.01773	56.4053	0.31773	3.1473	8.4452	2.6833
12	23.2981	0.0429	0.01345	74.3270	0.31345	3.1903	8.9173	2.7952
13	30.2875	0.0330	0.01024	97.6250	0.31024	3.2233	9.3135	2.8895
14	39.3738	0.0254	0.00782	127.9125	0.30782	3.2487	9.6437	2.9685
15	51.1859	0.0195	0.00598	167.2863	0.30598	3.2682	9.9172	3.0344
16	66.5417	0.0150	0.00458	218.4722	0.30458	3.2832	10.1426	3.0892
17	86.5042	0.0116	0.00351	285.0139	0.30351	3.2948	10.3276	3.1345
18	112.4554	0.0089	0.00269	371.5180	0.30269	3.3037	10.4788	3.1718
19	146.1920	0.0068	0.00207	483.9734	0.30207	3.3105	10.6019	3.2025
20	190.0496	0.0053	0.00159	630.1655	0.30159	3.3158	10.7019	3.2275
22	321.1839	0.0031	0.00094	1067.28	0.30094	3.3230	10.8482	3.2646
24	542.8008	0.0018	0.00055	1806.00	0.30055	3.3272	10.9433	3.2890
25	705.6410	0.0014	0.00043	2348.80	0.30043	3.3286	10.9773	3.2979
26	917.3333	0.0011	0.00033	3054.44	0.30033	3.3297	11.0045	3.3050
28	1550.29	0.0006	0.00019	5164.31	0.30019	3.3312	11.0437	3.3153
30	2620.00	0.0004	0.00011	8729.99	0.30011	3.3321	11.0687	3.3219
32	4427.79	0.0002	0.00007	14756	0.30007	3.3326	11.0845	3.3261
34	7482.97	0.0001	0.00004	24940	0.30004	3.3329	11.0945	3.3288
35	9727.86	0.0001	0.00003	32423	0.30003	3.3330	11.0980	3.3297

35%			TABLE 27	Discrete Cash Flow: Compound Interest Factors				35%
	Single Payments		Uniform Series Payments				Arithmetic Gradients	
	Compound Amount F/P	Present Worth P/F	Sinking Fund A/F	Compound Amount F/A	Capital Recovery A/P	Present Worth P/A	Gradient Present Worth P/G	Gradient Uniform Series A/G
n								
1	1.3500	0.7407	1.00000	1.0000	1.35000	0.7407		
2	1.8225	0.5487	0.42553	2.3500	0.77553	1.2894	0.5487	0.4255
3	2.4604	0.4064	0.23966	4.1725	0.58966	1.6959	1.3616	0.8029
4	3.3215	0.3011	0.15076	6.6329	0.50076	1.9969	2.2648	1.1341
5	4.4840	0.2230	0.10046	9.9544	0.45046	2.2200	3.1568	1.4220
6	6.0534	0.1652	0.06926	14.4384	0.41926	2.3852	3.9828	1.6698
7	8.1722	0.1224	0.04880	20.4919	0.39880	2.5075	4.7170	1.8811
8	11.0324	0.0906	0.03489	28.6640	0.38489	2.5982	5.3515	2.0597
9	14.8937	0.0671	0.02519	39.6964	0.37519	2.6653	5.8886	2.2094
10	20.1066	0.0497	0.01832	54.5902	0.36832	2.7150	6.3363	2.3338
11	27.1439	0.0368	0.01339	74.6967	0.36339	2.7519	6.7047	2.4364
12	36.6442	0.0273	0.00982	101.8406	0.35982	2.7792	7.0049	2.5205
13	49.4697	0.0202	0.00722	138.4848	0.35722	2.7994	7.2474	2.5889
14	66.7841	0.0150	0.00532	187.9544	0.35532	2.8144	7.4421	2.6443
15	90.1585	0.0111	0.00393	254.7385	0.35393	2.8255	7.5974	2.6889
16	121.7139	0.0082	0.00290	344.8970	0.35290	2.8337	7.7206	2.7246
17	164.3138	0.0061	0.00214	466.6109	0.35214	2.8398	7.8180	2.7530
18	221.8236	0.0045	0.00158	630.9247	0.35158	2.8443	7.8946	2.7756
19	299.4619	0.0033	0.00117	852.7483	0.35117	2.8476	7.9547	2.7935
20	404.2736	0.0025	0.00087	1152.21	0.35087	2.8501	8.0017	2.8075
22	736.7886	0.0014	0.00048	2102.25	0.35048	2.8533	8.0669	2.8272
24	1342.80	0.0007	0.00026	3833.71	0.35026	2.8550	8.1061	2.8393
25	1812.78	0.0006	0.00019	5176.50	0.35019	2.8556	8.1194	2.8433
26	2447.25	0.0004	0.00014	6989.28	0.35014	2.8560	8.1296	2.8465
28	4460.11	0.0002	0.00008	12740	0.35008	2.8565	8.1435	2.8509
30	8128.55	0.0001	0.00004	23222	0.35004	2.8568	8.1517	2.8535
32	14814	0.0001	0.00002	42324	0.35002	2.8569	8.1565	2.8550
34	26999		0.00001	77137	0.35001	2.8570	8.1594	2.8559
35	36449		0.00001		0.35001	2.8571	8.1603	2.8562

40%			TABLE 28	Discrete Cash Flow: Compound Interest Factors				40%
	Single Payments		Uniform Series Payments				Arithmetic Gradients	
	Compound Amount F/P	Present Worth P/F	Sinking Fund A/F	Compound Amount F/A	Capital Recovery A/P	Present Worth P/A	Gradient Present Worth P/G	Gradient Uniform Series A/G
n								
1	1.4000	0.7143	1.00000	1.0000	1.40000	0.7143		
2	1.9600	0.5102	0.41667	2.4000	0.81667	1.2245	0.5102	0.4167
3	2.7440	0.3644	0.22936	4.3600	0.62936	1.5889	1.2391	0.7798
4	3.8416	0.2603	0.14077	7.1040	0.54077	1.8492	2.0200	1.0923
5	5.3782	0.1859	0.09136	10.9456	0.49136	2.0352	2.7637	1.3580
6	7.5295	0.1328	0.06126	16.3238	0.46126	2.1680	3.4278	1.5811
7	10.5414	0.0949	0.04192	23.8534	0.44192	2.2628	3.9970	1.7664
8	14.7579	0.0678	0.02907	34.3947	0.42907	2.3306	4.4713	1.9185
9	20.6610	0.0484	0.02034	49.1526	0.42034	2.3790	4.8585	2.0422
10	28.9255	0.0346	0.01432	69.8137	0.41432	2.4136	5.1696	2.1419
11	40.4957	0.0247	0.01013	98.7391	0.41013	2.4383	5.4166	2.2215
12	56.6939	0.0176	0.00718	139.2348	0.40718	2.4559	5.6106	2.2845
13	79.3715	0.0126	0.00510	195.9287	0.40510	2.4685	5.7618	2.3341
14	111.1201	0.0090	0.00363	275.3002	0.40363	2.4775	5.8788	2.3729
15	155.5681	0.0064	0.00259	386.4202	0.40259	2.4839	5.9688	2.4030
16	217.7953	0.0046	0.00185	541.9883	0.40185	2.4885	6.0376	2.4262
17	304.9135	0.0033	0.00132	759.7837	0.40132	2.4918	6.0901	2.4441
18	426.8789	0.0023	0.00094	1064.70	0.40094	2.4941	6.1299	2.4577
19	597.6304	0.0017	0.00067	1491.58	0.40067	2.4958	6.1601	2.4682
20	836.6826	0.0012	0.00048	2089.21	0.40048	2.4970	6.1828	2.4761
22	1639.90	0.0006	0.00024	4097.24	0.40024	2.4985	6.2127	2.4866
24	3214.20	0.0003	0.00012	8033.00	0.40012	2.4992	6.2294	2.4925
25	4499.88	0.0002	0.00009	11247	0.40009	2.4994	6.2347	2.4944
26	6299.83	0.0002	0.00006	15747	0.40006	2.4996	6.2387	2.4959
28	12348	0.0001	0.00003	30867	0.40003	2.4998	6.2438	2.4977
30	24201		0.00002	60501	0.40002	2.4999	6.2466	2.4988
32	47435		0.00001		0.40001	2.4999	6.2482	2.4993
34	92972				0.40000	2.5000	6.2490	2.4996
35					0.40000	2.5000	6.2493	2.4997

50%			TABLE 29	Discrete Cash Flow: Compound Interest Factors				50%
	Single Payments		**Uniform Series Payments**				**Arithmetic Gradients**	
	Compound Amount	Present Worth	Sinking Fund	Compound Amount	Capital Recovery	Present Worth	Gradient Present Worth	Gradient Uniform Series
n	F/P	P/F	A/F	F/A	A/P	P/A	P/G	A/G
1	1.5000	0.6667	1.00000	1.0000	1.50000	0.6667		
2	2.2500	0.4444	0.40000	2.5000	0.90000	1.1111	0.4444	0.4000
3	3.3750	0.2963	0.21053	4.7500	0.71053	1.4074	1.0370	0.7368
4	5.0625	0.1975	0.12308	8.1250	0.62308	1.6049	1.6296	1.0154
5	7.5938	0.1317	0.07583	13.1875	0.57583	1.7366	2.1564	1.2417
6	11.3906	0.0878	0.04812	20.7813	0.54812	1.8244	2.5953	1.4226
7	17.0859	0.0585	0.03108	32.1719	0.53108	1.8829	2.9465	1.5648
8	25.6289	0.0390	0.02030	49.2578	0.52030	1.9220	3.2196	1.6752
9	38.4434	0.0260	0.01335	74.8867	0.51335	1.9480	3.4277	1.7596
10	57.6650	0.0173	0.00882	113.3301	0.50882	1.9653	3.5838	1.8235
11	86.4976	0.0116	0.00585	170.9951	0.50585	1.9769	3.6994	1.8713
12	129.7463	0.0077	0.00388	257.4927	0.50388	1.9846	3.7842	1.9068
13	194.6195	0.0051	0.00258	387.2390	0.50258	1.9897	3.8459	1.9329
14	291.9293	0.0034	0.00172	581.8585	0.50172	1.9931	3.8904	1.9519
15	437.8939	0.0023	0.00114	873.7878	0.50114	1.9954	3.9224	1.9657
16	656.8408	0.0015	0.00076	1311.68	0.50076	1.9970	3.9452	1.9756
17	985.2613	0.0010	0.00051	1968.52	0.50051	1.9980	3.9614	1.9827
18	1477.89	0.0007	0.00034	2953.78	0.50034	1.9986	3.9729	1.9878
19	2216.84	0.0005	0.00023	4431.68	0.50023	1.9991	3.9811	1.9914
20	3325.26	0.0003	0.00015	6648.51	0.50015	1.9994	3.9868	1.9940
22	7481.83	0.0001	0.00007	14962	0.50007	1.9997	3.9936	1.9971
24	16834	0.0001	0.00003	33666	0.50003	1.9999	3.9969	1.9986
25	25251		0.00002	50500	0.50002	1.9999	3.9979	1.9990
26	37877		0.00001	75752	0.50001	1.9999	3.9985	1.9993
28	85223		0.00001		0.50001	2.0000	3.9993	1.9997
30					0.50000	2.0000	3.9997	1.9998
32					0.50000	2.0000	3.9998	1.9999
34					0.50000	2.0000	3.9999	2.0000
35					0.50000	2.0000	3.9999	2.0000

INDEX

Glossary of Common Terms

Term	Symbol	Description (with initial section reference in parentheses)
Annual amount or worth	A or AW	Equivalent uniform annual worth of all cash inflows and outflows over estimated life (1.7, 6.1).
Annual operating cost	AOC	Estimated annual costs to maintain and support an alternative (1.3).
Benefit-cost ratio	BCR	Ratio of a project's benefits to costs expressed in PW, AW, or FW terms (9.2).
Breakeven point	Q_{BE}	Quantity at which revenues and costs are equal, or two alternatives are equivalent (13.1).
Book value	BV	Remaining capital investment in an asset after depreciation is accounted for (15.1).
Capital budget	b	Amount of money available for capital investment projects (12.1).
Capital recovery	CR or A	Equivalent annual cost of owning an asset plus the required return on the initial investment (6.2).
Capitalized cost	CC or P	Present worth of an alternative that will last forever (or a long time) (5.5).
Cash flow	CF	Actual cash amounts which are receipts (inflow) and disbursements (outflow) (1.10).
Cash flow before or after taxes	CFBT or CFAT	Cash flow amount before relevant taxes or after taxes are applied (16.2).
Capital cost allowance	CCA	Annual rate for reducing the value of assets using Canadian depreciation procedure (15.2).
Composite rate of return	i'	Unique rate of return when a reinvestment rate c is applied to a multiple-rate cash flow series (7.5).
Cost of capital	i or WACC	Interest rate paid for the use of capital funds; includes both debt and equity funds. For debt and equity considered, it is weighted average cost of capital (10.2–3).
Debt-equity mix	D-E	Percentages of debt and equity investment capital used by a corporation (1.9, 10.3).
Depreciation	D	Reduction in the value of assets using specific models and rules; there are book and tax depreciation methods (15.1).
Depreciation rate	d_t	Annual rate for reducing the value of assets using depreciation models (15.1).
Economic service life	ESL or n	Number of years at which the AW of costs is a minimum (11.2).
Expected value (average)	$\overline{X}$, μ, or $E(X)$	Long-run expected average if a random variable is sampled many times (17.3, 18.4).
Expenses	E	All corporate costs incurred in transacting business (16.1).
First cost or cost basis	P	Total initial cost—purchase, construction, setup, etc. (1.3, 15.1).

(*Continued*)